# Selected Titles in This Series

(*Continued in the back of this publication*)

Conference Participants

# CONTEMPORARY MATHEMATICS

197

# Matroid Theory

AMS-IMS-SIAM Joint Summer Research Conference
on Matroid Theory
July 2–6, 1995
University of Washington, Seattle

Joseph E. Bonin
James G. Oxley
Brigitte Servatius
Editors

**American Mathematical Society**
Providence, Rhode Island

## EDITORIAL COMMITTEE

Dennis DeTurck, managing editor

Andy Magid      Michael Vogelius
Clark Robinson      Peter M. Winkler

The 1995 AMS-IMS-SIAM Joint Summer Research Conference on Matroid Theory was held at the University of Washington, Seattle, from July 2 to July 6, 1995, with support from National Science Foundation Grant No. DMS-9221892-003 and National Security Agency Grant No. MDA 904-95-1-1063.

1991 *Mathematics Subject Classification.* Primary 05B35, 52C25;
Secondary 51E20, 05C15, 68U07.

---

**Library of Congress Cataloging-in-Publication Data**

AMS-IMS-SIAM Joint Summer Research Conference on Matroid Theory (1995 : University of Washington)
    Matroid theory : AMS-IMS-SIAM Joint Summer Research Conference on Matroid Theory, July 2–6, 1995, University of Washington, Seattle / Joseph E. Bonin, James G. Oxley, Brigitte Servatius, editors.
    p. cm. — (Contemporary mathematics, ISSN 0271-4132; 197)
    Includes bibliographical references (p.  –  ).
    ISBN 0-8218-0508-8 (alk. paper)
    1. Matroids—Congresses. I. Bonin, Joseph E. (Joseph Edmond), 1962– . II. Oxley, J. G. III. Servatius, Brigitte, 1954– . IV. Title. V. Series: Contemporary mathematics (American Mathematical Society); v. 197.
QA166.6.A45    1995
511′.6—dc20
                                                    96-18251
                                                    CIP

---

# Contents

# Preface

With his 1935 paper *On the abstract properties of linear dependence*, Hassler Whitney founded the theory of matroids. The richness of Whitney's work can be attributed in part to the variety of fields from which he drew inspiration, including algebra, geometry, and graph theory. Since Whitney's paper, numerous authors have recognized the natural occurrence of matroids in a wide diversity of areas, and the interplay between matroid theory and other fields has flourished.

This volume contains the proceedings of the 1995 AMS-IMS-SIAM Joint Summer Research Conference *Matroid Theory*, held at the University of Washington, Seattle, from July 2 until July 6, 1995. The conference focused on four major areas within matroid theory and its fields of application: the critical problem; structure theory and connectivity; rigidity and discrete applied geometry; and oriented matroids and arrangements of hyperplanes. The conference was structured to achieve the dual goals of fostering greater interaction among researchers in different specialties and presenting the latest research within each specialty. Each of the four chosen areas was surveyed by a leading researcher in the specialty. This volume begins with survey papers by Joseph Kung, James Oxley, and Walter Whiteley. These papers expand on the presentations made at the conference and blend the background material needed to make the papers accessible with numerous new results and research questions. Günter Ziegler's survey of oriented matroids and arrangements of hyperplanes will be developed into a separate book.

The survey lectures at the conference were complemented by more specialized talks and poster presentations. Papers resulting from these appear after the survey papers. The book concludes with a chapter of open problems. We hope that the contents of this volume will be interesting to a wide audience, and will advance further developments in matroid theory and its applications.

We thank the National Science Foundation for its financial support and the American Mathematical Society for its organizational support. Wayne Drady, of the AMS meetings and conferences department, did an excellent job with local arrangements, bookkeeping, and on-site assistance; Donna Harmon, of the AMS publications department, provided valuable guidance throughout the publication process. We are grateful to the referees. Finally, we thank those whose contributions are the core of this project: those who gave lectures and poster presentations at the conference, and those who contributed to this volume.

Joseph E. Bonin
James G. Oxley
Brigitte Servatius

Contemporary Mathematics
Volume **197**, 1996

# Conference Program

## Sunday, July 2

9:00–10:00   James Oxley, *Structure theory and connectivity for matroids. Part* I.

10:30–11:30   James Oxley, *Structure theory and connectivity for matroids. Part* II.

2:00–2:45   Geoff Whittle, *Ternary matroids representable over other fields.*

3:00–3:45   Dirk Vertigan, *Matroid minors and structure.*

4:00–4:45   Neil Robertson* and Jack Dharmatilake, *Binary matroids of branch-width three.*

7:00–8:30   Poster Session 1

- Gary Gordon* and Elizabeth McMahon, *An algorithmic approach to activities for matroids, antimatroids, and greedoids.*
- Arthur Hobbs, *Uniformly dense matroids.*
- Sandra Kingan, *A generalization of a graph result by D.W. Hall.*
- John Leo, *On coefficients of the Tutte polynomial.*
- Allan Mills, *Matroid reconstruction and relaxation.*

## Monday, July 3

9:00–10:00   Walter Whiteley, *Matroids in discrete applied geometry. Part* I: *rigidity of frameworks.*

10:30–11:30   Walter Whiteley, *Matroids in discrete applied geometry. Part* II: *splines, pictures, and CAD.*

2:00–2:45   Jack E. Graver, *The matroid duality operator.*

3:00–3:45   Robert Connelly, *Is global rigidity a generic property?*

4:00–4:45   T. S. Tay, *Rigidity and the number of faces of polytopes.*

7:00–8:30   Poster Session 2

- Laura Anderson, *Combinatorial differential manifolds.*
- Seth Chaiken, *Oriented matroid pairs: theory and an electric application.*
- Camille C. Cooper, *Bracing zonahedral frameworks.*
- Robert Jamison, *Monotactic matroids.*
- Andras Recski, *Some recent results on the combinatorial properties of square and cubic grids.*
- Paul Terwilliger, *Quantum matroids.*

## Tuesday, July 4

9:00–10:00   Henry Crapo, *Tilings by related zonotopes, with a fresh look at oriented matroids.*

10:30–11:30  Thomas Brylawski, *A matroid theory generalization of the contravariant form in representation theory.*

## Wednesday, July 5

9:00–10:00   Joseph P. S. Kung, *The critical problem: past and future. Part* I: *history and survey.*

10:30–11:30  Joseph P. S. Kung, *The critical problem: past and future. Part* II: *problems and methods.*

2:00–2:45    Dominic Welsh, *Randomised algorithms for computing numerical invariants.*

3:00–3:45    Neil White, *Matroids generalized to Coxeter groups — the* $(W, P)$-*matroids of Gelfand et al.*

7:00–8:30    Poster Session 3

o Laura Anderson* and Rephael Wenger, *Oriented matroids and hyperplane transversals.*

o Manoj K. Chari, *On topology and enumeration in matroids.*

o Hong-Jian Lai* and Zhi-Hong Chen, *Connectivity of cycle matroids and bicircular matroids.*

o William Miller, *Reconstructing matroids from Tutte polynomials.*

o Charles Semple, *Matroids representable over subgroups of fields.*

o Haidong Wu, *On contractible and vertically contractible elements in 3-connected matroids and graphs.*

## Thursday, July 6

9:00–10:00   Günter M. Ziegler, *Real arrangements, complex arrangements, and their (oriented) matroids. Part* I.

10:30–11:30  Günter M. Ziegler, *Real arrangements, complex arrangements, and their (oriented) matroids. Part* II.

2:00–2:45    Jürgen Richter-Gebert, *Nonrealizability proofs for (oriented) matroids and automatic theorem proving.*

3:00–3:45    Michael J. Falk, *Applications of matroid theory to generalized hypergeometric functions.*

4:00–4:45    Paul Edelman, *Discriminantal arrangements, free arrangements, and enumeration.*

Contemporary Mathematics
Volume **197**, 1996

# Participants List for Matroid Theory
## July 2–6, 1995, University of Washington, Seattle

Ian Affleck
Simon Fraser University
Canada

Laura Anderson
Indiana University at Bloomington
USA

Kenneth Bogart
Dartmouth College
USA

Joseph Bonin
The George Washington University
USA

Thomas Brylawski
Univ. of North Carolina, Chapel Hill
USA

Heidi Burgiel
University of Washington
USA

Seth Chaiken
SUNY at Albany
USA

Manoj Chari
Louisiana State University
USA

Robert Connelly
Cornell University
USA

Camille Cooper
York University
Canada

Henry Crapo
INRIA
France

Thomas Dowling
Ohio State University
USA

Paul Edelman
University of Minnesota
USA

Michael Falk
Northern Arizona University
USA

Luis Goddyn
Simon Fraser University
Canada

Gary Gordon
Lafayette College
USA

Jack Graver
Syracuse University
USA

Arthur Hobbs
Texas A & M University
USA

Robert Jamison
Clemson University
USA

Jürgen Richter-Gebert
Technische Universität Berlin
Germany

André Kézdy
University of Louisville
USA

Neil Robertson
Ohio State University
USA

Sandra Kingan
Oakland University
USA

Charles Semple
Victoria University of Wellington
New Zealand

Joseph Kung
University of North Texas
USA

Brigitte Servatius
Worcester Polytechnic Institute
USA

Hong-Jian Lai
West Virginia University
USA

Tiong-Seng Tay
National University of Singapore
Singapore

John Leo
Louisiana State University
USA

Paul Terwilliger
University of Wisconsin
USA

Jennifer McNulty
University of Montana
USA

Dirk Vertigan
Louisiana State University
USA

William Miller
The George Washington University
USA

Dominic Welsh
Mathematical Institute, Oxford
England

Allan Mills
Louisiana State University
USA

Neil White
University of Florida
USA

James Oxley
Louisiana State University
USA

Walter Whiteley
York University
Canada

Mark Purtill
Texas A & M University-Kingsville
USA

Geoffrey Whittle
Victoria University of Wellington
New Zealand

Andras Recski
Technical University of Budapest
Hungary

Haidong Wu
Southern University
USA

Talmage James Reid
University of Mississippi
USA

Günter Ziegler
Technische Universität Berlin
Germany

Contemporary Mathematics
Volume **197**, 1996

# Critical problems

## Joseph P. S. Kung

Dedicated to Gian-Carlo Rota on his Sixty-fourth Birthday

## 1. Introduction

Our aim in this paper is threefold: to give a survey of most of the work done on the critical problem in matroid theory, to describe the mathematical environment in which this critical problem has its habitat, and to indicate some of the open problems and problem areas. Thus, this paper combines three papers. The reader may therefore experience some disconcerting jumps in exposition, similar to those in the unfinished story *Kater Murr* by E. T. A. Hoffmann, most of which consists of a philosophical treatise accidentally written by a human and a cat on alternate pages. For example, sketches of baroque theories yet to be developed alternate with elementary calculations of critical exponents of specific matroids. But this merely reflects the present state of the subject: there are vast unexplored areas, both in theory and practice. It might therefore be useful to say to the reader, human or otherwise, that many sections can be omitted, often with a *gain* in continuity.

The material dealing with critical problems in matroid theory starts in Section 4. Sections 4, 5, 7 and 8 are perhaps the core of this paper for matroid theorists. These sections are best read in the intended order. Section 6 depends only on Sections 4.1 and 5.2 and can be read independently. In Section 2, we attempt to give a history of the critical problem by giving an account of two precursor problems. The first is Veblen's "algebraic" reformulation of the 4-color conjecture. The second is from algebraic tiling theory. This problem, formulated by Rédei, is to find a zeta-function proof of Hajós' theorem for abelian groups. We hope that experts in algebraic tiling theory will read Section 2 with a certain indulgence. In Section 3, we study the critical problem for relations. A relation is perhaps the most general mathematical structure on which a critical problem can be defined. Nonetheless, most of the enumerative theorems for matroids have analogues for relations. Relations also allow us to formulate the problem of finding the minimum number of generators of an algebraic object as a critical problem. Finally, in the appendix, we take the opportunity to correct a technical error in our earlier survey paper "Extremal matroid theory" [**81**].

1991 *Mathematics Subject Classification.* Primary 05B35; Secondary 05B20, 05C15, 05C35, 05D99, 06C10, 51E20.

There is some new material in this paper. It may be useful to the expert to give a list of the new topics: Frattini relations for closure operators (Section 3.2), Eulerian functions for matroids (Section 3.3), a mixed-characteristic critical problem for matroids (Section 4.1), cross-section matroids for polymatroids (Section 4.3), abstract linear functionals on Dowling group geometries (Section 4.5), row vectors of linear functionals and their applications (Section 4.7), a probabilistic algorithm for finding critical exponents (Section 4.7), extensions of various results relating critical exponents and sizes of bonds (Section 4.8), a dual version of the critical problem and explicit calculations of critical exponents of orthogonal duals of projective and representable Dowling group geometries (Section 4.9), a rank-4 Desargues' theorem for matroids (Section 5.6), a modular factorization theorem for Rédei functions (Section 5.8), a complete list of higher-weight rank-$n$ Dowling geometries with critical exponent $n - 1$ and an almost complete list of those with critical exponent $n - 2$, together with an explicit calculation of their characteristic polynomials (Sections 6.3 to 6.6), extensions of Mader's theorem and Wagner's theorem for graphs with no $K_m$-subcontractions to gain-graphic geometries (Sections 7.4 and 7.5), an inequality between the critical exponent of a representable geometry and the chromatic number of a certain graph (Section 7.6), a determination of all the rank-3 tangential 1-blocks over $GF(4)$ (Section 8.3), a characterization of minimal and tangential blocks with modular copoints (Section 8.4), and a formula for the characteristic polynomial of the $q$-lift of a geometry (Section 8.6). There are also surveys of two problem areas which have not been much studied. In Section 5.5, we discuss the problem of characterizing zero multisets of supersolvable geometries in a given class of geometries. In Section 5.6, we discuss the problem of finding all the geometries having the same characteristic polynomials as the three "classical" examples. Finally, we describe two theories which are in their gestation stage. The first is a theory of critical problems for higher-rank flats in matroids represented as sets of vectors (Section 4.6). The second is a representation-free formulation of the critical problem using strong maps (Section 4.10). A topic which we will not discuss in this paper is the theory of critical problems in orthogonal and symplectic analogues of matroids. Axioms for these analogues appeared in 1978 in Kung [**69,70**]. The first installment of this theory can be found in Kung [**86**].

We assume a basic knowledge of matroid theory. Some references are Crapo and Rota [**36**], Kung [**76**], Oxley [**106**], Welsh [**145**], and White [**150,151,152**]. Our approach to matroids is geometric and we think of them, for the most part, as sets of points in projective space. Partly for this reason, we shall call a simple matroid a geometry. We shall use the following convention for contractions of geometries. Let $x$ be a point in the geometry $G$. The geometry $G/x$ obtained by *contracting* $x$ from $G$ is the geometry on the set of lines in $G$ containing $x$ with lattice of flats the upper interval $[x, \hat{1}]$. In particular, $G/x$ is isomorphic to the simplification of the matroid $G/x$ as it is usually defined. This convention will be especially important in Sections 7 and 8 when we discuss minor-closed classes.

We shall find it useful to define characteristic polynomials for both matroids and geometric lattices. The *characteristic polynomial* $\chi(G; \lambda)$ of a matroid $G(S)$ on the set $S$ of elements is defined to be the following polynomial in the variable $\lambda$ :

$$\sum_{A:A\subseteq S} (-1)^{|A|} \lambda^{\mathrm{rank}(S)-\mathrm{rank}(A)}.$$

The characteristic polynomial of a geometric lattice $L$ is defined by the following equation:

$$\chi(L; \lambda) = \sum_{X: X \in L} \mu(\hat{0}, X) \lambda^{\text{rank}(\hat{1}) - \text{rank}(X)},$$

where $\mu$ is the Möbius function in the lattice $L$. If $G$ contains no loops, then $\chi(G; \lambda) = \chi(L(G); \lambda)$, where $L(G)$ is the lattice of flats of $G$. If $G$ contains loops, then $\chi(G; \lambda) = 0$.

We shall use the following notation throughout the paper. The standard basis vectors in a $d$-dimensional vector space are the vectors $e_1, e_2, \ldots, e_d$, where $e_i$ is the vector with $i$th coordinate 1 and all other coordinates 0. If $Y$ is a set of vectors in the vector space $\mathbb{F}^d$ or a set consisting of points or the zero element in the projective geometry $\text{PG}(d-1, \mathbb{F})$, then the *linear span* $\text{lin}(Y)$ is the subspace spanned by $Y$ in $\mathbb{F}^d$ or $\text{PG}(d-1, \mathbb{F})$. The *uniform matroid* $U_{n,k}$ is the matroid consisting of $k$ points in general position in a rank-$n$ space. The class $\mathcal{U}(q)$ is the class of matroids not containing the $(q+2)$-point line as a minor. The class $\mathcal{L}(q)$ is the class of $\text{GF}(q)$-representable matroids. The class $\mathcal{Z}(A)$ is the class of gain-graphic matroids with gains in the finite group $A$. A brief description of gain-graphic matroids can be found in Section 4.5.

Most of the matroids we consider are representable. A matroid $G(S)$ is *representable over the field* $\mathbb{F}$ if there exists a function $\phi$ defined from $S$ to the set of vectors in the vector space $\mathbb{F}^d$ or the set consisting of the points and the zero element in the projective geometry $\text{PG}(d-1, \mathbb{F})$ such that for every subset $A \subseteq S$,

$$\text{rank}_G(A) = \text{rank}(\phi(A)),$$

where the rank function on the right-hand side is rank in $\mathbb{F}^d$ or $\text{PG}(d-1, \mathbb{F})$. We shall find it useful to consider matroids with a specific representation $\phi$. To keep the notation simple, we shall not explicitly mention the function $\phi$ unless absolutely necessary. Instead, we shall say that a matroid is represented as "a set of vectors in $\mathbb{F}^d$" or "a set of points in $\text{PG}(d-1, \mathbb{F})$". This is not meant to be taken literally; for example, two elements in the same parallel class can be mapped by $\phi$ to the same vector or point and hence, a matroid can be represented only as a multiset of vectors or a multiset of points and the zero element. This slight inaccuracy is harmless.

In Sections 4.1, 4.10 and 8.7, we shall need the notion of a quotient.[1] Intuitively, a quotient $H$ of a matroid $G$ is the image of $G$ under a linear transformation. Because the matroid structure is invariant under changes of bases, quotients are images of projections. There are two ways of defining quotients. The "internal" definition abstracts the fact that the inverse image of a subspace under a linear transformation is a subspace. Let $G$ and $H$ be two matroids on the same set $S$ of elements. Then $H$ is a *quotient* of $G$ if every $H$-flat is also a $G$-flat. The "external" definition abstracts the idea of a projection. The matroid $H$ is a quotient of $G$ if there exists an extension $G^+$ of $G$ by a set $Q$ of elements (disjoint from $S$) so that

(1.1) $$H = G^+(S \cup Q)/Q;$$

in other words, a quotient is a matroid obtainable by an extension followed by a contraction. The equivalence of these two definitions follows from the Higgs' factorization theorem for strong maps (Higgs [61]). It is sometimes useful to think

---

[1]See Kung [72] for a more detailed exposition.

of the relation between $G$ and $H$ as a map: if $H$ is a quotient of $G$, then we say that the identity map from $S$ to itself induces a *quotient (strong) map* $G \to H$ from $G$ to $H$. An extension $G^+$ of $G$ satisfying equation (1.1) is said to be a *major* of the quotient map $G \to H$.

An example of a quotient is the *Brown* or *(complete) principal truncation* $T_X(G)$ of the rank-$n$ matroid $G$ by a rank-$r$ flat $X$ in $G$ (Brown [17]; see also Brylawski [20]). This is the rank-$(n - r + 1)$ quotient of $G$ whose flats are

    (1) the flats of $G$ containing $X$, and

    (2) the flats $Y$ of $G$ such that $\text{rank}(Y \vee X) = \text{rank}(Y) + r$.

If $G$ is represented as a set $S$ of vectors in $[\text{GF}(q)]^d$ or points in $\text{PG}(d - 1, q)$, then there is a natural way to obtain a quotient of $G$. Let $Q$ be a subspace in $[\text{GF}(q)]^d$ or $\text{PG}(d - 1, q)$. Then the matroid $G//Q$ on the set $S$ is the matroid constructed in two steps: first extend the matroid $G$ by adding a *copy* of $Q$ to $S$ (so that there will be an additional copy of any vector which is in both $S$ and $Q$), and then contract by $Q$. This is equivalent to considering the elements in $S$ as vectors in the quotient space $[\text{GF}(q)]^d/Q$, or as points or the zero element in the contraction $\text{PG}(d - 1, q)/Q$. The quotient $G//Q$ has no loops if and only if $Q \cap S = \emptyset$. For example, the principal truncation $T_X(G)$ can be obtained by taking $Q$ to be a rank-$(r-1)$ subspace such that $Q \subset \text{lin}(X)$ and $Q$ is "in general position" relative to $G$.

By construction, the quotient $G//Q$ is representable over $\text{GF}(q)$. A natural conjecture, given the equivalence between the internal and external definitions, is that all the $\text{GF}(q)$-representable quotients of a given $\text{GF}(q)$-representable matroid are of this form.

1.1. CONJECTURE. *Let $G$ be a $\text{GF}(q)$-representable matroid and let $H$ be a $\text{GF}(q)$-representable quotient of $G$. Then there exists a $\text{GF}(q)$-representable major $G^+$ of the quotient map $G \to H$.*

It is a useful fact that $G$ and $G//Q$ can be represented naturally in the same projective space. Let $G$ be a matroid represented in $\text{PG}(d - 1, q)$. Then the set $S$ of elements of $G//Q$ can be represented by flats of the form $x \vee Q$, where $x$ is a point in $S$. If $x \notin Q$, then $x \vee Q$ covers (and does not equal) $Q$ and $x \vee Q$ is a point in the projective space $\text{PG}(d - 1, q)/Q$. If $x \in Q$, then $x \vee Q$ equals $Q$, $x$ is a loop in $G//Q$, and $x$ is represented by the zero element in $\text{PG}(d - 1, q)/Q$. If $Y$ is a subset of $S$, then the linear span of the set $\{x \vee Q : x \in Y\}$ equals $\text{lin}(Y) \vee Q$. Hence, $Y$ (as a subset of $S$) is a $G//Q$-flat if and only if

$$Y = (\text{lin}(Y) \vee Q) \cap S.$$

In this paper, we shall be discussing a wide variety of critical problems. Central to all these critical problems are the related ideas of a "distinguishing" $s$-tuple and a "critical exponent". It will be cumbersome and pedantic to give distinct names to each occurrence of these ideas. Thus, the meaning of these words will always depend on the critical problem being discussed.

There have been several earlier surveys of the critical problem in matroids: Brylawski and Oxley [31], Welsh [146,147,148,149], and Zaslavsky [169]. It is not entirely fortuitous that the approaches in these papers are in some sense orthogonal to our approach in this paper. Brylawski, Oxley, and Zaslavsky emphasized the method of contraction and deletion. Welsh emphasized critical problems inspired by graph theory and the use of Seymour's decomposition theory. The three approaches are complementary and a complete picture can be obtained only by reading all five authors.

The publication of this paper coincides with the sixty-fourth birthday of Gian-Carlo Rota, the founder of the theory of critical problems. I had the privilege and good fortune to be his student and have learned many things from him, the most important, perhaps, is that combinatorics should not be studied in isolation but as part of a great *mathematical* tradition. Rota's *tao* of mathematics flows through this paper and it is my great pleasure to be able to dedicate this paper to him.

## 2. Rédei zeta functions

In 1970, Crapo and Rota ([**36**], Chapter 16; see also Kelly and Rota [**68**] and Rota [**118,119,120**]) formulated the *critical problem for matroids*:

> In a vector space $V_n$ of dimension $n$ over a field $GF(q)$, we consider a set $S$ of points not including the origin. The *critical problem* for the set $S$ is the problem of finding the minimum number $c$ of projective hyperplanes $H_1, H_2, \ldots, H_c$ with the property that the intersection $H_1 \cap H_2 \cap \ldots \cap H_c \cap S$ is null, that is, for every point $p \in S$, there exists at least one hyperplane $H_i$ such that $p \notin H_i$. Stated in slightly different terms, we seek the minimum number of linear functionals $L_1, L_2, \ldots, L_c$ such that for every point $p \in S$ there exists at least one linear functional $L_i$ for which $L_i(p) \neq 0$.

This problem includes many combinatorial problems as special cases and is now a standard topic in matroid theory. However, how the problem emerged and reached its final form remains somewhat obscure. The aim of this section is to give an account of the mathematical ideas surrounding the formulation of the critical problem.

The critical problem first appeared, in almost its definitive form for graphs, in the 1912 paper [**140**] of Veblen.[2] Veblen was interested in the four-color conjecture and stated his results in terms of maps. Rephrased in terms of graphs, Veblen proved that coloring a graph with four colors is equivalent to solving a system of inequalities over $GF(4)$. Let $\Gamma$ be a graph with $n$ vertices and let $y_1, y_2, \ldots, y_n$ be a set of variables with the variable $y_i$ corresponding to the vertex $v_i$ of $\Gamma$. Consider the following system of inequalities:

$$(2.1) \qquad y_i + y_j \neq 0, \text{ where } \{i, j\} \text{ is an edge of } \Gamma.$$

If $y_i = c_i$ is a solution of these inequalities over $GF(4)$, then assigning $c_i$ to the vertex $v_i$ yields a proper 4-coloring of $\Gamma$. Veblen showed that solving the system (2.1) is equivalent to finding a hyperplane or subspace of codimension-1 in the vector space $[GF(4)]^n$ disjoint from the set of vectors

$$\{e_i + e_j : \{i, j\} \text{ is an edge in } \Gamma\},$$

where $e_k$ is a standard basis vector. This surprisingly modern paper must have baffled most of Veblen's contemporaries. In 1966, Tutte [**136**] extended Veblen's problem to binary matroids. This extension will be described in detail in Section 8.

---

[2]This paper is reprinted in Chapter 8 of Biggs, Lloyd and Wilson [**8**]. In the same chapter is a description of earlier related work by Heawood.

A lesser known source for the critical problem is the following conjecture by Minkowski made between 1897 and 1907: In a lattice tiling of real $n$-dimensional space $\mathbb{R}^n$, there exist two tiles that share an $(n-1)$-face. This difficult conjecture remained open until 1942, when it was proved by Hajós. Hajós reformulated Minkowski's conjecture into an equivalent algebraic result about finite abelian groups (Hajós [54]). In this section, the binary operation in abelian groups will be multiplication.

Roughly speaking, Hajós' theorem says that if a finite abelian group can be factored into a product of cyclic subsets, then one of the cyclic subsets is a cyclic subgroup.

2.1. HAJÓS' THEOREM FOR FINITE ABELIAN GROUPS. *Let $G$ be a finite abelian group. Suppose that $X_1, X_2, \ldots, X_r$ are subsets of $G$ satisfying the following two properties:*

*(1) Each $X_i$ is of the form*

$$\{1, a_i, a_i^2, a_i^3, \ldots, a_i^{m_i-1}\}$$

*for some element $a_i$ in $G$. (Note that $m_i$ need not be the order of $a_i$.)*

*(2) Every element $g \in G$ can be written uniquely as a product*

$$g = x_1 x_2 \cdots x_r,$$

*where $x_i \in X_i$.*

*Then at least one of the subsets $X_i$ forms a (cyclic) subgroup of $G$.*

Theorem 2.1 is quite similar to the well-known structure theorem for finite abelian groups due to Frobenius and Stickelberger [51]. This theorem says that if $G$ is a finite abelian group, then there exist cyclic subgroups $X_1, X_2, \ldots, X_r$ such that every element $g \in G$ can be written uniquely as a product $g = x_1 x_2 \cdots x_r$, where $x_i \in X_i$. In fact, Hajós' theorem can be obtained from the structure theorem by interchanging an existential and a universal quantifier. For this reason, Rédei [115] called these two theorems the two fundamental theorems for abelian groups. It seems that Rédei was fascinated with Hajós' theorem; at any rate, he published several different ways of approaching Hajós' theorem with the aim of finding a transparent proof [112,113,114,115].[3]

Rédei was also interested in extending the notion of a zeta function to abelian groups and other algebraic structures [111]. Rédei defined the zeta function $\rho$ of a finite (non-empty) collection $\{A_1, A_2, \ldots, A_r\}$ of subgroups of an abelian group $G$ by the following formula:

$$\rho(s; A_1, A_2, \ldots, A_r) = \sum_{\{i_1, i_2, \ldots, i_m\} \subseteq \{1,2,\ldots,r\}} \frac{(-1)^m}{|A_{i_1} A_{i_2} \cdots A_{i_m}|^s},$$

where $|A|$ is the order of the group $A$ and $A_{i_1} A_{i_2} \cdots A_{i_m}$ is the subgroup generated by the subgroups $A_{i_1}, A_{i_2}, \ldots, A_{i_m}$. Note that

$$\rho(s; A_1, A_2, \ldots, A_r) = \sum_{X : X \in L} \mu(\hat{0}, X) |X|^{-s},$$

---

[3]An elementary account of some of this material can be found in the Carus monograph of Stein and Szabó [127]. In particular, an account of how Minkowski's conjecture is implied by Hajós' theorem can be found in Chapter 1. The proof of Hajós' theorem in this book is based on Rédei's proof in [114] and is similar to Rédei's proof given in [115].

where $\mu$ is the Möbius function in the lattice $L$ formed by the subgroups of the form $A_{i_1} A_{i_2} \cdots A_{i_m}$, where $\{i_1, i_2, \ldots, i_m\}$ is a subset of $\{1, 2, \ldots, r\}$, under set-theoretic containment. For more on the combinatorics of Rédei zeta functions, see Kung, Murty and Rota [86].

By taking a profinite limit of finite cyclic groups, one obtains as a limit of Rédei zeta functions of finite cyclic groups the Dirichlet series

$$\frac{1}{\zeta(s)} = \sum_{n=1}^{\infty} \frac{\mu(n)}{n^s},$$

where $\mu(n)$ is the number-theoretic Möbius function. From this, one sees that Rédei's "zeta" function is an analogue of the *reciprocal* of the Riemann zeta function. Nonetheless, Rédei called it a zeta function and this inaccurate terminology has become standard.

Rédei showed in his 1955 paper [112] that his two interests had non-empty intersection. He reformulated Hajós' theorem in terms of zeta functions of abelian groups. We shall describe the ideas behind this reformulation.

We begin by noting that the hypothesis in Hajós' theorem can be compactly written using the group ring $\mathbb{Q}G$. The *group ring* $\mathbb{Q}G$ of the group $G$ over the rationals $\mathbb{Q}$ is the ring of all formal linear combinations $\sum \alpha_g g$ of group elements in $G$ with rational coefficients $\alpha_g$. Multiplication is defined to be group multiplication for the basis elements and extended linearly to the formal linear combinations. Using the same notation as in Theorem 2.1, consider the following product in $\mathbb{Q}G$:

$$(1 + a_1 + a_1^2 + \ldots + a_1^{m_1 - 1})(1 + a_2 + a_2^2 + \ldots + a_2^{m_2 - 1}) \cdots (1 + a_r + a_r^2 + \ldots + a_r^{m_r - 1}).$$

If every element in $G$ can be written uniquely as a product $x_1 x_2 \cdots x_r$, where $x_i \in X_i$, then this product equals

$$\sum_{g \in G} g.$$

Writing

$$[A] = \sum_{g \in A} g$$

for a subset $A$ of elements of $G$, the hypothesis in Hajós' theorem can be written

$$[G] = [X_1][X_2] \cdots [X_r].$$

This product identity remains valid when acted on by a linear character. A *(linear) character* $\chi$ of an abelian group $G$ is a homomorphism of $G$ into the unit circle consisting of those complex numbers with modulus 1 in the complex plane. The *trivial* character $\chi^1$ is the character sending every element in $G$ to 1. Given a character $\chi$ of $G$, we can extend its domain to the group ring $\mathbb{Q}G$ by linearity. Assuming the hypothesis in Hajós' theorem, a simple expansion shows that

$$\chi([G]) = \chi([X_1])\chi([X_2]) \cdots \chi([X_r]).$$

If $\chi$ is not the trivial character, then, by an orthogonality relation for characters, $\chi([G]) = 0$; hence, one of the terms $\chi([X_j])$ must be zero. One of the difficulties in proving Hajós theorem is that while $\chi([X]) = 0$ if $X$ is a subgroup, the converse is not true.[4]

Next, we note that if the size $m_i$ of the cyclic set $X_i$ is not prime, then $X_i$ can be factored further into smaller cyclic subsets. Hence, we can assume that the numbers $m_i$ are prime. We shall change our notation to conform with this assumption and write $m_i = p_i$. By an easy reduction lemma of Rédei [**112,113**], we can also assume that $p_i$ divides the order of the element $a_i$.

Rédei observed that condition (2) in Hajós' theorem implies that products of the form

$$a_1^{k_1} a_2^{k_2} \cdots a_r^{k_r}, \text{ where } p_i \nmid k_i \text{ for all } i,$$

never equal the identity $e$. In terms of the group ring, this says that if $A_i$ is the cyclic subgroup generated by $a_i$ and $B_i = A_i^{p_i}$ is the subgroup of $A_i$ consisting of all the $p_i$th powers in $A_i$, then the coefficient of the identity in the product

$$\prod_{i=1}^{r} ([A_i] - [B_i])$$

in the group ring $\mathbb{Q}G$ is zero. On the other hand, we can expand this product. A typical term in this product has the form

$$(-1)^{r-m} [A_{i_1}][A_{i_2}] \cdots [A_{i_m}][B_{j_1}][B_{j_2}] \cdots [B_{j_{r-m}}],$$

where $\{i_1, i_2, \ldots, i_m\}$ is a subset of $\{1, 2, \ldots, r\}$ and $\{j_1, j_2, \ldots, j_{r-m}\}$ is its complementary subset. Using some elementary group theory, the coefficient of the identity in this term is

$$(-1)^{r-m} \frac{|A_{i_1}||A_{i_2}| \cdots |A_{i_m}||B_{j_1}||B_{j_2}| \cdots |B_{j_{r-m}}|}{|A_{i_1} A_{i_2} \cdots A_{i_m} B_{j_1} B_{j_2} \cdots B_{j_{r-m}}|}.$$

Because we can assume that $p_i$ divides the order of $a_i$, $|B_i| = |A_i|/p_i$. Hence the coefficient of the identity in the product equals

$$(-1)^r |A_1||A_2| \cdots |A_r| \sum_{\{i_1, i_2, \ldots, i_m\}} \frac{(-1)^m}{p_{j_1} p_{j_2} \cdots p_{j_{r-m}} |A_{i_1} A_{i_2} \cdots A_{i_m} B_{j_1} B_{j_2} \cdots B_{j_{r-m}}|},$$

where the sum ranges over all subsets $\{i_1, i_2, \ldots, i_m\}$ of $\{1, 2, \ldots, r\}$. Except for a common factor of $(-1)^r |A_1||A_2| \cdots |A_r|$ and various factors of $p_j$ in the summands, this expression resembles a multiple of a zeta function evaluated at 1.

Rédei's observation holds not only in $G$ but in all subgroups of the form $A_M$, where $M = \{i_1, i_2, \ldots, i_k\}$ is any non-empty subset of $\{1, 2, \ldots, r\}$ and $A_M = A_{i_1} A_{i_2} \cdots A_{i_k}$. Define $\Delta_M(s)$ by

$$\Delta_M(s) = \sum_{N \subseteq M} \frac{(-1)^{|N|}}{\left(\prod_{j \in M \setminus N} p_j^s\right) \left|\left(\prod_{i \in N} A_i\right)\left(\prod_{j \in M \setminus N} B_j\right)\right|^s}.$$

Then by the same argument, $\Delta_M(1)$ is the coefficient of the identity in the product

$$\prod_{i \in M} ([A_i] - [B_i])$$

---

[4] To see this, observe that the coefficient of $\lambda^{d-1}$ of a degree-$d$ cyclotomic polynomial in the variable $\lambda$ is a sum of roots of unity and there are cyclotomic polynomials for which this coefficient is zero.

and it equals 0 when the conditions in Hajós' theorem hold. Rédei's argument can be easily reversed and he concluded that the conditions in Hajós' theorem are equivalent to the following equations:

(2.2)    $\Delta_M(1) = 0$ for all non-empty subsets $M$ contained in $\{1, 2, \ldots, r\}$.

The functions $\Delta_M(s)$ are related to zeta functions by the following identity:

$$\frac{1}{\prod_{j \in \{1,2,\ldots,r\}} p_j^s} - \frac{1}{|\prod_{i \in \{1,2,\ldots,r\}} A_i|^s} + \sum_{M \subseteq \{1,\ldots,r\}, \, M \neq \emptyset} \frac{\Delta_M(s)}{\prod_{j \in \{1,2,\ldots,r\} \setminus M} p_j^s}$$

$$= \sum_{M \subset \{1,\ldots,r\}} \frac{\rho(s; M)}{(\prod_{j \in \{1,2,\ldots,r\} \setminus M} p_j^s)|\prod_{i \in M} A_i|^s},$$

where

$$\rho(s; M) = \rho(s; B_{j_1} A_M / A_M, B_{j_2} A_M / A_M, \ldots, B_{j_k} A_M / A_M)$$

and $\{j_1, j_2, \ldots, j_k\}$ is the complement of $M$ in $\{1, 2, \ldots, r\}$. This identity can be proved by interchanging the order of summation on both sides of the identity. Rédei noted that all coefficients in this identity are positive. He also noted that if

(2.3)                          $|A_1 A_2 \cdots A_r| = p_1 p_2 \cdots p_r,$

then the two reciprocals on the left-hand side cancel. Thus, assuming equation (2.3) holds, then one can prove that the system (2.2) of equations is equivalent to the system:

(2.4)              $\rho(1; M) = 0$ for all proper subsets $M \subset \{1, 2, \ldots, r\}$

by showing that $\Delta_M(1) \geq 0$ and $\rho(1; M) \geq 0$ for all subsets $M$ of $\{1, 2, \ldots, r\}$. Rédei proved that $\Delta_M(1) \geq 0$ by induction. That $\rho(1; M) \geq 0$ follows from a "weight theorem" in his paper [**111**] for zeta functions of collections of subgroups of an abelian group.

2.2. RÉDEI'S TRÄGHEITSATZ. *Let $\{A_1, A_2, \ldots, A_r\}$ be a non-empty collection of subgroups of a finite abelian group $G$ and let $s$ be a positive integer. Then*

$$0 \leq \rho(s; A_1, A_2, \ldots, A_r) < 1.$$

Rédei proved the *Trägheitsatz* by an inductive argument. Replacing the conditions in Hajós' theorem by equation (2.3) and the system (2.4), Rédei obtained the following equivalent version of Hajós' theorem.

2.3. THEOREM. *Let $A_1, A_2, \ldots, A_r$ be cyclic subgroups of a finite abelian group $G$, let $p_1, p_2, \ldots, p_r$ be prime numbers such that $p_i$ divides $|A_i|$, and let $B_i = A_i^{p_i} = \{x^{p_i} : x \in A_i\}$ be the subgroup of $p_i$th powers of elements in $A_i$. Suppose that*
   (1) *$|A_1 A_2 \cdots A_r| = p_1 p_2 \cdots p_r$, and*
   (2) *for every proper subset $M = \{i_1, i_2, \ldots, i_m\}$ of $\{1, 2, \ldots, r\}$,*

$$\rho(1; M) = 0.$$

*Then for all integers $s$ greater than 1,*

$$\rho(s; B_1, B_2, \ldots, B_r) = 0,$$

*or, equivalently, one of the subgroups $B_i$ is the identity subgroup.*

Rédei did not succeed in finding an independent zeta-function proof of this version of Hajós' theorem. Although Rédei published another proof of Hajós' theorem [114,115] in 1965, he seems not to have pursued this approach further.

As the reader might already have guessed, the link to the critical problem is the *Trägheitsatz*. From a combinatorial perspective, the way to show that a number lies between 0 and 1 is to interpret it as a probability. This is clear now, but it was a significant step when Rota proved the following result around 1965 (see Rota [120] and Kung, Murty and Rota [86]). Let $A_1, A_2, \ldots, A_m$ be a collection of subgroups of the abelian group $G$. An $s$-tuple $(\chi_1, \chi_2, \ldots, \chi_s)$ of linear characters of $G$ is said to *distinguish* $A_1, A_2, \ldots, A_m$ if either of the following equivalent conditions holds:

(1) For every subgroup $A_i$, there is a character $\chi_j$ such that $\chi_j$ restricted to $A_i$ is not the trivial character, that is, the character $\chi_j$ does not send every element in $A_i$ to 1.

(2) For every subgroup $A_i$ in the collection,

$$A_i \not\subseteq \ker \chi_1 \cap \ker \chi_2 \cap \ldots \cap \ker \chi_s.$$

2.4. THEOREM (ROTA). *Let $A_1, A_2, \ldots, A_r$ be a collection of subgroups of the abelian group $G$ and let $s$ be a positive integer. Then*

$$\rho(s; A_1, A_2, \ldots, A_r)$$

*is the probability that an $s$-tuple $(\chi_1, \chi_2, \ldots, \chi_s)$ of linear characters of $G$ distinguishes $A_1, A_2, \ldots, A_r$.*

To prove this theorem, recall that the set of (linear) characters of a finite abelian group $G$ forms an abelian group isomorphic to $G$. Hence, the number of linear characters on $A$ equals $|A|$. Let $A_{i_1}, A_{i_2}, \ldots, A_{i_m}$ be a collection of subgroups. A character $\chi$ of $G$ is trivial on a subgroup $A$ if and only if it defines a character on the quotient $G/A$. Moreover, $\chi$ is trivial on the subgroups $A$ and $A'$ if and only if $\chi$ is trivial on the subgroup $AA'$ generated by $A$ and $A'$. Hence, if $\{A_{i_1}, A_{i_2}, \ldots, A_{i_m}\}$ is a subcollection of the given collection of subgroups, then the number of $s$-tuples $(\chi_1, \chi_2, \ldots, \chi_s)$ of characters such that for all $k, 1 \leq k \leq m$,

$$A_{i_k} \subseteq \ker \chi_1 \cap \ker \chi_2 \cap \ldots \cap \ker \chi_s$$

equals

$$\left[ \frac{|G|}{|A_{i_1} A_{i_2} \cdots A_{i_m}|} \right]^s.$$

By the principle of inclusion and exclusion, the number of $s$-tuples $(\chi_1, \chi_2, \ldots, \chi_s)$ such that none of the subgroups $A_i$ is contained in $\ker \chi_1 \cap \ker \chi_2 \cap \ldots \cap \ker \chi_s$ equals

$$|G|^s \left( \sum_{\{i_1, i_2, \ldots, i_m\} \subseteq \{1, 2, \ldots, r\}} \frac{(-1)^m}{|A_{i_1} A_{i_2} \cdots A_{i_m}|^s} \right).$$

Dividing by $|G|^s$, the number of ways of choosing any $s$-tuple of characters, we conclude that $\rho(s; A_1, A_2, \ldots, A_r)$ is the probability of choosing an $s$-tuple distinguishing $A_1, A_2, \ldots, A_r$. This completes the proof of Rota's theorem.

Note that because the $s$-tuple $(\chi^1, \chi^1, \ldots, \chi^1)$, where $\chi^1$ is the trivial character on $G$, does not distinguish the (non-empty) collection $\{A_1, A_2, \ldots, A_r\}$ of subgroups, $|G|^s \rho(s; A_1, A_2, \ldots, A_r)$ is strictly less than 1. Thus, the *Trägheitsatz* follows from Rota's theorem.

Much remains to be done on critical problems for collections of subgroups of a finite abelian group. The outstanding problem is to give a combinatorial proof of Hajós' theorem. Perhaps the idea of a critical problem can be used directly to do this. Rota [121] has observed that the lattice of subgroups of an abelian group is a modular lattice (which may not be atomic). Thus, collections of subgroups of an abelian group are similar to polymatroids, which are abstractions of collections of subspaces in a vector space. The combinatorics of collections of subgroups of abelian groups should be a rewarding area of study.[5]

The counting proof of Theorem 2.4 motivated the enumerative approach to the critical problem and, in particular, Theorem 4.1. Theorem 4.1, which shows that the critical problem is an intrinsically matroidal problem, is the cornerstone of the "modern" theory of the critical problem for matroids.

## 3. Critical problems for relations

It is evident from Section 2 that critical problems exist in other areas of mathematics. The objective of this section is to develop a general theory of critical problems which includes most of the known examples.

### 3.1. Rédei functions for relations

A general form of the critical problem is the one defined for relations (Kung [71]). Let $R \subseteq S \times T$ be a relation between the finite sets $S$ and $T$. When $(x, u) \in R$, we say that $x$ *is related to* $u$. If $A \subseteq S$ and $B \subseteq T$, then $R : A \times B$ is the relation between $A$ and $B$ obtained by taking the intersection of $R$ with $A \times B$. In particular, the original relation $R$ is the relation $R : S \times T$. If $C \subseteq S$, its *perpendicular* $C^\perp$ is the set defined by

$$C^\perp = \{u : u \in T \text{ and for all } x \in C, (x, u) \notin R\}.$$

The perpendicular of a subset of $T$ is defined analogously. We shall write $a^\perp$ instead of $\{a\}^\perp$ for the perpendicular of a one-element set. The perpendicular operator defines a Galois connection between the lattices $2^S$ and $2^T$ of subsets of the sets $S$ and $T$. In particular, the map $A \mapsto A^{\perp\perp}$ defines closure operators on $S$ and $T$. We shall denote the lattice of closed sets in $S$ by $\mathrm{Lat}(S)$.

Let $\underline{u} = (u_1, u_2, \ldots, u_s)$ be an $s$-tuple of elements from $T$. The *kernel* $\ker \underline{u}$ of the $s$-tuple $\underline{u}$ is the subset of $S$ defined by

$$\ker \underline{u} = u_1^\perp \cap u_2^\perp \cap \ldots \cap u_s^\perp.$$

The $s$-tuple $\underline{u}$ is said to *distinguish* $S$ if for every element $x$ in $S$, there exists an index $i$ such that $(x, u_i) \in R$, or, equivalently,

$$\ker \underline{u} = \emptyset.$$

---

[5] An early paper in this area is Baer [4].

The *Rédei function* $\zeta(R{:}S \times T; s)$ is defined by:

$$\zeta(R{:}S \times T; s) = \text{number of } s\text{-tuples distinguishing } S.$$

If there exists an $s$-tuple distinguishing $S$ for some integer $s$, then the *critical exponent* of the relation $R$ is defined to be the minimum such integer. The critical exponent of $R$ is said to be *infinite* otherwise.

Despite the general setting, Rédei functions satisfy analogues of two basic properties of characteristic polynomials.

3.1. THEOREM. *Rédei functions satisfy the following identity called the* perpendicular decomposition:

$$(3.1) \qquad \zeta(R{:}S \times T; s) = \zeta(R{:}(S\backslash\{a\}) \times T; s) - \zeta(R{:}(S\backslash\{a\}) \times a^{\perp}; s).$$

*In addition,*

$$
\begin{aligned}
\zeta(R{:}S \times T; s) &= \sum_{B:B\subseteq S} (-1)^{|B|} |B^{\perp}|^s \\
&= \sum_{C:C\in\mathrm{Lat}(S)} \mu(\hat{0}, C)|C^{\perp}|^s.
\end{aligned}
$$

(3.2)

PROOF. Consider the set of $s$-tuples distinguishing $S\backslash\{a\}$ in the relation $R{:}$ $S\backslash\{a\} \times T$. This can be partitioned into two subsets:

(1) those $s$-tuples $\underline{u}$ for which $a$ is *not* in $u_1^{\perp} \cap u_2^{\perp} \cap \ldots \cap u_s^{\perp}$, and

(2) those $s$-tuples $\underline{u}$ for which $a$ is in $u_1^{\perp} \cap u_2^{\perp} \cap \ldots \cap u_s^{\perp}$.

Hence,

$$\zeta(R{:}S \times T; s) + \zeta(R{:}(S\backslash\{a\}) \times a^{\perp}; s) = \zeta(R{:}(S\backslash\{a\}) \times T; s).$$

There are two ways to prove the first part of equation (3.2): by induction using the perpendicular decomposition and by the principle of inclusion-exclusion. The second part of equation (3.2) is simply a restatement of the first part using the theory of Möbius functions. It can also be proved directly using Möbius inversion. For more details, see [71].                                                                 □

The classical case of a Rédei function is the characteristic polynomial of a representable matroid. Let $S$ be a subset of vectors in $[\mathrm{GF}(q)]^d$ and let $T$ be the dual space of the linear functionals on $[\mathrm{GF}(q)]^d$. Let $R$ be the relation

$$(x, L) \in R \Leftrightarrow L(x) \neq 0.$$

Then the lattice $\mathrm{Lat}(S)$ of $\perp$-closed sets is the lattice of flats $L(G)$ and

$$\zeta(R{:}S \times T; s) = q^{s(d-\mathrm{rank}(S))}\chi(G; q^s),$$

where $G$ is the matroid on $S$ specified by linear dependence. In this case, the perpendicular decomposition specializes to the contraction-and-deletion decomposition for characteristic polynomials (see Section 5.1). Note that there is no need to distinguish the case when $a$ is an isthmus. The notion of perpendicularity takes care of this case automatically. Almost all known identities for characteristic polynomials have analogues for Rédei functions. These analogues will be described in

Section 5.8. Farr [**49**] has developed a theory of generalized Whitney rank generating functions using "quasi-rank functions". Farr's rank generating functions are closely related to Rédei functions.

## 3.2. Frattini relations

A *closure operator* $A \mapsto A^*$ on the set $T$ is a function defined from subsets of $T$ to subsets of $T$ satisfying three conditions:

(1) $A \subseteq A^*$.
(2) If $A \subseteq B$, then $A^* \subseteq B^*$.
(3) $A^{**} = A^*$.

We recall several elementary definitions and results about closure operators. A subset $C \subseteq T$ is *closed* if $C^* = C$. If $C$ is a closed set and $A \subseteq C$, then $A$ *spans* $C$ if $A^* = C$. Intersections of closed sets are closed and the closure $A^*$ of a set $A$ equals the intersection of all the closed sets containing it. The collection of closed sets forms a lattice $\mathrm{Lat}^*(T)$. A closed set $M$ is *maximal* if $M \neq T$ and there are no closed sets $N$ such that $M \subset N \subset T$. Note that maximal closed sets are proper subsets of $T$ by definition.

Let $A \mapsto A^*$ be a closure operator on $T$ and let $\mathcal{M}$ be the collection of maximal closed subsets. The *Frattini relation* is the relation $F \subseteq \mathcal{M} \times T$ defined by

$$(M, x) \in F \Leftrightarrow x \notin M.$$

3.2. LEMMA. *An s-tuple $\underline{x} = (x_1, x_2, \ldots, x_s)$ distinguishes $\mathcal{M}$ if and only if the set $\{x_1, x_2, \ldots, x_s\}$ spans $T$.*

The proof is an abstraction of a classical argument of Frattini [**50**] in group theory. Because the closure of a set $A$ is contained in any closed set containing $A$,

$$(x_1, x_2, \ldots, x_s) \text{ does not distinguish } \mathcal{M}$$
$$\Leftrightarrow \text{ there exists } M \in \mathcal{M} \text{ such that } \{x_1, x_2, \ldots, x_s\} \subseteq M$$
$$\Leftrightarrow \text{ there exists } M \in \mathcal{M} \text{ such that } \{x_1, x_2, \ldots, x_s\}^* \subseteq M \subset T$$
$$\Leftrightarrow \{x_1, x_2, \ldots, x_s\} \text{ does not span.}$$

This proves the lemma.

The original Frattini relation is when $G$ is a finite group and the closure of a subset is the subgroup generated by that subset. In this case, the Rédei function is the *Eulerian function* $\phi(G; s)$ defined by Philip Hall [**55**].

To calculate the Rédei function $\zeta(F; s)$ of a Frattini relation $F$, observe that if $M$ is a maximal closed set in $\mathcal{M}$, then $M^\perp = M$. Hence, if $M_1, M_2, \ldots, M_k \in \mathcal{M}$,

$$M_1^\perp \cap M_2^\perp \cap \ldots \cap M_k^\perp = M_1 \cap M_2 \cap \ldots \cap M_k.$$

Therefore, the lattice $\mathrm{Lat}^\perp(\mathcal{M})$ of $\perp$-closed sets is a sublattice of the order dual of the lattice $\mathrm{Lat}^*(T)$ of $*$-closed sets. It consists of those $*$-closed sets which are intersections of maximal closed sets. By Theorem 3.1,

$$\zeta(F; s) = \sum_{X : X \in \mathrm{Lat}^\perp(\mathcal{M})} \mu(X, T)|X|^s.$$

Because the Möbius function is zero unless a closed set is an intersection of maximal closed sets,[6] the sum can also range over the lattice $\text{Lat}^*(T)$. In the case of groups, this yields

$$\phi(G; s) = \sum_{H \in L(G)} \mu(H, G)|H|^s,$$

where $L(G)$ is the lattice of subgroups of $G$. The critical exponent is the minimum number of generators for the group $G$. An account of work done on Eulerian functions of groups can be found in Kung [85].

### 3.3. Eulerian functions for matroids

For us, the natural closure operator to study is closure in a matroid. Let $M$ be a rank-$n$ matroid on the set of elements $S$ and let $L(M)$ be its lattice of flats. We define the *Eulerian function* $\phi(M; s)$ of $M$ to be the Rédei function of the Frattini relation of the closure operator of $M$. Thus,

$$\phi(M; s) = \text{number of } s\text{-tuples spanning } S$$
$$= \sum_{X : X \in L(M)} \mu(X, S)|X|^s.$$

The Eulerian function $\phi(M; s)$ behaves in many ways like the order-dual of the characteristic polynomial.

For the Frattini relation of a matroid closure, the critical problem is easily solved. The critical exponent is the rank $n$ of $M$ and $\phi(M; n)/n!$ is the number of bases in $M$. In particular, $\phi(M; s) = 0$ for $0 \leq s < n$. Thus, the theory of Eulerian functions yields a set of identities which must be satisfied by the Möbius function of the lattice $L(M)$ of flats of a matroid $M$:

(3.3)     $$\sum_{X \in L(M)} \mu(X, S)|X|^s = 0 \quad \text{for } 0 \leq s < \text{rank}(M).$$

From the Eulerian function, we can obtain the number $\bar{\phi}(M; s)$ of $s$-subsets spanning $S$ in $M$. By Möbius inversion,

$$\bar{\phi}(M; s) = \sum_{X \in L(M)} \mu(X, S) \binom{|X|}{s}.$$

Using the identity

(3.4)     $$\binom{\lambda}{s} = \frac{1}{s!} \sum_{j=0}^{s} (-1)^{s-j} t(s, j) \lambda^j,$$

where $t(s, j)$ is the signless Stirling numbers of the first kind, we obtain:

$$\bar{\phi}(M; s) = \frac{1}{s!} \sum_{j=0}^{s} (-1)^{s-j} t(s, j) \phi(M; j).$$

---

[6]This follows from one of Philip Hall's theorems about Möbius functions. This application is why Hall proved that theorem.

Closed forms for the Eulerian function are known in several cases. One case is when $M$ is the *matroid* consisting of *all* vectors in the vector space $[\mathrm{GF}(q)]^n$. In this case,

$$\phi([\mathrm{GF}(q)]^n; s) = \sum_{j=0}^{n}(-1)^{n-j}q^{\binom{n-j}{2}}\begin{bmatrix} n \\ j \end{bmatrix}_q (q^j)^s$$
$$= (q^s - 1)(q^s - q)\cdots(q^s - q^{n-1}).$$

The second step can be justified by observing that the sum is a reindexed version of the characteristic polynomial of $\mathrm{PG}(n-1, q)$. This observation is really the following identity of Cauchy:

$$(3.5) \qquad \sum_{j=0}^{n}(-1)^j q^{\binom{j}{2}}\begin{bmatrix} n \\ j \end{bmatrix}_q \lambda^{n-j} = (\lambda - 1)(\lambda - q)\cdots(\lambda - q^{n-1}).$$

A quick proof of Cauchy's identity can be given using Eulerian functions: by equation (3.3), the monic polynomial of degree $n$ on the left hand side of equation (3.5) has zeroes at $\lambda = q^j, 0 \leq j \leq n - 1$.

The Eulerian function of the projective geometry $\mathrm{PG}(n - 1, q)$ can also be calculated. Reindexing the sum from the definition, we have

$$\phi(\mathrm{PG}(n - 1, q); s) = \sum_{j=0}^{n}(-1)^j q^{\binom{j}{2}}\begin{bmatrix} n \\ j \end{bmatrix}_q \left(\frac{q^{n-j} - 1}{q - 1}\right)^s.$$

Expanding $(q^{n-j} - 1)^s$ using the binomial theorem, interchanging the order of summation, and using formula (3.5), we obtain

$$\phi(\mathrm{PG}(n - 1, q); s) = \frac{1}{(q - 1)^s}\sum_{j=0}^{s}(-1)^{s-j}\binom{s}{j}\prod_{k=0}^{n-1}(q^j - q^k).$$

The similarity between the Eulerian functions and the characteristic polynomials of vector and projective spaces is not surprising because the critical problem for the Frattini relation *is* the order dual of the classical critical problem for these matroids.[7]

For uniform geometries, the Eulerian function $\phi(U_{n,k}; s)$ equals the number of $s$-tuples $(x_1, x_2, \ldots, x_s)$ of elements of $U_{n,k}$ such that the *set* $\{x_1, x_2, \ldots, x_s\}$ has at least $n$ elements. A simple counting argument yields

$$\phi(U_{n,k}; s) = n!\binom{k}{n}S(s, n) + (n + 1)!\binom{k}{n + 1}S(s, n + 1) +$$

$$\ldots + (k - 1)!\binom{k}{k - 1}S(s, k - 1) + k!S(s, k).$$

Here, $S(j, k)$ is the number of partitions of a set of size $j$ into $k$ blocks. The formula for $\bar{\phi}(U_{n,k}; s)$ is simpler: it equals $\binom{k}{s}$ if $s \geq n$ and 0 otherwise.

---

[7]In an analogous way, for a finite abelian group, the Rédei zeta function is the "order dual" of the Eulerian function. This suggests that there is an extension of the Rédei zeta function to finite non-abelian groups.

In particular, for the free geometry or Boolean algebra $U_{n,n}$,

$$\phi(U_{n,n}; s) = \sum_{j=0}^{n} (-1)^{n-j} \binom{n}{j} j^s$$

$$= n! S(s, n).$$

The perpendicular decomposition is awkward to use for Frattini relations since the deletion of a copoint is not compatible with the matroid structure. A recursion which stays within Frattini relations of matroids can be obtained by deleting all the copoints not on a given element.

3.3. PROPOSITION. *Let $M(S)$ be a matroid on the set $S$ and let $a \in S$ be an element which is not a loop. Then*

$$(3.6) \qquad \phi(M; s) = \phi(M/a \oplus \{a\}; s) - \sum_{C: a \notin C} \phi(M|C; s),$$

*where the sum is over all the copoints $C$ not containing the element $a$, $M|C$ is the restriction of $M$ to the copoint $C$, and, as the notation indicates, $M/a \oplus \{a\}$ is the matroid obtained by contracting $M$ by $a$ and then adding $a$ back to the matroid $M/a$ as a loop.*

Proposition 3.3 was discovered and can be proved by iterating the perpendicular decomposition; it can also be proved using Weisner's theorem for Möbius functions. There is also a direct counting proof. Observe that the set of $s$-tuples $(x_1, x_2, \ldots, x_s)$ spanning $M/a \oplus \{a\}$ can be partitioned into two subsets: those that span $M$ and those that do not. If $\{x_1, x_2, \ldots, x_s\}$ does not span $M$, then $\{x_1, x_2, \ldots, x_s, a\}$ spans $M$, and hence, $\{x_1, x_2, \ldots, x_s\}$ spans a copoint $C$ not containing $a$.

Equation (3.6) can be simplified further with the following formula. If $c$ is a loop in the matroid $M$, then

$$\phi(M; s) = \sum_{j=0}^{s-1} \binom{s}{j} \phi(M \setminus \{c\}; s - j).$$

### 3.4. Two other examples

We end this section by showing that two difficult and central areas in mathematics are *really* about solving critical problems.

Using the classification theorem for finite simple groups, it can be shown that every finite simple group can be generated by two elements.

3.4. THEOREM. *Let $G$ be a finite simple group and $\phi(G; s)$ its Eulerian function. Then*

$$\phi(G; 2) > 0.$$

It has been observed that much of the classification theorem can be proved in a relatively easy way if one assumes Theorem 3.4 as a starting point. Thus, finding critical exponents *could* be a central problem in the study of finite simple groups.

The number-theoretic function $\pi(n)$, the number of prime numbers less than or equal to $n$, can be interpreted as a critical exponent in a similar way using the closure operator on the set $\{1, 2, \ldots, n\}$ which sends a subset $A \subseteq \{1, 2, \ldots, n\}$ to the set of integers in $\{1, 2, \ldots, n\}$ which are products of integers in $A$. For a genuine application of the critical problem to number theory, see Matthews [**93**].

## 4. Critical problems in finite vector spaces

### 4.1. The classical critical problem for matroids

We begin with the classical critical problem formulated by Crapo and Rota in 1970 [**36**]. There are two equivalent ways to pose the critical problem, the functional or algebraic way and the geometric way. We begin with the *algebraic* way. Let $G(S)$ be a matroid represented as a set of vectors in the $d$-dimensional vector space $[\mathrm{GF}(q)]^d$ over the finite field $\mathrm{GF}(q)$. An $s$-tuple $\underline{L} = (L_1, L_2, \ldots, L_s)$ of linear functionals is said to *distinguish* $G(S)$ if for every vector $x$ in $S$, there is a linear functional $L_i$ such that $L_i(x) \neq 0$.

The *kernel* $\ker L$ of a linear functional $L$ is the subspace $\{x : L(x) = 0\}$ in $[\mathrm{GF}(q)]^d$. If $L$ is not identically zero, $\ker L$ is a *hyperplane* or subspace of codimension 1. The *kernel* of an $s$-tuple $\underline{L} = (L_1, L_2, \ldots, L_s)$ is defined by

$$\ker \underline{L} = \ker L_1 \cap \ker L_2 \cap \ldots \cap \ker L_s.$$

In this notation, an $s$-tuple $\underline{L}$ distinguishes $G(S)$ if and only if $\ker \underline{L} \cap S = \emptyset$.

4.1. THEOREM (CRAPO AND ROTA). *Let $G(S)$ be a rank-$n$ matroid represented as a set $S$ of vectors in $[\mathrm{GF}(q)]^d$. Then the number of $s$-tuples distinguishing $S$ equals*

$$q^{s(d-n)}\chi(G; q^s),$$

*where $\chi(G; \lambda)$ is the characteristic polynomial of the matroid $G$.*

PROOF. If $\underline{L} = (L_1, L_2, \ldots, L_s)$ is an $s$-tuple of linear functionals, its $G$-kernel is the subset $G$-$\ker \underline{L}$ defined by

$$G\text{-}\ker \underline{L} = \ker \underline{L} \cap S.$$

Because it is an intersection of $S$ with a subspace of $[\mathrm{GF}(q)]^d$, the $G$-kernel of $\underline{L}$ is a flat of $G$.

If $X$ is a flat in $G$ and $L$ is a linear functional, then the condition that $\ker L \geq X$ is equivalent to the system of $\mathrm{rank}(X)$ linearly independent equations,

$$L(x) = 0, \; x \in B,$$

where $B$ is a basis for $X$. Hence, the set of linear functionals $L$ such that $\ker L \geq X$ is a subspace of dimension $d - \mathrm{rank}(X)$ in the dual space of $[\mathrm{GF}(q)]^d$. In particular, the number of $s$-tuples $\underline{L}$ of linear functionals such that $G$-$\ker \underline{L} \geq X$ equals

$$(q^{d-\mathrm{rank}(X)})^s.$$

By Möbius inversion, we conclude that the number of $s$-tuples of linear functionals distinguishing $S$, which equals the number of $s$-tuples with $G$-kernel equal to $\hat{0}$, equals

$$\sum_{X:X\in L(G)} \mu(\hat{0}, X)q^{s(d-\mathrm{rank}(X))} = q^{s(d-n)}\chi(G; q^s).$$

Another way to prove this result is to use the contraction-and-deletion method. A detailed account can be found in Welsh [**145**], Chapter 15. □

Note that when $G$ has loops, then $\chi(G; \lambda)$ is identically zero by definition. This is consistent with the fact that when $G$ has loops, then $S$ contains the zero vector and there are no $s$-tuples distinguishing $G$.

Theorem 4.1 implies that the number of $s$-tuples distinguishing $G$ in $[\mathrm{GF}(q)]^d$ depends only on $q$, $d$ and the lattice of flats $L(G)$. It is independent of the representation of $G$ in $[\mathrm{GF}(q)]^d$. Therefore, if $G$ is a $\mathrm{GF}(q)$-representable matroid with no loops, we define the *critical exponent* $c(G; q)$ *over* $\mathrm{GF}(q)$ to be the minimum non-negative integer $s$ such that there exists an $s$-tuple of linear functionals distinguishing $G$ in any representation of $G$ over $\mathrm{GF}(q)$. If $G$ has loops, then its critical exponent $c(G; q)$ is defined to be *infinite*. An equivalent definition is the following:

$$(4.1) \qquad c(G; q) = \min\{s : \chi(G; q^s) \neq 0\}.$$

From this definition, it is clear that $c(G; q)$ depends only on $q$ and $L(G)$. It follows from Theorem 4.1 that for any positive integer $t$, $t \geq c(G; q)$ implies $\chi(G; q^t) > 0$. Note that if $G$ is the matroid of rank zero on the empty set, then $\chi(G; \lambda) = 1$ and $c(G; q) = 0$ for every prime power $q$.

We remark that every $n$-tuple of linear functionals forming a basis for the dual space of $[\mathrm{GF}(q)]^n$ has kernel equal to the zero subspace. Hence, if $G$ has no loops, $\mathrm{rank}(G) = n$, and $G$ is represented in $[\mathrm{GF}(q)]^n$, then there exists an $n$-tuple of linear functionals distinguishing $G$. We conclude that

$$c(G; q) \leq \mathrm{rank}(G).$$

The critical exponent can also be defined *geometrically* in terms of hyperplanes. An $s$-tuple $(H_1, H_2, \ldots, H_s)$ of hyperplanes in $[\mathrm{GF}(q)]^d$ is said to *distinguish* $G$ if for every point $x \in S$, there exists a hyperplane $H_i$ such that $x \notin H_i$. The critical exponent $c(G; q)$ equals the minimum positive integer $c$ such that there exists a $c$-tuple $(H_1, H_2, \ldots, H_c)$ of hyperplanes in $[\mathrm{GF}(q)]^d$ distinguishing $G$. The geometric definition using hyperplanes works without change in projective spaces. Let $G(S)$ be a matroid without loops represented as a set $S$ of points in the projective space $\mathrm{PG}(d-1, q)$. Taking the intersection of $c$-tuples of hyperplanes, we conclude that the critical exponent $c(G; q)$ also equals the minimum positive integer $c$ such that there exists a subspace $U$ of rank $d - c$ in $[\mathrm{GF}(q)]^d$ or $\mathrm{PG}(d-1, q)$ disjoint from $S$. Because the complement of a hyperplane is affine (by definition), $c(G; q)$ equals the minimum number $c$ such that the point set $S$ can be partitioned into $c$ subsets $S_i$ so that the restrictions $G|S_i$ are affine in $\mathrm{PG}(d-1, q)$.

Using the natural injection of the field $\mathrm{GF}(q)$ into its extension field $\mathrm{GF}(q^r)$, we obtain natural injections $[\mathrm{GF}(q)]^d \hookrightarrow [\mathrm{GF}(q^r)]^d$ and $\mathrm{PG}(d-1, q) \hookrightarrow \mathrm{PG}(d-1, q^r)$. Therefore, given a representation $\phi$ of $G(S)$ in $[\mathrm{GF}(q)]^d$ or $\mathrm{PG}(d-1, q)$, we can obtain a representation of $G(S)$ over $\mathrm{GF}(q^r)$ by composing it with the natural injections. Using equation (4.1), we obtain the equivalence

$$(4.2) \qquad c(G; q) = c \iff c = \min\{s : c(G; q^s) = 1\}.$$

In terms of projective spaces, the critical exponent $c(G; q)$ is the minimum degree of an extension field $\mathrm{GF}(q^c)$ of $\mathrm{GF}(q)$ such that $G$ is affine in the projective space $\mathrm{PG}(d-1, q^c)$.

Equivalence (4.2) can also be proved directly. If $L$ is a linear functional on $[\mathrm{GF}(q)]^d$, then it can be written as a linear combination of the linear functionals $E_1, E_2, \ldots, E_d$ dual to the standard basis vectors $e_1, e_2, \ldots, e_d$. In this form, $L$ can be extended naturally to a linear functional on $[\mathrm{GF}(q^r)]^d$, where $\mathrm{GF}(q^r)$ is any extension field of GF($q$). Let $\{\alpha_1, \alpha_2, \ldots, \alpha_s\}$ be a basis of the extension field GF($q^s$) considered as a vector space over the ground field GF($q$). Suppose that $(L_1, L_2, \ldots, L_s)$ is an $s$-tuple of linear functionals over GF($q$) distinguishing $G$, then

$$\alpha_1 L_1 + \alpha_2 L_2 + \ldots + \alpha_s L_s$$

is a linear functional over GF($q^s$) distinguishing $G(S)$. Conversely, if $L$ is a linear functional over GF($q^s$) distinguishing $G$, then $L$ can be expressed as a linear combination $\sum_{i=1}^{d} \beta_i E_i$, where $\beta_i \in$ GF($q^s$), of the linear functionals $E_i$. Expanding the coefficients $\beta_i$ in terms of the basis $\{\alpha_1, \alpha_2, \ldots, \alpha_s\}$, we obtain

$$L = \sum_{i=1}^{d} [\sum_{j=1}^{s} \gamma_{ij} \alpha_j] E_i = \sum_{j=1}^{s} \alpha_j [\sum_{i=1}^{d} \gamma_{ij} E_i].$$

It is easy to check that the $s$-tuple $(L_1, L_2, \ldots, L_s)$, where

$$L_j = \sum_{i=1}^{d} \gamma_{ij} E_i,$$

distinguishes $G$.

In its ideal form, the *critical problem* is to "find" the critical exponent of a matroid $G$. In practice, the *theory of critical problems* is the study of the relation amongst the critical exponent, the characteristic polynomial and similar invariants of a matroid, and the structure of the matroid.

The Möbius inversion proof of Theorem 4.1 can be modified to show the following result (Kung [**83**]).

4.2. LEMMA.
*(a) Let $G(S)$ be a rank-$n$ matroid represented as a set $S$ of vectors in $[\mathrm{GF}(q)]^d$ and let $U$ be a rank-$k$ subspace in $[\mathrm{GF}(q)]^d$. Then the number of $s$-tuples $\underline{L}$ distinguishing $G(S)$ such that $U \subseteq \ker \underline{L}$ equals*

$$q^{s(d-n)} \chi(G//U; q^s),$$

*where $G//U$ is the rank-$(n-k)$ quotient of $G(S)$ obtained by regarding the vectors in $S$ as vectors in the quotient space $[\mathrm{GF}(q)]^d/U$.*
*(b) If $X$ is a flat of $G$, then*

$$q^{s(d-n)} \chi(G/X; q^s),$$

*is the number of $s$-tuples $\underline{L}$ of linear functionals such that $\ker \underline{L} \cap S = X$.*

Note that if $U \cap S \neq \emptyset$, then $G//U$ has loops and $\chi(G//U; \lambda)$ is identically zero.

To prove Lemma 4.2, let $G$ be a loopless matroid represented as a set $S$ of nonzero vectors in $[\mathrm{GF}(q)]^d$. Let $\underline{L}$ be an $s$-tuple with $U \subseteq \ker \underline{L}$ and let $X = \ker \underline{L} \cap S$. Although $U$ is not necessarily a subset of $X$, it is the case that

$$\mathrm{lin}(U \cup X) \cap S = \ker \underline{L} \cap S = X,$$

where $\mathrm{lin}(Y)$ is the linear span of $Y$ in $[\mathrm{GF}(q)]^d$. Hence, $X$ is a closed set under the closure

$$A \mapsto \mathrm{lin}(U \cup A) \cap S$$

on $S$. This closure is precisely the closure of the quotient matroid $G//U$ obtained by regarding the vectors in $S$ as vectors in the quotient space $[\mathrm{GF}(q)]^d/U$.

To finish the proof, observe that if $X$ is a flat in the lattice $L(G//U)$ of flats of $G//U$, then the number of $s$-tuples $\underline{L}$ such that $U \subseteq \ker \underline{L}$ and $X \subseteq \ker \underline{L}$ equals

$$q^{s(d-\mathrm{rank}(X \cup U))},$$

where rank is the rank function in the vector space $[\mathrm{GF}(q)]^d$. Hence, by Möbius inversion in $L(G//U)$, the number of $s$-tuples $\underline{L}$ distinguishing $G(S)$ with $U \subseteq \ker \underline{L}$ equals

$$\sum_{X:X\in L(G//U)} \mu_{G//U}(\hat{0}, X) q^{s(d-\mathrm{rank}(X \cup U))},$$

where $\mu_{G//U}$ is the Möbius function in $L(G//U)$. Because the rank function of the quotient $G//U$ is given by the formula: for $A \subseteq S$,

$$\mathrm{rank}_{G//U}(A) = \mathrm{rank}(A \cup U) - \mathrm{rank}(U) = \mathrm{rank}(A \cup U) - k,$$

we have

$$d - \mathrm{rank}(X \cup U) = (d-n) + (n-k) - \mathrm{rank}_{G//U}(X).$$

Hence, the sum equals $q^{s(d-n)}\chi(G//U; q^s)$. This completes the proof of part (a) of Lemma 4.2. The proof of part (b) is similar and is left to the reader.

The Möbius inversion proof of Theorem 4.1 suggests an extension of the critical problem. This extension is a *mixed-characteristic* critical problem which applies to geometries representable over several finite fields. Let $G(S)$ be a matroid representable over the finite fields $\mathrm{GF}(q_i), i = 1, 2, \ldots, s$. The orders $q_i$ of the fields are not required to be distinct. Let $\phi_i : S \to V_i$, where

$$V_i = [\mathrm{GF}(q_i)]^{d_i},$$

be representations of $G$. An $s$-tuple $(L_1, L_2, \ldots, L_s)$, where $L_i$ is a linear functional on $V_i$, is said to *distinguish* $G$ if for every vector $x$ in $S$, there is a linear functional $L_i$ such that $L_i(\phi_i(x)) \neq 0$.

4.3.   THEOREM. *Let $G(S)$ be a rank-$n$ matroid represented as above over* $\mathrm{GF}(q_i)$. *The number of $s$-tuples distinguishing $G$ equals*

$$q_1^{d_1-n} q_2^{d_2-n} \cdots q_s^{d_s-n} \chi(G; q_1 q_2 \cdots q_s).$$

The proof is a simple modification of the Möbius inversion argument. Let $L_i$ be a linear functional on $V_i$. Its $G$-kernel is the flat of $G$ defined by

$$G\text{-}\ker L_i = \{x \in S : L_i(\phi_i(x)) = 0\}.$$

If $\underline{L} = (L_1, L_2, \ldots, L_s)$ is an $s$-tuple with $L_i$ a linear functional on $V_i$, then its *G-kernel* is the subset $G\text{-}\ker \underline{L}$ defined by

$$G\text{-}\ker \underline{L} = \{x \in S : L_i(\phi_i(x)) = 0 \text{ for all } i\}$$
$$= G\text{-}\ker L_1 \cap G\text{-}\ker L_2 \cap \ldots \cap G\text{-}\ker L_s.$$

Because $G\text{-}\ker L$ is an intersection of flats of $G$, it is a flat of $G$.

For any flat $X$ of $G$, the number of $s$-tuples $\underline{L}$ such that $G\text{-}\ker \underline{L} \geq X$ equals

$$q_1^{d_1-\mathrm{rank}(X)} q_2^{d_2-\mathrm{rank}(X)} \cdots q_s^{d_s-\mathrm{rank}(X)}.$$

By Möbius inversion, the number of $s$-tuples distinguishing $G$ equals

$$\sum_{X:X\in L(G)} \mu(\hat{0}, X)q_1^{d_1-\operatorname{rank}(X)}q_2^{d_2-\operatorname{rank}(X)}\cdots q_s^{d_s-\operatorname{rank}(X)}$$

$$= q_1^{d_1-n}q_2^{d_2-n}\cdots q_s^{d_s-n}\chi(G; q_1q_2\cdots q_s).$$

This completes the proof of Theorem 4.3.

Theorem 4.3 gives a critical problem interpretation for evaluations of the characteristic polynomial over certain integers which are not prime powers. In particular, for a regular matroid $G$ with no loops, Theorem 4.3 provides an interpretation of $\chi(G; n)$ for all positive integers $n$.

The notion of a critical exponent does not transfer directly to the mixed critical problem. For the mixed critical problem, one is usually interested in finding the minimum positive integer $n$ such that $\chi(G; n) \neq 0$. A reasonable analogue of the critical exponent would then be the integer defined in the following way. The *critical number* $c'(G)$ of a loopless matroid $G(S)$ representable over some field is the minimum positive integer $n$ satisfying two properties:

(1) there exists a factorization $n = q_1q_2\cdots q_s$, where $q_i$ are prime powers such that $G(S)$ is representable over $\operatorname{GF}(q_i)$, and

(2) $\chi(G; n) \neq 0$.

Note that if $m$ is a power of $c'(G)$, then $\chi(G; m) > 0$. But there exist matroids $G$ such that $\chi(G; m) = 0$ for some integer $m$ greater than $c'(G)$. The ternary affine geometry $AG(2,3)$ is an example (see Section 5.4). But such examples seem to be rare and it might be possible to classify them.

## 4.2. Colorings and flows in graphs

The critical problem is a generalization of certain cases of the coloring problem in graph theory. Let $\Gamma$ be a graph with vertex set $V$ and edge set $E$. We shall orient each edge $e = \{a, b\}$ by specifying one vertex $a = \operatorname{head}(e)$ as its *head* and the other vertex $b = \operatorname{tail}(e)$ as its *tail*. In particular, if $e$ is a loop at the vertex $a$, then $\operatorname{head}(e) = a = \operatorname{tail}(e)$. The *cycle matroid* $M(\Gamma)$ of a graph $\Gamma$ is the matroid on the edge set $E$ whose circuits are the cycles of $\Gamma$. It can be represented over every field by the oriented vertex-edge incidence matrix $[\sigma(a, e)]$ of $\Gamma$, where

$$\sigma(a, e) = \begin{cases} 1 & \text{if } a = \operatorname{head}(e), \\ -1 & \text{if } a = \operatorname{tail}(e), \\ 0 & \text{otherwise.} \end{cases}$$

The rank function of $M(\Gamma)$ is given by the formula: if $T \subseteq E$,

$$\operatorname{rank}(T) = |V| - p(T),$$

where $p(T)$ is the number of connected components of the subgraph $\Gamma|T$ of $\Gamma$ with vertex set $V$ and edge set $T$. A *k-coloring* of the graph $\Gamma$ is a function $\omega : V \to K$, where $K$ is a $k$-element set, called the set of *colors*. If $\omega$ is a coloring of $\Gamma$, its *kernel* is the set of edges $e = \{a, b\}$ such that $\omega(a) = \omega(b)$. Suppose the edges $e_1, e_2, e_3, \ldots, e_m$ form a cycle and $e_1, e_2, e_3, \ldots, e_{m-1}$ are in the kernel of a coloring. Then all the vertices incident on the edges $e_1, e_2, e_3, \ldots, e_{m-1}$ are assigned the same color. Hence, the vertices incident on $e_m$ are also assigned the same color and $e_m$ is in the kernel. We conclude that kernels of colorings are flats in the cycle matroid

$M(\Gamma)$. If $X$ is a flat of $M(\Gamma)$, then there are $k^{p(X)}$ $k$-colorings whose kernels contain $X$.

A $k$-coloring $\omega$ is said to be *proper* if its kernel is the empty set, or, equivalently, if for every edge $e = \{a, b\}$, $\omega(a) \neq \omega(b)$. The *chromatic number* of a loopless graph is the minimum positive integer $k$ such that there exists a proper $k$-coloring of $\Gamma$. Rota [**117**] observed that the number of proper $k$-colorings can be obtained by evaluating a characteristic polynomial.

4.4. THEOREM. *Let $\Gamma$ be a graph. Then the number of proper $k$-colorings of $\Gamma$ equals*

$$k^p \chi(M(\Gamma); k),$$

*where $p$ is the number of connected components in $\Gamma$.*

Again, the proof is a Möbius inversion argument.

It follows from Theorem 4.4 that if $k$ is a positive integer and $\chi(M(\Gamma); k) \neq 0$, then $\chi(M(\Gamma); k') \neq 0$ for all positive integers $k'$ greater than $k$. From this, one concludes that if $k$ is the chromatic number of $\Gamma$, then

$$c(M(\Gamma); q) = \lceil \log_q k \rceil,$$

where $\log_q$ is logarithm to base $q$.

The *chromatic polynomial* $p(\Gamma; \lambda)$ of the graph $\Gamma$ is the polynomial defined by the condition: for every positive integer $k$, $p(\Gamma; k)$ is the number of proper $k$-colorings of $\Gamma$. By Theorem 4.4,

$$p(\Gamma; \lambda) = \lambda^p \chi(M(\Gamma); \lambda).$$

By Theorem 4.4 again, $\chi(M(\Gamma); 2) \neq 0$ if and only if $\Gamma$ can be properly 2-colored, that is, if and only if $\Gamma$ is bipartite. Therefore, $M(\Gamma)$ is affine over GF(2) if and only if $\Gamma$ is bipartite. Thus, the critical problem for a cycle matroid $M(\Gamma)$ over GF(2) is equivalent to the problem of finding the minimum integer $c$ satisfying the condition: there exists a partition of the edge set $E$ into $c$ subsets $E_1, E_2, \ldots, E_c$ such that the subgraphs $\Gamma|E_i$ are bipartite.

The *bond* or *cocycle* matroid $M^\perp(\Gamma)$ is the matroid on the edge set $E$ whose circuits are the minimal cutsets of $\Gamma$. As the notation implies, $M^\perp(\Gamma)$ is the orthogonal dual of the cycle matroid $M(\Gamma)$. Thus, the bases of $M^\perp(\Gamma)$ are the complements of spanning forests of $\Gamma$. By duality, the rank function $\mathrm{rank}^\perp$ of $M^\perp(\Gamma)$ is given by the formula: for $T \subseteq E$,

$$\mathrm{rank}^\perp(T) = \mathrm{nullity}(E) - \mathrm{nullity}(E \backslash T),$$

where nullity is the nullity function of the cycle matroid $M(\Gamma)$. Because $\mathrm{rank}^\perp(E) = \mathrm{nullity}(E)$,

$$\mathrm{corank}^\perp(T) = \mathrm{nullity}(E \backslash T)$$
$$= |E \backslash T| - |V| + p(E \backslash T).$$

A *flow* in a graph $\Gamma$ with values in an abelian group $A$ (written additively) is a function $f : E \to A$ satisfying the following *conservation equation* at every vertex $a$,

$$\sum_{e : e \text{ is incident on } a} \sigma(a, e) f(e) = 0.$$

Because every minimal cut-set is a symmetric difference of cutsets separating a vertex from the rest of the graph, the conservation equations imply that the total flow across any minimal cutset is zero. This implies that if a flow $f$ is known to be zero on all except one edge in a minimal cut set, then $f$ is also zero on that edge. Hence, the *kernel* $\ker f$ of the flow $f$, defined to be the set of edges $e$ for which $f(e) = 0$, is a flat in the cocycle matroid.

4.5. LEMMA. *Let $X$ be a flat in the cocycle matroid $M^{\perp}(\Gamma)$. Then the number of flows $f$ with values in the finite abelian group $A$ such that $\ker f \geq X$ equals*

$$|A|^{|E \setminus X| - |V| + p(E \setminus X)}.$$

PROOF. The proof uses the observation that a flow on $\Gamma$ is determined once we know its values on the complement of a spanning forest, which is a graph-theoretic statement of the fact that a linear functional is determined by its values on a basis. Choose a spanning forest $F$ in the graph $\Gamma|(E \setminus X)$ on the vertex set $V$ and edge set $E \setminus X$. Then every flow $f$ with kernel containing $X$ can be constructed in the following way. On the complement $E \setminus F$, let $f(e)$ be assigned $0$ if $e \in X$ and let $f(e)$ be assigned any element in $A$ if $e \in E \setminus X$. This assignment is extended to all the edges in the following way. Let $e$ be an edge in $E \setminus F$. When $e$ is added to the spanning forest $F$, the union $F \cup \{e\}$ contains a unique cycle $C_e$ in $\Gamma$ containing $e$. The edges in the cycle $C_e$ form the fundamental circuit of $e$ relative to the basis $F$ in the cycle matroid $M(\Gamma)$. Let $f_e$ be the flow that assigns the value $f(e)$ to $e$, the value $0$ to any edge not in $C_e$, and the value $f(e)$ or $-f(e)$ to every edge in $C_e$, depending on the orientation, so that the flow $f_e$ satisfies the conservation equation at each vertex. Note that if $e$ is an edge in $X$, then the flow $f_e$ is identically zero. Let $f$ be the flow defined by the equation

$$f = \sum_{e \in E \setminus F} f_e.$$

Then $f$ is a flow with kernel containing $X$. Conversely, every flow with kernel containing $X$ can be expressed uniquely in this form.

Because there are $|V| - p(E \setminus X)$ edges in $F$, there are $|E| - |X| - |V| + p(E \setminus X)$ edges which can be assigned any value in $A$. This proves the lemma. $\square$

A flow is *nowhere-zero* if $f(e) \neq 0$ for every edge $e$. Just as in the case of colorings, Möbius inversion can be used to prove the following theorem stated in Rota [117].

4.6. THEOREM. *Let $\Gamma$ be a graph and let $A$ be a finite abelian group. Then the number of nowhere-zero $A$-flows on $\Gamma$ equals*

$$\chi(M^{\perp}(\Gamma); |A|).$$

We remark that Theorems 4.4 and 4.6 can also be proved by a contraction-and-deletion argument. See Brylawski and Oxley [31] for a detailed account.

It follows from Theorem 4.6 that $\chi(M^{\perp}(\Gamma); 2) \neq 0$ if and only if the function with values in GF(2) assigning $1$ to every edge of $\Gamma$ is a flow. Therefore, $M^{\perp}(\Gamma)$ is affine over GF(2) if and only if the edge set of $\Gamma$ is a disjoint union of cycles. From graph theory, this is equivalent to the condition that every vertex in $\Gamma$ has even degree, or the condition that $\Gamma$ has an Eulerian "circuit".

Another consequence of Theorem 4.6 is that the number of nowhere-zero flows on a graph with values in an abelian group $A$ depends only on the order $|A|$ of the group. A graph $\Gamma$ is said to have a *nowhere-zero $n$-flow* if it has a nowhere-zero $A$-flow, where $A$ is any abelian group of order $n$. If $\Gamma$ has a nowhere-zero $n$-flow, it has a nowhere-zero $A$-flow for *every* abelian group $A$ of order $n$. Tutte [133] has shown that if $\Gamma$ has a nowhere-zero flow over the integers modulo $n$, then $\Gamma$ has a nowhere-zero flow $f$ over the integers such that $-n < f(e) < n$ for every edge $e$. Crapo [34] has generalized the notion of a flow to all regular matroids. Using Crapo's generalization, Lindström [88] proved that for a regular matroid $G$, if $\chi(G;t) > 0$, then $\chi(G;t') > 0$ for every integer $t' \geq t$. Lindström's result implies that the set of integer zeroes of the characteristic polynomial of a regular matroid is an initial segment of the positive integers, that is, it is a set of the form $\{1, 2, \ldots, t-1\}$, where $t \geq 2$.

Because of Theorem 4.6, $\chi(M^\perp(\Gamma); \lambda)$ is sometimes called the *flow polynomial* of $\Gamma$. Like the chromatic polynomial, the flow polynomial can be calculated for "small" graphs using the method of contraction-and-deletion (see Section 5.1). For two examples ($K_5$ and $K_{3,3}$), see Brylawski and Oxley [31], p. 201. If $\Gamma$ is planar, then its dual is a planar graph. Hence, the flow polynomial of a planar graph can be obtained by calculating a chromatic polynomial. Note that if $\Gamma$ is a cycle, then there are $|A| - 1$ nowhere-zero $A$-flows obtained by assigning a constant non-zero value in $A$ to all the edges in the cycle. Hence, $\chi(M^\perp(\Gamma); \lambda) = \lambda - 1$. The only other non-trivial infinite family of graphs for which the flow polynomials are known is the family of complete graphs. Tutte [137] has obtained a formula and a generating function for the dichromatic polynomials of complete graphs.[8] By specializing Tutte's formula, one obtains the following formula for the flow polynomial of $M(K_n)$ :

$$(-1)^{\binom{n}{2}} \lambda^n \chi(M^\perp(K_n); \lambda) =$$
$$\sum_{(b_1, b_2, \ldots, b_n)} \left[ \frac{n!}{b_1!(1!)^{b_1} b_2!(2!)^{b_2} \cdots b_n!(n!)^{b_n}} \right] \lambda_{(b_1 + b_2 + \ldots + b_n)} (1 - \lambda)^{\sum_{i=1}^{n} \binom{i}{2} b_i},$$

where $\lambda_{(r)}$ is the falling factorial $\lambda(\lambda-1)(\lambda-2)\cdots(\lambda-r+1)$ and the sum ranges over all $n$-tuples $(b_1, b_2, \ldots, b_n)$ of non-negative integers such that $b_1 1 + b_2 2 + \ldots + b_n n = n$. Tutte's generating function yields the following generating function:

$$\sum_{n=0}^{\infty} \frac{(-1)^{\binom{n}{2}} \lambda^n u^n \chi(M^\perp(K_n); \lambda)}{n!} = \left[ \sum_{n=0}^{\infty} \frac{(1-\lambda)^{\binom{n}{2}} u^n}{n!} \right]^\lambda.$$

One of the best-known critical problems is Tutte's 5-flow conjecture [133].

4.7. TUTTE'S 5-FLOW CONJECTURE. *Every graph with no isthmuses has a nowhere-zero 5-flow.*

Jaeger [63] has shown using matroid theory that every graph with no isthmuses has an 8-flow. We will say more about Jaeger's methods in Section 7.2. Using Jaeger's theorem and Seymour's decomposition theorem, Walton and Welsh [143] have shown that every graph with no isthmuses and no $K_{3,3}$-minors has a nowhere-zero 4-flow.

---

[8]Tutte's formula can also be derived using Brylawski's intersection theory. See [25].

Seymour [123] has improved Jaeger's result to a 6-flow theorem. From the viewpoint of the mixed critical problem, Seymour's theorem is equivalent to the statement that every cocycle matroid with no loops can be partitioned into two sets $S_1$ and $S_2$ such that the restriction $G|S_1$ is affine over GF(2) and the restriction $G|S_2$ is affine over GF(3). It would be of great interest to have an independent geometric proof of Seymour's theorem.

For more about flows in graphs, see the survey article of Jaeger [65].

### 4.3. The critical problem for representable polymatroids

Another extension of the critical problem, to representable polymatroids, is due to Helgason [57] and Whittle [164].[9] A *polymatroid* $G$ on the set $S$ of elements can be specified by a rank function $f : 2^S \to \mathbb{N}$ satisfying:

(1) $f(\emptyset) = 0$,
(2) if $A \subseteq B$, then $f(A) \leq f(B)$, and
(3) if $A, B \subseteq S$, then $f(A \cup B) + f(A \cap B) \leq f(A) + f(B)$.

The *rank* of $G$ is the rank $f(S)$ of the set of elements. Roughly speaking, a polymatroid is a matroid in which elements can have rank greater than one. One way to represent a polymatroid is to represent elements as subsets of vectors in vector spaces. More precisely, a GF($q$)-representation of the polymatroid $G(S)$ with rank function $f$ is a function $\phi$ from $S$ to the collection of subsets of vectors of the vector space $[\text{GF}(q)]^d$ or the collection of subsets of points of the projective space $\text{PG}(d-1, q)$ such that for all subsets $A \subseteq S$,

$$f(A) = \text{rank}(\bigcup_{a \in A} \phi(a)).$$

We can replace the subset $\phi(a)$ by the subspace spanned by $\phi(a)$ without changing the rank function. Doing so gives a geometric picture of a representable polymatroid as a collection of subspaces.[10] Because points in $\text{PG}(d-1, q)$ are equivalence classes of vectors in $[\text{GF}(q)]^d$, every representation of a polymatroid $G$ as a collection of subsets of $\text{PG}(d-1, q)$ yields a representation of $G$ as a collection of subsets in $[\text{GF}(q)]^d$. We shall state and prove our results for representations in $[\text{GF}(q)]^d$; however, our examples will be represented in $\text{PG}(d-1, q)$.

The *closure* of a subset $A \subseteq S$ is the subset $\{a : f(A \cup \{a\}) = f(A)\}$. A *flat* is a closed set and the collection of flats forms a lattice $L(G)$. This lattice is not

---

[9]Except for the summaries [58,59], Helgason's work appeared only in his M. I. T. thesis [57]. Given a hypergraph $\Gamma$, Helgason defined a *coloring closure* on its set $E$ of hyperedges by: if $A \subseteq E$, the closure of $A$ is the set of all hyperedges $e$ such that for all colorings $\omega$, if every edge in $A$ is monochromatic under $\omega$, then $e$ is monochromatic under $\omega$. This closure defines the same polymatroid as the one defined later in this section. Helgason determined those hypergraphs whose polymatroids are matroids: apart from degenerate examples, these hypergraphs are (ordinary) graphs. He also studied *strong* colorings, that is, colorings $\omega$ for which $\omega(v) \neq \omega(u)$ for every pair of distinct vertices $u$ and $v$ in an hyperedge. Strong colorings are related to the critical problem for higher rank flats discussed in Section 4.6. These results on hypergraph colorings appeared in [58,59]. The unpublished portion of Helgason's thesis includes the following topics: a critical problem for representable polymatroids (described in detail in this section), a contraction-and-deletion theory for polymatroids (similar to the theory developed in Whittle [162,164]), a polymatroid analogue of Crapo's identity (described in Section 5.7), and a theory of flows on certain hypergraphs.

[10]This collection is really a "multicollection" because a subspace may occur more than once as an image of $\phi$.

geometric in general: indeed, Dilworth (see Crawley and Dilworth [**37**], Chapter 14) has shown that every finite lattice is the lattice of flats of some polymatroid.[11] When the polymatroid $G(S)$ is represented as a collection $S$ of subsets of $[\mathrm{GF}(q)]^d$, then the flats are subsets of $S$ having the form $\{a \in S : a \subseteq U\}$, where $U$ is a subspace of $[\mathrm{GF}(q)]^d$. The *weighted characteristic polynomial* $\chi(G; \lambda)$ of $G(S)$ is the polynomial

$$\sum_{A:A\subseteq S} (-1)^{|A|} \lambda^{f(S)-f(A)}.$$

If $G$ contains no loops (that is, elements $a$ such that $f(a) = 0$), then

$$\chi(G; \lambda) = \sum_{X:X\in L(G)} \mu(\hat{0}, X)\lambda^{f(S)-f(X)};$$

if $G$ contains loops, then $\chi(G; \lambda) = 0$. Note that because $f$ is not necessarily the rank function of $L(G)$ in those cases when $L(G)$ is a ranked lattice, the weighted characteristic polynomial is not necessarily the characteristic polynomial of $L(G)$. For more about weighted characteristic polynomials, see Whittle [**163**].

Let $G(S)$ be a polymatroid represented as a collection $S$ of subsets in $[\mathrm{GF}(q)]^d$. An $s$-tuple $(L_1, L_2, \ldots, L_s)$ of linear functionals is said to *distinguish* $G$ if for every subspace $a \in S$, there exists a linear functional $L_i$ such that $L_i$ restricted to $a$ is not identically zero, or, equivalently, $a \not\subseteq \ker L_i$. Helgason and Whittle proved the following polymatroid analogue of Theorem 4.1.

4.8.  THEOREM. *Suppose that the polymatroid $G(S)$ is represented as a collection of subsets of vectors in $[\mathrm{GF}(q)]^d$. The number of $s$-tuples distinguishing $G$ equals*

$$q^{s(d-\mathrm{rank}(G))}\chi(G; q^s),$$

*where $\chi(G; \lambda)$ is the weighted characteristic polynomial of the lattice of flats of $G$.*

PROOF. Once again, the crucial fact is that if $L$ is a linear functional, then the subset $\{a \in S : a \subseteq \ker L\}$ is a flat of $G$. The theorem now follows by Möbius inversion.                                                                       □

The *critical exponent* $c(G; q)$ of the loopless polymatroid $G$ over $\mathrm{GF}(q)$ is the minimum integer $c$ such that there exists a $c$-tuple of linear functionals distinguishing $G$ in any representation $\phi$ of $G$ over $\mathrm{GF}(q)$. Equivalently, when $G$ is represented as a collection $S$ of subsets in $[\mathrm{GF}(q)]^d$, $c(G; q)$ is the minimum integer $c$ such that there exists a subspace $U$ of codimension $c$ such that $\phi(a) \not\subseteq U$ for every element $a$ in $S$. It is straight-forward to define a mixed critical problem for polymatroids and obtain a polymatroid analogue of Theorem 4.3. We remark that because subspaces are subgroups, the critical problem for polymatroids is almost the same as the critical problem for abelian groups stated in Section 2.

The problem of finding the critical exponent of a representable polymatroid can be reduced to the problem of finding the critical exponent of a matroid. Let $G$ be a polymatroid without loops represented as a collection $S$ of subsets of $[\mathrm{GF}(q)]^d$ (or

---

[11]Dilworth also showed that there is a "functorial" way to associate a matroid with any polymatroid. This is the Dilworth completion in its most general form. A natural conjecture is that if a polymatroid is representable over $\mathrm{GF}(q)$, then the associated matroid is representable over an extension of $\mathrm{GF}(q)$. For the special case of Dilworth truncations, this is true. See Brylawski [**26**].

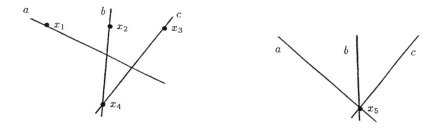

FIGURE 1. Two representations of a polymatroid.

PG$(d-1, q)$). A set $T$ of non-zero vectors in $[\mathrm{GF}(q)]^d$ (or points in PG$(d-1, q)$) is a *cross-section* of the collection $S$ if for every subset $a \in S$, there exists a vector $x$ in $T$ such that $x \in \mathrm{lin}(a)$, where $\mathrm{lin}(a)$ is the subspace in $[\mathrm{GF}(q)]^d$ (or PG$(d-1, q)$) spanned by $a$. An obvious way to obtain a cross-section is to simply take the union $\bigcup_{a \in S} a$ of all the subsets in $S$, but there are usually smaller cross-sections. A cross-section $T$ defines a matroid $H(T)$ by linear dependence. A matroid $H(T)$ obtained in this way from a cross-section of some representation of $G$ over $\mathrm{GF}(q)$ is called a *cross-section matroid (over $\mathrm{GF}(q)$)* for $G$. By definition, a cross-section matroid is representable over $\mathrm{GF}(q)$.

4.9. THEOREM. *Suppose that the polymatroid $G(S)$ is represented as a collection of subsets of $[\mathrm{GF}(q)]^d$ or PG$(d-1, q)$. Let $H(T)$ be a cross-section matroid for $G(S)$. Then*

$$(4.3) \qquad\qquad c(G; q) \le c(H; q).$$

*In addition, there exists a cross-section matroid $H$ such that $c(G; q) = c(H; q)$.*

PROOF. Suppose that $G(S)$ is represented as a collection $S$ of subsets in $[\mathrm{GF}(q)]^d$. Let $c = c(H; q)$ and let $\underline{L} = (L_1, L_2, \ldots, L_c)$ be a $c$-tuple of linear functionals distinguishing $H$. We will show that $\underline{L}$ also distinguishes $G$. Let $a$ be a subset in $S$ and let $x_a$ be a vector in $T$ such that $x_a \in \mathrm{lin}(a)$. Because $\underline{L}$ distinguishes $H$, there exists a linear functional $L_i$ such that $L_i(x_a) \ne 0$, that is, $\mathrm{lin}(a) \not\subseteq \ker L_i$. But $a$ contains a basis of $\mathrm{lin}(a)$. Hence, $a \not\subseteq \ker L_i$.

Now let $c = c(G; q)$ and let $\underline{L} = (L_1, L_2, \ldots, L_c)$ be a $c$-tuple of linear functionals distinguishing $G$. For each subset $a \in S$, choose a non-zero vector $x_a$ in the following way. First choose a linear functional $L_i$ such that $a \not\subseteq \ker L_i$. Next, choose $x_a$ to be one of the vectors $x$ in $\mathrm{lin}(a)$ such that $L_i(x) \ne 0$. Note that $x_a$ need not be in $a$; however, it can always be chosen to be in $a$. Let $T$ be the set of vectors obtained in this way. Then the cross-section matroid $H(T)$ has critical exponent at most $c(G; q)$. By inequality (4.3), $c(H; q)$ is exactly $c(G; q)$. □

As the following example shows, the behavior of cross-section matroids can be quite subtle. Consider the polymatroid $G$ on the collection $\{a, b, c\}$, given by the rank function

$$f(\emptyset) = 0,$$
$$f(\{a\}) = f(\{b\}) = f(\{c\}) = 2,$$
$$f(\{a, b\}) = f(\{a, c\}) = f(\{b, c\}) = f(\{a, b, c\}) = 3.$$

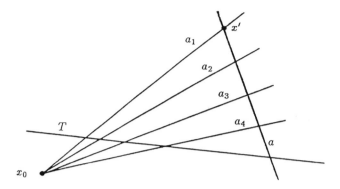

FIGURE 2. A minimal cross-section over GF(4).

This polymatroid can be represented in $[\mathrm{GF}(q)]^3$ for all sufficiently large $q$ by three lines. These three lines can be in general position or they can meet at a point. Figure 1 shows these two representations. The sets $\{x_1, x_2, x_3\}$ and $\{x_1, x_4\}$ are cross-sections for the first representation. The set $\{x_5\}$ is a cross-section for the second. Thus, the uniform matroids $U_{1,1}$, $U_{2,2}$, and $U_{3,3}$ (as well as other matroids) occur as cross-section matroids. The matroid $U_{1,1}$ can only be obtained by taking a cross-section in the second representation. All three matroids have critical exponent 1 and the polymatroid $G$ also has critical exponent 1.

Whittle [**165**] has posed the problem of characterizing the cross-sections which have the same critical exponent as the polymatroid. A cross-section $T$ of a collection $S$ of subsets in $[\mathrm{GF}(q)]^n$ is *minimal* if none of the proper subsets of $T$ is a cross-section of $S$. The following examples show that a minimal cross-section can have a critical exponent strictly greater than the polymatroid. Given a prime power $q$, let $G(S)$ be the polymatroid represented by the collection $S = \{a, a_1, a_2, \ldots, a_q\}$ of lines in the projective plane $\mathrm{PG}(2, q)$ where $a_1, a_2, \ldots, a_q$ are $q$ lines passing through a common point $x_0$ and $a$ is a line *not* containing the point $x_0$. Because $a$ contains $(q + 1)$ points, there is a (unique) point $x_1$ on $a$ not on any of the lines $a_1, a_2, \ldots, a_q$. Observing that $\{x_0, x'\}$, where $x'$ is any point on $a$, is a cross-section of $S$, we conclude that $c(G; q) = 1$. On the other hand, let $T$ be a line not equal to $a$ passing through $x_1$ but not through $x_0$. Then $T$ is a combinatorial and geometric transversal of the collection $S$ of lines. Because $T$ meets every line in $S$ exactly once, it is a minimal cross-section. However, $T$ has critical exponent 2 over $\mathrm{GF}(q)$. The polymatroid $G(S)$ and its cross-section $T$ in $\mathrm{PG}(2, 4)$ are shown in Figure 2.

The notion of cross-section matroids gives another statement of the critical problem for matroids. The *$m$-subspace polymatroid* $\mathrm{PG}(n-1, q; m)$ is the polymatroid consisting of all the subspaces of rank $m$ in $\mathrm{PG}(n-1, q)$. Let $G$ be a loopless rank-$n$ matroid represented as a set $S$ of vectors in $\mathrm{GF}(q)$. Then $c(G; q) > m$ if and only if $G$ intersects every subspace of codimension $m$. Hence, $c(G; q) > m$ if and only if $G$ is a cross-section matroid of the polymatroid $\mathrm{PG}(n-1, q; n-m)$. By taking other collections of subspaces in $\mathrm{PG}(n-1, q)$, one can define critical problems relative to given configurations of subspaces.[12]

---

[12]I do not know of any interesting examples at present.

The idea of a cross-section matroid originated in the proof of the following theorem in Helgason's thesis [57]. This theorem generalizes the fact that an independent set is affine.[13]

4.10. HELGASON'S THEOREM. *Let $G(S)$ be a polymatroid with rank function $f$. Suppose that $G$ is representable over* $\mathrm{GF}(q)$ *and for every subset $A \subseteq S$,*

$$f(A) \geq |A|.$$

*Then $c(G; q) = 1$.*

PROOF. Observe that $G$ contains no loops; otherwise, for some $a \in S$, $f(\{a\}) = 0 < 1 = |\{a\}|$. Choose a specific representation of $G$ as a collection $S$ of subsets in $[\mathrm{GF}(q)]^d$. Consider the relation $R \subseteq S \times [\mathrm{GF}(q)]^d$ defined by

$$a \, R \, x \quad \text{whenever} \quad x \in a.$$

Then for every subset $A \subseteq S$,

$$\mathrm{rank}(R(A)) = \mathrm{rank}(\bigcup_{a \in A} a) = f(A) \geq |A|,$$

where rank is the rank function in $[\mathrm{GF}(q)]^d$. By the marriage theorem for matroids,[14] there exists an independent transversal $T = \{x_a : a \in S\}$. This transversal $T$ is a cross-section of $S$, its matroid $H(T)$ is a free matroid, and $c(H; q) = 1$. Hence, by Theorem 4.9, $c(G; q) = 1$. □

Just as in the case of matroids, the critical problem for polymatroids extends a special case of a coloring problem (Helgason [57,58,59] and Whittle [162]). A *"simple" hypergraph* $\Gamma$ on the vertex set $V$ is specified by a collection $E$ of subsets of size at least 2 of $V$. The sets in $E$ are called *hyperedges*. *A proper $k$-coloring* of $\Gamma$ is a function $\omega : V \to K$, where $K$ is a set of size $k$, such that there are no *monochromatic* hyperedges, that is, for every hyperedge $\{v_1, \ldots, v_m\}$, there are two vertices $v_i$ and $v_j$ such that $\omega(v_i) \neq \omega(v_j)$. A *connected component* of $\Gamma$ is a minimal subset $U \subseteq V$ of vertices such that for every hyperedge $e \in E$, either $e \subseteq U$ or $e \cap U = \emptyset$. If $A \subseteq E$ is a set of hyperedges, the set $V_A$ is the set of vertices incident on some edge of $A$, that is,

$$V_A = \bigcup_{e \in A} e.$$

The *restriction* $\Gamma | A$ of $\Gamma$ to $A$ is the hypergraph on the vertex set $V_A$ and edge set $A$.

The polymatroid $M(\Gamma)$ associated with the coloring problem on hypergraphs was constructed by Helgason and Whittle. Its rank function $f$ is given by the formula: for $A \subseteq E$,

$$f(A) = |V_A| - p(\Gamma | A),$$

where $p(\Gamma | A)$ is the number of connected components of the restriction $\Gamma | A$. An intuitive way to visualize $M(\Gamma)$ is through the following "canonical" geometrical

---

[13]Instead of Theorem 4.9, Helgason used an argument based on a polymatroid analogue of Crapo's identity (Theorem 5.17 in Section 5.7). The idea of a cross-section matroid was implicit in that argument.

[14]This theorem is due to Rado [108]. Expositions can be found in Crapo and Rota [36], Chapter 8, Oxley [106], Chapter 12, or Welsh [145], Chapter 7.

representation found by Whittle [**162**]. Let $\Gamma$ be a hypergraph on the vertices $\{1, 2, \ldots, n\}$. In the vector space $[\mathrm{GF}(2)]^n$, let the standard basis vector $e_i$ represent the vertex $i$. Let $H$ be the hyperplane $\{(x_1, x_2, \ldots, x_n) : x_1 + x_2 + \ldots + x_n = 0\}$. Represent the hyperedge $\{i_1, i_2, \ldots, i_k\}$ by the subspace

$$(e_{i_1} \vee e_{i_2} \vee \ldots \vee e_{i_k}) \wedge H.$$

This subspace is the $(k-1)$-dimensional subspace spanned by the vectors $e_{i_1} + e_{i_2}, e_{i_2} + e_{i_3}, \ldots, e_{i_{k-1}} + e_{i_k}$. This construction can be carried out in any matroid containing a basis $B$ and a modular copoint $H$ such that $B \cap H = \emptyset$. Hence, the polymatroid of a hypergraph can be represented in any projective geometry or Dowling group geometry. Whittle's representation is a generalization of the construction of $M(K_n)$ using the Dilworth truncation in Crapo and Rota [**36**], Chapter 6. This construction also shows that the polymatroid of a hypergraph is a "comap image" of a Boolean algebra.[15]

Helgason and Whittle showed that the number of proper $k$-coloring of $\Gamma$ equals $k^{p(\Gamma)}\chi(M(\Gamma); k)$. When the number of colors is a prime power $q^s$, a direct one-to-one correspondence between $s$-tuples of linear functionals distinguishing $M(\Gamma)$ in the canonical geometric representation over $\mathrm{GF}(q)$ and proper $q^s$-colorings of $\Gamma$ with colors in $[\mathrm{GF}(q)]^s$ is given by:

$$(L_1, L_2, \ldots, L_s) \quad \longleftrightarrow \quad \omega : i \mapsto (L_1(e_i), L_2(e_i), \ldots, L_s(e_i)).$$

When specialized to hypergraphs, Theorem 4.10 yields the following two-color theorem conjectured by Erdős and proved by Lovász [**89**].

4.11. COROLLARY. *Let $\Gamma$ be a hypergraph such that for every subset $A$ of hyperedges,*

$$\left| \bigcup_{e \in A} e \right| > |A|.$$

*Then $\Gamma$ has a proper 2-coloring.*

PROOF. If $p(\Gamma|A) = 1$, then $f(A) \geq |A|$. If $p(\Gamma|A) = p > 1$, then $A$ can be partitioned into non-empty subsets $A_1, A_2, \ldots, A_p$ so that for every $i$, $p(\Gamma|A_i) = 1$. Summing up the inequalities $f(A_i) \geq |A_i|$, we obtain $f(A) \geq |A|$. We can now apply Helgason's theorem over $\mathrm{GF}(2)$ to finish the proof.                $\square$

A research area with great potential in the theory of polymatroids is to use matroid methods to study colorings of hypergraphs.

### 4.4. Critical problems from embeddings

A representation of $G$ is an *embedding* or rank-preserving injection of the elements of $G$ into the linear matroid formed by all the vectors in a vector space. One may therefore look for interesting critical problems resulting from embeddings into other types of matroids. Because the algebraic structure of the dual space of linear

---

[15]Strictly speaking, comaps have only been defined between geometric lattices. Intuitively, a comap is a function from a geometric lattice $L$ to a geometric lattice $M$ such that $M$ is obtained from $L$ by taking intersections with a modular flat added to $L$. Thus, the definition of a comap can be extended so that the image is the lattice of flats of a polymatroid. Whittle's construction is a special case of this. It should be worthwhile to study more closely the relation between comaps and polymatroids. See Crapo [**32**] and Kung [**72,73**] for introductions to comaps.

functionals does not exist in general, we have to use hyperplanes or flats. In this section, we shall give an elementary development of this theory suggested by the following papers: Brylawski [**23,24,25**], Dowling [**44**], and Whittle [**161**].

Let $G(S)$ and $P(E)$ be matroids with no loops. We say that $G(S) \hookrightarrow P(E)$ is an *embedding* if there is an injective map $\iota : S \to E$ such that the restriction $P|\iota(S)$ is isomorphic to $G$. By relabelling the element $x$ in $S$ with $\iota(x)$, we can assume that $S$ is a subset of $E$ and that $G$ is the restriction $P|S$. We shall call $P$ the *ambient space*, and the copoints in $P$ hyperplanes.

There are two critical problems for embeddings in general. The first uses hyperplanes in the ambient space. Let $G(S) \hookrightarrow P(E)$ be an embedding. An $s$-tuple of hyperplanes $(H_1, H_2, \ldots, H_s)$ *distinguishes* $S$ if for every point $x \in S$, there is a hyperplane $H_i$ such that $x \notin H_i$. The *hyperplane critical exponent* $c_H(G \hookrightarrow P)$ is the minimum integer $c$ such that there exists a $c$-tuple of hyperplanes distinguishing $G$. The second critical problem uses subspaces in $P(E)$. The *subspace critical exponent* $c_S(G \hookrightarrow P)$ is the minimum integer $c'$ such that there exists a $P$-flat (or "subspace") $U$ of corank $c'$ such that $U \cap S = \emptyset$. In the classical case, when $P$ is a vector space or projective geometry, the two critical exponents are equal. Because hyperplanes may not be modular in $P$, this is false for embeddings in general. One only knows that

$$c_H(G \hookrightarrow P) \leq c_S(G \hookrightarrow P).$$

The next result is an analogue of Theorem 4.1 for embeddings.

4.12. LEMMA. *Let $G(S)$ be a matroid embedded in the matroid $P(E)$. The number of $s$-tuples of hyperplanes distinguishing $S$ equals*

$$(4.4) \qquad \sum_{X : X \in L(G)} \mu(\hat{0}, X) h(X)^s,$$

*where $h(X)$ is the number of hyperplanes in $P$ containing the $G$-flat $X$.*

PROOF. If $X$ is a flat in $G$, then the number of $s$-tuples $(H_1, H_2, \ldots, H_s)$ of hyperplanes such that $X \subseteq H_1 \cap H_2 \cap \ldots \cap H_s \cap S$ equals $h(X)^s$. Because an $s$-tuple $(H_1, H_2, \ldots, H_s)$ distinguishes $S$ if and only if $H_1 \cap H_2 \cap \ldots \cap H_s \cap S = \emptyset$, the result follows by Möbius inversion. $\qquad \square$

Formula (4.4) becomes more manageable when $h(X)$ depends only on numerical matroid invariants of $X$ and $P(E)$. An example is the classical case when the ambient space is $[\mathrm{GF}(q)]^d$ or $\mathrm{PG}(d-1, q)$. This case was studied by Dowling [**44**]. In the expository account [**169**], Zaslavsky gave a direct proof of the following result of Dowling and suggested the shorter proof given here.[16]

4.13. PROPOSITION. *Let $G(S)$ be a rank-$n$ matroid represented as a set $S$ of non-zero vectors in $[\mathrm{GF}(q)]^d$ or a set of points in $\mathrm{PG}(d-1, q)$. The number of $s$-tuples of hyperplanes in $[\mathrm{GF}(q)]^d$ or $\mathrm{PG}(d-1, q)$ distinguishing $G$ equals*

$$(4.5) \qquad \frac{1}{(q-1)^s} \sum_{j=0}^{s} (-1)^{s-j} \binom{s}{j} q^{j(d-n)} \chi(G; q^j).$$

---

[16]Note that a binomial coefficient was inadvertently omitted in Zaslavsky's formula on p. 131 of [**169**].

*In particular, the number of hyperplanes in* $[\mathrm{GF}(q)]^d$ *or* $\mathrm{PG}(d-1,q)$ *not containing any point of* $G$ *equals*

$$\frac{q^{d-n}\chi(G;q)}{q-1}.$$

PROOF. Let $X$ be a flat of $G$. Then[17]

$$h(X) = \frac{q^{d-\mathrm{rank}(X)} - 1}{q-1}.$$

Raising both sides to the $s$th power and expanding the right hand side by the binomial theorem, we obtain

$$[h(X)]^s = \frac{1}{(q-1)^s}\sum_{j=0}^{s}(-1)^{s-j}\binom{s}{j}q^{j(d-\mathrm{rank}(X))}.$$

We can now substitute $[h(X)]^s$ into equation (4.4) and interchange the order of summation to obtain equation (4.5). □

Proposition 4.13 also holds for a set $S$ of points in a (non-Desarguesian) projective plane of order $q$ and gives the following result. *Let* $G(S)$ *be a subgeometry of a projective plane* $P$ *of order* $q$. *Then the number of lines in* $P$ *disjoint from* $S$ *equals*

$$\frac{q^{3-\mathrm{rank}(G)}\chi(G;q)}{q-1}.$$

Using the argument in Lemma 4.12, one can also obtain a formula for the number of corank-$k$ $P$-flats disjoint from $S$ :

$$\sum_{X:X\in L(G)} \mu(\hat{0},X)h(X,k),$$

where $h(X,k)$ is the number of corank-$k$ $P$-flats containing $X$. In particular, if $P$ is $[\mathrm{GF}(q)]^d$ or $\mathrm{PG}(d-1,q)$, then this formula gives

$$\sum_{X:X\in L(G)} \mu(\hat{0},X)\frac{\prod_{j=0}^{k-1}(q^{d-\mathrm{rank}(X)} - q^j)}{\prod_{j=0}^{k-1}(q^k - q^j)}.$$

Using Cauchy's formula (3.5) and interchanging summations, we obtain the following result due to Dowling [44]:

4.14. PROPOSITION. *Let* $S$ *be a set of vectors in* $[\mathrm{GF}(q)]^d$ *or a set of points in* $\mathrm{PG}(d-1,q)$. *Let* $G$ *be the matroid on* $S$ *defined by linear dependence. The number of corank-$k$ subspaces disjoint from* $S$ *equals*

$$\frac{1}{\prod_{j=0}^{k-1}(q^k - q^j)} \sum_{j=0}^{k}(-1)^j q^{\binom{j}{2}} \begin{bmatrix} k \\ j \end{bmatrix}_q q^{(k-j)(d-\mathrm{rank}(G))}\chi(G;q^{k-j}).$$

Another interesting case is when the ambient space is the Dowling group geometry $Q_d(A)$ over a finite group $A$. From Dowling's recursion for the Whitney numbers of $Q_d(A)$ (see p. 77 of [46] and the *erratum* to that paper), or, more

---

[17]This formula makes clear the relationship between hyperplanes and linear functionals. Each hyperplane is the kernel of $q-1$ non-zero linear functionals. The entire space is the kernel of a unique linear functional, the identically zero linear functional.

directly, from his interpretation of the flats of $Q_d(A)$ as partial $G$-partitions, the number of hyperplanes in $Q_d(A)$ containing a given flat $X$ of rank $r$ equals

$$(4.6) \qquad \frac{(|A|+1)^{d-r}-1}{|A|},$$

a number depending only on $r$ and $|A|$. When $A$ is the multiplicative group of $GF(q)$, this formula implies that every hyperplane in $PG(d-1, q)$ is also a hyperplane in $Q_d(A)$. From formula (4.4) and the method in the proof of Proposition 4.13, we obtain the following result due to Whittle [161].

4.15. PROPOSITION. *Let $G(S)$ be a rank-$n$ subgeometry of the Dowling group geometry $Q_d(A)$. The number of $s$-tuples $N(G, d, A, s)$ of hyperplanes in $Q_d(A)$ distinguishing $G$ equals*

$$(4.7) \qquad \frac{1}{|A|^s} \sum_{j=0}^{s} (-1)^{s-j} \binom{s}{j} (|A|+1)^{j(d-n)} \chi(G; (|A|+1)^j).$$

The number $N(G, d, A, s)$ given by formula (4.7) depends only on the characteristic polynomial of $G$, $d$, $|A|$, and $s$. Because the integer $N(G, d, A, s)$ is a linear combination of the integers $\chi(G; (|A|+1)^j), j = 1, 2, \ldots, s$, we conclude that

$$\min\{s : \chi(G; (|A|+1)^s) \neq 0\} = \min\{s : N(G, d, A, s) \neq 0\}.$$

Hence, the hyperplane critical exponent $c_H(G \hookrightarrow Q_d(A))$ depends only on $|A|$ and the lattice of flats of $G$. In particular, it is independent of the rank $d$ of the ambient Dowling group geometry. As in the classical case, we can define the *critical exponent* $c(G; A)$ of a geometry embeddable in a Dowling group geometry over the group $A$ to be the integer $c_H(G \hookrightarrow Q_d(A))$, where $G \hookrightarrow Q_d(A)$ is any embedding of $G$ into a Dowling group geometry $Q_d(A)$. If $G$ is a subgeometry of the Dowling geometry $Q_d(GF(q)^\times)$ over the multiplicative group $GF(q)^\times$ of a finite field $GF(q)$, then $G$ is representable over $GF(q)$. When this is the case, the critical exponent $c(G; GF(q)^\times)$ over the group $GF(q)^\times$ equals the "classical" critical exponent $c(G; q)$ over the field $GF(q)$. We shall give a more direct approach to the critical problem over Dowling group geometries in the next section.

Subgeometries of Dowling group geometries can be thought of as cycle matroids of gain graphs. Zaslavsky [170] has defined several ways of coloring a gain graph. No one has as yet figured out whether there is a relation between colorings and the critical problem stated here.

## 4.5. Abstract linear functionals in Dowling group geometries

The similarity between the formulas (4.5) and (4.7) suggests that there should be a direct interpretation of the numbers $\chi(G; (|A|+1)^s)$ when $G$ is a subgeometry of $Q_d(A)$. Such an interpretation is provided by a "Hamming-weight-two-or-less" analogue of linear algebra.

The basic component of this analogue is the following construction of the Dowling group geometry $Q_d(A)$ over a finite group $A$. The point set of $Q_d(A)$ consists of a basis $\{p_1, p_2, \ldots, p_d\}$ and points of the form $\alpha_{ij}$, where $\alpha$ is a group element in $A$ and $1 \leq i < j \leq d$. The points in the basis are called *joints* and the other points are called *internal points*. The dependencies in $Q_d(A)$ are generated by 3-element circuits of the following four forms:

$$\{p_i, \alpha_{ij}, p_j\}, \{p_i, \alpha_{ij}, \beta_{ij}\}, \{\alpha_{ij}, \beta_{ij}, \gamma_{ij}\}, \{\alpha_{ij}, \beta_{jk}, (\alpha\beta)_{ik}\}.$$

These circuits are called *atomic* circuits. For a brief but complete treatment, see Section 7 of Kahn and Kung [**67**]. The account in [**67**] is based on work in Doubilet, Rota, and Stanley [**42**], Section 5.3, Dowling [**45**], and Zaslavsky [**168**].

To do linear algebra on $Q_d(A)$, we interpret the internal point $\alpha_{ij}$ as the vector $p_i - \alpha p_j$. We also need to have a zero scalar element and we supply this by adding a formal zero element 0 to the group $A$ and extending the multiplication by the axiom $0\alpha = \alpha 0 = 0$ for every element $\alpha \in A$. An *abstract linear functional* on $Q_d(A)$ is a $d$-tuple $L = (l_1, l_2, \ldots, l_d)$ with elements from $A \cup \{0\}$. The abstract linear functional $L$ is said to be *non-zero* if $L \neq (0, 0, \ldots, 0)$. Although $L$ is not really a function on $Q_d(A)$, we can define when its value is zero or non-zero in this way:

(1)  $L$ is non-zero on a joint $p_i$ if $l_i \neq 0$; $L$ is zero on $p_i$ if $l_i = 0$;

(2)  $L$ is non-zero on an internal point $\alpha_{ij}$ if $l_i \neq \alpha l_j$; $L$ is zero on $\alpha_{ij}$ if $l_i = \alpha l_j$.

By an easy induction starting from the atomic circuits, we can show that abstract linear functionals are *linear* in the following sense.

4.16.  LEMMA.  *If an abstract linear functional $L$ is zero on all but one point $x$ of a circuit, then $L$ is also zero on $x$.*

Lemma 4.16 implies that the *kernel* of $L$, defined by

$$\ker L = \{x \in Q_d(A) : L \text{ is zero on } x\},$$

is a flat of $Q_d(A)$. When $L$ is non-zero, its kernel is a hyperplane. To prove this, we transfer the standard linear algebra argument. Let $A$ be the set of positions $i$ in $L$ such that $l_i = 0$ and $B$ be the complement of $A$. If $i \in A$, then the joint $p_i$ is in $\ker L$. If $B$ is the one-element set $\{r\}$, then $\ker L$ equals the copoint spanned by $\{p_1, p_2, \ldots, p_{r-1}, p_{r+1}, \ldots, p_d\}$. Otherwise, let $B = \{i_1, i_2, i_3, \ldots, i_t\}$, where $i_1 < i_2 < i_3 < \ldots < i_t$. Then the following internal points are in the kernel of $L$ :

$$p_{i_1} - l_{i_1} l_{i_2}^{-1} p_{i_2}, \ p_{i_2} - l_{i_2} l_{i_3}^{-1} p_{i_3}, \quad \ldots, \quad p_{i_{t-1}} - l_{i_{t-1}} l_{i_t}^{-1} p_{i_t}.$$

It is now routine to check that these points, together with joints $p_i, i \in A$, form a set of $d-1$ independent points spanning $\ker L$.

Because the non-zero abstract linear functionals $(l_1, l_2, \ldots, l_d)$ and $(\alpha l_1, \alpha l_2, \ldots, \alpha l_d)$, where $\alpha \in A$, have the same hyperplane as kernel, there are exactly $|A|$ abstract linear functionals having a given hyperplane as their kernel. Applied to the contraction of $Q_d(A)$ by a flat of rank $r$, this gives a direct proof of formula (4.6). A similar method shows that if $U$ is a flat in $Q_d(A)$, the number of $s$-tuples of abstract linear functionals $\underline{L}$ such that $\ker \underline{L} \geq U$ equals

$$(|A| + 1)^{s(d - \text{rank}(U))}.$$

An $s$-tuple $\underline{L} = (L_1, L_2, \ldots, L_s)$ of abstract linear functionals *distinguishes* a subgeometry $G$ of $Q_d(A)$ if for every point $x$ in $G$, there exists an abstract linear functional $L_i$ such that $L_i$ is non-zero on $x$. The standard Möbius inversion argument yields the following theorem.

4.17.  THEOREM.  *Let $G(S)$ be a rank-$n$ subgeometry of the Dowling group geometry $Q_d(A)$. The number of $s$-tuples of abstract linear functionals of $Q_d(A)$ distinguishing $G$ equals*

$$(|A| + 1)^{s(d-n)} \chi(G; (|A| + 1)^s).$$

*In particular, the critical exponent $c(G; A)$ equals the minimum integer $c$ such that there exists a $c$-tuple of abstract linear functionals of $Q_d(A)$ distinguishing $G$.*

In addition to the critical problem, this lean analogue of linear algebra can also be used to prove geometric theorems in Dowling group geometries by transfering over linear algebra proofs. In particular, theorems involving only lines have proofs which use only 3-element circuits and these proofs transfer to yield valid proofs in Dowling group geometries. For examples of such theorems, see Bennett, Bogart and Bonin [**7**].

## 4.6.  The critical problem for flats of a given rank

In this section, we shall describe two critical problems for flats of a representable matroid. The first (algebraic) critical problem appeared in Rota's Bowdoin lectures [**119**].

A *bracket* or *determinant function* on a $d$-dimensional vector space $V$ over the field $\mathbb{F}$ is the function from the $d$-fold direct product $V^d$ to the field $\mathbb{F}$ given by

$$[x_1, x_2, \ldots, x_d] = \det(x_{ij})_{1 \le i,j \le d},$$

where $x_i = (x_{i1}, x_{i2}, \ldots, x_{id})$ relative to a chosen basis $e_1, e_2, \ldots, e_d$. Because a change of basis is equivalent to multiplication by a non-singular matrix, the *multiplicative property* $\det(AB) = \det(A)\det(B)$ of determinants implies that any bracket can be obtained from another bracket by multiplying it with a non-zero scalar. Indeed, the bracket is defined up to a non-zero scalar multiple as a function from $V^d$ to $\mathbb{F}$ by the properties: it is non-degenerate (that is, not identically zero), multilinear, and alternating.

Now let $u_1, u_2, \ldots, u_{d-1}$ be a set of $d - 1$ linearly independent vectors in $V$. Then the function

$$x \mapsto [u_1, u_2, \ldots, u_{d-1}, x]$$

is a linear functional on $V$. Conversely, given a linear functional $L$, we can represent it as a bracket in the following way. The kernel of $L$ is a hyperplane $H$ in $V$. Choose a basis $u_1, u_2, \ldots, u_{d-1}$ for $H$. Then

$$L(x) = \gamma[u_1, u_2, \ldots, u_{d-1}, x] = [\gamma u_1, u_2, \ldots, u_{d-1}, x],$$

for some non-zero constant $\gamma$. This way of representing linear functionals suggests two extensions of the critical problem to flats of higher rank. These extensions are best described in the language of exterior algebra.

Let $V$ be a $d$-dimensional vector space over a field $\mathbb{F}$. A *decomposable $k$-tensor* or *$k$-extensor* of $V$ is an expression of the form

$$v_1 \wedge v_2 \wedge \ldots \wedge v_k,$$

where $v_i \in V$. A $k$-tensor is a linear combination of decomposable $k$-tensors.[18] The *wedge product* $\wedge$ is defined to satisfy two properties:

---

[18]Strictly speaking, our tensors are *alternating* tensors.

*Alternation.* For any permutation $\sigma$ of $\{1, 2, \ldots, k\}$,

$$v_{\sigma(1)} \wedge v_{\sigma(2)} \wedge \ldots \wedge v_{\sigma(k)} = \text{sign}(\sigma)(v_1 \wedge v_2 \wedge \ldots \wedge v_k).$$

*Multilinearity.*

$$(\alpha v_1 + \beta u_1) \wedge v_2 \wedge \ldots \wedge v_k = \alpha(v_1 \wedge v_2 \wedge \ldots \wedge v_k) + \beta(u_1 \wedge v_2 \wedge \ldots \wedge v_k).$$

The *k-fold exterior power* $\bigwedge^k(V)$ is the vector space of *k*-tensors. The following basic results can be derived from the properties of alternation and multilinearity:

(EP1) If $\{e_1, e_2, \ldots, e_d\}$ is a basis of $V$, then the *k*-tensors

$$e_{i_1} \wedge e_{i_2} \wedge \ldots \wedge e_{i_k}, \quad i_1 < i_2 < \ldots < i_k$$

form a basis for $\bigwedge^k(V)$. In particular, $\bigwedge^k(V)$ has dimension $\binom{d}{k}$.

(EP2) $v_1 \wedge v_2 \wedge \ldots \wedge v_k \neq 0$ if and only if $\{v_1, v_2, \ldots, v_k\}$ is a linearly independent set having size $k$.

(EP3) Suppose $v_1 \wedge v_2 \wedge \ldots \wedge v_k$ and $u_1 \wedge u_2 \wedge \ldots \wedge u_k$ are non-zero decomposable *k*-tensors. Then

$$v_1 \wedge v_2 \wedge \ldots \wedge v_k = \alpha(u_1 \wedge u_2 \wedge \ldots \wedge u_k)$$

for some non-zero scalar $\alpha$ if and only if the vectors $v_1, v_2, \ldots, v_k$ and $u_1, u_2, \ldots, u_k$ span the same subspace $U$ in $V$. The scalar $\alpha$ is the determinant of the change-of-basis matrix from $v_i$ to $u_i$. We call the subspace $U$ the *underlying subspace* of the *k*-tensor $v_1 \wedge v_2 \wedge \ldots \wedge v_k$.

The *d*-fold exterior power is a 1-dimensional vector space and by choosing the vector $e_1 \wedge e_2 \wedge \ldots \wedge e_d$ as a basis vector in $\bigwedge^d(V)$, one obtains the bracket by the identity:

$$x_1 \wedge x_2 \wedge \ldots \wedge x_d = [x_1, x_2, \ldots, x_d](e_1 \wedge e_2 \wedge \ldots \wedge e_d).$$

Thus, we can identify the bracket $[x_1, x_2, \ldots, x_d]$ with the decomposable *d*-tensor $x_1 \wedge x_2 \wedge \ldots \wedge x_d$.

Let $k$ be an integer such that $1 \leq k \leq d-1$. Given any decomposable $(d-k)$-tensor $u_1 \wedge u_2 \wedge \ldots \wedge u_{d-k}$ of vectors in $V$, we can define a function from the *k*-fold exterior product $\bigwedge^k(V)$ to $\mathbb{F}$ by:

$$x_1 \wedge x_2 \wedge \ldots \wedge x_k \mapsto u_1 \wedge u_2 \wedge \ldots \wedge u_{d-k} \wedge x_1 \wedge x_2 \ldots \wedge x_k.$$

We call such functions *decomposable linear $(d-k)$-functionals* on $V$. In fact, since $\bigwedge^{d-k}(V)$ is the vector space dual to $\bigwedge^k(V)$, a decomposable $(d-k)$-functional is a special kind of linear functional on $\bigwedge^k(V)$. To obtain all linear functionals on $\bigwedge^k(V)$, we take all linear combinations of decomposable $(d-k)$-functionals.

Consider a matroid $G(S)$ with no loops represented as a set $S$ of non-zero vectors in $V$. If $X$ is a *k*-flat of $G$, then $X$ defines a decomposable *k*-tensor in the following way: choose a basis $x_1, x_2, \ldots, x_k$ of $X$ and form the *k*-tensor $x_1 \wedge x_2 \wedge \ldots \wedge x_k$. By Property (EP3), any two *k*-tensors constructed in this way differ by a non-zero scalar multiple. We shall use $\wedge X$ to denote any (non-zero) *k*-tensor obtained in this way.

We can now state the *algebraic critical problem for rank-k flats*. Let $\phi : S \rightarrow [\text{GF}(q)]^d$ be a representation of the matroid $G(S)$. An *s*-tuple $(L_1, L_2, \ldots, L_s)$ of linear functionals in the dual of $\bigwedge^k([\text{GF}(q)]^d)$ is said to *distinguish the k-flats of $G$*

in the representation $\phi$ if for any $k$-flat $X$ of $G$, there is a linear functional $L_i$ such that

(4.8) $$L_i(\wedge X) \neq 0.$$

The *algebraic critical exponent* $c(G, \phi, k, q)$ *for* $k$-*flats of the representation* $\phi$ of $G$ is the minimum integer $c$ such that there exists a $c$-tuple of linear functionals distinguishing the $k$-flats. The reason for stressing the representation is that it is not known for $k \geq 2$ that the critical exponent for $k$-flats depends only on the matroid structure of $G$. As we shall see, there are matroids $G$ for which the number of $s$-tuples distinguishing the $k$-flats depends on the representation.

Because a $k$-flat can be represented as a vector in the $k$th exterior power $\bigwedge^k(V)$, the algebraic critical problem for $k$-flats can be reduced to a critical problem on vectors in $\bigwedge^k(V)$. Indeed, by (EP3), every $k$-flat corresponds to a unique point in the projective space $\mathrm{PG}(\bigwedge^k(V))$ associated with the vector space $\bigwedge^k(V)$. Thus, given a representation $\phi$ of $G$ over $\mathrm{GF}(q)$, we define the $k$-*Grassmannian matroid* $\bigwedge^k(G, \phi)$ to be the geometry defined by the set of points in $\mathrm{PG}(\bigwedge^k(V))$ of the form $\wedge X$, where $X$ is a $k$-flat of $G$. The $k$-Grassmannian matroid $\bigwedge^k(G, \phi)$ depends on the representation $\phi$.

*Example 1.* Consider $U_{3,6}$, the uniform matroid with 6 points $x_1, x_2, x_3, x_4, x_5, x_6$ in general position in a plane. For any sufficiently large prime power $q$, there are two projectively inequivalent representations of $U_{3,6}$ over $\mathrm{PG}(2, q)$ : $\phi_1$, in which the six points are in general position, and $\phi_2$, in which the three lines $x_1 \vee x_2$, $x_3 \vee x_4$, and $x_5 \vee x_6$ intersect at a common point (not in $U_{3,6}$). For the first representation, the $\binom{6}{2} = 15$ lines are in general position in the rank-3 projective space $\mathrm{PG}(\bigwedge^2([\mathrm{GF}(q)]^3))$ and hence, $\bigwedge^2(G, \phi_1) \cong U_{3,15}$. For the second representation, the three lines which are copunctual are collinear and form a 3-point line in $\mathrm{PG}(\bigwedge^2([\mathrm{GF}(q)]^3))$. We conclude that the representations $\phi_1$ and $\phi_2$ yield non-isomorphic 2-Grassmannian matroids. The 1-tensors of $[\mathrm{GF}(q)]^3$ are vectors and every 1-tensor is decomposable. A vector (or more correctly, a 1-tuple of vectors) distinguishes the lines of $U_{3,5}$ if and only if it is not on the linear span of any of the lines in $U_{3,5}$. It is clear geometrically that the number of such vectors are different for the two representations. Finally, because $c(G, \phi_1, 2, q) = c(G, \phi_2, 2, q) = 1$, the critical exponent for lines are equal. At the time of writing, there are no known examples for which the critical exponent depends on the representation.

4.18. LEMMA. *Let* $G(S)$ *be a matroid represented over* $\mathrm{GF}(q)$ *by the representation* $\phi$. *Then*

$$c(G, \phi, k, q) = c(\textstyle\bigwedge^k(G, \phi); q).$$

A disadvantage of the algebraic critical problem is that arbitrary linear functionals $L_i$ on $\bigwedge^k([\mathrm{GF}(q)]^d)$ have no obvious geometric interpretation in the original vector space $[\mathrm{GF}(q)]^d$. Decomposable linear $(d - k)$-functionals, however, correspond directly to $(d - k)$-dimensional subspaces. Let $L$ be the decomposable linear $(d - k)$-functional defined by the $(d - k)$-tensor $\wedge U = u_1 \wedge u_2 \wedge \ldots \wedge u_{d-k}$. If $\wedge X = x_1 \wedge x_2 \wedge \ldots \wedge x_k$, then

$$L(\wedge X) \neq 0 \Leftrightarrow (\wedge U) \wedge (\wedge X) = [u_1, u_2, \ldots, u_{d-k}, x_1, x_2, \ldots, x_k] \neq 0.$$

Hence, the following conditions are equivalent:

(1) $L(\wedge X) \neq 0.$

(2) The underlying subspace $U$ spanned by $u_1, u_2, \ldots, u_{d-k}$ is *complementary* to the subspace spanned by the $k$-flat $X$.

(3) The join of the subspaces $U$ and $X$ is the entire space $V$.

Roughly speaking, the *geometric critical problem for rank-$k$ flats* is the algebraic critical problem with the linear functionals restricted to those arising from decomposable tensors. However, we shall state it in its purely geometric form. Let $\phi : S \to [\mathrm{GF}(q)]^d$ be a representation of the matroid $G(S)$ over $\mathrm{GF}(q)$. An $s$-tuple $(U_1, U_2, \ldots, U_s)$ of $(d-k)$-dimensional subspaces in $[\mathrm{GF}(q)]^d$ is said to *distinguish the $k$-flats of $G$ in the representation $\phi$* if for any $k$-flat $X$ of $G$, there is a subspace $U_i$ such that $U_i$ is complementary to $X$. The *geometric critical exponent* $\hat{c}(G, \phi, k, q)$ *for $k$-flats of the representation $\phi$ of $G$* is the minimum integer $c$ such that there exists a $c$-tuple of $(d-k)$-subspaces distinguishing all the $k$-flats of $G$. When $k = 1$, the classical case, and $k = n - 1$, the case of copoints, every linear $(n - k)$-functional is decomposable. Therefore, the algebraic and geometric critical problems are the same in these two cases. We also have the inequality

$$\hat{c}(G, \phi, k, q) \geq c(G, \phi, k, q).$$

This inequality can be a strict inequality.

*Example 2.* Let $\phi$ be a representation of the uniform matroid $U_{4,4}$ in $[\mathrm{GF}(2)]^4$ that sends the four points in $U_{4,4}$ to the standard basis vectors $e_1, e_2, e_3, e_4$. Then the 2-Grassmannian matroid $\bigwedge^2(G, \phi)$ consists of the six decomposable 2-tensors $e_i \wedge e_j, 1 \leq i < j \leq 4$. Because the 2-functional

$$\sum_{1 \leq i < j \leq 4} e_i \wedge e_j$$

distinguishes $\bigwedge^2(G, \phi)$, the critical exponent $c(G, \phi, 2, q)$ equals 1. However, the union of the six lines $e_i \vee e_j$ in $\mathrm{PG}(3, 2)$ is a 10-point geometry $H$ isomorphic to $M(K_5)$. Because $M(K_5)$ has critical exponent 3 over $\mathrm{GF}(2)$, every line in $\mathrm{PG}(3, 2)$ has non-empty intersection with $H$. Hence, there does not exist a line in $\mathrm{PG}(3, 2)$ complementary to all six lines $e_i \vee e_j$. We conclude that

$$\hat{c}(G, \phi, 2, q) > 1 = c(G, \phi, 2, q).$$

It can be easily checked that $\hat{c}(G, \phi, 2, q)$ equals 2.

The geometric critical problem can also be defined for subsets of $k$-flats of $G$. One reason for doing this is that geometric critical exponents of subsets of $k$-flats are related to critical exponents of points. The following lemma gives an example of such a result. It can be proved using the alternative identity for tensors (see Doubilet, Rota and Stein [**43**]).

4.19. LEMMA. *Let $G(S)$ be a matroid without loops represented as a set $S$ of non-zero vectors in $[\mathrm{GF}(q)]^d$. Let $u_1 \wedge u_2 \wedge \ldots \wedge u_{d-k}$ be a decomposable $(d-k)$-tensor distinguishing the set of $k$-flats $X_1, X_2, \ldots, X_m$ in $G$. Then the restriction of $G$ to the union $X_1 \cup X_2 \cup \ldots \cup X_m$ has critical exponent at most $k$.*

I intend to discuss the two higher-rank critical problems in more detail in future papers.

## 4.7. Finding critical exponents using matrix operations

In this section, we describe some elementary methods to "find" the critical exponent of a given matroid over a given finite field.

Let $G(S)$ be a rank-$n$ matroid with no loops. Let the set $S$ of elements in $G$ be listed in a fixed order, $x, y, \ldots, z$. Suppose $\phi : G \to [\mathrm{GF}(q)]^d$ is a representation of $G$ over the field $\mathrm{GF}(q)$. Then, we can visualize the representation $\phi$ by putting the $d$-dimensional column vectors $\phi(x), \phi(y), \ldots, \phi(z)$, side by side according to the ordering of $S$. This yields a $d \times |S|$ matrix $M(\phi)$. A matrix $M(\phi)$ obtained in this way is called a *representation matrix* of $G$ (*over* $\mathrm{GF}(q)$). The columns of $M(\phi)$ are indexed by $S$ and the rows are indexed by $\{1, 2, \ldots, d\}$. The rows are not linearly independent unless $d = n$. The *row space* of $M(\phi)$, that is, the subspace in $[\mathrm{GF}(q)]^{|S|}$ spanned by the rows, has dimension $n$.

There is a close relation between the row vectors in the row space of $M(\phi)$ and linear functionals. Consider the "$i$th coordinate" linear functional $E_i : [\mathrm{GF}(q)]^d \to \mathrm{GF}(q)$ defined by the formula

$$E_i((x_1, x_2, \ldots, x_d)) = x_i.$$

The linear functionals $E_1, E_2, \ldots, E_d$ form a basis dual to the standard basis vectors $e_1, e_2, \ldots, e_d$ in the following sense:

$$E_i(e_j) = \delta_{ij} = \begin{cases} 1 \text{ if } i = j, \\ 0 \text{ otherwise.} \end{cases}$$

The $i$th row of $M(\phi)$ is the row vector

$$(E_i(x), E_i(y), \ldots, E_i(z))_{x,y,\ldots,z \in S}.$$

Generalizing this, we define the *row vector* $\mathrm{row}(L)$ *of a linear functional* $L$ *(for the representation matrix* $M(\phi)$ *of* $G$*)* to be the $|S|$-dimensional vector

$$(L(x), L(y), \ldots, L(z))_{x,y,\ldots,z \in S}.$$

Because $L$ is a linear combination of the dual basis vectors $E_i$, $\mathrm{row}(L)$ is a linear combination of the rows of $M(\phi)$. Because a linear functional is determined by its values on a basis of $[\mathrm{GF}(q)]^d$, the row vector $\mathrm{row}(L)$ determines $L$ when $d = n$, the rank of $G$. This yields the following lemma.

4.20.   LEMMA. *Let* $M(\phi)$ *be the matrix of a representation* $\phi$ *of a rank-$n$ matroid* $G(S)$ *in* $[\mathrm{GF}(q)]^n$. *Then the function* $L \mapsto \mathrm{row}(L)$ *is a bijection between the dual space of* $[\mathrm{GF}(q)]^n$ *and the row space of* $M(\phi)$.

Note that if $\phi$ is a representation of the rank-$n$ matroid $G(S)$ in $[\mathrm{GF}(q)]^d$, then each vector in the row space of $M(\phi)$ is the row vector of $q^{d-n}$ linear functionals on $[\mathrm{GF}(q)]^d$.

Using the relation between linear functionals and row vectors, we can reformulate the critical problem in terms of row vectors in the row space of a representation matrix. The *support* $\mathrm{supp}(u)$ of a row vector $u$ in $[\mathrm{GF}(q)]^{|S|}$ is the subset of elements in $S$ which have non-zero coordinates. Note that if $\alpha$ and $\beta$ are non-zero scalars and $u$ and $v$ are row vectors, then

(4.9)        $\mathrm{supp}(u) \,\triangle\, \mathrm{supp}(v) \subseteq \mathrm{supp}(\alpha u + \beta v) \subseteq \mathrm{supp}(u) \cup \mathrm{supp}(v),$

where $\triangle$ is symmetric difference of sets.

4.21. LEMMA. *The critical exponent $c(G; q)$ is the minimum integer $c$ such that there exist $c$ row vectors $u_1, u_2, \ldots, u_c$ in $[\mathrm{GF}(q)]^{|S|}$ satisfying the conditions:*

(1) *every row vector $u_i$ is a linear combination of the rows of a (fixed) representation matrix $M$ of $G$ over $\mathrm{GF}(q)$, and*

(2) *the union of the supports of the vectors $u_1, u_2, \ldots, u_c$ is all of $S$.*

Equivalent forms of Lemma 4.21 can be found in the earlier papers: Mullin and Stanton [**95**] (for binary matroids) and Asano *et al.* [**3**].

A set of row vectors satisfying conditions (1) and (2) in Lemma 4.21 is said to *distinguish* $G$. Because $c(G; q)$ is the minimum such integer, equation (4.9) implies that the row vectors $u_1, u_2, \ldots, u_c$ are linearly independent.[19] Thus, we can obtain a new representation matrix $M'$ of $G$ by taking $u_1, u_2, \ldots, u_c$ as the first $c$ rows and extending these rows to a representation matrix by adding suitable rows from $M$. The new matrix $M'$ is obtained by row operations from the original matrix $M$. Equivalently, $M'$ is obtained from $M$ by multiplication on the left by a non-singular square matrix in the general linear group $\mathrm{GL}(d, q)$. This suggests a naive algorithm for finding the critical exponent assuming the existence of a procedure MATRIX for generating all the matrices in a general linear group.[20] If $G(S)$ has rank $n$, then one can obtain an $n \times |S|$ representation matrix from any representation matrix by deleting rows. Because an algorithm using an $n \times |S|$ representation matrix is more efficient than one using a larger matrix, we shall state the algorithm only for $n \times |S|$ representation matrices.

4.22. ALGORITHM. *Given a positive integer $k$ and an $n \times |S|$ representation matrix $M$ over $\mathrm{GF}(q)$ of a rank-$n$ matroid $G(S)$ with no loops, this algorithm decides if $c(G; q) \leq k$.*

*Input a matrix $A$ from* MATRIX. *Calculate the matrix product $AM$ and check if the union of the supports of the first $k$ rows is all of $S$. If it is, output 'Yes' and stop; if not, repeat this step until* MATRIX *has generated all the matrices in $\mathrm{GL}(n, q)$. Output 'No' at the end.*

We remark that about $\log_2 n$ applications of Algorithm 4.22 will yield the exact critical exponent by a binary search on the integer interval $\{1, 2, \ldots, n\}$.

Algorithm 4.22 can be randomized by using a procedure for generating a random matrix from $\mathrm{GL}(n, q)$.[21] Note that by Lemma 4.20, the probability that the

---

[19]This is also clear from the hyperplane interpretation of the critical problem.

[20]No algorithm, polynomial-time or otherwise, has ever been proposed for finding the critical exponent of a matroid. Algorithm 4.22 basically lists all possible solutions. The problem of finding critical exponents is related to computationally intractable problems. For example, Jaeger, Vertigan and Welsh [**66**] have shown that finding the value $\chi(G; k)$ of the characteristic polynomial of a matroid $G$ at a given integer $k$ is #$P$-hard in general. The decision problem, whether $\chi(G; k) > 0$, is $NP$-complete for the following reason: it is $NP$, and it includes the problem of finding the chromatic number of a graph, an $NP$-complete problem, as a special case. However, if one specifies a finite field $\mathrm{GF}(q)$, then the decision problem, whether $c(G; q) \geq k$, for $G$ a $\mathrm{GF}(q)$-representable matroid and $k$ a positive integer, does not seem to include the problem of finding the chromatic number of a graph. The complexity of this special decision problem is not known.

[21]One way to generate all the matrices in $\mathrm{GL}(n, q)$ is to try to find a Hamiltonian path in a suitable Cayley graph of $\mathrm{GL}(n, q)$. A random matrix generator can also be obtained by taking a random walk on such a Cayley graph. Since the usual generators for $\mathrm{GL}(n, q)$ are in fact

first $k$ rows distinguishes $G$ is

$$\frac{\chi(G; q^k)}{q^{kn}} = 1 - \frac{w_1}{q^k} + \frac{w_2}{q^{2k}} - \ldots \pm \frac{w_n}{q^{nk}}.$$

where $\chi(G; \lambda) = \sum_{j=0}^{n} (-1)^j w_j \lambda^{n-j}$. This probability is close to 1 if $k$ is large compared with the actual critical exponent. Hence, the randomized algorithm should be reasonably effective for finding upper bounds. It would be interesting to have a careful probabilistic analysis of this algorithm.

One way to find the critical exponent by hand calculations to try to replace two row vectors by one. The following technical lemma allows us to combine two row vectors whose supports have small overlap.

4.23. LEMMA. *Let $u$ and $v$ be row vectors for a representation matrix $M(\phi)$ of a matroid $G(S)$ over $\mathrm{GF}(q)$. Suppose that*

$$|\mathrm{supp}(u) \cap \mathrm{supp}(v)| \leq q - 2.$$

*Then there exists a linear combination $u - \beta v$ such that*

$$\mathrm{supp}(u - \beta v) = \mathrm{supp}(u) \cup \mathrm{supp}(v).$$

PROOF. Let $u = (u_1, u_2, \ldots, u_{|S|})$ and $v = (v_1, v_2, \ldots, v_{|S|})$. Relabelling if necessary, let the supports of $u$ and $v$ intersect in the first $k$ coordinate positions. Consider the ratios $u_i/v_i$. These are non-zero elements in $\mathrm{GF}(q)$. Because $k \leq q - 2$, there exists a non-zero element $\beta$ in $\mathrm{GF}(q)$ such that $u_i \neq \beta v_i$ for every $i = 1, 2, \ldots, k$. Hence, none of the coordinates in the first $k$ positions in $u - \beta v$ is zero. By equation (4.9), we conclude that $\mathrm{supp}(u - \beta v) = \mathrm{supp}(u) \cup \mathrm{supp}(v)$. $\square$

A natural question that can be answered by looking at representation matrices is the relation between *girth*, the minimum size of a circuit, and the critical exponent. Because parallel elements give rise to 2-element circuits which are irrelevant for the critical problem, the question is best answered for geometries rather than matroids. Rather surprising, a rather crude argument yields the following sharp inequality.

4.24. LEMMA. *Let $G(S)$ be a rank-n geometry with positive nullity representable over $\mathrm{GF}(q)$. Suppose that there is a basis $B$ in $G$ such that all the fundamental circuits relative to $B$ have size at least $k$. Then*

$$c(G; q) \leq n - k + 3.$$

PROOF. Represent $G$ as a set of non-zero vectors in $[\mathrm{GF}(q)]^n$ so that the basis $B$ is represented by the standard basis vectors $\{e_1, e_2, \ldots, e_n\}$. Let $M$ be the representation matrix. If $x \in S \backslash B$, then, because the fundamental circuit of $x$ relative to $B$ contains at least $k - 1$ basis vectors, there are at least $k - 1$ non-zero entries in the column indexed by $x$ in the representation matrix $M$. Choose a set $U$ of $n - k + 2$ row vectors. Because any subset of size at least $k - 1$ has non-empty

---

elementary row operations, an algorithm using Cayley graphs can be incorporated directly into Algorithm 4.22. If this is done, then one may be able to make use of the fact that we are only interested in matrices which change the first $k$ rows. Finding effective algorithms for generating random matrices (or random vectors) is an area of intense research at present.

intersection with a (fixed) subset of size $n - k + 2$ in a set of size $n$, at least one of the non-zero entries in the column indexed by $x$ occurs in a row in $U$. Therefore,

$$S \backslash B \subseteq \bigcup_{u \in U} \text{supp}(u)$$

and we have distinguished all the vectors in $S \backslash B$. To distinguish the basis vectors, we add the sum $w$ of all row vectors in $M$ to the set of $n - k + 2$ rows chosen earlier. We conclude that $c(G; q) \leq n - k + 3$.                                                $\square$

Note that $k \geq g$, where $g$ is the girth of the geometry $G$. Thus, it follows immediately from Lemma 4.24 that

(4.10)                                    $c(G; q) \leq n - g + 3.$

Because a $k$-connected matroid with at least $2k - 2$ elements has no circuits of size $k - 1$ or less, Lemma 4.24 implies that a rank-$n$ $k$-connected GF$(q)$-representable geometry with at least $2k - 2$ points has critical exponent at most $n - k + 3$ over GF$(q)$.

Both the inequality in Lemma 4.24 and inequality (4.10) are sharp. For example, the projective geometry PG$(n - 1, q)$ has rank $n$, girth 3, and critical exponent $n$ over GF$(q)$. For another class of examples, consider the rank-$n$ geometry $H(n, q)$ obtained by taking a basis $B = \{e_1, e_2, \dots, e_n\}$ in PG$(n - 1, q)$ and all the points in PG$(n - 1, q)$ of the form $\alpha_1 e_1 + \alpha_2 e_2 + \dots + \alpha_n e_n$, where none of the coefficients $\alpha_i$ is zero. (These are the points having "Hamming weight" equal to $n$.) By construction, all the fundamental circuits relative to the basis $B$ have size equal to $n + 1$. Note, however, that when $n \geq 3$, the geometries $H(n, q)$ have smaller girth. When $q = 2$ and $n$ is even, or when $q$ is a prime power not equal to 2 and $n \geq 2$, it is easy to check that $H(n, q)$ is not affine and $c(H(n, q); q) = 2$. Hence, the inequality in Lemma 4.24 is sharp for these geometries.

## 4.8. Some bounds on critical exponents

A *bond* or *cocircuit* of a matroid $G(S)$ is the complement $S \backslash X$ of a copoint $X$ of $G$. Because a linear functional is non-zero off a copoint, the structure of bonds in a matroid should have some connection with its critical exponent. This is confirmed by the following results.

4.25. LEMMA. *Let $G(S)$ be a matroid representable over* GF$(q)$. *Suppose that there exist bonds $D_1, D_2, \dots, D_m$ such that*
   *(1)  $D_1 \cup D_2 \cup \dots \cup D_m = S$, and*
   *(2)  for $2 \leq i \leq m$, $|(D_1 \cup D_2 \cup \dots \cup D_{i-1}) \cap D_i| \leq q^k - 2$.*
*Then $c(G; q) \leq k$.*

PROOF. It suffices to show that $c(G; q^k) = 1$. Note that condition (1) implies that there are no loops in $G$. Represent $G$ as a set $S$ of non-zero vectors in $[\text{GF}(q^k)]^d$. If $X$ is a copoint of $G$, let $L_X$ be a (non-zero) linear functional on $[\text{GF}(q^k)]^d$ with kernel $\text{lin}(X)$, the hyperplane spanned by $X$ in $[\text{GF}(q^k)]^d$. Then for $x \in S$, $L_X(x) \neq 0$ if and only if $x$ is in the bond $S \backslash X$. Hence, the row vector $\text{row}(L_X)$ has support $X^c$.

Now let $X_i$ be the copoint for which $D_i = S \backslash X_i$ and let $u_i$ be the row vector of the linear functional $L_{X_i}$. Applying Lemma 4.23 iteratively, we obtain a linear combination $u = \alpha_1 u_1 + \alpha_2 u_2 + \ldots + \alpha_m u_m$ of the row vectors $u_i$ having support $S$. We conclude that $c(G; q^k) = 1$. ☐

The special case of Lemma 4.25 when the bonds $D_i$ are pairwise disjoint was proved by Oxley [**101**]. Note that when $q = 2$ and $k = 1$, condition (2) is equivalent to the condition that the bonds $D_i$ are pairwise disjoint. Using Lemma 4.25, we obtain the following extension of a result of Lindström [**88**].

4.26. LEMMA. *Let $G(S)$ be a matroid representable over* GF$(q)$. *Suppose that there exist bonds $D_1, D_2, \ldots, D_m$ such that*
   *(1)  $D_1 \cup D_2 \cup \ldots \cup D_m = S$, and*
   *(2)  for $2 \leq i \leq m$, $|D_i| \leq q^k - 1$.*
*Then $c(G; q) \leq k$.*

PROOF. We shall show that $c(G; q^k) = 1$. To do this, it suffices to find a subsequence of bonds satisfying the conditions in Lemma 4.25. Starting with the bonds $D_1$ and $D_2$, we proceed as follows. If $D_j \subseteq D_1 \cup D_2 \cup \ldots \cup D_{j-1}$, then $D_j$ can removed without violating condition (1). If $D_j \not\subseteq D_1 \cup D_2 \cup \ldots \cup D_{j-1}$, then

$$|(D_1 \cup D_2 \cup \ldots \cup D_{j-1}) \cap D_j| < |D_j| \leq q^k - 1$$

and condition (2) in Lemma 4.25 is satisfied. ☐

The following example shows that Lemma 4.26 is "tight". Consider the cycle matroid $M(K_{q^k})$ of the complete graph on the vertices $\{1, 2, \ldots, q^k\}$. The collection of bonds $D_i$, where $D_i$ is the cutset of all edges incident on the vertex $i$, satisfies condition (1). In addition, $|D_i| = q^k - 1$ for every $i$, and $c(M(K_{q^k}); q) = k$.

The idea of combining two linear functionals yields the following technical lemma.

4.27. LEMMA. *Let $G(S)$ be a matroid representable over* GF$(q)$. *Suppose that there exists a copoint $X$ in $G$ such that*
   *(1)  the restriction $G|X$ has critical exponent not exceeding $k$, and*
   *(2)  the bond $S \backslash X$ contains at most $q^k - 1$ points.*
*Then $G$ has critical exponent not exceeding $k$.*

PROOF. It suffices to show that $c(G; q^k) = 1$. Represent $G$ over GF$(q^k)$. Let $L$ be a linear functional distinguishing $G|X$ and let $L_X$ be a linear functional with kernel the linear span $\text{lin}(X)$ of $X$. If $L(x) \neq 0$ for every $x$ in the bond $S \backslash X$, then we are done; otherwise, $\text{supp}(L) \cap \text{supp}(L_X) \leq q^k - 2$ and we can use Lemma 4.23 to combine $L$ and $L_X$ into one linear functional distinguishing $G$. ☐

Using Lemma 4.27 inductively, we obtain the following result.

4.28. COROLLARY. *Let $\phi : S \to [$GF$(q)]^n$ be a representation of the rank-n matroid $G(S)$. Suppose the representation matrix $M(\phi)$ is an $n \times |S|$ "staircase" matrix*

$$[I | N_2 | N_3 | \cdots | N_m],$$

*where $I$ is a submatrix of the $n \times n$ identity matrix and the submatrix $N_i$ is an $n \times h_i$ matrix such that*
   *(1)  $0 \leq h_i \leq q^k - 2$, that is, $N_i$ has at most $q^k - 2$ columns,*
   *(2)  all the entries in the ith row are non-zero, and*

*(3) all the entries in the $i+1$st row, the $i+2$nd row, ..., and the $n$th row are zero.*

Then $c(G;q) \leq k$.

The next result is a special case of Corollary 4.28. When $q \geq 3$, it generalizes the well-known fact that independent sets are affine.

4.29. COROLLARY. *Let $G(S)$ be a geometry representable over $\mathrm{GF}(q)$. If $G$ has nullity less than or equal to $q^k - 2$, then $c(G;q) \leq k$. In particular, if $G$ has nullity less than or equal to $q - 2$, then $G$ is affine.*

Corollary 4.29 is the best possible result when $k = 1$ because the direct sum $U_{2,q+1} \oplus U_{n-2,n-2}$ has critical exponent 2 over $\mathrm{GF}(q)$. For higher values of $k$, the following improvement (due to Mullin and Stanton [95] for $q = 2$ and Oxley [102] for general prime powers $q$) is known: *Let $G(S)$ be a $\mathrm{GF}(q)$-representable geometry having nullity less than or equal to*

$$\frac{q^{k+1} - 1}{q - 1} - k - 2.$$

Then $c(G;q) \leq k$. The result can be proved by an easy induction. See Oxley [102]. Oxley's result is the best possible result because the critical exponent $c(\mathrm{PG}(k,q) \oplus U_{n-k-1,n-k-1};q)$ equals $k + 1$.

## 4.9. Orthogonal duality and critical exponents

Orthogonal duality[22] suggests yet another matrix approach to the critical problem. Once again, let $G(S)$ be a rank-$n$ matroid with no loops representable over $\mathrm{GF}(q)$. Whitney [154] proved that if $M$ is a representation matrix for the matroid $G$ over $\mathrm{GF}(q)$, then any matrix $M^\perp$ whose row space is an orthogonal complement to the row space of $M$ in $[\mathrm{GF}(q)]^{|S|}$ is a representation matrix of the orthogonal dual $G^\perp$.[23] Here, orthogonality of vectors is defined relative to the standard inner product:

$$\langle (u_1, u_2, \ldots, u_{|S|}), (v_1, v_2, \ldots, v_{|S|}) \rangle = u_1 v_1 + u_2 v_2 + \ldots + u_{|S|} v_{|S|}.$$

From this, we draw the following conclusion. Let $N$ be a representation matrix for the orthogonal dual $G^\perp$. Then $u$ is the row vector $\mathrm{row}(L)$ of some linear functional on the representation of $G$ given by the matrix $N^\perp$ if and only if $u$ is orthogonal to every row of $N$. Therefore, by Lemma 4.21, the critical problem is equivalent to the following matrix problem.

---

[22]See Crapo [35] and Whitney [154]. Sections 13 to 15 of Whitney's classic paper inspired the material in Section 4.9.

[23]A neat way to produce $M^\perp$, described in Section 14 of Whitney's paper, is to construct the circuit matrix of the representation matrix $M$. Let $C$ be a circuit of $G$. Consider the columns $y_1, y_2, \ldots, y_k$ in $M$ representing the elements of the circuit. These columns are linearly dependent. Thus, there exist scalars $\alpha_i$ such that

$$\sum_{i=1}^{k} \alpha_i y_i = 0.$$

Because a circuit is a minimal dependent set, every scalar $\alpha_i$ is non-zero. Let $u_C$ be the row vector indexed by the elements of $S$ with the $x$-coordinate equal to $\alpha_i$ if $x$ equals one of the elements $y_i$ in $C$ and 0 if $x$ is not in $C$. By minimality, $u_C$ is determined up to a non-zero scalar multiple. The *circuit matrix* is the matrix with columns indexed by $S$ and rows indexed by the circuits of $G$, with the row indexed by the circuit $C$ equal to $u_C$.

4.30. PROBLEM. *Let $N$ be an $m \times t$ matrix over $\mathrm{GF}(q)$. Find the minimum number $c$ so that there exist $c$ $t$-dimensional row vectors $u_1, u_2, \ldots, u_c$ satisfying the conditions:*

*(1) $u_i$ is orthogonal to every row vector of $N$, and*

*(2) the union of the supports of the $c$ vectors $u_1, u_2, \ldots, u_c$ equals $S$.*

In the remainder of this section, we shall use this formulation of the critical problem to find the critical exponent of orthogonal duals of projective and representable Dowling group geometries.

4.31. PROPOSITION. *Suppose $n \geq 2$.*

*(a) $c([[\mathrm{GF}(q)]^n]^\perp; q) = 1$.*

*(b) $c(\mathrm{AG}(n-1, q)^\perp; q) = 1$.*

*(c) Except when $n = 2$ and $q = 3$, $c(\mathrm{PG}(n-1, q)^\perp; q) = 1$.*

*(d) $c(\mathrm{PG}(1, 3)^\perp; 3) = 2$.*

PROOF. Represent the matroid $[\mathrm{GF}(q)]^n$ by the $n \times q^n$ matrix $M_n$ with all possible $q^n$ vectors as column vectors. To prove (a), it suffices to show that the $q^n$-dimensional row vector $\underline{1}$ with all its coordinates 1 is orthogonal to every row of $M$. Observe that in any row $u$ of $M$, every element of $\mathrm{GF}(q)$ occurs exactly $q^{n-1}$ times. Hence,

$$(4.11) \qquad \langle \underline{1}, u \rangle = q^{n-1}\omega,$$

where $\omega$ is the sum of all the elements in $\mathrm{GF}(q)$. Because the characteristic of $\mathrm{GF}(q)$ divides $q$, the inner product in equation (4.11) is zero.

To prove parts (b) and (c), we first construct a representation matrix $P_n$ for $\mathrm{PG}(n-1, q)$. The projective geometry $\mathrm{PG}(n-1, q)$ can be obtained from $[\mathrm{GF}(q)]^n$ by removing the zero vector and choosing one vector from each one-dimensional subspace. We will construct $P_n$ in $n$ steps. First, choose all the columns from $M_n$ with first entry equal to 1. Next, choose all the columns with first entry equal to 0 and second entry equal to 1. Continuing in this way, choose at the $j$th step all the columns whose first to $(j-1)$st entries equal 0 and whose $j$th entry equals 1.

The affine geometry $\mathrm{AG}(n-1, q)$ is the subgeometry obtained from $\mathrm{PG}(n-1, q)$ by deleting a hyperplane. A representation matrix for $\mathrm{AG}(n-1, q)$ is the matrix $A_n$ consisting of all the columns from $M$ with first entry equal to 1. The first row of the $n \times q^{n-1}$ matrix $A_n$ is the row vector $\underline{1}$. The submatrix consisting of the second to $n$th rows is the matrix $M_{n-1}$. One concludes from this that the row vector $\underline{1}$ is orthogonal to every row of $A_n$. This proves part (b).

To prove part (c), observe that

$$P_n = [A_n | P'_{n-1}],$$

where $P'_{n-1}$ is the matrix obtained by putting a zero row on top of $P_{n-1}$. Hence, if $u$ is a row vector orthogonal to every row of $P_{n-1}$, then the row vector $(\underline{1}|u)$ obtained by adding $q^{n-1}$ 1's to $u$ is orthogonal to every row of $P_n$. Thus, we can prove the cases $q \neq 3$ by induction on $n$ if we can prove that $\mathrm{PG}(1, q)^\perp$ has critical exponent 1.

The representation matrix of $\mathrm{PG}(1, q)$ that we have chosen is

$$\begin{pmatrix} 1 & 1 & 1 & \ldots & 1 & 0 \\ 0 & \alpha_2 & \alpha_3 & \ldots & \alpha_q & 1 \end{pmatrix}.$$

Choose non-zero elements $\omega_2, \omega_3, \ldots, \omega_q$ in $GF(q)$ so that $\xi = \omega_2 + \omega_3 + \ldots + \omega_q \neq 0$ and $\eta = \omega_2 \alpha_2 + \omega_3 \alpha_3 + \ldots + \omega_q \alpha_q \neq 0$. [It is easy to check that this can be done if and only if $q \neq 3$.] The row vector

$$(-\xi \quad \omega_2 \quad \omega_3 \quad \ldots \quad \omega_q \quad -\eta)$$

is orthogonal to both rows of the representation matrix. An alternative argument to show that $c(PG(1,q)^\perp; q) = 1$ is to observe that $PG(1,q)^\perp \cong U_{2,q+1}^\perp = U_{q-1,q+1}$. The characteristic polynomial of $U_{q-1,q+1}$ can be calculated and shown not to be zero at $\lambda = q$ in a variety of ways. Note also that $PG(0,q)$, which is a rank-1 geometry, is *not* affine.

When $q = 3$, $PG(1,3)$ is isomorphic to $U_{2,4}$. Because $U_{2,4}^\perp$ equals $U_{2,4}$ and $U_{2,4}$ has critical exponent 2 over $GF(3)$, $c(PG(1,3)^\perp; 3) = 2$. This proves part (d). To finish the proof of part (c), we need to show that $[PG(2,3)]^\perp$ has critical exponent 1; once this is done, we can proceed by induction as in the cases $q \neq 3$. The representation matrix we have chosen for $PG(2,3)$ is

$$\begin{pmatrix} 1 & 1 & 1 & 1 & 1 & 1 & 1 & 1 & 1 & 0 & 0 & 0 & 0 \\ 0 & 0 & 0 & 1 & 1 & 1 & -1 & -1 & -1 & 1 & 1 & 1 & 0 \\ 0 & -1 & 1 & 0 & -1 & 1 & 0 & -1 & 1 & 0 & 1 & -1 & 1 \end{pmatrix}.$$

The row vector

$$(-1 \quad 1 \quad 1 \quad 1 \quad -1 \quad 1 \quad 1 \quad -1 \quad 1 \quad 0 \quad 0 \quad 0 \quad -1)$$

is one of many row vectors orthogonal to all three row vectors in this representation matrix. $\qquad \square$

Most of the cases in Proposition 4.31 can also be obtained from dualizing Lemma 4.26. A *covering by t-circuits* of a matroid $G(S)$ is a collection of circuits $C_1, C_2, \ldots, C_m$ of $G$ such that $C_1 \cup C_2 \cup \ldots \cup C_m = S$ and $|C_i| \leq t$ for $2 \leq i \leq m$. A *long line* is a line or rank-2 flat containing at least three points or rank-1 flats. A *covering by long lines* of a matroid $G(S)$ is a collection of long lines $L_1, L_2, \ldots, L_m$ of $G$ such that $L_1 \cup L_2 \cup \ldots \cup L_m = S$. Since a long line is a union of circuits of size 3 or less, if $G$ has a covering by long lines, then $G$ has a covering by 3-circuits.[24]

4.32. LEMMA. *Let $G(S)$ be a matroid representable over $GF(q)$. If $G$ has a covering by t-circuits and $t \leq q^k - 1$, then the orthogonal dual $G^\perp$ has critical exponent at most $k$. In particular, if $q \geq 4$ and $G$ has a covering by long lines, then $c(G^\perp; q) = 1$.*

From our results, we can find $c(M^\perp(K_{n+1}); 2)$. From Theorem 4.6, we already know that $c(M^\perp(K_{n+1}); 2) = 1$ if and only if $n$ is even. By Lemma 4.32, we now know that $c(M^\perp(K_{n+1}); 4) = 1$. Hence,

$$c(M^\perp(K_{n+1}); 2) = \begin{cases} 1 & \text{if } n \text{ is even,} \\ 2 & \text{if } n \text{ is odd.} \end{cases}$$

We can also deduce from Lemma 4.32 that for $q \geq 4$,

$$c(Q_n(GF(q)^\times)^\perp; q) = 1.$$

---

[24]We remark that if a loopless matroid $G$ has a covering by long lines, then it has a covering by circuits having size *exactly* three.

As an exercise, the reader could settle the remaining cases and find the critical exponents $c(M^\perp(K_{n+1}); 3)$ and $c(Q_n(\mathrm{GF}(3)^\times)^\perp; 3)$. Note that the value of the critical exponent $c(M^\perp(K_{n+1}); 3)$ can, in principle, be deduced from Tutte's generating function given in [**133**].

Note that when $n \geq 3$ and $|A| \geq 2$, the orthogonal dual $Q_n(A)^\perp$ is not embeddable in $Q_d(A)$ for any $d$. The counting argument in Oxley [**106**], p. 90, proving that $M^\perp(K_5)$ and $M^\perp(K_{3,3})$ are not graphic, can be easily modified to prove this.

### 4.10. A representation-free formulation of the critical problem

An inconsistency within the critical problem is that while the critical exponent depends only on the matroid structure, the critical problem itself is formulated in terms of a specific representation of the matroid. One way to "solve" this philosophical problem is to find a representation-free formulation (Rota [**121**]). Using the ideas in Section 4.7, we propose a purely matroid-theoretic critical problem using the theory of strong maps and quotients.

To do this, we need to have a purely matroid-theoretic description of deleting rows from a representation matrix. Let $M$ be a representation matrix of $G(S)$ and let $M'$ be the matrix obtained from $M$ by deleting, say, the first $k$ rows. Then $M'$ can be obtained from $M$ in two steps:

(1) Add the standard column basis vectors $e_1, e_2, \ldots, e_k$ to $M$ to obtain the augmented matrix $M^+$.

(2) Contract the added vectors $e_1, e_2, \ldots, e_k$.

If $H(S)$ is the matroid represented by $M'$, then

$$(4.12) \qquad\qquad H = G^+(S \cup A)/A,$$

where $A = \{e_1, e_2, \ldots, e_k\}$ and $G^+(S \cup A)$ is the matroid on the disjoint union $S \cup A$ represented by the augmented matrix $M^+$. In the terminology of the theory of strong maps, the matroid $H$ is a quotient of $G$. An important point to note is that when we are deleting rows from a matrix, all three matroids, $G$, $G^+$, and $H$ are representable over $\mathrm{GF}(q)$. In this language, the critical problem can be stated in the following way.

4.33. LEMMA. *The critical exponent $c(G; q)$ of a matroid $G(S)$ without loops representable over $\mathrm{GF}(q)$ is the minimum rank of a quotient $H(S)$ of $G(S)$ satisfying the conditions:*

*(1) there exists a major of the quotient map $G \to H$ which is representable over $\mathrm{GF}(q)$, and*

*(2) none of the elements in $S$ are loops in $H$.*

Note that if Conjecture 1.1 holds, then condition (1) can be replaced by the simpler condition: $H$ is $\mathrm{GF}(q)$-representable.

This formulation allows us to extend the critical problem to classes of matroids. Let $\mathcal{C}$ be a minor-closed class of matroids. The *critical exponent $c(G; \mathcal{C})$ over the class $\mathcal{C}$* of a loopless matroid $G(S)$ in $\mathcal{C}$ is the minimum rank of a quotient $H(S)$ of $G(S)$ satisfying the conditions:

(1) there exists a major of the quotient map $G \to H$ which is in $\mathcal{C}$, and

(2) none of the elements in $S$ are loops in $H$.

By Lemma 4.33, $c(G; \mathcal{L}(q)) = c(G; q)$. A reasonable minor-closed class to use instead of $\mathcal{L}(q)$ is $\mathcal{U}(q)$. The class $\mathcal{U}(q)$ captures much of the numerical constraints in $\mathcal{L}(q)$

without complicated representability conditions. It is natural to conjecture that if $G$ is a matroid in $\mathcal{L}(q)$, then

$$c(G; \mathcal{U}(q)) = c(G; \mathcal{L}(q)).$$

Note that if $G$ is a gain-graphic geometry over the finite group $A$, then, in general, the critical exponent $c(G; \mathcal{Z}(A))$ does *not* equal the critical exponent $c(G; A)$ as defined in Section 4.4. But it seems plausible that $c(G; A) = c(G; \mathcal{U}(|A| + 1))$. We plan to study these and other problems in future work.

We end Section 4 with another philosophical problem posed by Rota [121]. This problem is to find a continuous (that is, real, complex, or $p$-adic) analogue of the critical problem. A model for such an analogue is the Gamma function $\Gamma(x)$, which is a continuous analogue of the factorial function $n!$.

## 5. Characteristic polynomials

Three types of identities are known for characteristic polynomials: contraction-and-deletion identities, identities derived from Galois connections, and factorization identities.

### 5.1. Contraction and deletion

The best known identity for characteristic polynomials is the contraction-and-deletion identity: if $G$ is a matroid and $a$ is not an isthmus of $G$, then

$$\chi(G; \lambda) = \chi(G \backslash a; \lambda) - \chi(G/a; \lambda);$$

if $a$ is an isthmus, then

$$\chi(G; \lambda) = (\lambda - 1)\chi(G \backslash a; \lambda).$$

This identity is sometimes called the *Tutte-Grothendieck decomposition*. In his 1947 paper [132], Tutte defined a universal ring of functions on graphs invariant under the contraction-and-deletion decomposition. Rota observed in his 1967 Hedrick lectures that much of Tutte's work extends without change to matroids and pointed out its fundamental importance. He also observed that because the triple $(G, G \backslash a, G/a)$ may be regarded as an exact sequence, the ring of decomposition invariants may be regarded as the Grothendieck ring for a certain category of graphs. This is the reason for Rota's terminology. It is not well-known, however, that the identity was first discovered by R. G. Foster[25] for chromatic polynomials of graphs and appeared in an addendum to Whitney's 1932 paper [153]. Foster was one of the neglected pioneers in graph theory, but it is perhaps too late to give him proper credit. For this reason, we have decided to use a neutral descriptive name in this paper. For a comprehensive survey of the contraction-and-deletion method, see Brylawski and Oxley [31].

Rota's observation can be made technically precise. One way is to use Orlik-Solomon algebras (see, Orlik and Solomon [99] or Orlik and Terao [100]). Let $A(G)$ be the Orlik-Solomon algebra of a geometric lattice $G$ over some field $\mathbb{F}$. Then, $A$ is a functor from the category of geometric lattices and strong maps to

---

[25]Foster's name was misspelled in Tutte [132].

the category $\mathcal{OS}$ of Orlik-Solomon algebras over $\mathbb{F}$ and $\mathbb{F}$-algebra homomorphisms (see [**99**], p. 171). If $a$ is neither a loop nor an isthmus, then

$$0 \to A(G\backslash a) \to A(G) \to A(G/a) \to 0$$

is an exact sequence (see [**100**], p. 76). Hence, in the Grothendieck ring $K_0(\mathcal{OS})$ of the category $\mathcal{OS}$, every Orlik-Solomon algebra can be reduced, by the usual contraction-and-deletion process, to a linear combination of Orlik-Solomon algebras of Boolean algebras (which are lattices of flats of free geometries $U_{n,n}$). For the Boolean algebra $B_n$, the Orlik-Solomon algebra $A(B_n)$ equals $X \otimes X \otimes \ldots \otimes X$, where $X$ is the one-dimensional Orlik-Solomon algebra of $B_1$. Hence, the Grothendieck ring $K_0(\mathcal{OS})$ over $\mathbb{Z}$ (or any integral domain) of $\mathcal{OS}$ equals the polynomial ring $\mathbb{Z}[X]$. This is not surprising since the Orlik-Solomon algebra models the characteristic polynomial of a matroid. An interesting problem is to find an algebra similar to the Orlik-Solomon algebra such that the Grothendieck ring is isomorphic to $\mathbb{Z}[X, Y]$, the Tutte-Grothendieck ring in matroid theory. It should also be possible to calculate $K_1(\mathcal{OS})$ and do higher $K$-theory in $\mathcal{OS}$. Doing so might lead to an *interesting* higher $K$-theory for matroids.

Using the contraction-and-deletion identity, Oxley obtained the following identity [**101,104**]:

5.1. OXLEY'S IDENTITY. *Let* $\{a_1, a_2, \ldots, a_t\}$ *be the set of points not contained in a copoint* $X$ *in a geometry* $G$. *Then*

$$\chi(G; \lambda) = \chi(G|X; \lambda)(\lambda - t)$$

$$+ \sum_{j=2}^{t} \left[ \sum_{i=1}^{j-1} \chi((G\backslash\{a_1, \ldots, a_{i-1}, a_{i+1}, \ldots, a_{j-1}\})/\{a_i, a_j\}; \lambda) \right].$$

*Moreover,*

$$\chi(G; \lambda) = \chi(G|X; \lambda)(\lambda - t)$$

*if and only if* $X$ *is modular.*

With this identity, Oxley [**101**] showed that if $G$ is a matroid with no loops, then the maximum (positive) real root of the characteristic polynomial $\chi(G; \lambda)$ is bounded above by the maximum size of a bond in a simplification of $G$.

## 5.2. Identities from embeddings

Suppose $G$ is a subgeometry of the geometry $H$. How are their characteristic polynomials related? The simplest way of expressing this relation is through Crapo's identity.

5.2. CRAPO'S IDENTITY. *Let* $P(E)$ *be a geometry on the set* $E$ *and let* $G$ *be the subgeometry on the subset* $S \subseteq E$. *Then*

$$\lambda^{\mathrm{rank}(P)-\mathrm{rank}(G)} \chi(G; \lambda) = \sum_{Z: Z \in L(P) \text{ and } Z \cap S = \emptyset} \chi([Z, \hat{1}]; \lambda),$$

*the sum ranging over all the* $P$-*flats* $Z$ *containing no points in* $S$.

Crapo's identity is a special case of an identity about characteristic polynomials of geometries related by strong maps (Crapo [**33**]). An analogue of it, for Rédei zeta functions, appeared earlier in Rédei's work [**111**] as his *Hauptsatz*. See also Kung,

Murty and Rota [**86**]. Rédei's proof is inductive. All the other proofs of Crapo's identity uses Rota's Galois connection theorem for Möbius functions ([**117**], p. 347) in some form.

For the special case of a geometry $G(S)$ represented as a set $S$ of points in the projective space $\mathrm{PG}(d-1,q)$, Crapo's identity yields the following corollary.

5.3. COROLLARY. *Let $G$ be a rank-$n$ geometry represented as a set $S$ of points in the projective space $\mathrm{PG}(d-1,q)$. Then*

$$(5.1) \qquad \lambda^{d-n}\chi(G;\lambda) = \sum_{k=0}^{d} C_k \prod_{j=0}^{d-k-1} (\lambda - q^j),$$

*where $C_k$ is the number of subspaces $U$ in $\mathrm{PG}(d-1,q)$ such that $\mathrm{rank}(U) = k$ and $U \cap S = \emptyset$.*

Corollary 5.3 gives explicitly the expansion of $\chi(G;\lambda)$ in terms of the $q$-falling factorials. It is the analogue of the following identity for the chromatic polynomial (see, for example, Read and Tutte [**110**], p. 16):

$$(5.2) \qquad p(\Gamma;\lambda) = \sum_{k=1}^{|V|} c_k \prod_{j=0}^{k-1}(\lambda - j)$$

where $c_k$ is the number of ways of partitioning the vertex set $V$ of $\Gamma$ into $k$ non-empty *stable* subsets, that is, subsets such that no edge of $\Gamma$ joins two vertices in the same subset. Identity (5.2) can be obtained as a special case of Crapo's identity by considering a graphic geometry as a subgeometry of the cycle geometry of a complete graph.

It is worth noting that Corollary 5.3 can be proved by a simple counting argument. Let $\underline{L} = (L_1, L_2, \ldots, L_s)$ be an $s$-tuple of linear functionals distinguishing $G$. Then $\ker \underline{L} \cap S = \emptyset$ and $\ker \underline{L}$ is a subspace of $\mathrm{PG}(d-1,q)$ disjoint from $S$. If $Z$ is a subspace in $\mathrm{PG}(d-1,q)$ disjoint from $S$, then, by Lemma 4.2(b), the number of $s$-tuples $\underline{L}$ with kernel equal to $Z$ equals

$$\chi(\mathrm{PG}(d-1,q)/Z;q^s) = \chi(\mathrm{PG}(d-\mathrm{rank}(Z)-1,q);q^s)$$

$$= \prod_{j=0}^{d-\mathrm{rank}(Z)-1} (q^s - q^j).$$

Summing over all subspaces $Z$ in $\mathrm{PG}(d-1,q)$ disjoint from $S$, we conclude that equation (5.1) holds at $\lambda = q^s$. Because $s$ is an arbitrary positive integer, equation (5.1) holds as a polynomial identity in $\lambda$. A more complicated version of this counting argument can be used to prove Theorem 5.2 when both $G(S)$ and $P(E)$ are represented as subgeometries of $\mathrm{PG}(n-1,q)$.

From Corollary 5.3 and the fact that the affine geometry $\mathrm{AG}(n-1,q)$ is obtained from $\mathrm{PG}(n-1,q)$ by removing a hyperplane, one obtains

$$(5.3) \qquad \chi(\mathrm{AG}(n-1,q);\lambda) = \sum_{i=0}^{n-1} \begin{bmatrix} n-1 \\ i \end{bmatrix}_q \prod_{j=0}^{n-i-1} (\lambda - q^j),$$

where the $q$-binomial coefficient $\begin{bmatrix} n-1 \\ i \end{bmatrix}_q$ is the number of subspaces of rank $i$ in the rank-$(n-1)$ projective geometry $\mathrm{PG}(n-2,q)$.

Another application, due to Brylawski [23,24,25], is a formula for the inter-section matrix of a geometry embedded in a uniform geometry. If $P$ is a geometry and $U$ is a flat of $P$, let

(1) $w(U, c)$ be the coefficient of $\lambda^c$ in the characteristic polynomial $\chi([U, \hat{1}]; \lambda)$ of the contraction $[U, \hat{1}]$, and

(2) $W(U, c)$ be the number of flats of corank $c$ in the contraction $[U, \hat{1}]$, or, equivalently, the number of flats of corank $c$ in $P$ containing $U$.

The numbers $w(U, c)$ (respectively, $W(U, c)$) are the *Whitney numbers of the first* (respectively, *second*) *kind* of $[U, \hat{1}]$. A geometry $P$ is said to be *upper uniform*[26] if it satisfies the condition:

(U$_1$) For every flat $U$ in $P$, the characteristic polynomial $\chi([U, \hat{1}]; \lambda)$ depends only on the corank $r$ of $U$; equivalently, for every flat $U$ in $P$ and every integer $c$, $0 \leq c \leq r$, $w(U, c) = w(r, c)$, a number depending only on $c$ and $r$.

The following lemma about uniform geometries was stated in Brylawski's 1977 paper [23]. It has the same proof as a slightly weaker result in Dowling's 1972 paper [46].

5.4. LEMMA. *Let $P$ be a geometry satisfying condition (U$_1$) and let $[U, \hat{1}]$ be any corank-$r$ upper interval in $L(P)$. Then the numbers $W(U, c)$ satisfy the lower triangular system of linear equations:*

$$\sum_{c=0}^{r} W(U, c) w(c, d) = \delta_{rd}, \quad d = 0, 1, \ldots, r.$$

PROOF. See [46], p. 75.                                                     □

Brylawski [23] drew the following consequences from Lemma 5.4. The Whitney numbers $W(U, c)$ are solutions of the non-singular system of linear equations given in Lemma 5.4. Therefore, they are uniquely determined by the integers $w(c, d)$ which depend only on the corank $r$ of $U$. Hence, condition (U$_1$) is equivalent to the following condition:

(U$_2$) for every flat $U$ in $P$ and every integer $c$, $0 \leq c \leq \text{corank}(U)$, $W(U, c) = W(r, c)$, a number depending only on $c$ and $r$.

In addition, for a uniform geometry $P$, the lower triangular matrices $[w(r, c)]$ and $[W(r, c)]$ are inverses of each other.

The *intersection matrix* of the embedding $G(S) \hookrightarrow P(E)$ is the matrix $[I_{ij}]$, where $1 \leq i \leq |S|, 1 \leq j \leq \text{rank}(P)$ and the entry $I_{ij}$ is the number of $P$-flats $U$ of corank $j$ such that $|U \cap S| = i$. Observe that because $U \cap S$ is a $G$-flat, the $i$th row is zero if there are no $G$-flats with exactly $i$ points. The *$\chi$-matrix* of the geometry $G(S)$ is the matrix $[\chi_{ic}]$ whose entries are defined by:

$$\chi_{ic} = \sum_{X : |X| = i} w(G/X, c),$$

where the sum ranges over all the $G$-flats $X$ containing exactly $i$ points.

---

[26]Upper uniform geometries are simply called uniform in Brylawski's papers. Our terminol-ogy is intended to eliminate confusion between them and the uniform geometries $U_{k,n}$. Note that uniform geometries *are* upper uniform.

5.5. THEOREM (BRYLAWSKI). *Let $G(S) \hookrightarrow P(E)$ be an embedding of $G$ into an upper uniform geometry $P$ having the same rank as $G$. Then the following matrix identity holds:*

$$[I_{ik}] = [\chi_{ic}][W(c,k)].$$

PROOF. Let $X$ be a $G$-flat and let $\overline{X}$ be its closure in $P$. The embedding $G \hookrightarrow P$ yields an embedding of the contractions $G/X \hookrightarrow P/\overline{X}$. Applying Crapo's identity to the latter embedding, we obtain

$$\chi(G/X; \lambda) = \sum_{U:U \in L(P) \text{ and } U \cap S = X} \chi([U, \hat{1}]; \lambda).$$

Summing over all $G$-flats $X$ with $|X| = i$ and equating coefficients of $\lambda^c$, we obtain

$$\chi_{ic} = \sum_{X:|X|=i} w(G/X, c)$$

$$= \sum_{k=0}^{\text{rank}(P)} I_{ik} w(k, c).$$

Hence, we have the matrix identity

$$[\chi_{ic}] = [I_{ik}][w(k,c)].$$

Because the inverse of $[w(k,c)]$ is $[W(k,c)]$, this completes the proof of the theorem. $\qquad \square$

The subspace critical exponent $c_S(G \hookrightarrow P)$ of the embedding $G \hookrightarrow P$ (defined in Section 4.4) equals the minimum integer $c$ such that the entry $I_{0c}$ is non-zero. When $P$ is an upper uniform geometry, the intersection matrix depends only on the $\chi$-matrix and the matrix $[W(k,c)]$. Both matrices depend only on the matroid structure of $G$ and $P$. In particular, as in the classical case when $P$ is a finite projective geometry, the subspace critical exponent $c_S(G \hookrightarrow P)$ does not depend on the embedding. Using the same ideas, it can also be shown that when $P$ is an upper uniform geometry, the hyperplane critical exponent $c_H(G \hookrightarrow P)$ does not depend on the embedding. For another treatment of the intersection matrix, see Brylawski and Oxley [31].

### 5.3. Modular factorization identities

In his 1971 paper [125], Stanley showed that if $X$ is a modular rank-$k$ flat in a rank-$n$ geometry $G$, then

$$(5.4) \qquad \chi(G; \lambda) = \chi(G|X; \lambda) \left[ \sum_{U:U \wedge X = \hat{0}} \mu(\hat{0}, U) \lambda^{n-k-\text{rank}(U)} \right].$$

Shortly afterwards, Brylawski observed in [20] that the sum on the right hand side equals $\chi(T_X(G); \lambda)/(\lambda - 1)$, where $T_X(G)$ is the (complete) principal truncation of $G$ at $X$.

5.6. THE MODULAR FACTORIZATION THEOREM. *Let $X$ be a modular flat in a geometry $G$. Then*

$$\chi(G; \lambda) = \frac{\chi(G|X; \lambda)\chi(T_X(G); \lambda)}{\lambda - 1}.$$

A rank-$n$ geometry $G$ is said to be *supersolvable* if there exists a *modular flag* or a saturated chain of modular flats $X_0 < X_1 < X_2 < \ldots < X_n$. Note that it follows from the definition that $\text{rank}(X_i) = i$. Stanley [125,126] obtained the following explicit formula for the characteristic polynomial of a supersolvable geometry.

5.7. THEOREM. *Let $G$ be a rank-$n$ supersolvable geometry with a modular flag $X_0 < X_1 < X_2 < \ldots < X_n$. Then*

$$\chi(G; \lambda) = (\lambda - a_1)(\lambda - a_2) \cdots (\lambda - a_n),$$

*where $a_i = |X_i \backslash X_{i-1}|$.*

The "three classical examples," the free geometry $U_{n,n}$, the projective space $\text{PG}(n-1, q)$, and the Dowling group geometry $Q_n(A)$, are all supersolvable. Thus, Theorem 5.7 yields their characteristic polynomials:

$$\chi(U_{n,n}; \lambda) = (\lambda - 1)^n,$$

$$\chi(\text{PG}(n-1, q); \lambda) = (\lambda - 1)(\lambda - q)(\lambda - q^2) \cdots (\lambda - q^{n-1}),$$

$$\chi(Q_n(A); \lambda) = (\lambda - 1)(\lambda - |A| - 1)(\lambda - 2|A| - 1) \cdots (\lambda - (n-1)|A| - 1).$$

A natural way to extend Theorem 5.6 is to ask what is the remainder when one divides $\chi(G; \lambda)$ by $\chi(G|X; \lambda)$ in the case of a non-modular flat $X$. There seems to be no neat answer to this question. However, the closely related question of finding a formula for the *correction term*

$$\chi(G; \lambda) - \frac{\chi(G|X; \lambda)\chi(T_X(G); \lambda)}{\lambda - 1}$$

has a reasonable answer (Kung [83]; see also [29] for earlier partial results).

Let $U$ be a set of points in $S \backslash X$. We define the matroid $(G|X)_U$ to be the matroid on the set $X$ obtained by contracting the restriction $G|(X \cup U)$ by $U$, that is,

$$(G|X)_U = (G|(X \cup U))/U.$$

The matroid $(G|X)_U$ is a quotient of $G|X$ and its rank equals $\text{rank}_G(U \vee X) - \text{rank}_G(U)$. An element in $X$ is a loop in $(G|X)_U$ if and only if it is in the intersection $\overline{U} \cap X$ of the closure of $U$ and $X$.

5.8. THEOREM. *Let $X$ be a rank-$k$ flat in a rank-$n$ geometry $G$. Then,*

$$\chi(G; \lambda) = \frac{\chi(G|X; \lambda)\chi(T_X(G); \lambda)}{\lambda - 1} + \sum_U \mu(\hat{0}, U)\lambda^{n - \text{rank}(U \vee X)}\chi((G|X)_U; \lambda),$$

*where the sum ranges over all the flats $U$ in $L(G)$ such that*
*(1) $\text{rank}(U \vee X) < \text{rank}(U) + k$, and*
*(2) $U \cap X = \emptyset$.*
*Moreover,*

$$\chi(G; \lambda) = \chi(G|X; \lambda)\chi(T_X(G); \lambda)/(\lambda - 1)$$

*if and only if $X$ is modular.*

Note that the correction term has degree at most $n - 2$. Therefore, when $X$ is a copoint, the correction term gives the remainder.

5.9. COROLLARY. *Let $X$ be a copoint in a geometry $G$. Then,*

$$\chi(G; \lambda) = \chi(G|X; \lambda)(\lambda - t) + \sum_{U:U \in L(G),\, \mathrm{rank}(U) \geq 2 \text{ and } U \cap X = \emptyset} \mu(\hat{0}, U)\chi((G|X)_U; \lambda),$$

*where $t$ is the number of points in $G$ not in $X$.*

Corollary 5.9 and Oxley's identity 5.1 give two different expressions for the remainder when $X$ is a copoint. The exact relation between the two expressions is not clear. From Oxley's identity 5.1, Theorem 5.8 and Corollary 5.9, many inequalities involving Whitney numbers of the first kind can be derived. See Kung [82,83] and Oxley [104].

There are several ways to prove Theorems 5.6 and 5.8. Stanley [125] uses Crapo's complementation theorem and other results in the theory of Möbius functions. Brylawski [20] proved Theorem 5.6 using a contraction-and-deletion argument. Later, in [22], he gave a proof using the broken circuit complex. Theorem 5.8 can be proved when $G$ is representable by counting distinguishing (1-tuples of) hyperplanes. The general case is proved using the broken circuit complex. For both proofs, see Kung [83].

Surveys of work on the broken circuit complex (in particular, how it factors topologically in the presence of a modular flat) can be found in Björner and Ziegler [10], Brylawski and Oxley [29,30], and the references in these papers. Modular flats also induce factorizations of Orlik-Solomon algebras. See Falk [48] and Terao [129,130] for work in this area.

### 5.4. Hand calculation of characteristic polynomials

Following the tradition of Read and Tutte in their expository papers on the chromatic polynomial (Read [109], Read and Tutte [110]), we give several examples of hand calculations of characteristic polynomials of "small" geometries. Parts of this section are intended to be read in close conjunction with Oxley's catalogue of geometries [106], Appendix, pp. 501–522.

We begin with rank-3 geometries. Here, the following special case (Kung [83]; see also Brylawski [27]) of Theorem 5.8 is helpful.[27]

5.10. LEMMA. *Let $G$ be a rank-3 geometry and let $L$ be a line in $G$. Then*

$$\chi(G; \lambda) = (\lambda - 1)[(\lambda - |L| + 1)(\lambda - |G| + |L|) + \sum_{M:M \cap L = \emptyset} (|M| - 1)],$$

*with the sum ranging over all lines $M$ disjoint from $L$.*

Using this lemma, we can calculate the characteristic polynomials of the Pappus geometry $P$, the Non-Pappus geometry $NP$, and the ternary affine plane $\mathrm{AG}(2,3)$ :

$$\chi(P; \lambda) = (\lambda - 1)(\lambda^2 - 8\lambda + 19),$$
$$\chi(NP; \lambda) = (\lambda - 1)(\lambda^2 - 8\lambda + 20),$$
$$\chi(\mathrm{AG}(2,3); \lambda) = (\lambda - 1)(\lambda - 4)^2.$$

---

[27] This lemma implies that if a rank-3 geometry $G$ has three real roots, then one of them is 1 and the other two is between $|L| - 1$ and $|G| - |L|$ and located symmetrically relative to the midpoint $(|G| - 1)/2$. This fact was carelessly stated in [83], p. 49; there, it was incorrectly assumed that $|L| - 1 \leq |G| - |L|$.

FIGURE 3. The cocycle matroid of $K_{3,3}$.

Note that $P \neq NP$. In a similar way, we obtain the following formula for the characteristic polynomial of the affine plane $AG(2, q)$ over $GF(q)$ :

$$\chi(AG(2, q); \lambda) = (\lambda - 1)[\lambda^2 - (q^2 - 1)\lambda + (q + 1)(q - 1)^2].$$

For rank-4 geometries, Theorem 5.8 is harder to use. For example, let $G$ be the cocycle geometry $M^\perp(K_{3,3})$ of the bipartite Kuratowski graph and let $X$ be one of the 5-point planes consisting of the union of two 3-point lines. From the affine representation in Figure 3, we see that (a) every plane intersects the plane $X$, and (b) there are two lines not intersecting $X$. We conclude that

$$\chi(M^\perp(K_{3,3}); \lambda) = (\lambda - 1)[(\lambda - 2)^2(\lambda - 4) + 2(\lambda - 2)]$$
$$= (\lambda - 1)(\lambda - 2)(\lambda^2 - 6\lambda + 10)$$
$$= (\lambda - 1)(\lambda^3 - 8\lambda^2 + 22\lambda - 20).$$

As another example, consider the Vámos cube $V_8$. Because $V_8$ has only five non-trivial planes, it is easier to calculate its characteristic polynomial directly from the definition. Using the following facts:

(1) $V_8$ has 8 points, 28 lines all of which have 2 points, 36 planes with 3 points and 5 planes with 4 points,
(2) for a 4-point plane $X$, $\mu(\hat{0}, X) = -3$, and
(3) $\chi(G; 1) = 0$ for every matroid $G$,

we conclude that

$$\chi(V_8; \lambda) = \lambda^4 - 8\lambda^3 + 28\lambda^2 - 51\lambda + 30$$
$$= (\lambda - 1)(\lambda^3 - 7\lambda^2 + 21\lambda - 30).$$

Next we calculate the characteristic polynomial of $R_{10}$, the 10-element rank-5 matroid appearing in Seymour's decomposition theorem [122] for regular matroids. In this case, we make use of the fact that for any point $a$ in $R_{10}$,

$$R_{10}/a \cong M^\perp(K_{3,3}) \quad \text{and} \quad R_{10} \backslash a \cong M(K_{3,3}).$$

Because $M(K_{3,3})$ is graphic, $\chi(M(K_{3,3}); \lambda)$ can be calculated using the theory of chromatic polynomials. Using a theorem of Read ([109], p. 60) or equation (5.2),

$$\lambda \chi(M(K_{3,3}); \lambda) = p(K_{3,3}; \lambda) = \lambda_{(6)} + 6\lambda_{(5)} + 11\lambda_{(4)} + 6\lambda_{(3)} + \lambda_{(2)},$$

where $\lambda_{(r)} = \lambda(\lambda - 1) \cdots (\lambda - r + 1)$ is a falling factorial. Dividing by $\lambda$ and expanding, we obtain

$$\chi(M(K_{3,3}); \lambda) = (\lambda - 1)(\lambda^4 - 8\lambda^3 + 28\lambda^2 - 47\lambda + 31).$$

By the contraction-and-deletion identity,

$$\chi(R_{10}; \lambda) = \chi(M(K_{3,3}); \lambda) - \chi(M^\perp(K_{3,3}); \lambda)$$
$$= (\lambda - 1)(\lambda^4 - 9\lambda^3 + 36\lambda^2 - 69\lambda + 51).$$

Our final example is to calculate the characteristic polynomial of the jointless Dowling group geometry $Q'_n(A)$, obtained by deleting all the joints $\{p_1, p_2, \ldots, p_n\}$ from the Dowling geometry $Q_n(A)$ over a finite group $A$ having order at least 2. This calculation was done using an inductive method by Whittle [**161**]. We use Crapo's identity 5.2 for the embedding $Q'_n(A) \hookrightarrow Q_n(A)$. The flats in $Q_n(A)$ disjoint from $Q'_n(A)$ are the empty flat and the $n$ rank-1 flats $\{p_i\}$. Hence,

$$\chi(Q'_n(A); \lambda) = \left[ \prod_{j=0}^{n-1} (\lambda - j|A| - 1) \right] + n \left[ \prod_{j=0}^{n-2} (\lambda - j|A| - 1) \right]$$
$$= [\lambda - (n-1)(|A| - 1)] \prod_{j=0}^{n-2} (\lambda - j|A| - 1).$$

From this calculation, one sees that the fact that the deleted points are joints is not really relevant: as long as we delete a set of points not containing a line, then the same calculation holds. More precisely, we have the following result. Let $D$ be a set of points in $Q_n(A)$ not containing any lines. Then

$$\chi(Q_n(A)\backslash D; \lambda) = [\lambda - (n-1)|A| + |D| - 1] \prod_{j=0}^{n-2} (\lambda - j|A| - 1).$$

By choosing $D$ judiciously, we can construct many examples of geometries which contain no modular copoints but have characteristic polynomials all of whose zeroes are integers.[28] We shall see another example of this phenomenom in Section 6.

### 5.5. Zero sequences and zero multisets of supersolvable geometries

Let $\mathcal{C}$ be a class of geometries. A sequence $(1, a_2, a_3, \ldots, a_n)$ of positive integers is said to be a *zero sequence (for a supersolvable geometry) in* $\mathcal{C}$ if there exists a rank-$n$ supersolvable geometry $G$ in the class $\mathcal{C}$ with modular flag $X_0 < X_1 < \ldots < X_{n-1} < X_n$ such that $a_i = |X_i\backslash X_{i-1}|$. A multiset $\{1, a_2, a_3, \ldots, a_n\}$ is said to be a *zero multiset for* $\mathcal{C}$ if it can be ordered so that its elements form a zero sequence for $\mathcal{C}$. Three related questions arise naturally.

  (1)  Which sequences $(1, a_2, a_3, \ldots, a_n)$ are zero sequences for a given class $\mathcal{C}$ of geometries?
  (2)  Which multisets $\{1, a_2, a_3, \ldots, a_n\}$ are zero multisets for a given class $\mathcal{C}$ of geometries?

---

[28]When $A = \{1, -1\}$, the group of order 2, the geometry $Q'_n(A)$ is the geometry of the root system $D_n$. Several people in algebraic combinatorics have considered the problem of "understanding" why $\chi(D_n; \lambda)$ has integer zeroes.

(3)  Given a zero multiset for a class $\mathcal{C}$, which orderings of it yield zero sequences for the class $\mathcal{C}$?

For the class of all geometries, Stanley [126] answered all three questions completely. He observed that the parallel connection at a common point of lines $L_2, L_3, \ldots, L_n$, where $L_i$ contains $a_i + 1$ points, is a supersolvable geometry with characteristic polynomial equal to $(\lambda - 1)(\lambda - a_2) \cdots (\lambda - a_n)$. In fact, one can also take arbitrary parallel connections of the lines $L_i$ at (different) points. Hence, all sequences of positive integers $(1, a_2, a_3, \ldots, a_n)$ are zero sequences of rank-$n$ geometries. Stanley's construction works in any class of geometries containing $k$-point lines for every positive integer $k$ and closed under parallel connections at a point. In particular, it works in the class of geometries representable over the reals and the class of transversal geometries.

Another consequence of Stanley's construction is that every sequence of positive integers $(1, a_2, a_3, \ldots, a_n)$ with $a_i \leq q$ is a zero sequence for the class of $GF(q)$-representable geometries. A weaker sufficient condition can be obtained using parallel connections at flats of higher rank. Let $(1, a_2, a_3, \ldots, a_n)$ be a sequence satisfying three conditions:

(C1)  There exist *special* indices $1 = c_0 < c_1 < c_2 < \ldots < c_m$ such that

$$a_{c_i} = q^i.$$

(C2)  For every index $j$ less than the $i$th special index $c_i$, $a_j \leq q^i$.

(C3)  For every index $j$ greater than the last special index $c_m$, $a_j \leq q^{m+1}$.

We can construct a rank-$n$ $GF(q)$-representable geometry $G$ the given zero sequence in the following way. Let $e_1, e_2, \ldots, e_n$ be a basis for $PG(n-1, q)$. First take all the points in the linear span

$$\text{lin}(\{e_{c_0}, e_{c_1}, e_{c_2}, \ldots, e_{c_m}\}),$$

thereby obtaining a subgeometry isomorphic to the rank-$(m+1)$ projective geometry $PG(m, q)$. Let

$$P_r = \text{lin}(\{e_{c_0}, e_{c_1}, e_{c_2}, \ldots, e_{c_r}\}).$$

For every $r$, the subgeometry $P_r$ is modular in any $GF(q)$-representable geometry containing it. Let $j$ be an index not equal to one of the special indices and let $k = \lceil \log_q a_j \rceil$, where $\log_q$ is logarithm to base $q$. Consider the rank-$(k+1)$ affine subgeometry

$$A = \text{lin}(\{e_{c_0}, e_{c_1}, e_{c_2}, \ldots, e_{c_{k-1}}, e_j\}) \setminus P_k$$

in $PG(n-1, q)$. It has $q^k$ points. Because $q^{k-1} < a_j \leq q^k$, the index $c_{k-1}$ is strictly less than $j$ and we can choose $a_j$ points from the affine subgeometry $A$. Doing this for every index $j$ which is not a special index, we obtain a $GF(q)$-representable geometry $G$ which is constructed by taking a sequence of generalized parallel connections along modular flats of $P_m$. From this, one concludes that $G$ is supersolvable and has characteristic polynomial $\prod_{i=1}^{n}(\lambda - a_i)$. We have thus proved the following result.

5.11.  PROPOSITION. *A sequence* $(1, a_2, a_3, \ldots, a_n)$ *satisfying the conditions* (C1), (C2) *and* (C3) *is a zero sequence for the class of* $GF(q)$-*representable geometries.*

As an example, let $q = 2$ and consider the sequence $(1, 2, 3, 4, 5)$. Carrying out the construction, we obtain the rank-5 binary geometry constructed by taking the parallel connection of the cycle geometry $M(K_4)$ with the binary geometry $D_{12}$ along a 3-point line. The geometry $D_{12}$ is the 12-point rank-4 binary geometry obtained by deleting three non-collinear points from $\mathrm{PG}(3, 2)$. The geometry $D_{12}$ contains a Fano plane as a subgeometry. There are two non-isomorphic 12-point rank-4 binary geometries. The other one, $C_{12}$, is obtained by deleting a 3-point line from $\mathrm{PG}(3, 2)$. It contains no subgeometry isomorphic to the Fano plane. Taking the parallel connection of $M(K_4)$ and $C_{12}$ along a 3-point line also results in a supersolvable binary geometry with characteristic polynomial $\prod_{i=1}^{5}(\lambda - i)$.

We note that the following result can be derived from the $q$-lift construction described in Section 8.6: *if* $(1, a_2, a_3, \dots, a_n)$ *is a zero sequence for* $\mathrm{GF}(q)$-*representable supersolvable geometries, then so is the sequence* $(1, q, qa_2, qa_3, \dots, qa_n)$. This result is a consequence of equation (8.5).

All the examples so far can be obtained by taking parallel connections. A more difficult situation arises when we impose connectivity conditions. The right notion of connectivity to use here seems to be Whitney connectivity rather than Tutte connectivity.[29] A geometry $G$ *splits* if its point set is the union of two proper flats; it is *non-splitting* if it does not split (Kahn and Kung [**67**]). We shall give one example of such a result.

5.12. THEOREM. *Let* $(1, a, b)$ *be a zero sequence for a non-splitting rank-3 supersolvable geometry* $G$ *representable over the reals. If* $b$ *is even, then* $b \leq a + 1$; *if* $b$ *is odd, then* $b \leq a + 2$.

This theorem is a disguised version of Ungar's theorem about the number of slopes determined by points in the plane $\mathbb{R}^2$. Given $n$ points $(x_i, y_i), 1 \leq i \leq n$ in $\mathbb{R}^2$, not all on a line, how many different slopes

$$\frac{y_i - y_j}{x_i - x_j}$$

do they determine? Ungar [**139**] shows that $2k$ points determine at least $2k$ distinct slopes and $2k + 1$ points determine at least $2k$ distinct slopes. Two lines have the same slope when they are parallel. Therefore, the number of distinct slopes equals the number of parallelism classes of lines determined by the given points. Every line in the same parallelism class meets the line at infinity at a common point. Hence, the number of slopes is the number of points of intersection of lines determined by the given points with the line at infinity. To obtain Theorem 5.12 from Ungar's theorem, observe that because $G$ is non-splitting, $G$ is not the union of two lines. Hence, the $b$ points not on $L$ are not all collinear. Represent the geometry $G$ in the real projective plane so that the modular line $L$ is represented by points on the line at infinity. Then $a + 1$ is at least the number of slopes determined by $b$

---

[29]Recall that a matroid $G(S)$ has a $k$-*separation* if there is a partition of $S$ into two subsets $X$ and $Y$ such that

$$\mathrm{rank}(X) + \mathrm{rank}(Y) \leq \mathrm{rank}(S) + k - 1.$$

The subsets $X$ and $Y$ are required to satisfy $|X|, |Y| \geq k$ in the case of Tutte connectivity and $\mathrm{rank}(X), \mathrm{rank}(Y) \geq k$ in the case of Whitney connectivity. The condition that a matroid does not split is equivalent to its having infinite Whitney connectivity. When $k \geq 4$, there are no Tutte-$k$-connected supersolvable matroids. This follows from the fact that when $k \geq 4$, every line in a Tutte-$k$-connected matroid contains exactly two points. Thus, Tutte connectivity is not the right notion of connectivity to use when studying supersolvable matroids.

points outside $L$. A generalization of Theorem 5.12 to higher rank would be of great interest.

A natural but difficult extension of this research area is to study zero multisets of geometries which may not be supersolvable. A multiset $\{1, a_2, a_3, \ldots, a_n\}$ of positive integers is said to be a *zero multiset of a geometry in a class $\mathcal{C}$* if there exists a rank-$n$ geometry $G$ in $\mathcal{C}$ such that

$$\chi(G; \lambda) = (\lambda - 1)(\lambda - a_2)(\lambda - a_3) \cdots (\lambda - a_n).$$

By Stanley's construction, any multiset of positive integers containing 1 is the zero multiset of a geometry in a class $\mathcal{C}$ containing lines of all possible sizes and closed under parallel connections at a point. For the class $\mathcal{L}(q)$, the situation is more complicated. For example, $\{1, 4, 4\}$ is the zero multiset of the ternary affine plane, but it is not the zero multiset of any ternary supersolvable geometry. On the other hand, all known zero multisets of binary geometries are also zero multisets of supersolvable binary geometries.[30] A plausible line of attack, suggested by Theorem 5.8, is that every zero multiset for geometries in $\mathcal{L}(q)$ can be obtained by "perturbing slightly" a zero multiset of a supersolvable geometry in $\mathcal{L}(q)$. If this heuristic can be make precise, then it would be a reasonable solution to the problem of characterizing all geometries whose characteristic polynomials factor completely over the integers.

## 5.6. Geometries with given characteristic polynomials

Two geometries may have the same characteristic polynomial.[31] Even so, because the characteristic polynomials of the three classical examples (see Section 5.3) have such special forms, a natural problem is to classify all geometries having those polynomials as their characteristic polynomials.

Because a rank-$n$ geometry having $n$ points must be the free geometry $U_{n,n}$, there is only one geometry with characteristic polynomial $(\lambda - 1)^n$.

Bogart and Stonesifer [11] initiated the program of classifying the geometries having the "shifted" falling factorials

$$(\lambda - 1)_{(n)} = (\lambda - 1)(\lambda - 2) \cdots (\lambda - n)$$

as their characteristic polynomials. There are two kinds of examples of geometries with characteristic polynomial $(\lambda - 1)_{(n)}$. The first is the cycle geometry $M(K_{n+1})$. The second are the examples obtained from the sequence $(1, 2, \ldots, n)$ using the constructions given in the previous section.

Given the examples, there is a natural conjecture, which Bogart and Stonsifer used as a working hypothesis: *every binary geometry with characteristic polynomial $(\lambda - 1)_{(n)}$ is supersolvable.* One might also note that amongst the known examples, $M(K_{n+1})$ is the only geometry which is not a parallel connection. Thus, another natural conjecture is: *if a non-splitting geometry has characteristic polynomial $(\lambda - 1)_{(n)}$, then it is isomorphic to $M(K_{n+1})$.*

Not much progress has been made on these conjectures, due mainly to the absence of any method to prove the existence of modular copoints. Assuming

---

[30] There exist graphic and binary non-supersolvable geometries whose characteristic polynomials factor completely over the integers. See Read and Tutte [110] and Section 6.3 for some examples.

[31] There is a vast literature on the subject, especially for chromatic polynomials. Two surveys containing references are Read and Tutte [110] and Brylawski and Oxley [31].

the existence of modular copoints, several partial results can be obtained. See [**11,166,167**]. Another partial result of this kind is the following.

5.13. THEOREM. *Let $G(S)$ be a non-splitting rank-n geometry with a modular copoint and (exactly) $\binom{n+1}{2}$ points. Then $G$ is isomorphic to $M(K_{n+1})$.*

Theorem 5.13 is a consequence of the following useful technical lemma. Weaker versions of this lemma have appeared in the literature. See, for example, Kung [**74**] and Whittle [**157**].

5.14. LEMMA. *Let $G(S)$ be a geometry satisfying the following conditions:*
*(1)  $G$ has a modular copoint $X$.*
*(2)  The complement $S \backslash X$ of the copoint $X$ has rank at least $m$.*
*Then $G$ contains a subgeometry isomorphic to $M(K_{m+1})$.*

PROOF. Let $\{e_1, e_{12}, e_{13}, \dots, e_{1m}\}$ be an independent set of size $m$ in $X^c$. Because $X$ is modular, the line $e_1 \vee e_{1i}$ intersects $X$ at a point $e_i$. By modularity again, the line $e_{1i} \vee e_{1j}$ intersects $X$ at a point $e_{ij}$. Because the set $\{e_1, e_{12}, e_{13}, \dots, e_{1m}\}$ is independent, the points of intersections are distinct. The points $e_i$ and $e_{ij}$ form a rank-$m$ subgeometry with $\binom{m+1}{2}$ points which is *almost* a $M(K_{m+1})$. However, we do not yet know that the triples $\{e_{ij}, e_{jk}, e_{ik}\}, 2 \le i < j < k \le m$ contained in the copoint $X$ are collinear. The following theorem says that they are indeed collinear.                                                                                    □

5.15. THE RANK-4 DESARGUES' THEOREM FOR MATROIDS. *Let $G$ be a rank-4 10-point geometry consisting of a basis $e_1, e_2, e_3, e_4$ and six points $e_{ij}, 1 \le i < j \le 4$, where $e_{ij}$ is on the line $e_i \vee e_j$. If the three triples $\{e_{12}, e_{13}, e_{23}\}$, $\{e_{12}, e_{14}, e_{24}\}$, and $\{e_{13}, e_{14}, e_{34}\}$ are collinear, then the fourth triple $\{e_{23}, e_{24}, e_{34}\}$ is also collinear.*

PROOF. We shall give two easy proofs. The first is a variation on a method in Kahn and Kung [**67**], p. 491. Let $N$ be the rank-4 "configuration" with $\{e_{23}, e_{24}, e_{34}\}$ an independent set. Consider the contraction $N/e_{24}$. From Figure 4, we see that $N/e_{24}$ is a not a matroid. Hence, $N$ is not a matroid.

The second geometric proof was suggested by J. Bonin [**15**]. The set $\{e_{23}, e_{24}, e_{34}\}$ lies in the intersection of the planes $e_{12} \vee e_{13} \vee e_{14}$ and $e_2 \vee e_3 \vee e_4$. Hence, by the semimodular inequality, $\{e_{23}, e_{24}, e_{34}\}$ has rank 2 and the points $e_{23}, e_{24}, e_{34}$ are collinear.                                                                                    □

Theorem 5.15 is rather surprising in view of the fact that in rank-3, the non-Pappus configuration and the non-Desargues configuration are matroids (see Mac Lane [**91**]; see also Ingleton [**62**] and Oxley [**106**], p. 517–518).

For the other classical examples, even less is known. Yoon [**166**] has proved that if $G$ is a geometry satisfying (a) $G$ contains a modular copoint, (b) any two upper intervals of the same rank in $L(G)$ are isomorphic, and (c) $\chi(G; \lambda) = \prod_{j=0}^{n-1}(\lambda - q^j)$, then $G$ is isomorphic to the projective geometry $PG(n-1, q)$. The cases of Dowling geometries for groups of order greater than 1 is wide open.

An easier related problem is to characterize the upper uniform geometries (see Section 5.2 for the definition) with classical characteristic polynomials. This problem is also related to the problem of finding all upper uniform geometries (see Aigner [**1,2**]). Many cases of this problem can be resolved by using known results.

5.16. THEOREM.

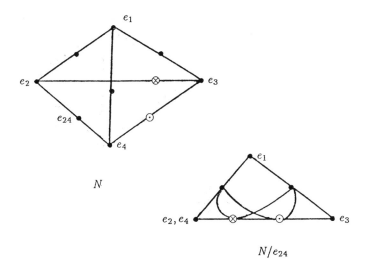

FIGURE 4. The non-matroidal configuration $N$ and its contraction $N/e_{24}$. The third point on the line $e_i \vee e_j$ is the point $e_{ij}$. The three 3-point lines $\{e_{12}, e_{13}, e_{23}\}$, $\{e_{12}, e_{14}, e_{24}\}$, and $\{e_{13}, e_{14}, e_{34}\}$ in $N$ are not shown.

*(a) Let $G$ be an upper uniform rank-$n$ geometry in which every rank-$k$ upper interval has characteristic polynomial $\prod_{j=0}^{k-1}(\lambda - q^j)$. Then $G$ is isomorphic to a rank-$n$ projective geometry of order $q$.*

*(b) Let $G$ be an upper uniform rank-$n$ geometry in which every rank-$k$ upper interval has characteristic polynomial $(\lambda - 1)_{(k)}$. Then $G$ is isomorphic to $M(K_{n+1})$.*

SKETCH OF PROOF. To prove (a), observe that all the rank-2 upper intervals in $G$ are $(q+1)$-point lines. Hence, $G$ contains no $(q+2)$-point-line-minor. In addition, $G$ has $1 + q + q^2 + \ldots + q^{n-1}$ points. Hence, by Theorem 4.3 in Kung [**81**], $G$ is isomorphic to $\mathrm{PG}(n-1, q)$ when $n \neq 3$ and to $\mathrm{PG}(2, q)$ or a projective plane of order $q$ when $n = 3$. Note that our proof holds under the weaker hypothesis: every rank-2 upper interval has at most $q + 1$ points and $G$ has $1 + q + q^2 + \ldots + q^{n-1}$ points.

To prove (b), observe that all the rank-2 upper intervals in $G$ are 3-point lines. Hence, $G$ is binary. All the rank-3 upper intervals have 6 points and hence are isomorphic to $M(K_4)$. Hence, $G$ has no minor isomorphic to the Fano plane $F_7$. Finally, $G$ contains $\binom{n+1}{2}$ points. Therefore, by the proof of Heller's theorem given in [**60**], $G$ is isomorphic to $M(K_{n+1})$. An alternate approach is to use Tutte's forbidden minor characterization of graphic geometries [**135**] as was done in Aigner [**1**]. $\square$

A natural conjecture is that an analogue of Theorem 5.16(b) holds for Dowling group geometries. Bonin [**15**] has observed that an analogue of Theorem 5.16(a) holds for affine geometries. Let $G$ be a rank-$n$ geometry satisfying the conditions:

(1) If $0 \leq k < n$, every rank-$k$ upper interval has characteristic polynomial $\prod_{j=0}^{k-1}(\lambda - q^j)$.

(2) $\chi(G; \lambda) = \chi(\mathrm{AG}(n - 1, q); \lambda)$.

Then $G$ is isomorphic to a rank-$n$ affine geometry of order $q$. (Equation (5.3) in Section 5.2 gives an explicit formula for $\chi(\mathrm{AG}(n - 1, q); \lambda)$.) To prove this result, observe that the number of points in $G$ is given by the absolute value of the coefficient of $\lambda^{n-1}$ in $\chi(G; \lambda)$. Hence, there are $q^{n-1}$ points in $G$. Next, observe that all the rank-2 upper intervals in $G$ are $(q+1)$-point lines. Hence, $G$ contains no $(q+2)$-point-line minor. From these two fact, one concludes, by a theorem in Bonin [14], that $G$ is can be embedded in a rank-$n$ projective geometry of order $q$. By condition (2), $\chi(G; q) \neq 0$ and $G$ is affine. Because $G$ has $q^{n-1}$ points, we conclude that $G$ is isomorphic to a (full) rank-$n$ affine geometry of order $q$. We remark that this proof uses only condition (2) and the hypothesis that $G$ contains no $(q + 2)$-point-line minor.

### 5.7. Characteristic polynomials of polymatroids

Most of the identities for characteristic polynomials of matroids have analogues for polymatroids. For example, an analogue of the contraction-and-deletion identity holds. See Helgason [57] and Whittle [162,164]. Defining a flat $X$ to be modular if

$$f(X \cup U) + f(X \cap U) = f(X) + f(U)$$

for every flat $U$, Whittle [163] has obtained an analogue of the modular factorization identity.

There is also an analogue of Crapo's identity for polymatroids. The general form can be obtained from the abstract version of Rédei's *Hauptsatz* as stated in Kung, Murty and Rota [86]. We shall state a simpler but useful version here.

5.17. THEOREM. *Let $G(S)$ be a rank-$n$ polymatroid represented as a collection $S$ of subspaces in $[\mathrm{GF}(q)]^d$. Then*

$$\lambda^{d-n}\chi(G; \lambda) = \sum_{k=0}^{d} C_k \prod_{j=0}^{d-k-1} (\lambda - q^j),$$

*where $C_k$ is the number of subspaces of rank $k$ not containing any subspace in $S$.*

The proof is an easy modification of the counting proof of Corollary 5.3 given in Section 5.2.

Using Theorem 5.17, we can calculate the characteristic polynomial of the $m$-subspace polymatroid $\mathrm{PG}(n - 1, q; m)$ consisting of all the subspaces of rank $m$ in $\mathrm{PG}(n - 1, q)$. Using the fact that a subspace $U$ contains no subspace of rank $m$ if and only if $U$ has rank at most $m - 1$, we conclude that

$$\chi(\mathrm{PG}(n - 1, q; m); \lambda) = \sum_{i=0}^{m-1} \begin{bmatrix} n \\ i \end{bmatrix}_q \prod_{j=0}^{n-i-1} (\lambda - q^j).$$

In particular, $\chi(\text{PG}(n-1,q;m);\lambda)$ has zeroes at $1,q,q^2,\ldots,q^{n-m}$. For example, the characteristic polynomial of a line polymatroid is given by the formula

$$\chi(\text{PG}(n-1,q;2);\lambda) = (1+q+\ldots+q^{n-1})\prod_{j=0}^{n-2}(\lambda-q^j) + \prod_{j=0}^{n-1}(\lambda-q^j)$$

$$= (\lambda+1+q+\ldots+q^{n-2})\prod_{j=0}^{n-2}(\lambda-q^j).$$

This example shows that characteristic polynomials of polymatroids can have zeroes which are negative integers. It is easier to calculate the characteristic polynomial of the hyperplane polymatroid $\text{PG}(n-1,q;n-1)$ from the basic definition. Doing so, we obtain

$$\chi(\text{PG}(n-1,q;n-1);\lambda) = \lambda^n - \left(\frac{q^n-1}{q-1}\right)\lambda + \left(\frac{q^n-q}{q-1}\right).$$

Note that when $2 \leq m \leq n-1$, none of the proper flats of the $m$-subspace polymatroids $\text{PG}(n-1,q;m)$ are modular in the sense of Whittle [163].

There is a direct analogue of formula (5.2) for the characteristic polynomial of a hypergraph:

$$\lambda^{p(\Gamma)}\chi(M(\Gamma);\lambda) = \sum_{k=1}^{|V|} c_k \prod_{j=0}^{k-1}(\lambda-j),$$

where $c_k$ is the number of partitions of the vertex set $V$ of $\Gamma$ into $k$ non-empty subsets such that no subset contains a hyperedge. From this analogue, we derive the following formula for the characteristic polynomial of the "complete" hypergraph $K[n,m]$ on the vertex set $\{1,2,\ldots,n\}$ with hyperedges all $m$-subsets of $\{1,2,\ldots,n\}$:

$$\chi(K[n,m];\lambda) = \sum_{k=\lceil\frac{n}{m-1}\rceil}^{n} S(n,k,m)\prod_{j=1}^{k-1}(\lambda-j),$$

where $S(n,k,m)$ is the number of partitions of $\{1,2,\ldots,n\}$ into $k$ (non-empty) blocks such that no block has size exceeding $m-1$. If $m=3$, then

$$S(n,k,3) = \prod_{i=1}^{n-k}\binom{n-2k+2}{2}.$$

(Note that the empty product equals 1.) Therefore,

$$\chi(K[n,3];\lambda) = \sum_{k=\lceil\frac{n}{2}\rceil}^{n}\left[\prod_{i=1}^{n-k}\binom{n-2k+2}{2}\right]\prod_{j=1}^{k-1}(\lambda-j).$$

Note that $\chi(K[n,m];\lambda)$ does not factor completely over the integers when $m \geq 3$ and that $K[n,m]$ can be properly colored with $\lceil\frac{n}{m-1}\rceil$ or more colors. Just as for the $m$-subspace polymatroids, the polymatroids of the complete hypergraphs $K[n,m]$ have no proper modular flats.

A worthwhile project would be to study the characteristic polynomials of other naturally occurring polymatroids, such as the 2-polymatroids in Oxley and Whittle [107].

### 5.8. Identities for Rédei functions

Most of the identities for characteristic polynomials have analogues for Rédei functions of relations. The analogue of the contraction-and-deletion identity has already been described in Theorem 3.1. The following proposition gives an analogue of Crapo's identity.

5.18. PROPOSITION. *Let $R : E \times T$ be a relation and let $S \subseteq E$. Let $R : S \times T$ be the subrelation obtained by restricting $R$ to $S \times T$. Then*

$$\zeta(R : S \times T; s) = \sum_{Z : Z \in \mathrm{Lat}(E) \text{ and } Z \cap S = \emptyset} \zeta(R : (E \backslash Z) \times Z^{\perp}; s).$$

PROOF. Let $\underline{u}$ be an $s$-tuple distinguishing $S$. Then the kernel of $\underline{u}$ in the relation $R : E \times T$ is a $\perp$-closed subset $Z$ (in $\mathrm{Lat}(E)$) disjoint from $S$. The $s$-tuples distinguishing $S$ are partitioned according to their kernel $Z$ in $\mathrm{Lat}(E)$.

Let $Z$ be a $\perp$-closed subset such that $Z \cap S = \emptyset$. Then the following two conditions are equivalent for an $s$-tuple $\underline{u} = (u_1, u_2, \dots, u_s)$ :
   (1)   $\ker \underline{u} = Z$ in the relation $R : E \times T$.
   (2)   Every component $u_i$ of $\underline{u}$ is in $Z^{\perp}$ and $\underline{u}$ distinguishes $E \backslash Z$ in the relation $R : (E \backslash Z) \times Z^{\perp}$.
To prove this equivalence, suppose that condition (1) holds. Because $\ker \underline{u} = u_1^{\perp} \cap u_2^{\perp} \cap \dots \cap u_s^{\perp}$ (by definition), $Z \subseteq u_i^{\perp}$. Taking perpendiculars of both sides, we obtain

$$u_i^{\perp\perp} \subseteq Z^{\perp}.$$

Since $u_i \in u_i^{\perp\perp}$, this implies that $u_i \in Z^{\perp}$. Moreover, in the relation $R : E \times T$, $\ker \underline{u} \subseteq Z$ if and only if $\ker \underline{u} \cap (E \backslash Z) = \emptyset$. We conclude that condition (1) implies condition (2). Conversely, if condition (2) holds, then $Z \subseteq \ker \underline{u}$ and $\ker \underline{u} \cap (E \backslash Z) = \emptyset$. Hence, condition (1) holds.

From the equivalence of conditions (1) and (2), we conclude that the number of $s$-tuples $\underline{u}$ satisfying the condition $\ker \underline{u} = Z$ equals

$$\zeta(R : (E \backslash Z) \times Z^{\perp}; s).$$

This completes the proof of Proposition 5.18.                                    □

An alternate way to prove Proposition 5.18 is to show the more general theorem that an upper interval of a lattice of $\perp$-closed sets is a lattice of the same type. More precisely, this theorem states that if $Z$ is a $\perp$-closed set in the lattice $\mathrm{Lat}(E)$ of $\perp$-closed sets of the relation $R : E \times T$, then the upper interval $[Z, E]$ in $\mathrm{Lat}(E)$ is isomorphic to the lattice $\mathrm{Lat}(E \backslash Z)$ of $\perp$-closed sets of the relation $R : (E \backslash Z) \times Z^{\perp}$.

The analogue of the modular factorization theorem has a fascinating history. A factorization theorem for Eulerian functions of groups appeared in the 1959 paper [52] of Gaschütz, before the 1971 paper [125] of Stanley.

5.19. GASCHÜTZ'S FACTORIZATION THEOREM FOR NORMAL SUBGROUPS. *Let $N$ be a normal subgroup in the finite group $G$. Then*

$$\phi(G; s) = \phi(G/N; s)\phi(G \downarrow N; s),$$

*where*

$$\phi(G \downarrow N; s) = \sum_{H : H \leq G \text{ and } NH = G} \mu(H, G)|N \cap H|^s.$$

Gaschütz's formula for $\phi(G \downarrow N; s)$ in [**52**] was a sum with fewer terms involving maximal subgroups and their intersections which is equivalent (by one of Philip Hall's theorems on Möbius functions) to the one given here.

Gaschütz gave a counting proof of this identity. The group $G$ is partitioned by the cosets of $N$. Hence, every element $x \in G$ is in a unique coset of $N$. Therefore, each $s$-tuple $(x_1, x_2, \ldots, x_s)$ of elements in $G$ is associated with a unique $s$-tuple $(Ng_1, Ng_2, \ldots, Ng_s)$ of cosets such that $x_1 \in Ng_1, x_2 \in Ng_2, \ldots$, and $x_s \in Ng_s$. Moreover, if $(x_1, x_2, \ldots, x_s)$ generates $G$, then $(Ng_1, Ng_2, \ldots, Ng_s)$ generates the quotient group $G/N$.

Thus, to prove Gaschütz's theorem, it suffices to show that for a given $s$-tuple of cosets $(Ng_1, Ng_2, \ldots, Ng_s)$ generating $G/N$, the number of $s$-tuples $(x_1, x_2, \ldots, x_s)$ generating $G$ such that $x_i \in Ng_i$ equals $\phi(G \downarrow N; s)$, a number depending only on $N$. To do so, we use the following lemma.

5.20. LEMMA. *Let $(Ng_1, Ng_2, \ldots, Ng_s)$ be an $s$-tuple of cosets and let $H$ be a subgroup of $G$. Let $C(H, s)$ be the number of $s$-tuples $(x_1, x_2, \ldots, x_s)$ such that $x_i \in Ng_i$ and $(x_1, x_2, \ldots, x_s)$ generates a subgroup of $H$. Then*

$$C(H, s) = \begin{cases} |H \cap N|^s & \text{if for all } i, \ H \cap Ng_i \neq \emptyset, \\ 0 & \text{otherwise.} \end{cases}$$

PROOF. An $s$-tuple $(x_1, x_2, \ldots, x_s)$ such that $x_i \in Ng_i$ generates a subgroup contained in $H$ if and only if for every $i$, $x_i \in H \cap Ng_i$. Therefore,

$$C(H, s) = |H \cap Ng_1||H \cap Ng_2| \cdots |H \cap Ng_s|.$$

Consider a set of the form $H \cap Ng$. If this set is non-empty and $x \in H \cap Ng$, then $Ng = Nx$. The function $G \to G, g \mapsto gx^{-1}$ is a bijection on $G$ and it maps $Nx$ to $N$ and $H$ to $H$. Hence,

$$|H \cap Ng| = |H \cap N|.$$

We conclude that $|H \cap Ng|$ equals $|H \cap N|$ if $H \cap Ng \neq \emptyset$ and 0 if $H \cap Ng = \emptyset$. $\square$

Let $(Ng_1, Ng_2, \ldots, Ng_s)$ be a given $s$-tuple of cosets generating $G/N$. By Möbius inversion on the lattice of subgroups, the number of $s$-tuples $(x_1, x_2, \ldots, x_s)$ such that for all $i$, $x_i \in Ng_i$ and $\{x_1, x_2, \ldots, x_s\}$ generating $G$ equals

$$(5.5) \qquad\qquad \sum_{H:H \in L(G)} \mu(H, G)C(H, s).$$

By Lemma 5.20, the number $C(H, s)$ equals 0 unless $Ng_i \cap H \neq \emptyset$ for all $i$. Because $(Ng_1, Ng_2, \ldots, Ng_s)$ generates $G/N$, this condition implies that $H/N$ generates $G/N$, that is, $NH = G$. Therefore the sum can be restricted to subgroups $H$ such that $NH = G$. For such subgroups, $C(H, s) = |N \cap H|^s$. Hence, the sum (5.5) equals $\phi(G \downarrow N; s)$. This completes the proof of Gaschütz's theorem.

Gaschütz's theorem and the modular factorization theorem can be extended to a factorization theorem for Rédei functions of relations. To do so, we need to abstract set-theoretically those properties of the partition of $G$ into cosets $Ng_i$ which are used in the proof of Gaschütz's theorem. Let $R \subseteq S \times T$ be a relation and let $X \subseteq S$. A partition of $T$ into blocks $T_1, T_2, \ldots, T_l$ is said to be $X$-modular if it satisfies the following conditions:

($X$M1) If $u$ and $v$ are in the same block $T_i$, then

$$R^{-1}(u) \cap X = R^{-1}(v) \cap X,$$

or, equivalently,

$$u^{\perp} \cap X = v^{\perp} \cap X.$$

($X$M2) For every closed set $U$ in $\mathrm{Lat}(S)$ such that $U \wedge X = \hat{0}$ and every block $T_i$, the number $|U^{\perp} \cap T_i|$ equals an integer $\gamma_U$ depending on $U$ but not on $T_i$.

Given an $X$-modular partition of $T$, let $\tilde{T} = \{T_1, T_2, \ldots, T_l\}$ be the set of blocks. We define the relation $\tilde{R} \colon X \times \tilde{T}$ by the condition: for $x \in X$ and $T_i \in \tilde{T}$,

$$(x, T_i) \in \tilde{R} \iff (x, t) \in R \text{ for some } t \text{ in } T_i.$$

There are two archetypical examples of an $X$-modular partition. The first example appeared implicitly in Gaschütz's theorem. In this example, the relation is the Frattini relation of a finite group $G$ and the $N$-modular partition is the partition of $G$ into cosets of a normal subgroup $N$.[32] To describe the second, let $G$ be a rank-$n$ loopless matroid represented as a set $S$ of non-zero vectors in $[\mathrm{GF}(q)]^d$, let $X$ be a rank-$k$ flat of $G$, let $T$ be the dual space of linear functionals on $[\mathrm{GF}(q)]^d$, and let $R \colon S \times T$ be the relation given by

$$(x, L) \in R \iff L(x) \neq 0.$$

Consider the equivalence relation $\sim_X$ on the set $T$ defined in the following way: two linear functionals in $T$ are equivalent whenever their restrictions to the subspace $\mathrm{lin}(X)$ spanned by $X$ are equal, or, equivalently, their restrictions to the set $X$ are equal. A block or equivalence class of $\sim_X$ consists of all extensions of a fixed linear functional $L'$ defined on $\mathrm{lin}(X)$. In particular, there are $q^k$ blocks.

If $X$ is modular, then the partition given by the equivalence relation $\sim_X$ is an $X$-modular partition for the relation $R$. Condition ($X$M1) follows immediately from the definition of $\sim_X$. To check condition ($X$M2), let $U$ be a flat in $G$ such that $U \wedge X = \emptyset$. Let $L'$ be a linear functional on $\mathrm{lin}(X)$ and let $T_i$ be the block of $\sim_X$ consisting of all the linear functionals $L$ on $[\mathrm{GF}(q)]^d$ which are extensions of $L'$. Then the set $U^{\perp} \cap T_i$ consists of all the linear functionals $L$ on $[\mathrm{GF}(q)]^d$ such that

(5.6)            the restriction $L|_{\mathrm{lin}(X)}$ equals $L'$ and $U \subseteq \ker L$.

Because $X$ is modular and $U \wedge X = \emptyset$, the intersection of the subspaces $\mathrm{lin}(U)$ and $\mathrm{lin}(X)$ is the zero subspace $\{0\}$. Hence, the two sets of linear constraints in (5.6) are linearly independent and impose a total of $k + \mathrm{rank}(U)$ linear constraints on the linear functional $L$. We conclude that

$$|U^{\perp} \cap T_i| = q^{d-k-\mathrm{rank}(U)},$$

a number depending on $U$ but not on $T_i$.

The following theorem is a common generalization of Gaschütz theorem and Stanley's modular factorization identity (equation (5.4)).

---

[32] Note that a normal subgroup is modular as an element of the lattice of subgroups.

5.21. THEOREM. *Let $R \subseteq S \times T$ be a relation, let $X$ be a subset of $S$, and let $T_1, T_2, \ldots, T_l$ be an $X$-modular partition of $T$. Then*

$$\zeta(R\colon S \times T; s) = \zeta(\tilde{R}\colon X \times \tilde{T}; s) \left( \sum_{U\colon U \in \mathrm{Lat}(S) \text{ and } U \wedge X = \hat{0}} \mu(\hat{0}, U) \gamma_U^s \right),$$

*where $\gamma_U$ is the common value of $|U^\perp \cap T_i|$.*

The proof is an abstraction of the proof of Gaschütz's theorem given earlier in this section. Let $\underline{u} = (u_1, u_2, \ldots, u_s)$ be an $s$-tuple distinguishing $S$. Then there is a unique $s$-tuple of blocks $\underline{T} = (T_{i_1}, T_{i_2}, \ldots, T_{i_s})$ such that $u_j \in T_{i_j}$ for all $j, 1 \le j \le s$. Because $\underline{u}$ distinguishes $S$ with respect to the relation $R$, $\ker \underline{u} = \emptyset$. By condition $(X\mathrm{M}1)$, this implies that $\ker \underline{T} = \emptyset$. Hence, $\underline{T}$ distinguishes $X$ with respect to the relation $\tilde{R}$.

As in the proof of Theorem 5.19, it suffices to show that for a fixed $s$-tuple $\underline{T} = (T_{i_1}, T_{i_2}, \ldots, T_{i_s})$ distinguishing $X$ in the relation $\tilde{R}$, the number of $s$-tuples $(u_1, u_2, \ldots, u_s)$ distinguishing $S$ such that $u_j$ is in $T_{i_j}$ equals

$$\sum_{U\colon U \in \mathrm{Lat}(S) \text{ and } U \wedge X = \hat{0}} \mu(\hat{0}, U) \gamma_U^s.$$

Consider the kernel of such an $s$-tuple. Because $\underline{T}$ distinguishes $X$, the kernel of $(u_1, u_2, \ldots, u_s)$ is a closed set in $\mathrm{Lat}(S)$ disjoint from $X$. Given a closed set $U$ in $\mathrm{Lat}(S)$ disjoint from $X$, there are

$$|U^\perp \cap T_{i_1}||U^\perp \cap T_{i_2}| \cdots |U^\perp \cap T_{i_s}|$$

$s$-tuples $(u_1, u_2, \ldots, u_s)$ with $u_j$ in $T_{i_j}$ whose kernel contains or equals $U$. Hence, by Möbius inversion on the order ideal of closed sets in $\mathrm{Lat}(S)$ disjoint from $X$, we conclude that the number of $s$-tuples $(u_1, u_2, \ldots, u_s)$ with $u_j$ in $T_{i_j}$ with kernel equal to $\hat{0}$ is

$$\sum_{U\colon U \in \mathrm{Lat}(S) \text{ and } U \wedge X = \hat{0}} \mu(\hat{0}, U)|U^\perp \cap T_{i_1}||U^\perp \cap T_{i_2}| \cdots |U^\perp \cap T_{i_s}|.$$

We can now finish the proof using condition $(X\mathrm{M}2)$ that the cardinality $|U^\perp \cap T_{i_j}|$ is a number $\gamma_U$ depending only on $U$. Note that this proof gives a counting proof of Stanley's identity (5.4) when $G$ is a representable geometry.

We remark that because our interest is in combinatorics, we have considered Rédei functions as functions with a non-negative integer argument $s$. One can also regard Rédei functions as Dirichlet polynomials with a complex argument $s$. In [**52**], Gaschütz proved that if an identity amongst Dirichlet polynomials holds for all positive integers $s$, then that identity also holds as an identity for Dirichlet polynomials with complex argument $s$. Thus, the identities for Rédei functions proved in this paper hold as identities between Dirichlet polynomials.

## 6. Dowling geometries and linear codes

The discovery by Dowling in his 1971 paper [44] that one of the fundamental problems of coding theory is an instance of the critical problem provided strong support to the contention by Crapo and Rota that "the critical problem is the central problem of extremal combinatorial theory" ([36], Chapter 16). In this section, we shall describe the developments arising from Dowling's work.

### 6.1. Matroids defined by Hamming weights

Let $x = (x_1, x_2, \ldots, x_n)$ be a vector in the vector space $[\mathrm{GF}(q)]^n$ of $n$-tuples over $\mathrm{GF}(q)$. The *support* of $x$ is the set $\{i : x_i \neq 0\}$ of (coordinate) positions on which $x$ has non-zero coordinates. The *(Hamming) weight* $\mathrm{wt}(x)$ of $x$ is the number of non-zero coordinates in $x$. It equals the size of the support of $x$. An $(n, k)$-*linear code C* is a subspace of dimension $k$ in $[\mathrm{GF}(q)]^n$. The *minimum weight* (or *minimum distance*) of the linear code $C$ is the minimum weight of a non-zero vector in $C$. One of the fundamental problems of coding theory – as opposed to coding "practice", which is more concerned with particular codes – is the following.

6.1. PROBLEM. *Given parameters n, t, and q, where n and t are positive integers and q is a prime power, find the maximum dimension k of a linear code C in $[\mathrm{GF}(q)]^n$ with minimum weight $t + 1$.*

Because a set $S$ of non-zero vectors in $[\mathrm{GF}(q)]^n$ has critical exponent $n - k$ if and only if the maximum dimension of a subspace disjoint from $S$ has dimension $k$, Problem 6.1 can be recast as a critical problem. The *weight-t Dowling matroid* $\tilde{B}_{n,t}(q)$ is the matroid consisting of all non-zero $n$-tuples in $[\mathrm{GF}(q)]^n$ having weight at most $t$. The set of $n$-tuples in $\tilde{B}_{n,t}(q)$ can be thought of as the punctured $t$-ball relative to the Hamming weight. Using Dowling matroids, we can reformulate Problem 6.1 as a critical problem.

6.2. PROBLEM. *Given parameters n, t, and q, find the critical exponent of the weight-t Dowling matroid $\tilde{B}_{n,t}(q)$.*

One way to "solve" Problem 6.2 is to explicitly calculate the characteristic polynomials of the Dowling matroids. As these matroids have multiple points, it is more convenient to consider them as subsets of points in projective space $\mathrm{PG}(n - 1, q)$. We shall think of $\mathrm{PG}(n - 1, q)$ as the set of all non-zero $n$-tuples in $[\mathrm{GF}(q)]^n$, modulo the equivalence relation $x \sim y$ whenever $y = \alpha x$ for some non-zero scalar $\alpha$. We shall often confuse a point (or equivalence class of non-zero vectors) in $\mathrm{PG}(n-1, q)$ with one of the $n$-tuples in it. The Hamming weight is the same for all the vectors in a point. Therefore, we can define the weight of a point in $\mathrm{PG}(n-1, q)$ to be the weight of any vector in it. The *weight-t Dowling geometry* $B_{n,t}(q)$ is the geometry consisting of all points in $\mathrm{PG}(n - 1, q)$ having weight at most $t$. It is a simplification of the Dowling matroid $\tilde{B}_{n,t}(q)$. The number $b_{n,t,q}$ of points in $B_{n,t}(q)$ is given by the formula

$$b_{n,t,q} = \sum_{i=1}^{t} \binom{n}{i} (q - 1)^{i-1}.$$

Note that the Dowling group geometry $Q_n(\mathrm{GF}(q)^{\times})$ over the multiplicative group of the field $\mathrm{GF}(q)$ is the weight-2 Dowling geometry $B_{n,2}(q)$.

## 6.2. Supersolvable Dowling geometries

In [**45,46**], Dowling showed that the lattice of flats of a weight-2 Dowling geometry can be represented as a lattice of "$q$-partitions". Using the fact that contractions of weight-2 Dowling geometries are weight-2 Dowling geometries of lower ranks, Dowling used Crapo's identity 5.2 to calculate their characteristic polynomials:

$$(6.1) \qquad \chi(B_{n,2}(q); \lambda) = \prod_{i=0}^{n-1} (\lambda - (q-1)i - 1).$$

This formula also follows from Theorem 5.7 and the fact that weight-2 Dowling geometries are supersolvable.

Bonin [**12**] has shown that a flat is modular in $B_{n,t}(q)$ if and only if it is a *coordinate flat*, that is, a flat which contains all the points in its linear span in $PG(n-1, q)$. Hence, there are exactly three other infinite families of supersolvable Dowling geometries. The first family consists of the weight-1 Dowling geometries. The lattices of flats of these geometries are Boolean algebras. The second family consists of the weight-$n$ Dowling geometries $B_{n,n}(q)$, which are the projective geometries $PG(n-1, q)$. The last family consists of the weight-$(n-1)$ Dowling geometries $B_{n,n-1}(q)$. Their characteristic polynomials are given by the following formula:

$$\chi(B_{n,n-1}(q); \lambda) = (\lambda - 1)(\lambda - q)(\lambda - q^2) \cdots (\lambda - q^{n-2})(\lambda - (q^{n-1} - (q-1)^{n-1})).$$

Bonin also calculated the characteristic polynomials of the Dowling geometries $B_{n,n-2}(q)$ and obtained the following formula:

$$\chi(B_{n,n-2}(q); \lambda) = [(\lambda - q^{n-2})(\lambda - q^{n-1}) + (\lambda - q^{n-2})((q-1)^{n-1} + n(q-1)^{n-2}) +$$
$$(q-1)^{n-1}(q-2)(q-3) \cdots (q-n+2)] \prod_{i=0}^{n-3} (\lambda - q^i).$$

Bonin's method is to observe that $B_{n,n-2}(q)$ has critical exponent at least $n-2$. Therefore, by determining the points and lines disjoint from $B_{n,n-2}(q)$, their characteristic polynomials can be calculated using Crapo's identity 5.2. Bonin's method can be extended to other values of $t$ close to $n$. We shall describe this extension in the next three sections.

## 6.3. Dowling geometries with critical exponent $n-1$

We first determine the values of $t$ for which $B_{n,t}(q)$ has critical exponent $n-1$.

6.3. THEOREM. *The weight-$t$ Dowling geometry $B_{n,t}(q)$ has critical exponent $n-1$ if and only if*

$$n - 1 \geq t \geq n - \left\lceil \frac{n}{q+1} \right\rceil.$$

PROOF. Suppose that $n - 1 \geq t \geq n - \lceil \frac{n}{q+1} \rceil$. Because points of weight $n$ are not in $B_{n,t}(q)$, its critical exponent is at most $n-1$. To prove that the critical exponent is exactly $n-1$, it suffices to show that if $x$ and $y$ are two points in $PG(n-1, q)$ having weight $t+1$ or greater, then there exists a point on the line $x \vee y$ with weight at most $t$.

Suppose that $x = (x_1, x_2, \ldots, x_n)$ and $y = (y_1, y_2, \ldots, y_n)$. Define their *common support* to be the set $M$ of (coordinate) positions $i$ on which both coordinates $x_i$ and $y_i$ are non-zero. The number of such positions is at least

$$\text{wt}(x) + \text{wt}(y) - n \geq n - 2 \left\lceil \frac{n}{q+1} \right\rceil + 2$$

$$\geq (q-1) \left\lfloor \frac{n}{q+1} \right\rfloor + 1.$$

Consider the $q - 1$ subsets of $M$

$$\{i : i \in M \text{ and } \frac{x_i}{y_i} = \alpha\},$$

where $\alpha$ ranges over the $q-1$ non-zero elements of $\text{GF}(q)$. These subsets are disjoint and their union is $M$. Because $M$ contains more than $(q-1)\lfloor \frac{n}{q+1} \rfloor$ elements, one of these subsets, say the subset $J$ for which $x_i/y_i = \beta$, has size at least

$$\left\lfloor \frac{n}{q+1} \right\rfloor + 1 \geq \left\lceil \frac{n}{q+1} \right\rceil.$$

At every position $j$ in $J$, the point $x - \beta y$ has coordinate zero. Hence, the point $x - \beta y$ on the line $x \vee y$ has weight at most $t$.

To finish the proof, we shall construct a line disjoint from $B_{n,t}(q)$ when $t < n - \lceil \frac{n}{q+1} \rceil$. Let $n = a(q+1) + b$, where $0 \leq b \leq q$. Partition the set of coordinate positions into $b$ subsets $A_1, A_2, \ldots, A_b$ of size $a + 1$ and $q + 1 - b$ subsets $A_{b+1}, A_{b+2}, \ldots, A_q, A_{q+1}$ of size $a$. For $1 \leq i \leq q+1$, let $u_i$ be a point in $\text{PG}(n-1, q)$ with support equal to $A_i$. Let $\alpha_1, \alpha_2, \ldots, \alpha_{q-1}$ be an ordering of the non-zero elements in $\text{GF}(q)$. Let

$$x = \alpha_1 u_1 + \alpha_2 u_2 + \ldots + \alpha_{q-1} u_{q-1} + u_q$$

and

$$y = u_1 + u_2 + \ldots + u_{q-1} + u_{q+1}.$$

Because the support of $x$ equals $A_1 \cup A_2 \cup \ldots A_{q-1} \cup A_q$ and the support of $y$ equals $A_1 \cup A_2 \cup \ldots A_{q-1} \cup A_{q+1}$, both $x$ and $y$ have weight greater than $t$. Moreover, the point $x - \alpha_i y$ on the line $x \vee y$ has zero coordinates precisely in the positions $A_i$ and hence, it also has weight greater than $t$. We conclude that every point on the line $x \vee y$ has weight greater than $t$.                                                 $\square$

Theorem 6.3 implies that $1, q, q^2, \ldots, q^{n-2}$ are roots of the characteristic polynomial of $B_{n,t}(q)$ when $t \geq n - \lceil \frac{n}{q+1} \rceil$. Because we also know the number of points in $B_{n,t}(q)$, we can calculate the characteristic polynomial of $B_{n,t}(q)$.

6.4. COROLLARY. *Let $n - 1 \geq t \geq n - \lceil \frac{n}{q+1} \rceil$. Then*

$$\chi(B_{n,t}(q); \lambda) = (\lambda - 1)(\lambda - q)(\lambda - q^2) \cdots (\lambda - q^{n-2})(\lambda - c_{n,t,q}),$$

*where*

$$c_{n,t,q} = b_{n,t,q} - [1 + q + q^2 + \ldots + q^{n-2}].$$

When $n - 2 \geq t \geq n - \lceil \frac{n}{q+1} \rceil$, the weight-$t$ Dowling geometries $B_{n,t}(q)$ are examples of non-supersolvable geometries whose characteristic polynomials factor completely in integers. Because these Dowling geometries contain $PG(2, q)$ as sub-geometries, they are representable only over fields of characteristic equal to the prime characteristic of $GF(q)$.

The partitioning idea in the proof of Theorem 6.3 can be used to determine most of the values of $t$ for which $B_{n,t}(q)$ has critical exponent $n - 2$. Because the work needed to do this is intricate but elementary, Sections 6.4 and 6.5 are somewhat technical.

## 6.4. Lines in projective geometries

We begin with a combinatorial description of lines in $PG(n - 1, q)$. Suppose $L$ is a line in $PG(n - 1, q)$. Choose two distinct points $x = (x_1, x_2, \ldots, x_n)$ and $y = (y_1, y_2, \ldots, y_n)$ on $L$. We define a collection of $q + 2$ subsets of the (coordinate) positions in the following way. Let

$$A_0 = \{i : x_i = 0 \text{ and } y_i = 0\}.$$

The set $A_0$ is the set of positions $i$ such that the $i$th coordinate is zero in every point on $L$ and it will play a special role. Next, let

$$A' = \{i : x_i = 0 \text{ but } y_i \neq 0\},$$
$$A'' = \{i : y_i = 0 \text{ but } x_i \neq 0\},$$

and

$$A_\alpha = \{i : \frac{x_i}{y_i} = \alpha\},$$

where $\alpha$ ranges over all the non-zero elements in $GF(q)$. The subsets $A_0, A', A'', A_\alpha$ are pairwise disjoint and their union is $\{1, 2, \ldots, n\}$. Some of these subsets may be empty. Let $P$ be the multiset with elements the $q + 1$ subsets $A', A'', A_\alpha$. The non-empty subsets in $P$ occur with multiplicity 1. Because $x$ and $y$ are distinct points in projective space, the multiset $P$ contains at least two non-empty subsets. Thus, $P$ may contain the empty set with any multiplicity from 0 to $q - 1$.

If $z = x - \beta y$ is a point on $L$, then $z_i = 0$ if $i \in A_0$ or $i \in A_\beta$ and

$$z_i = x_i - \beta y_i = (\alpha - \beta) y_i$$

if $i \in A_\alpha$. From this, we deduce that the subset $A_0$ and the multiset $P$ are independent of the choice of the two points $x$ and $y$. We call the pair $[A_0, P]$ the *layout* of the line $L$.

A pair $[A_0, P]$ is a *layout* if $A_0$ is a proper subset of $\{1, 2, \ldots, n\}$ and $P$ is a multiset of $q + 1$ subsets of $\{1, 2, \ldots, n\} \setminus A_0$ satisfying the following properties:

(1) the subsets are pairwise disjoint,
(2) their union is $\{1, 2, \ldots, n\} \setminus A_0$, and
(3) at least two subsets are non-empty.

Note that by condition (1), the only subset which can occur with multiplicity greater than 1 is the empty set. Given a layout $[A_0, P]$, we can construct all lines having this pair as its layout by the following algorithm:

*Step 1.* Choose a subset $A'$ from $P$. Construct a point $x = (x_1, x_2, \ldots, x_n)$ by setting $x_i = 0$ if $i \in A_0 \cup A'$. Fill in the remaining positions in any way with non-zero elements in $GF(q)$.

*Step 2.* Choose another subset $A''$ from $P$. There are now $q - 1$ subsets in $P$ that have not been chosen. Choose a bijection from these subsets to the set of non-zero elements in $\mathrm{GF}(q)$. Label the set $A$ mapped to $\alpha$ by $A_\alpha$. Construct a point $y = (y_1, y_2, \ldots, y_n)$ by setting $y_i = 0$ if $i \in A_0 \cup A''$ and $y_i = \alpha x_i$ if $i \in A_\alpha$. Fill in the remaining positions in $A'$ in any way with non-zero elements in $\mathrm{GF}(q)$.

The line $L = x \vee y$ has layout $[A_0, P]$. Because the algorithm chooses all possible bases for a line $L$ regarded as a 2-dimensional subspace of $[\mathrm{GF}(q)]^n$, the line $L$ appears as the output

$$(q^2 - 1)(q^2 - q) = q(q - 1)^2(q + 1)$$

times.

As an example of this construction, take $n = 13$ and $q = 3$. Choose the layout given by $A_0 = \{1\}$ and $P = \{\{2, 3, 4\}, \{5, 6, 7\}, \{8, 9, 10\}, \{11, 12, 13\}\}$. Choose $A' = \{11, 12, 13\}$ and $A'' = \{8, 9, 10\}$. Finally, choose $A_{-1} = \{2, 3, 4\}$ and $A_1 = \{5, 6, 7\}$, where 1 and $-1$ are elements in $\mathrm{GF}(3)$. Then one way of filling in the coordinates yields

$$x = (0, \quad 1, -1, 1, \quad -1, -1, 1, \quad -1, 1, 1, \quad 0, 0, 0)$$
$$y = (0, \quad -1, 1, -1, \quad -1, -1, 1, \quad 0, 0, 0, \quad -1, -1, 1).$$

Let $[A_0, P]$ be a layout. We define its *size sequence* to be the sequence $\underline{a} = (a_0, a_1, a_2, \ldots, a_{q+1})$, where $a_0 = |A_0|$ and $a_1, a_2, \ldots, a_{q+1}$ is the sequence obtained by arranging the multiset $\{|A_1|, |A_2|, \ldots, |A_{q+1}|\}$ of sizes of the sets in $P$ in non-increasing order. Let $l[\underline{a}]$ be the number defined by

$$l[\underline{a}] = \frac{(q - 1)^{n - a_0 - 2}}{q(q + 1)}[(q - 1)(q - 2) \cdots (t - 1)$$
$$+ 2(q + 1 - t)(q - 1)(q - 2) \cdots (t)$$
$$+ (q + 1 - t)(q - t)(q - 1)(q - 2) \cdots (t + 1)],$$

where $t$ is the number of terms which are zero in the sequence $a_1, a_2, \ldots, a_{q+1}$.

6.5. **Lemma.** *Let $[A_0, P]$ be a layout having size sequence $\underline{a}$. Then the number of lines in $\mathrm{PG}(n - 1, q)$ having layout $[A_0, P]$ equals $l[\underline{a}]$. In particular, the number of lines with layout $[A_0, P]$ depends only on $|A_0|$ and the number of empty sets in $P$.*

The proof consists of counting the number of choices at each step of the algorithm. Note that (a) there are three cases, depending on whether both $A'$ and $A''$ are empty, one of them is empty, or neither is empty, and, (b) there are a total of $n - a_0$ coordinates in $x$ and $y$ to be filled in arbitrarily with non-zero elements from $\mathrm{GF}(q)$.

## 6.5. Dowling geometries with critical exponent $n - 2$

In this section, we shall find most of the values of $t$ for which the Dowling geometry $B_{n,t}(q)$ has critical exponent $n - 2$. The following theorem covers most of the cases.

6.6. THEOREM. *Let*

$$e = \left\lfloor \frac{1}{q+1+\frac{1}{q}} \left\lceil \frac{n}{q+1} \right\rceil \right\rfloor.$$

*Suppose that $e \geq 1$ and*

$$n - \left\lceil \frac{n}{q+1} \right\rceil - 1 \geq t \geq n - \left\lceil \frac{n}{q+1} \right\rceil - e.$$

*Then the Dowling geometry $B_{n,t}(q)$ has critical exponent $n - 2$.*

PROOF. By Theorem 6.3, there exist lines $L$ in $\mathrm{PG}(n-1,q)$ disjoint from $B_{n,t}(q)$. Hence the critical exponent of $B_{n,t}(q)$ is at most $n-2$. To prove that it is exactly $n-2$, it suffices to show that if $x$ is a point with weight exceeding $t$ not on $L$, then the plane $L \vee x$ contains a point having weight at most $t$.

Let $L$ be a line disjoint from $B_{n,t}(q)$ and let $[A_0, \{A_1, A_2, \ldots, A_{q+1}\}]$ be its layout. Let $x$ be a point having weight exceeding $t$, let $H$ be the set of positions $i$ such that the $i$th coordinate in $x$ is zero, and let $h = |H|$. Let $h' = |H \cap A_0|$, the number of positions $i$ such that the $i$th coordinate in $x$ and the $i$th coordinate in all the points in $L$ are zero. The remaining positions in $H \backslash (H \cap A_0)$ are distributed into $q+1$ subsets $A_1, A_2, \ldots, A_{q+1}$ in the partition of $L$. Hence, one of these subsets receives at least $\lceil \frac{h-h'}{q+1} \rceil$ positions. Disjoint from these positions are the $h'$ positions which have zero coordinates in $x$ and all points of $L$. Since

$$\left\lceil \frac{h - h'}{q+1} \right\rceil + h' \geq \left\lceil \frac{h}{q+1} \right\rceil,$$

we conclude that there exists a point $y$ on the line $L$ such that $x$ and $y$ have $\lceil \frac{h}{q+1} \rceil$ or more positions on which both of their coordinates are zero. Note that these positions will also have zero coordinates for any point on the line $x \vee y$.

Observing that $x$ and $y$ are supported on a set of size $n - \lceil \frac{h}{q+1} \rceil$ or less, we conclude that their common support has size at least

$$\begin{aligned}
& \mathrm{wt}(x) + \mathrm{wt}(y) - \left( n - \left\lceil \frac{h}{q+1} \right\rceil \right) \\
\geq\ & \left( n - \left\lceil \frac{n}{q+1} \right\rceil - h + \left\lceil \frac{n}{q+1} \right\rceil \right) + \left( n - \left\lceil \frac{n}{q+1} \right\rceil - e + 1 \right) - \left( n - \left\lceil \frac{h}{q+1} \right\rceil \right) \\
=\ & \left( n - 2 \left\lceil \frac{n}{q+1} \right\rceil + 1 \right) - \left( h - \left\lceil \frac{h}{q+1} \right\rceil \right) + \left( \left\lceil \frac{n}{q+1} \right\rceil - e \right) \\
\geq\ & (q-1) \left\lfloor \frac{n}{q+1} \right\rfloor + \left( \left\lceil \frac{n}{q+1} \right\rceil - e - h + \left\lceil \frac{h}{q+1} \right\rceil \right).
\end{aligned}$$

As in the proof of Theorem 6.3, we conclude that there is a point $z$ on the line $x \vee y$ with at least

$$\left\lfloor \frac{n}{q+1} \right\rfloor + \frac{1}{q-1} \left( \left\lceil \frac{n}{q+1} \right\rceil - e - h + \left\lceil \frac{h}{q+1} \right\rceil \right)$$

positions with zero coordinates in the common support of $x$ and $y$. Hence, the total number $N$ of positions on which $z$ has zero coordinates is at least

$$\left\lfloor \frac{n}{q+1} \right\rfloor + \frac{1}{q-1} \left( \left\lceil \frac{n}{q+1} \right\rceil - e - h + \left\lceil \frac{h}{q+1} \right\rceil \right) + \left\lceil \frac{h}{q+1} \right\rceil$$

$$= \left\lfloor \frac{n}{q+1} \right\rfloor + \frac{1}{q-1} \left( \left\lceil \frac{n}{q+1} \right\rceil - e + q \left\lceil \frac{h}{q+1} \right\rceil - h \right)$$

$$\geq \left\lfloor \frac{n}{q+1} \right\rfloor + \frac{1}{q-1} \left( \left\lceil \frac{n}{q+1} \right\rceil - e - \left\lfloor \frac{h}{q+1} \right\rfloor \right).$$

But $x$ has weight exceeding $t$. Therefore,

$$h < \left\lceil \frac{n}{q+1} \right\rceil + e.$$

Dividing by $q+1$, taking the floor on the left-hand side, and then moving all the terms to the right-hand side, we obtain

$$0 < \frac{1}{q+1} \left\lceil \frac{n}{q+1} \right\rceil + \frac{e}{q+1} - \left\lfloor \frac{h}{q+1} \right\rfloor.$$

Combining this with the estimate for $N$, we obtain

$$N \geq \left\lfloor \frac{n}{q+1} \right\rfloor + \frac{1}{q-1} \left( \frac{1}{q+1} \left\lceil \frac{n}{q+1} \right\rceil + \frac{e}{q+1} - \left\lfloor \frac{h}{q+1} \right\rfloor \right) +$$

$$\frac{1}{q-1} \left( \frac{q}{q+1} \left\lceil \frac{n}{q+1} \right\rceil - \left( \frac{q+2}{q+1} \right) e \right)$$

$$> \left\lfloor \frac{n}{q+1} \right\rfloor + \frac{1}{(q-1)(q+1)} \left( q \left\lceil \frac{n}{q+1} \right\rceil - (q+2)e \right).$$

The quantity inside the brackets in the second term can be simplified as follows.

$$q \left\lceil \frac{n}{q+1} \right\rceil - (q+2)e = q \left( q+1+\frac{1}{q} \right) \left( \frac{1}{q+1+\frac{1}{q}} \left\lceil \frac{n}{q+1} \right\rceil \right) - (q+2)e$$

$$\geq (q^2+q+1)e - (q+2)e$$

$$\geq (q^2-1)e.$$

We conclude that

$$N > \left\lfloor \frac{n}{q+1} \right\rfloor + e,$$

that is, the point $z$ on the plane $L \vee x$ has weight at most $t$.     $\square$

From the way the inequalities work in the proof, the lower bound in Theorem 6.6 should be almost the sharp bound, with a possible error arising from rounding up or down. Because of the number of cases, this error is difficult to write down exactly in general. However, given specific $n$ and $q$, the sharp bound should be obtainable by working through the proof carefully.

The next result shows that many of the cases when $e = 0$ can be settled easily.

6.7. THEOREM. *Let $t = n - \left\lceil \frac{n}{q+1} \right\rceil - 1$. Suppose that $n \not\equiv 1 \ (mod \ q+1)$. Then the Dowling geometry $B_{n,t}(q)$ has critical exponent $n-2$.*

PROOF. Since $t < n - \lceil \frac{n}{q+1} \rceil$, the critical exponent is at most $n-2$ by Theorem 6.3. Therefore, it suffices to show that the critical exponent is at least $n - 2$. The copoint $X$ in $B_{n,t}(q)$ consisting of the points with the last coordinate zero is isomorphic to $B_{n-1,t}(q)$. Because $n \not\equiv 1 \pmod{q+1}$,

$$t = (n-1) - \left\lceil \frac{n-1}{q+1} \right\rceil.$$

Hence, by Theorem 6.3, the restriction $B_{n,t}(q)|X$ has critical exponent $n - 1$ and every subspace of rank greater than 1 in the linear span of $X$ intersects $X$. Because the intersection of a subspace of rank $r$ in $\mathrm{PG}(n-1, q)$ with the linear span of $X$ is a subspace of rank $r - 1$, we conclude that every subspace in $\mathrm{PG}(n, q)$ disjoint from $B_{n,t}(q)$ has rank at most 2. □

When $n \equiv 1 \pmod{q+1}$ and $t = n - \lceil \frac{n}{q+1} \rceil - 1$, the Dowling geometry $B_{n,t}(q)$ may have critical exponent less than $n - 2$. For example, $B_{7,3}(2)$ has critical exponent 4 because all points in the plane spanned by

$$(0,1,1,0,1,0,1),\ (0,1,1,1,0,1,0),\ (1,1,0,0,0,1,1)$$

have weight 4.

It might be worth noting that Theorems 6.3 and 6.6 have the following form:

$$t \geq n - \frac{n}{q+1} \quad \text{approximately} \quad \Rightarrow \quad c(B_{n,t}(q); q) \leq 1,$$
$$t \geq n - \frac{n}{q+1} - \frac{n}{(q+1)^2} \quad \text{approximately} \quad \Rightarrow \quad c(B_{n,t}(q); q) \leq 2.$$

Perhaps there is a more general theorem.

To calculate the characteristic polynomials of $B_{n,t}(q)$, we need a formula for the number of lines $L$ disjoint from $B_{n,t}(q)$. This formula can be obtained using the methods in Section 6.4.

Let $[A_0, P]$ be the layout of a line $L$. Suppose every point on $L$ has weight exceeding $t$. Because a point $x - \alpha y$ on $L$ has zero coordinates exactly in the positions in $A_0 \cup A_\alpha$ and every point in $L$ has weight exceeding $t$,

$$n - |A_0| - |A_\alpha| \geq t + 1.$$

This motivates the following definition. A sequence $(a_0, a_1, a_2, \ldots, a_{q+1})$ of nonnegative integers is said to be a *t-partition* of the integer $n$ if
(1) $a_1 \geq a_2 \geq \ldots \geq a_{q+1} \geq 0$, and
(2) for every $i > 0$,

$$a_1 + a_2 + \ldots + a_{i-1} + a_{i+1} + \ldots + a_{q+1} = n - a_i - a_0 \geq t + 1.$$

The number of $t$-partitions of $n$ varies with $n$, $t$, and $q$. For example, when $n = 21$, $q = 3$, and $t = 14$, there are four $t$-partitions:

$$(1,5,5,5,5), (0,6,5,5,5), (0,6,6,5,4),\ \text{and}\ (0,6,6,6,3).$$

However, when $n = 22$, $q = 3$, and $t = 15$, there are only two:

$$(0,6,6,5,5)\ \text{and}\ (0,6,6,6,4).$$

When $n = b(q+1)$ and $t = n - b - 1 = bq - 1$, there is only one $t$-partition:

$$(0, b, b, \dots, b).$$

6.8. LEMMA. *Let $L$ be a line in $\mathrm{PG}(n-1, q)$. Then every point on the line $L$ has weight exceeding $t$ if and only if the layout of $L$ is a $t$-partition of $n$.*

In our earlier example, the size sequence of the layout is an 8-partition of 13. As predicted, the points $x$ and $y$ have weight 9. In addition, the other two points $x + y$ and $x - y$ on the line $x \vee y$ also have weight at least 9.

6.9. LEMMA. *The number of layouts which have a given sequence $(a_0, a_1, a_2, \dots, a_{q+1})$ as their size sequences equals*

$$\frac{1}{m_1! m_2! \cdots m_n!} \binom{n}{a_0, a_1, a_2, \dots, a_{q+1}},$$

*where $m_i$ is the multiplicity of the integer $i$ in the multiset $\{a_1, a_2, \dots, a_{q+1}\}$.*

Combining all our results and using the same notation, we obtain the following lemma.

6.10. LEMMA. *The number $l_{n,t}$ of lines in $\mathrm{PG}(n-1, q)$ all of whose points have weight exceeding $t$ equals*

$$\sum_{\underline{a}} \frac{1}{m_1! m_2! \cdots m_n!} \binom{n}{a_0, a_1, a_2, \dots, a_{q+1}} l[\underline{a}],$$

*where the sum ranges over all $t$-partitions of $n$.*

Using the previous lemmas and Crapo's identity 5.2, we obtain a formula for the characteristic polynomial of a rank-$n$ Dowling geometry with critical exponent $n - 2$.

6.11. COROLLARY. *Suppose the Dowling geometry $B_{n,t}(q)$ has critical exponent $n - 2$. Then*

$$\chi(B_{n,t}(q); \lambda) = [\lambda^2 - (q^{n-1} + q^{n-2} - P)\lambda + q^{2n-3} - Pq^{n-2} + l_{n,t}] \prod_{i=0}^{n-3} (\lambda - q^i).$$

*where*

$$P = [1 + q + q^2 + \dots + q^{n-1}] - b_{n,t,q}.$$

For coding theorists, the more interesting cases are when $t$ is small. A difficult problem is to find a formula, or, more realistically, an efficient algorithm, for calculating the characteristic polynomial of $B_{n,3}(q)$ and, more generally, the characteristic polynomial of $B_{n,t}(q)$ for "small" values of $t$.[33]

How Theorems 6.3, 6.6 and 6.7 fit into coding theory can be illustrated by giving two tables of critical exponents. The first is a table of the critical exponents $c$ of $B_{7,t}(2)$ :

$$t = 1, \ 2, \ 3, \ 4, \ 5, \ 6, \ 7$$
$$c = 1, \ 3, \ 4, \ 6, \ 6, \ 6, \ 7.$$

---

[33]The hope is that one can use matroid theory to do coding theory. However, one can cheat and use results in coding theory to do this problem. For example, when it is known that there is a unique isomorphism class of codes with parameters $(n, k, t+1)$, one should be able to compute the characteristic polynomial of $B_{n,t}(q)$ using this fact.

The values of $c$ for $t = 4, 5,$ and 6 are deduced from Theorems 6.3 and 6.6. The value of $c$ for $t = 3$ follows from the observation following Theorem 6.7. The value of $c$ for $t = 2$ is deduced from equation (6.1). The characteristic polynomials for $t = 3$ and 4 have been calculated explicitly by Bonin [15]:

$$\chi(B_{7,3}(2); \lambda) =$$
$$\lambda^7 - 63\lambda^6 + 1582\lambda^5 - 19810\lambda^4 + 128014\lambda^3 - 409612\lambda^2 + 584688\lambda - 284800$$

and

$$\chi(B_{7,4}(2); \lambda) =$$
$$\lambda^7 - 98\lambda^6 + 3507\lambda^5 - 56730\lambda^4 + 432264\lambda^3 - 1522752\lambda^2 + 2290688\lambda - 1146880.$$

The reader's computer can easily check that the expression for $\chi(B_{7,4}(2); \lambda)$ is the same as that given in Corollary 6.11.

Going to the case $n = 8$, we have the following table of critical exponents $c$ for $B_{8,t}(2)$ :

$$t = 2, 3, 4, 5, 6, 7, 8$$
$$c = 4, 4, 6, 7, 7, 7, 8.$$

For $t = 4$, the value of $c$ follows from Theorem 6.7. For $t = 5, 6,$ and 7, the value of $c$ follows from Theorem 6.3. For $t = 3$, the value of $c$ follows from from the existence of the extended Hamming $(8, 4)$-code. The value of $c$ for $t = 2$ is deduced from equation (6.1).

A detailed discussion of how the bounds in coding theory (known in 1971) apply to the problem of bounding $c$ given $n$, $t$ and $q$ can be found in Dowling [44]. (See also Brini [16].) Other applications of the theory of critical problems to coding theory can be found in Brylawski and Oxley [31], Section 6.5, and Greene [53]. Note that Proposition 4.14 gives a formula for the number of distinct linear codes with a given set of parameters in terms of the characteristic polynomial of $B_{n,t}(q)$. A related application can be found in Baker et al. [5].

Our calculations in Corollaries 6.4 and 6.11 depend on the fact that the geometries considered have high critical exponents. This idea can also be applied to the cocycle matroid $M^\perp(P_{10})$ of the Petersen graph $P_{10}$. Because $P_{10}$ has no nowhere-zero $k$-flows if $k \leq 4$ (see Tutte [188]), it follows from Theorem 4.6 that

$$\chi(M^\perp(P_{10}); \lambda) = (\lambda - 1)(\lambda - 2)(\lambda - 3)(\lambda - 4)(\lambda^2 - a\lambda + b).$$

Because $M^\perp(P_{10})$ has 15 points, equating coefficients of $\lambda^5$ yields $a = 5$. Next, observe that there are $\binom{15}{2} = 105$ independent sets of size 2 and exactly ten 3-point lines, the ten 3-element cutsets of edges incident on a vertex. Therefore, there are 75 2-point lines. Hence, the coefficient of $\lambda^4$ equals 95 and $b = 10$. We conclude[34] that

(6.2)          $$\chi(M^\perp(P_{10}); \lambda) = (\lambda - 1)(\lambda - 2)(\lambda - 3)(\lambda - 4)(\lambda^2 - 5\lambda + 10).$$

In particular, there are 240 nowhere-zero 5-flows on $P_{10}$.

---

[34]This result is in agreement with Welsh [149] and Brylawski and Oxley [31], p. 142. In these two papers, $\chi(M^\perp(P_{10}); \lambda)$ is calculated from first principles and the formula is then used to prove that $P_{10}$ has no 4-flows. An efficient way to calculate $\chi(M^\perp(P_{10}); \lambda)$ is to choose a 10-point copoint (by taking the complement of a length-5 cycle in the graph $P_{10}$) in $M^\perp(P_{10})$ and then use Oxley's identity 5.1 or Theorem 5.8.

# 7. Minor-closed classes of matroids

## 7.1. Basic definitions

A *class* $\mathcal{C}$ of geometries is a collection of geometries closed under isomorphisms, that is, if $G$ is isomorphic to $H$ and $G$ is in $\mathcal{C}$, then $H$ is in $\mathcal{C}$. A *class* $\mathcal{M}$ of matroids is a collection of matroids closed under simplifications, that is, the class $\mathcal{M}$ satisfies the condition: if $M$ and $N$ have isomorphic simplifications and $M$ is in $\mathcal{M}$, then $N$ is in $\mathcal{M}$.[35] A class $\mathcal{M}$ of matroids is determined by the subclass of geometries in it. For this reason, we can restrict our attention to classes of geometries.

A class $\mathcal{C}$ of geometries is said to be *closed under restrictions* or *subgeometries* if it satisfies the condition: if $G$ is a restriction of $H$ and $H \in \mathcal{C}$, then $G$ is in $\mathcal{C}$. A class $\mathcal{C}$ of geometries is said to be *minor-closed* if it satisfies the condition: if $G$ is isomorphic to a minor of $H$ and $H \in \mathcal{C}$, then $G$ is in $\mathcal{C}$.[36] Two important examples of minor-closed classes are the class $\mathcal{L}(q)$, the class of $GF(q)$-representable geometries, and $\mathcal{Z}(A)$, the class of gain-graphic geometries over the group $A$. One way to construct a minor-closed class is by *excluding* certain geometries as minors. More precisely, let $\{M_1, M_2, \dots\}$ be a collection of geometries. Then the class $\mathcal{EX}(M_1, M_2, \dots)$ of geometries containing none of the geometries $M_1, M_2, \dots$ as minors is a minor-closed class.

The class of all geometries forms a quasi-order (that is, a partial order in which antisymmetry may fail) under the order relation:

$$H \preceq G \text{ if } H \text{ is isomorphic to a minor of } G.$$

This quasi-order is called the *minor order* and it can be made into a partial order by identifying isomorphic geometries. If $\mathcal{C}$ is a class of *finite* geometries, then $\mathcal{C}$ has no infinite descending chains under the minor order. In particular, for any property of geometries, there exist geometries in $\mathcal{C}$ minimal in the minor order satisfying that property. Note also that a class of geometries is minor-closed if and only if it is an order ideal in the minor order.

The next lemma gives simple ways of constructing minor-closed classes. Analogous results hold for restriction-closed classes.

7.1. LEMMA.
(a) *An arbitrary union of minor-closed classes is minor-closed.*
(b) *An arbitrary intersection of minor-closed classes is minor-closed.*
(c) *Given a class $\mathcal{C}$, there is a unique minimal minor-closed class $\overline{\mathcal{C}}$ containing $\mathcal{C}$. The class $\overline{\mathcal{C}}$ is the intersection of all the minor-closed classes containing $\mathcal{C}$.*

By Lemma 7.1(a), for any given property of minor-closed classes, there is a unique *maximum* minor-closed class satisfying that property. This maximum class

---

[35] A *complication* of a geometry $G$ is a matroid $M$ whose simplification is isomorphic to $G$. Thus, a class of matroids is a collection closed under both simplifications and complications. Note that our definition of a class of matroids may not be standard.

[36] Readers familiar with the notion of a "variety" in universal algebra might want to add the condition that the class $\mathcal{C}$ be closed under direct sums. If $\mathcal{C}$ is a class, then the class $\mathrm{Dir}(\mathcal{C})$ is the class consisting of all geometries of the form $G_1 \oplus G_2 \oplus \dots \oplus G_n$, where $G_1, G_2, \dots, G_n$ are geometries in $\mathcal{C}$. If $\mathcal{C}$ is minor-closed, then $\mathrm{Dir}(\mathcal{C})$ is closed under minors and direct sums. Most of the conjectures considered in this paper hold or fail equally for $\mathcal{C}$ and $\mathrm{Dir}(\mathcal{C})$. The direct sum construction does not seem to be relevant for the critical problem. A case where the existence of direct sums is relevant is in the classification of varieties of finite geometries (Kahn and Kung [**67**]).

is obtained by taking the union of all the minor-closed classes satisfying that property. Similarly, maximum classes exist for properties of restriction-closed classes.

Let $\mathcal{C}$ be a class of geometries containing a geometry of rank $n$ for every non-negative integer $n$. The *size function* of $\mathcal{C}$ is the partial function $h(\mathcal{C}; n)$ on the non-negative integers defined by

$$h(\mathcal{C}; n) = \max\{|G| : \operatorname{rank}(G) = n \text{ and } G \in \mathcal{C}\},$$

whenever the maximum exists (and is finite). Here, $|G|$ is the number of points in the geometry $G$. A class $\mathcal{C}$ of geometries is said to have *linear growth* if there is a constant $a$ such that

$$h(\mathcal{C}; n) \leq an.$$

The *critical exponent* $c(\mathcal{C}; q)$ of a class $\mathcal{C}$ of geometries contained in $\mathcal{L}(q)$ is defined to be the maximum

$$\max\{c(G; q) : G \in \mathcal{C}\}$$

if this maximum exists (and is finite). The critical exponent $c(\mathcal{C}; q)$ is said to be *infinite* otherwise. The critical exponent $c(\mathcal{C}; A)$ of a class $\mathcal{C}$ of gain-graphic geometries contained in $\mathcal{Z}(A)$ is defined in an analogous manner. The basic question in the theory of critical problems over classes of geometries is:

*When and why does a class $\mathcal{C}$ of geometries have finite critical exponent?*

The possible answers to the basic question depend heavily on the structure of the class $\mathcal{C}$. For example, there is a simple answer when $\mathcal{C}$ is restriction-closed. A GF$(q)$-representable rank-$n$ geometry $G$ has critical exponent $c$ if and only if it is a subgeometry of PG$(n-1, q)\backslash X_{n-c}$, where $X_{n-c}$ is a subspace of dimension $n-c$. Hence, the restriction-closed class $\mathcal{R}(c; q)$ of all subgeometries of the geometries PG$(n-1, q)$, $0 \leq n \leq c$, and PG$(n-1, q)\backslash X_{n-c}$, $c \leq n < \infty$, is the maximum restriction-closed class of geometries in $\mathcal{L}(q)$ having critical exponent at most $c$. Put another way, a restriction-closed class $\mathcal{C}$ in $\mathcal{L}(q)$ has critical exponent $c$ or less if and only if it is contained in $\mathcal{R}(c; q)$. More about the relation between restriction-closed classes and critical exponents can be found in Section 3 of Kung [**81**].

Perhaps the most interesting case is the case of minor-closed classes. The two classical critical problems for graphs, the 4-color problem and the 5-flow problem, were stated for minor-closed classes of graphs. All the minor-closed classes known to have finite critical exponent have this property for one of two reasons: they have linear growth or they do not contain the cycle geometry $M(K_m)$ of the complete graph $K_m$ for some $m$. Most of the results and conjectures in Section 7 were motivated in part by this fact.

We end this preliminary section with some easy observations about the behaviour of critical exponents under matroid operations. If $G$ is representable over GF$(q)$ and $H$ is a subgeometry of $G$, then

(7.1) $$c(H; q) \leq c(G; q).$$

If $G$ and $H$ are representable over GF$(q)$, then

(7.2) $$c(G \oplus H; q) = \max\{c(G; q), c(H; q)\}.$$

Analogous results hold for critical exponents of gain-graphic geometries.

The critical exponent behaves unpredictably under contraction. For example, the affine geometry $\mathrm{AG}(n-1,q)$ has critical exponent 1 over $\mathrm{GF}(q)$, but every contraction by a point is isomorphic to $\mathrm{PG}(n-2,q)$ and has critical exponent $n-1$ over $\mathrm{GF}(q)$. The critical exponent also behaves unpredictably under weak maps or specializations. See Lucas [90] for some examples.

### 7.2. Jaeger's 8-flow theorem

In this section, we shall describe the original example of a general method to prove that the critical exponent of a class is finite. This example is Jaeger's proof of the 8-flow theorem.

As we have recounted in Section 4.2, Tutte conjectured that every graph with no isthmuses has a nowhere-zero 5-flow. This conjecture is equivalent to the conjecture that for a loopless cographic matroid $G$, $\chi(G;5) \neq 0$. Making the first significant progress on this conjecture, Jaeger proved in his 1979 paper [63] that $\chi(G;8) \neq 0$.

There are two steps in Jaeger's proof. The first step is to find the size function of the class $\mathcal{G}^{\perp}$ of cographic matroids.

7.2. LEMMA. *Let $G$ be a cographic geometry of rank $n$. Then*

$$|G| \leq 3n - 3.$$

To prove Lemma 7.2, let $G$ be a connected cographic geometry and let $G$ be the cocycle geometry of the graph $\Gamma$. Because $G$, and hence $\Gamma$, is connected, the cycle geometry $M(\Gamma)$ has rank $v-1$ and nullity $e-v+1$, where $v$ is the number of vertices and $e$ is the number of edges in $\Gamma$. Moreover, because the two edges incident on a vertex of degree 2 are parallel, every vertex of $\Gamma$ has degree at least 3, and hence, $3v \leq 2e$. From this, we conclude that

$$|G| \leq e \leq e + (2e - 3v) = 3(e - v + 1) - 3 = 3\mathrm{rank}(G) - 3.$$

The argument in the second part of this proof is due to Lindström. See Kung [74].

The second step is to use the matroid partition theorem (Edmonds [47] and Nash-Williams [96,97]) to partition $G$ into three subgeometries which are affine over $\mathrm{GF}(2)$.

7.3. THE MATROID PARTITION THEOREM. *The set $S$ of elements of the matroid $G$ can be partitioned into $k$ independent sets if and only if for every subset $A \subseteq S$,*

$$|A| \leq k\mathrm{rank}(A).$$

Because a restriction of a cographic geometry is cographic, the matroid partition theorem implies that every cographic geometry $G$ can be partitioned into 3 independent sets. Since independent sets are affine, we conclude that $G$ has critical exponent at most 3. This proves the following theorem.

7.4. JAEGER'S 8-FLOW THEOREM.

$$c(\mathcal{G}^{\perp};2) = 3.$$

It follows from Theorems 4.6 and 7.4 that for every graph $\Gamma$ with no isthmuses, $\chi(M^{\perp}(\Gamma);8) \neq 0$. Hence, $\Gamma$ has an 8-flow.

Jaeger's method can be used to prove the following technical lemma (Kung [75,81]; see also Oxley [105]).

7.5. LEMMA. *Let $C$ be a restriction-closed class of geometries in $\mathcal{L}(q)$ or $\mathcal{Z}(A)$. Suppose that there exists a positive integer $c$ such that for every geometry $G$ in $C$,*

$$|G| \leq \mathrm{crank}(G).$$

*Then, $c(C;q)$ or $c(C;A)$ is at most $c$.*

Because independent sets are the smallest possible affine subgeometries, the integer $c$ is very rarely a sharp bound. A difficult problem is to find sharper versions of Lemma 7.5.[37]

Another application of Lemma 7.5 is an 8-color theorem for planar graphs:

$$c(\mathcal{P}; 2) \leq 3,$$

where $\mathcal{P}$ is the class of planar graphic geometries. To prove this, replace Lemma 7.2 by Euler's inequality: if $G$ is the cycle matroid of a simple planar graph and $\mathrm{rank}(G) = n$, then $|G| \leq 3n - 3$.

There are other applications of Lemma 7.5. Most of these applications involve estimating the size function of minor-closed classes. The reader is referred to Kung [81] for a survey.

For restriction-closed classes, having linear growth is a sufficient condition for having finite critical exponent. However, it is not necessary. The class $\mathcal{A}(q)$ of all geometries which are affine over $\mathrm{GF}(q)$ has critical exponent 1 over $\mathrm{GF}(q)$, but $h(\mathcal{A}(q); n) = q^{n-1}$. However, all known examples of minor-closed classes having finite critical exponent also have linear growth. This led to the following conjecture (Kung [75,81]).

7.6. CONJECTURE. *Let $C$ be a minor-closed class of geometries in $\mathcal{L}(q)$. Then $c(C;q)$ is finite if and only if $C$ has linear growth.*

## 7.3. Excluding complete graphs

Because the cycle matroid $M(K_m)$ of the complete graph $K_m$ has critical exponent $\lceil \log_q m \rceil$ over $\mathrm{GF}(q)$, the class $\mathcal{G}$ of graphic geometries has infinite critical exponent over every finite field. Hence, if a class $C$ contains $\mathcal{G}$, its critical exponent cannot be finite. In particular, a minor-closed class $C$ with finite critical exponent cannot contain all the cycle matroids $M(K_m)$. This motivates the following conjecture.

7.7. CONJECTURE. *Let $C$ be a minor-closed class in $\mathcal{L}(q)$ not containing the cycle matroid $M(K_m)$. Then $C$ has finite critical exponent.*

Because the class $\mathcal{EX}(M(K_m)) \cap \mathcal{L}(q)$ is the maximum minor-closed class in $\mathcal{L}(q)$ not containing $M(K_m)$, Conjecture 7.7 is equivalent to:

7.8. CONJECTURE. *The class $\mathcal{EX}(M(K_m)) \cap \mathcal{L}(q)$ has finite critical exponent.*

Related to Conjecture 7.7 is the following conjecture which is the linear-quadratic portion of the growth rate conjecture. (For a complete account of the growth rate conjecture, see Kung [81].)

---

[37]Jaeger has posed two related problems. See Brylawski and Oxley [31], p. 208.

7.9. THE GROWTH RATE CONJECTURE. *Let $\mathcal{C}$ be a minor-closed class in $\mathcal{L}(q)$ not containing the cycle matroid $M(K_m)$. Then $\mathcal{C}$ has linear growth, that is, there exists a constant $a$ such that $h(\mathcal{C}; n) \leq an$.*

Because $M(K_m)$ is a geometry of rank $m-1$ having $\binom{m}{2}$ points, a class $\mathcal{C}$ with linear growth does not contain $M(K_m)$ for all sufficiently large $m$. Hence, the converse of Conjecture 7.9 holds.

When $\mathcal{C}$ is a minor-closed class, the three conjectures discussed so far are related in following way:

$$\text{linear growth} \quad \xleftarrow[\text{Growth rate conjecture}]{\hspace{3cm}} \quad \text{no } M(K_m)$$

$$\text{Conjecture 7.6} \diagdown \qquad\qquad \diagup \text{Conjecture 7.7}$$

$$\text{finite critical exponent}$$

where $\rightarrow$ indicates a conjectured implication. The converse of all the conjectured implications are proven implications. The growth rate conjecture is apparently the strongest conjecture, in the sense that its validity would imply the validity of the other two conjectures.

Several cases of Conjecture 7.8 have been proved. Because $M(K_3)$ is isomorphic to the 3-point line $U_{2,3}$, $\mathcal{EX}(M(K_3))$ is the class $\mathcal{U}(1)$ of free geometries. Hence,

$$c(\mathcal{EX}(M(K_3)); q) = 1.$$

It is also known that

$$c(\mathcal{EX}(M(K_4)) \cap \mathcal{L}(2); 2) = 2$$

and

(7.3)                $$c(\mathcal{EX}(M(K_4)) \cap \mathcal{L}(3); 3) = 2.$$

The first of these results is due essentially to Dirac, who proved in [41] the stronger theorem that graphs with no $M(K_4)$-minors have chromatic number not exceeding 3. Brylawski [18] gave a proof using characteristic polynomials and Kung [75] gave a proof using another theorem in Dirac [41] and Lemma 7.5. The second result was obtained by Oxley [105] using a decomposition theorem for ternary matroids with no $M(K_4)$-minor. It would be interesting to have a more direct proof of Oxley's result. For higher values of $q$, the following bounds are known (Kung [78]):

$$2 \leq c(\mathcal{EX}(M(K_4)) \cap \mathcal{L}(q); q) < 6q^3.$$

When $m = 5$, the only value of $q$ for which a bound is known is 2 (Kung [77]):

(7.4)                $$3 \leq c(\mathcal{EX}(M(K_5)) \cap \mathcal{L}(2); 2) \leq 8.$$

This bound is obtained from the following bound for the size function:

$$h(\mathcal{EX}(M(K_5)) \cap \mathcal{L}(2); 2) \leq 8n.$$

Walton and Welsh [143] have posed the question of deciding whether the critical exponent $c(\mathcal{EX}(M(K_5)) \cap \mathcal{L}(2); 2)$ equals 3.

There is a stronger, but still plausible, version of Conjecture 7.8.

7.10. CONJECTURE. *There exists an integer constant $\psi(m)$ depending only on m such that for all prime powers $q$,*

$$c(\mathcal{EX}(M(K_m)) \cap \mathcal{L}(q); q) \le \psi(m).$$

Brylawski [21] has conjectured that

$$c(\mathcal{EX}(M(K_4)) \cap \mathcal{L}(q); q) = 2.$$

This conjecture was verified for the smaller restriction-closed class $\mathcal{TR}$ of transversal geometries. Whittle proved in [155] that

$$c(\mathcal{TR} \cap \mathcal{L}(q); q) = 2$$

for every prime power $q$. Whittle [156] has conjectured the following extension of Brylawski's conjecture:

$$c(\mathcal{EX}(M(K_m)) \cap \mathcal{L}(q); q) = m - 2.$$

Because the rank-$(m-2)$ projective geometry $\mathrm{PG}(m-3, q)$ does not contain an $M(K_m)$-minor and has critical exponent $m-2$, the constant $\psi(m)$ is at least $m-2$.

### 7.4. Critical exponents of classes of gain-graphic geometries

Conjecture 7.10 can be regarded as a matroid analogue of a weaker form of *Hadwiger's conjecture*:

*The chromatic number of a graph with no $K_m$-minor (or subcontraction) is at most $m - 1$.*

Wagner proved in [141] that:

*When $m \ge 4$, the chromatic number of a graph with no $K_m$-minor is strictly less than $2^{m-2}$.*

Hence, if $\mathcal{G}$ is the class of graphic geometries,

$$c(\mathcal{EX}(M(K_m)) \cap \mathcal{G}; 2) \le m - 2.$$

Wagner's elegant argument is worth repeating here.[38] We proceed by induction on $m$, basing the induction on the known result of Dirac [41] that a graph with no $K_4$-minor has chromatic number at most 3. Let $\Gamma$ be a graph with chromatic number at least $2^{m-2}$. Taking a connected component if necessary, we can assume that $\Gamma$ is connected. Choose a vertex $v_0$ of $\Gamma$. Let $V_i$ be the vertices at graphical distance $i$ from $V_i$, and let

$$V_{odd} = \bigcup_{i: i \text{ odd}} V_i \quad \text{and} \quad V_{even} = \bigcup_{i: i \text{ even}} V_i.$$

Consider the subgraph $\Gamma_i$ induced by the vertex set $V_i$. If every such subgraph has chromatic number $2^{m-3} - 1$ or less, then $\Gamma$ can be colored with $2^{m-2} - 2$ colors

---

[38]Wagner's argument in [141] is more careful than the one given here. Using Wagner's argument and a more sophisticated theorem (such as the 4-color theorem) for the base of the induction, one can improve the upper bound. This improvement yields upper bounds having the same order of magnitude as the bounds given here. See Wagner's original paper [141] or the English version in Ore [98]. The argument given here is similar to that given by Thomassen in [128]. Thomassen observed that Wagner's argument yields a stronger theorem: the chromatic number of a graph with no series minor isomorphic to $K_m$ is strictly less than $2^{m-2}$. This suggests a strengthening of Conjecture 7.10 in which "minor" is replaced by "series minor".

in the following way. Partition the available colors into two disjoint subsets, each containing $2^{m-3} - 1$ colors. Using one of these subsets, color the vertices in $V_{odd}$ so that every subgraph $\Gamma_i$, where $i$ is odd, is properly colored. Using the other subset, properly color the subgraphs $\Gamma_i$, where $i$ is even. Because the distance between two vertices in different subsets $V_i$ and $V_j$, where $i$ and $j$ have the same parity, is at least 2, they cannot be adjacent in $\Gamma$. Hence, this coloring is a proper coloring of $\Gamma$. We conclude that if $\Gamma$ has chromatic number at least $2^{m-2}$, then at least one of the subgraphs, $\Gamma_j$, say, has chromatic number at least $2^{m-3}$. By induction, $\Gamma_j$ contains a $K_{m-1}$-minor. To finish the proof, we use the fact that every vertex of $\Gamma_j$ is joined by a path to $v_0$. Contracting the paths, we obtain a $K_m$-minor in $\Gamma$.

In the remainder of Section 7.4, we shall prove an analogue of Wagner's theorem for gain-graphic geometries. The technical tool needed to do this is contained in the following lemma.

7.11.  LEMMA. *Let $G(S)$ be a subgeometry of the Dowling group geometry $Q_d(A)$, let $\hat{S}$ be the subset of internal points in $S$ of the form $1_{ij}$, where $1$ is the identity in the gain group $A$, and let $\Xi$ be the graph on the vertex set $\{1, 2, \ldots, d\}$ with $\{i, j\}$ an edge whenever $1_{ij}$ is in $\hat{S}$. Then*

$$\lceil \log_{|A|+1} k \rceil \le c(G; A) \le \lceil \log_{|A|+1} k \rceil + 1,$$

*where $k$ is the chromatic number of the graph $\Xi$.*

PROOF. Let $\alpha$ be the abstract linear functional $(1, 1, \ldots, 1)$ all of whose co-ordinates are equal to the identity 1 of $A$. Then $\alpha$ is non-zero on any joint $p_i$ and any internal point $\omega_{ij}$, where $\omega$ is a group element not equal to the identity. Hence, $\alpha$ distinguishes all the points in $S \backslash \hat{S}$. To distinguish the remaining points, observe that the restriction $G|\hat{S}$ is isomorphic to the cycle geometry $M(\Xi)$. Let $k$ be the chromatic number of $\Xi$. Then $\chi(M(\Xi); k') \ne 0$ for every integer $k' \ge k$. In particular, $\chi(M(\Xi); (|A| + 1)^m) \ne 0$, where $m = \lceil \log_{|A|+1} k \rceil$. By Lemma 4.17, there exists an $m$-tuple of abstract linear functionals distinguishing $G|\hat{S}$. Adding $\alpha$ to this $m$-tuple, we obtain an $(m+1)$-tuple of abstract linear functionals distinguishing $G$. We conclude that $c(G; A) \le m + 1$. On the other hand, $c(G|\hat{S}; A) \le c(G; A)$. Since $c(G|\hat{S}; A)$ equals $m$, we conclude that $m \le c(G; A)$.                             □

Using Lemma 7.11, we obtain the following theorem.

7.12.  THEOREM. *Let $\mathcal{C}$ be a minor-closed class in $\mathcal{Z}(A)$ not containing the cycle geometry $M(K_m)$. Then*

$$c(\mathcal{C}; A) \le 1 + \lceil \log_{|A|+1} t \rceil,$$

*where $t$ is a number such that every graph with no $K_m$-minor has chromatic number at most $t$.*

The value $t$ obtained from Wagner's theorem is $2^{m-2} - 1$. Since

$$\lceil \log_{|A|+1}(2^{m-2} - 1) \rceil = \left\lceil \frac{\log_2(2^{m-2} - 1)}{\log_2(|A| + 1)} \right\rceil \le m - 2,$$

we have proved the following analogue of Conjecture 7.10 for gain-graphic geometries:

$$c(\mathcal{EX}(M(K_m)) \cap \mathcal{Z}(A); A) \le m - 1.$$

The upper bound of $m-1$ is far from sharp when the gain group $A$ is given. For example, for a given positive integer $m$ greater than 3,

$$c(\mathcal{EX}(M(K_m)) \cap \mathcal{Z}(A); A) = 2$$

for all groups $A$ such that $|A| \geq 2^{m-2} - 2$. (Equality holds because the $(|A|+1)$-point line does not contain an $M(K_m)$-minor and has critical exponent 2 over $A$.) In particular,

$$c(\mathcal{EX}(M(K_4)) \cap \mathcal{Z}(A); A) = 2$$

if $|A| \geq 2$. This bound also holds when $|A| = 1$ by Dirac's theorem [41]. Therefore, this upper bound holds for all groups $A$ and we have proved the analogue of Brylawski's conjecture for gain-graphic geometries.

A problem for further research is whether there is a useful modification of Wagner's argument (given earlier in this section) for matroids. This modification would complement the matroid partition argument described in Section 7.2.

### 7.5. Growth rates of classes of gain-graphic geometries

The growth rate conjecture 7.9 is true for the class of graphic geometries. This follows from Mader's theorem [92] in extremal graph theory:[39]

> If a graph $\Gamma$ with $v$ vertices contains at least $2^{t-3}v$ edges, then $\Gamma$ contains a $K_t$-minor.

In this section, we shall prove an analogue of Mader's theorem for gain-graphic geometries. To avoid technicalities, we shall not be overly concerned with getting the smallest possible constants.

Theorems from extremal graph theory yield analogous theorems about gain-graphic geometries because internal points in the Dowling group geometry $Q_d(A)$ behave as if they were edges of a graph. Let $P$ be the set $\{p_1, p_2, \ldots, p_d\}$ of joints of $Q_d(A)$ and let $a$ be an internal point on the "coordinate" line $p_i \vee p_j$. Then the geometry $Q_d(A)/a$ obtained by contracting $a$ can be identified with the rank-$(d-1)$ Dowling group geometry $Q_{d-1}(A)$ on the set of joints $(P \backslash \{p_i, p_j\}) \cup \{p\}$, where $p$ is the joint obtained from identifying the joints $p_i$ and $p_j$. If $S$ is a set of internal points in $Q_d(A)$, then, as in graph theory, the elements in $S$ not on the line $p_i \vee p_j$ is a multiset of internal points in $Q_{d-1}(A)$. Removing those points in $S$ which are on the line $p_i \vee p_j$ and all but one element from every parallel class, we obtain a set of internal points in $Q_{d-1}(A)$ called the *image of $S$ under contraction by $a$*.

Let $S$ be a set of internal points of $Q_d(A)$. The graph $\Gamma(S)$ associated with $S$ is the (ordinary) graph on the vertex set $\{p_1, p_2, \ldots, p_d\}$ of joints with $\{p_i, p_j\}$ an edge if and only if there exists an internal point in $S$ on the line $p_i \vee p_j$. Suppose that a graph $\Delta$ can be obtained from the associated graph $\Gamma(S)$ by a sequence of contractions and deletions. Then if we ignore the deletions and if we replace a graphical contraction by the edge $\{p_i, p_j\}$ in $\Gamma(S)$ with a matroidal contraction by an internal point $a$ in $S$ in $p_i \vee p_j$, then we obtain a contraction $Q_{d'}(A)$. In $Q_{d'}(A)$, the image of $S'$ under the sequence of contractions is a set of internal points such that the associated graph $\Gamma(S')$ contains $\Delta$ as a subgraph.

Next, suppose that the associated graph $\Gamma(S)$ is connected. Choose a spanning tree in $\Gamma$ and let $T \subseteq S$ be a subset formed by choosing exactly one internal point in $S$ from the line $p_i \vee p_j$ for each edge $\{p_i, p_j\}$ in the spanning tree. It is easy to

---

[39]See Kung [81], p. 22, for an expository account.

check that $T$ is an independent set, and hence, $|T| \leq \mathrm{rank}(S)$. Let $p$ be any joint in $P$. Then the closure $\overline{T \cup \{p\}}$ in $Q_d(A)$ contains $P$, and hence, $S$. We conclude that

$$(7.5) \qquad\qquad |P| - 1 = |T| \leq \mathrm{rank}(S) \leq |P|.$$

A set $S$ of internal points in $Q_t(A)$ is said to be a *mock (complete graph)* $K_t$ if its associated graph $\Gamma(S)$ is the complete graph $K_t$, that is, if for every pair of joints $p$ and $p'$ in $Q_t(A)$, there exists an internal point in $S$ on the line $p \vee p'$. From a sufficiently large mock complete graph, one can produce, by contraction, a "real" complete graph.

7.13. LEMMA. *Let*

$$t \geq \binom{m-1}{2}(|A| - 1) + m.$$

*Then a mock $K_t$ contains a minor isomorphic to $M(K_m)$.*

PROOF. Let $S$ be a mock $K_t$ in $Q_t(A)$ and let $C \mapsto \overline{C}$ be the closure operator in $Q_t(A)$. Choose a set, $\{p_1, p_2, \ldots, p_{m-1}\}$, say, of $m-1$ joints. A joint $p$ not equal to $p_1, p_2, \ldots, p_{m-1}$ satisfies the *f-property* if for every pair of points $a \in p \vee p_i$ and $b \in p \vee p_j$ in $S$ on distinct coordinate lines, the third point on the 3-point line $a \vee b$ (which lies on the coordinate line $p_i \vee p_j$) is also in $S$.

We shall construct an $M(K_m)$-minor of the restriction $Q_t(A)|S$ by contracting internal points onto the lines $p_i \vee p_j, 1 \leq i < j \leq m-1$ using the following procedure:

> Choose a joint $p$ not equal to $p_1, p_2, \ldots, p_{m-1}$. If $p$ satisfies the f-property, stop. Otherwise there exists a pair of points $a \in p \vee p_i$ and $b \in p \vee p_j$ such that the line $a \vee b$ does not meet $p_i \vee p_j$. Project an extra internal point, the image of $b$, onto $p_i \vee p_j$ by contracting the point $a$. Let $S'$ be the image of $S$ under contraction by $a$. Repeat this procedure with the set $S'$ of internal points in the contraction $Q_t(A)/a$. (Note that $Q_t(A)/a$ is isomorphic to $Q_{t-1}(A)$ and the image $S'$ is a mock $K_{t-1}$ in $Q_t(A)/a$.)

Because there are $\binom{m-1}{2}$ coordinate lines of the form $p_i \vee p_j, 1 \leq i < j \leq m-1$, and such a line contains at most $|A|$ internal points, one can project at most

$$\binom{m-1}{2}(|A| - 1)$$

additional internal points onto the lines $p_i \vee p_j, 1 \leq i < j \leq m-1$. Hence, at some stage in the procedure, we stop and obtain a contraction $Q_{t'}(A)$ of $Q_t(A)$ by a subset of points in $S$ satisfying the following conditions:

(1)  $t' \geq m$, and
(2)  there exists a joint $p$ in $Q_{t'}(A)$ not equal to $p_1, p_2, \ldots, p_{m-1}$ satisfying the f-property.

Let $p$ be a joint not equal to $p_1, p_2, \ldots, p_{m-1}$ satisfying the f-property. The internal points on the lines $p_i \vee p, 1 \leq i \leq m-1$, form a set of rank at least $m-1$. Hence, by the argument in the proof of Lemma 5.14, the restriction $Q_{d'}(A)|S'$ contains a subgeometry isomorphic to $M(K_m)$. $\qquad\square$

Note that in the proof of Lemma 7.13, we need only a set $S$ of internal points whose associated graph $\Gamma(S)$ consists of a $K_{m-1}$-subgraph together with $\binom{m-1}{2}(|A|-1)+1$ new vertices and all possible edges between every vertex in the $K_{m-1}$-subgraph and every new vertex.

7.14. THEOREM. *Let* $t = \binom{m-1}{2}(|A| - 1) + m$. *Then*

$$h(\mathcal{E}\mathcal{X}(M(K_m)) \cap \mathcal{Z}(A); n) < (2^{t-2}|A| + 1)n.$$

PROOF. Let $G(S)$ be a rank-$n$ geometry in $\mathcal{Z}(A)$ represented as a subset $S$ of points in the Dowling group geometry $Q_d(A)$. Suppose that

$$|S| \geq (2^{t-2}|A| + 1)n.$$

Because the set of joints is independent, $S$ contains at most $n$ joints. Hence, the set $S'$ of internal points in $S$ contains at least $2^{t-2}|A|\mathrm{rank}(S')$ points. Consider the graph $\Gamma(S')$ associated with $S'$. Let $\Delta$ be a connected component of the graph $\Gamma(S')$. Let $T$ be the maximum of all the subsets $T'$ in $S'$ such that the associated graph $\Gamma(T')$ equals $\Delta$. It is easy to check that $T$ is a separator of the restriction $G|S'$. Because the lower bound $2^{t-2}|A|\mathrm{rank}(S')$ is linear in the rank, there is at least one maximum subset $T$ such that $|T| \geq 2^{t-2}|A|\mathrm{rank}(T)$. Thus, we can assume that the associated graph $\Gamma(S')$ is connected and that

$$|S'| \geq 2^{t-2}|A|\mathrm{rank}(S').$$

Because a coordinate line contains at most $|A|$ internal points, there are at least $2^{t-2}\mathrm{rank}(S')$ edges in the graph $\Gamma(S')$. Let $P$ be the set of vertices in the graph $\Gamma(S')$. By inequality (7.5),

$$2^{t-2}\mathrm{rank}(S') \geq 2^{t-3}(\mathrm{rank}(S') + 1) \geq 2^{t-3}|P|.$$

Hence, the number of edges in $\Gamma(S')$ is at least $2^{t-3}|P|$. We conclude, by Mader's theorem, that $\Gamma(S')$ contains a $K_t$-subcontraction. Hence, $S$ contains a minor which is a mock $K_t$, and, by Lemma 7.13, $G$ contains an $M(K_m)$-minor. $\square$

### 7.6. $\alpha$-graphs

We end Section 7 with a result for representable geometries inspired by the proof of Lemma 7.11.

Let $G(S)$ be a geometry representable over $\mathrm{GF}(q)$, let $M$ be a $d \times |S|$ representation matrix of $G$ over $\mathrm{GF}(q)$, and let $\alpha = (\alpha_1, \alpha_2, \ldots, \alpha_d)$ be a $d$-tuple of non-zero elements from $\mathrm{GF}(q)$. Let $x = (x_1, x_2, \ldots, x_d)^T$ be a column vector in $M$. The vector $x$ is said to be $\alpha$-*even* if the inner product or weighted sum

$$\langle \alpha, x \rangle = \sum_{i=1}^{d} \alpha_i x_i = \alpha_1 x_1 + \alpha_2 x_2 + \ldots + \alpha_d x_d$$

equals zero. Recall that the *support* of the vector $x$ is the subset $\{i : x_i \neq 0\}$ of row indices $i$ for which the $i$th coordinate $x_i$ of $x$ is non-zero. The $\alpha$-*graph* $\Xi(M, \alpha)$ of the representation matrix $M$ of $G$ is the (simple) graph on the vertex set $\{1, 2, \ldots, d\}$ of row indices with $\{i, j\}$ an edge whenever there exists an $\alpha$-even column vector $x$ in $M$ such that both $i$ and $j$ are in the support of $x$.

7.15. PROPOSITION. *Let* $M$ *be a* $d \times |S|$ *representation matrix over* $\mathrm{GF}(q)$ *of the geometry* $G(S)$ *and let* $\alpha = (\alpha_1, \alpha_2, \ldots, \alpha_d)$ *be a* $d$-*tuple of non-zero elements of* $\mathrm{GF}(q)$. *Then*

(7.6)                                     $c(G; q) \leq k,$

*where $k$ is the chromatic number of the $\alpha$-graph $\Xi(M, \alpha)$.*

PROOF. Let $P_1, P_2, \ldots, P_k$ be a partition of the vertex set $\{1, 2, \ldots, d\}$ of the $\alpha$-graph $\Xi(M, \alpha)$ into stable subsets. We shall construct a $k$-tuple of linear functionals over $\mathrm{GF}(q)$ distinguishing $G$ in the following way. For each stable subset $P_t$, let

$$L_t = \sum_{i: i \in P_t} \alpha_i E_i,$$

where $E_i$ is the standard dual basis vector sending a column vector $x$ to its $i$th-coordinate. Suppose that $x$ is an $\alpha$-even column vector in $M$. Then, the support of $x$ intersects a stable subset at most one vertex. Let $P_t$ be a stable subset such that $\mathrm{supp}(x) \cap P_t = \{i\}$. Then $L_t(x) = \alpha_i x_i \neq 0$. From this, we conclude that the $k$-tuple of linear functionals $(L_1, L_2, \ldots, L_k)$ distinguishes the $\alpha$-even vectors in $M$. This $k$-tuple also distinguish the vectors which are not $\alpha$-even. To see this, suppose that $x = (x_1, x_2, \ldots, x_d)^T$ is a column vector which is not $\alpha$-even. Then, because the subsets $P_i$ partition $\{1, 2, \ldots, d\}$ and $x$ is not even,

$$L_1(x) + L_2(x) + \ldots + L_k(x) = \sum_{i=1}^{d} \alpha_i E_i(x) = \sum_{i=1}^{d} \alpha_i x_i \neq 0.$$

Hence, one of the function values $L_j(x)$ is non-zero.[40]                             $\square$

Rather surprisingly, the inequality is sharp. Let $M$ be an $n \times (q^n - 1)/(q - 1)$ representation matrix of the projective geometry $\mathrm{PG}(n - 1, q)$ and let $\alpha$ be the $n$-tuple $(1, 1, \ldots, 1)$ with all coordinates equal to 1. Then, the $\alpha$-graph $\Xi(M, \alpha)$ is the complete graph $K_n$. Because the critical exponent of $\mathrm{PG}(n - 1, q)$ over $\mathrm{GF}(q)$ is $n$ and the chromatic number of $K_n$ is also $n$, inequality (7.6) is sharp for this example.

Over the field $\mathrm{GF}(2)$, there is exactly one $d$-tuple of non-zero elements, the $d$-tuple $\alpha = (1, 1, \ldots, 1)$. In this case, a column vector $x$ is $\alpha$-even if and only if it has even Hamming weight.[41] Note that if we represent the cycle geometry $M(\Gamma)$ of a graph $\Gamma$ by the oriented vertex-edge incidence matrix $I$ of $\Gamma$ over any finite field, then the $\alpha$-graph $\Xi(I, \alpha)$ is simply the original graph $\Gamma$. Hence, Proposition 7.15 yields the obvious inequality: for every prime power $q$, the critical exponent $c(M(\Gamma); q)$ of the cycle matroid $M(\Gamma)$ over $\mathrm{GF}(q)$ is bounded above by the chromatic number of $\Gamma$.

We can also define $\alpha$-graphs for subgeometries of Dowling group geometries. However, because the bounds given in Lemma 7.11 are almost tight, $\alpha$-graphs are probably not very useful.

---

[40] Another way to look at Proposition 7.15 is to consider the hypergraph $\hat{\Xi}(M, \alpha)$ on the vertex set $\{1, 2, \ldots, d\}$ with hyperedges those subsets $e$ such that $e$ is the support of an $\alpha$-even vector and $|e| \geq 2$. From this point of view, a proper coloring of the graph $\Xi(M, \alpha)$ is a strong coloring of hypergraph $\hat{\Xi}(M, \alpha)$. The proof of Proposition 7.15 requires a strong coloring and not just a coloring of $\hat{\Xi}(M, \alpha)$. One can easily construct an example to show that Proposition 7.15 is false if $k$ is replaced by the chromatic number of the hypergraph $\hat{\Xi}(M, \alpha)$. For a brief account of hypergraph coloring, see Section 4.3.

[41] The definition of Hamming weight can be found in Section 6.1.

## 8. The theory of blocks

In the last section of this paper, we shall give an account of the theory of blocks. Section 8.1 contains the basic definitions and properties of the three kinds of blocks, "plain", minimal, and tangential. Results about minimal blocks can be found in Sections 8.2 and 8.4. The rest of the material is about tangential blocks. Some of the deepest problems in the study of the critical problem are about tangential blocks. *Non senza fatiga si giunge a fine.*

### 8.1. Blocks

In his 1966 paper [**136**], Tutte[42] formulated a critical problem for geometries represented over GF(2). He also introduced the useful terminology of blocks. Blocks can be defined over $\mathcal{L}(q)$, the class of geometries representable over GF($q$), and $\mathcal{Z}(A)$, the class of gain-graphic geometries with gains in the finite group $A$. The general theory is more or less the same. For simplicity, we shall state our results in $\mathcal{L}(q)$ in the main account, reserving the material on $\mathcal{Z}(A)$ for Section 8.11.

Let $k$ be a positive integer. A geometry $M$ in $\mathcal{L}(q)$ is said to be a *$k$-block over* GF($q$) if $M$ has critical exponent strictly greater than $k$ over GF($q$). Note that a $k$-block has rank at least $k + 1$. In addition, if $k' \leq k$, then a $k$-block is also a $k'$-block. A geometry $M$ in $\mathcal{L}(q)$ is a *minimal $k$-block over* GF($q$) if

(MB1)  $M$ has critical exponent strictly greater than $k$, and
(MB2)  every proper subgeometry of $M$ has critical exponent less than or equal to $k$.

Thus, $M$ is a restriction-minimal $k$-block in $\mathcal{L}(q)$. A geometry $M$ in $\mathcal{L}(q)$ is a *tangential $k$-block over* GF($q$) if

(TB1)  $M$ has critical exponent strictly greater than $k$, and
(TB2)  every proper minor of $M$ has critical exponent less than or equal to $k$.

Thus, a tangential $k$-block is a minor-minimal $k$-block in $\mathcal{L}(q)$. Note that a tangential $k$-block over GF($q$) is a minimal $k$-block over GF($q$).

The following lemma can be easily proved using equivalence (4.2) in Section 4.1. One of its consequences is that *in principle,* it suffices to study only 1-blocks.

8.1. LEMMA. *A $kk'$-block over* GF($q$) *is a $k'$-block over* GF($q^k$). *If a $k'$-block over* GF($q^k$) *is representable over* GF($q$), *then it is a $kk'$-block over* GF($q$). *In particular, a $k$-block over* GF($q$) *is a 1-block over* GF($q^k$). *These results hold for minimal and tangential blocks.*

Tutte's original definition of the three kinds of blocks over GF(2) is in terms of intersection conditions on a specific representation of a binary geometry. Combining Tutte's definition with Theorem 4.1, we obtain the following characterizations.

8.2. LEMMA. *Let $k$ be a positive integer and let $M(S)$ be a rank-$n$ geometry in $\mathcal{L}(q)$.*

*(a) The geometry $M$ is a $k$-block over* GF($q$) *if and only if for any representation of $M$ as a set $S$ of points in the projective space* PG($d - 1, q$), $S$ *intersects every subspace of codimension $k$ in* PG($d - 1, q$).

---

[42]See also Tutte [**138**].

*(b) The geometry $M$ is a minimal $k$-block over $\mathrm{GF}(q)$ if and only if $M$ is a $k$-block and the following condition holds for any representation of $M$ as a set $S$ of points in $\mathrm{PG}(d-1,q)$ :*

> *for every point $x \in S$, there exists a codimension-$k$ subspace $U$ in $\mathrm{PG}(d-1,q)$ such that $U \cap S = \{x\}$.*

*(c) The geometry $M$ is a tangential $k$-block if and only if $M$ is a $k$-block and the following condition holds for any representation of $M$ as a set $S$ of points in $\mathrm{PG}(d-1,q)$ :*

> *for every non-empty flat $X$ of $M$ having rank $n - k$ or less, there exists a codimension-$k$ subspace $U$ in $\mathrm{PG}(d-1,q)$ such that $U \cap S = X$.*

Let $M$ be a geometry represented as a set of points in $\mathrm{PG}(d-1,q)$ and let $X$ be a flat of $G$. A *tangent* of the flat $X$ is a subspace $U$ of $\mathrm{PG}(d-1,q)$ such that $U \cap S = X$. If $U$ is a tangent of $X$, we shall also say that $U$ is *tangent to the flat* $X$. In this terminology, a subset $S$ of points in $\mathrm{PG}(d-1,q)$ is the representation of a tangential $k$-block $M$ if and only if $S$ intersects every subspace of codimension $k$ and every non-empty flat of $M$ of rank $n - k$ or less has a codimension-$k$ tangent.

Similarly, if a minimal $k$-block $M$ is represented as a set $S$ of points in $\mathrm{PG}(d-1,q)$, then every point $x$ has a tangent $U$ of codimension $k$. In particular, in the contraction $\mathrm{PG}(d-1,q)/x$, the subspace $U/x$ of codimension $k$ is disjoint from the image $\{y \vee x : y \in S \backslash \{x\}\}$ of the set $S \backslash \{x\}$ under contraction by $x$. Hence, the geometry $M/x$ has critical exponent at most $k$. Conversely, if $M/x$ has critical exponent at most $k$, then we can reverse the argument to obtain a tangent of codimension $k$ for the point $x$. We conclude[43] that condition (MB2) in the definition of a minimal $k$-block can be replaced with the condition:

(MB2′)  for every point $x$ of $M$, the contraction $M/x$ has critical exponent less than or equal to $k$.

By a similar argument, condition (TB2) in the definition of a tangential $k$-block can be replaced by the apparently weaker condition:

(TB2′)  for every non-empty flat $X$ of $M$, the contraction $M/X$ has critical exponent less than or equal to $k$.

We remark that by Theorem 4.1, a $\mathrm{GF}(q)$-representable geometry $M(S)$ is a minimal $k$-block over $\mathrm{GF}(q)$ if and only if $\chi(M; q^k) = 0$ and $\chi(M/x; q^k) \neq 0$ for every point $x$ of $M$. By the same theorem, the geometry $M(S)$ is a tangential $k$-block over $\mathrm{GF}(q)$ if and only if $\chi(M; q^k) = 0$ and $\chi(M/X; q^k) \neq 0$ for any non-empty flat $X$ of $M$. If the geometry $M$ is represented as a set of points in $\mathrm{PG}(d-1,q)$, then a flat $X$ has a tangent of codimension $k$ in $\mathrm{PG}(d-1,q)$ if and only if $\chi(M/X; q^k) \neq 0$. This follows from Lemma 4.2(b). The number of codimension-$k$ tangents of a flat $X$ in the geometry $M$ can be expressed in terms of $d$ and the characteristic polynomial $\chi(M/X; \lambda)$ using Proposition 4.14. In particular, this number does not depend on the representation.

Tutte's description of blocks gives a geometric visualization of minimal and tangential blocks. It also makes clear several consequences of the definitions.

8.3. LEMMA.

---

[43]For a related result, see Asano *et al.* [**3**].

*(a) A geometry $M(S)$ is a $k$-block if and only if it contains a subgeometry which is a minimal $k$-block.*

*(b) If a geometry $M(S)$ is a $k$-block, then it contains a minor which is a tangential $k$-block.*

Part (a) of Lemma 8.3 follows immediately from equation (7.1). The proof of part (b) is an easy induction. Let $\operatorname{rank}(M) = n$. If every non-empty flat of rank at most $n - k$ in $M(S)$ has a tangent of codimension $k$, then $M(S)$ is a tangential $k$-block. Otherwise, let $X$ be a non-empty flat of rank at most $n - k$ with no tangent. Then the contraction $M/X$ is a $k$-block of smaller rank, and, by induction, contains a minor which is a tangential $k$-block.

The next lemma, due to Tutte [136], is also easy to prove geometrically. It is useful for inductive proofs.

8.4. LEMMA. *Let $M(S)$ be a $k$-block represented as a set $S$ of points in $\mathrm{PG}(d-1, q)$ and let $k'$ be a positive integer strictly less than $k$. Then the intersection $U \cap S$ of any codimension-$k'$ subspace $U$ with $S$ is a $(k - k')$-block. In particular,*

*(a) if $X$ is a copoint of $M$, then the restriction $M|X$ is a $(k - 1)$-block, and*

*(b) if $U$ is a subspace of codimension $k - 1$, then $U \cap S$ is a $1$-block.*

PROOF. Let $U$ be a subspace of codimension $k'$. Then every subspace $W$ of codimension $k - k'$ relative to $U$ is a subspace of codimension $k$ in $\mathrm{PG}(d - 1, q)$. Hence, $W \cap S \neq \emptyset$. Because $W \cap S \subseteq U \cap S$, the subset $U \cap S$ intersects every subspace contained in $U$ having codimension $k - k'$ relative to $U$. Therefore, $U \cap S$ is a $(k - k')$-block. $\qquad \square$

Lemma 8.4 clears up the following point in the definition of a minimal $k$-block. If $M$ is a minimal $k$-block, then $M$ cannot be a $(k + 1)$-block; otherwise, by Lemma 8.4, a copoint $X$ of $M$ would be a $k$-block, contradicting minimality. Hence, a minimal $k$-block has critical exponent exactly $k + 1$.

Because critical exponents could increase arbitrarily under contractions (see Section 7.1), the converse of part (b) of Lemma 8.3 is false. However, erratic behavior can occur only when the critical exponent increases, because *if the critical exponent does not increase*, then it remains constant or decreases by steps of $1$ relative to the minor order: more precisely, if $G$ and $H$ are in $\mathcal{L}(q)$, $G$ covers $H$ in the minor order, and $c(H, q) \leq c(G; q)$, then $c(H; q) = c(G; q)$ or $c(G; q) - 1$. To prove this, let $x$ be a point in a $\mathrm{GF}(q)$-representable geometry $G$ and let $X$ be a copoint not containing $x$. Then by Lemma 8.4,

$$c(G; q) - 1 \leq c(G|X; q) \leq c(G \backslash x; q) \leq c(G; q).$$

Because the copoint $X$ is a complement of the point $x$ in the lattice $L(G)$ of flats, the copoint $X$ embeds into the contraction $G/x$ as a subgeometry. Hence, by Lemma 8.4 again,

$$c(G; q) - 1 \leq c(G|X; q) \leq c(G/x; q).$$

It follows immediately from equation (7.2) that minimal and tangential blocks are connected.[44] Another general property of minimal and tangential blocks can be obtained from Lemma 4.27.

---

[44]Walton [142] has proved that a tangential block cannot be a 2-sum; hence, tangential blocks are 3-connected. In addition, Walton and Welsh [143] proved that a binary tangential block cannot be a 3-sum. Both proofs use identities between characteristic polynomials.

8.5. LEMMA. *Let $X$ be any copoint in a minimal or tangential $k$-block $M(S)$ over $GF(q)$. Then the bond $S \setminus X$ contains at least $q^k$ points.*

PROOF. Represent $M(S)$ over $GF(q^k)$. By minimality, $c(M|X; q) \leq k$ and $M|X$ is affine over $GF(q^k)$. If $S \setminus X$ contains fewer than $q^k$ points, then by Lemma 4.27, $c(M; q) \leq k$, a contradiction.                                              □

There are two "classical" families of tangential $k$-blocks over $GF(q)$.

*Projective geometries.* The rank-$(k+1)$ projective geometry $PG(k, q)$ is a tangential $k$-block over $GF(q)$. In particular, the $(q+1)$-point line $U_{2,q+1}$ is a tangential 1-block over $GF(q)$.

*Dowling group geometries.* When $A$ is a subgroup of the multiplicative group $GF(q)^\times$ and

$$(8.1) \qquad\qquad n = \frac{q^k - 1}{|A|} + 1,$$

the rank-$n$ Dowling group geometry $Q_n(A)$ is a tangential $k$-block over $GF(q)$. In particular, the rank-$q^k$ cycle matroid $M(K_{q^k+1})$ is a tangential $k$-block over $GF(q)$.

## 8.2. Minimal blocks

One way to solve the critical problem over $GF(q)$ is to classify all minimal $k$-blocks over $GF(q)$. This difficult problem has been solved completely in only the simplest case, when $k = 1$ and $q = 2$ (Tutte [136]).

8.6. TUTTE'S ODD STIGM LEMMA. *The minimal 1-blocks over $GF(2)$ are the odd circuits.*[45]

PROOF. Suppose $G$ is a binary rank-$n$ geometry all of whose circuits are even. Let $x_1, x_2, \ldots, x_n$ be a basis of $G$. Then in any representation of $G$ over $[GF(2)]^n$, the linear functional $L$ defined by $L(x_i) = 1, 1 \leq i \leq n$, distinguishes $G$. Hence, every 1-block over $GF(2)$ contains an odd circuit. On the other hand, it is easy to check that odd circuits are 1-blocks and hence, they are minimal 1-blocks.    □

When $q \geq 3$, it is easy to check that a rank-2 minimal 1-block over $GF(q)$ must be the $(q + 1)$-point lines $U_{2,q+1}$. Jaeger [64] has described a constructive method of obtaining all $k$-blocks over $GF(q)$. This method does not seem to be useful for finding minimal $k$-blocks.

An elegant way to produce minimal blocks was found by Oxley [103]. Let $G(S)$ be a rank-$n$ matroid and let $H(T)$ be a rank-$m$ matroid. Let $x_1$ be an element in $S$ and $x_2$ be an element in $T$. The *series connection* $S(G, H)$ of $G$ and $H$ (at the basepoints $x_1$ and $x_2$) is the matroid on the set $(S \setminus \{x_1\}) \cup (T \setminus \{x_2\}) \cup \{x\}$ whose circuits are the circuits of $G$ not containing $x_1$, the circuits of $H$ not containing $x_2$, and all sets of the form $(C_1 \setminus \{x_1\}) \cup (C_2 \setminus \{x_2\}) \cup \{x\}$, where $C_1$ is a circuit in $G$ containing $x_1$ and $C_2$ is a circuit in $H$ containing $x_2$. Let $\phi_1 : S \to [GF(q)]^{n+m}$ be a representation of $G$ such that its image is in the linear span $V_1$ of the first $n$ standard basis vectors $e_1, e_2, \ldots, e_n$. Let $\phi_2 : T \to [GF(q)]^{n+m}$ be a representation of $H$ such that its image is in the linear span $V_2$ of the last $m$ standard basis

---

[45] In Tutte's terminology, a circuit is called a "stigm".

vectors $e_{n+1}, e_{n+2}, \ldots, e_{n+m}$. Then the function $\phi : (S\backslash\{x_1\}) \cup (T\backslash\{x_2\}) \cup \{x\} \rightarrow [\mathrm{GF}(q)]^{n+m}$ defined by:

$$\phi(y) = \begin{cases} \phi_1(y) & \text{if } y \in S\backslash\{x_1\} \\ \phi_2(y) & \text{if } y \in T\backslash\{x_2\} \\ \phi_1(x_1) + \phi_2(x_2) & \text{if } y = x \end{cases}$$

is a representation of $S(G, H)$.

8.7. THEOREM (OXLEY). *The series connection of two minimal k-blocks over* $\mathrm{GF}(q)$ *(at any pair of basepoints) is a minimal k-block over* $\mathrm{GF}(q)$.

Oxley's proof of Theorem 8.7 uses an identity for characteristic polynomials of series connections. Theorem 8.7 can also be proved geometrically using the representation for series connections given above. Using the same notation, suppose that $G(S)$ and $H(T)$ are minimal $k$-blocks over $\mathrm{GF}(q)$. We first show that the series connection $S(G, H)$ at the basepoints $x_1$ and $x_2$ is a $k$-block. Suppose it is not. Represent $S(G, H)$ using the function $\phi$ described earlier. Let $\underline{L} = (L_1, L_2, \ldots, L_k)$ be a $k$-tuple of linear functionals distinguishing $S(G, H)$. Then for every point $y \in (S\backslash\{x_1\}) \cup (T\backslash\{x_2\}) \cup \{x\}$, there exists a linear functional $L_i$ such that $L_i(\phi(y)) \neq 0$. In particular, there is a linear functional $L_i$ such that

$$L_i(\phi(x)) = L_i(\phi_1(x_1)) + L_i(\phi_2(x_2)) \neq 0.$$

At least one of the values $L_i(\phi_1(x_1))$ or $L_i(\phi_2(x_2))$ is non-zero. Hence, the $k$-tuple $\underline{L}$ distinguishes at least one of the geometries $G(S)$ or $H(T)$, contradicting the assumption that both geometries are $k$-blocks.

Next let $z \in S\backslash\{x_1\}$. We shall prove that the deletion $S(G, H)\backslash z$ has critical exponent at most $k$. By minimality, the deletion $G\backslash z$ has critical exponent at most $k$. Hence, there is a $k$-tuple $\underline{L} = (L_1, L_2, \ldots, L_k)$ distinguishing the vectors $\phi_1(y), y \in S\backslash\{z\}$. Because the image of the representation $\phi_1$ lies in the linear span $V_1$ of $e_1, e_2, \ldots, e_n$, we can assume that every linear functional $L_i$ in $\underline{L}$ is *supported on* $V_1$, that is, $L_i(e_j) = 0$ for every $j, n + 1 \leq j \leq n + m$. Similarly, there is a $k$-tuple $\underline{L}' = (L_1', L_2', \ldots, L_k')$ of linear functionals supported on $V_2$ distinguishing the vectors $\phi_2(y), y \in T\backslash\{x_2\}$. Because $H$ is a $k$-block, $\underline{L}'$ does not distinguish $H$ and hence, $L_i'(\phi_2(x_2)) = 0$ for every $i$. Consider the $k$-tuple

$$\underline{L} + \underline{L}' = (L_1 + L_1', L_2 + L_2', \ldots, L_k + L_k').$$

Then, because $L_i'(\phi_2(x_2)) = 0$, we have

$$(L_i + L_i')(\phi(y)) = \begin{cases} L_i(\phi_1(y)) & \text{if } y \in S\backslash\{x_1, z\}, \\ L_i'(\phi_2(y)) & \text{if } y \in T\backslash\{x_2\}, \\ L_i(\phi_1(x_1)) & \text{if } y = x. \end{cases}$$

From this, we deduce that the $k$-tuple $\underline{L} + \underline{L}'$ distinguishes $S(G, H)\backslash z$ and hence, $S(G, H)\backslash z$ has critical exponent at most $k$. In a similar way, we can prove that when $z \in T\backslash\{x_2\}$, $S(G, H)\backslash z$ has critical exponent at most $k$. To finish the proof, observe that deleting the basepoint $x$ from $S(G, H)$ results in the direct sum $(G\backslash x_1) \oplus (H\backslash x_2)$. From this, it is easy to prove that $S(G, H)\backslash x$ has critical exponent at most $k$. This completes the proof of Theorem 8.7.

Because an odd circuit can be constructed by taking series connections of copies of 3-point lines, Tutte's odd stigm theorem suggests the conjecture that every minimal $k$-block can be constructed by taking series connections of tangential $k$-blocks. This attractive conjecture is false; counterexamples can be found in Oxley [102].

### 8.3. Tangential blocks

Another solution of the critical problem over $GF(q)$ is to find all the tangential $k$-blocks over $GF(q)$. Two cases are known (Tutte [136]and Walton and Welsh [144]).

8.8. THEOREM.

(a) *The only tangential 1-block over* $GF(2)$ *is the 3-point line* $U_{2,3}$.

(b) *There are precisely two tangential 1-blocks over* $GF(3)$ : *the 4-point line* $U_{2,4}$ *and the cycle matroid* $M(K_4)$.

PROOF. There are at least two easy ways to check that $U_{2,3}$ is a tangential 1-block over $GF(2)$. Because every odd circuit contains the 3-point circuit $U_{2,3}$ as a minor, part (a) follows from the odd stigm lemma 8.6. Alternatively, one can observe that a geometry $G$ with no $U_{2,3}$-minor cannot contain a circuit. Hence, $G$ consists of a basis and is affine.

To prove part (b), one needs to use more difficult theorems. By Tutte's theorem for binary matroids [134], a geometry with no $U_{2,4}$ minor is binary. Because all the forbidden minors in Tutte's theorem for graphic geometries (see [135]) contain $M(K_4)$ as a minor, a binary geometry with no $M(K_4)$-minor is graphic, and hence, is the cycle matroid of a series-parallel graph by a theorem first proved by Dirac [41]. To show that the cycle geometries of series-parallel graphs are affine over $GF(3)$, one can use Dirac's result [41] that such graphs are 3-colorable, or one can explicitly calculate their characteristic polynomials, as was done by Brylawski [18]. □

To see how difficult it is to go beyond Theorem 8.8, consider the case when $k = 2$ and $q = 2$. The Fano plane $F_7$ and the cycle geometry $M(K_5)$ are tangential 2-blocks over $GF(2)$. However, the critical exponent of the minor-closed class $\mathcal{EX}(F_7, M(K_5)) \cap \mathcal{L}(2)$ is at least 3 because the cocycle geometry $M^{\perp}(P_{10})$ of the Petersen graph $P_{10}$ has critical exponent 3 but does not contain $F_7$ or $M(K_5)$ as minors. (We shall show in Section 8.9 that $\mathcal{EX}(F_7, M(K_5)) \cap \mathcal{L}(2)$ has critical exponent exactly 3.) Tutte [136] has conjectured that $M^{\perp}(P_{10})$ is the only other tangential 2-block over $GF(2)$.

8.9. THE TANGENTIAL 2-BLOCK CONJECTURE. *There are precisely three tangential 2-blocks over* $GF(2)$: $F_7$, $M(K_5)$, *and* $M^{\perp}(P_{10})$.

Tutte [136] showed that Conjecture 8.9 holds up to rank 6.

An interesting case which includes the tangential 2-block conjecture is the case when $k = 1$ and $q = 4$. By Lemma 8.1, every tangential 2-block over $GF(2)$ is a tangential 1-block over $GF(4)$. Hence, finding all tangential 1-blocks over $GF(4)$ would resolve Conjecture 8.9. As a very small step towards this, we determine all the tangential 1-blocks over $GF(4)$ having rank 3 or less.[46] As one might expect, this determination involves a rather technical case analysis.

---

[46]These blocks have all appeared, as examples, in Whittle [157].

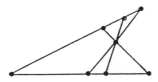

FIGURE 5. The geometry $T$.

The 5-point line $U_{2,5}$ is the only rank-2 tangential 1-block over GF(4). By minor-minimality, every tangential 1-block over GF(4) having rank greater than 2 contains no $U_{2,5}$-minor. This implies that in a tangential 1-block over GF(4) with rank at least 3, every 4-point line is modular.

Suppose that $M$ is a rank-3 tangential 1-block over GF(4).

*Case 1.* $M$ does not contain the 4-point line $U_{2,4}$ as a minor. Then by a theorem of Tutte [**134**], $M$ is binary and $M$ is a rank-3 tangential 2-block over GF(2). Hence, $M$ is isomorphic to the Fano plane $F_7$.

We can now assume that $M$ contains no $F_7$-subgeometry.

*Case 2.* $M$ does not contain $U_{3,5}$ as a subgeometry. By the forbidden-minor theorem for representability over GF(3) (see Oxley [**106**], Chapter 10, for an exposition), $M$ is ternary. By Proposition 2.6 in Kung [**80**], any ternary geometry with 10 or more points contains the ternary Reid geometry $R$. Because $R$ is representable only over fields of characteristic 3, no ternary geometry with 10 or more points is representable over GF(4).

There are three ternary geometries having 9 points: the ternary Reid geometry $R$, the rank-3 ternary Dowling geometry $Q_3(\mathrm{GF}(3)^\times)$, and the ternary affine plane AG(2, 3). Neither $R$ nor $Q_3(\mathrm{GF}(3)^\times)$ is representable over GF(4). However, AG(2, 3) is GF(4)-representable (see, for example, Ingleton [**62**]). In Section 5.4, it was shown that the characteristic polynomial of AG(2, 3) equals $(\lambda - 1)(\lambda - 4)^2$. From this, it is easy to check that AG(2, 3) is a tangential 1-block over GF(4). Next, consider the ternary rank-3 geometries with 8 points. All such geometries can be obtained by deleting a point from $R$, $Q_3(\mathrm{GF}(3)^\times)$, or AG(2, 3). There are two 8-point geometries with a 4-point line. One of them, the geometry $T$ shown in Figure 5, is obtained from $Q_3(\mathrm{GF}(3)^\times)$ by deleting an internal point; the other is obtained from $Q_3(\mathrm{GF}(3)^\times)$ by deleting a joint. Because a 4-point line is modular in a ternary geometry, both geometries are supersolvable and have characteristic polynomial $(\lambda - 1)(\lambda - 3)(\lambda - 4)$. However, only the geometry $T$ is GF(4)-representable. From this (or from Theorem 8.15 in the next section), it is easy to check that $T$ is a tangential 1-block over GF(4). All other ternary 8-point rank-3 geometries have no 4-point-line subgeometries and are subgeometries of AG(2, 3). Finally, any ternary 7-point rank-3 geometry is a subgeometry of $T$ or AG(2, 3). Hence, there are no further ternary rank-3 tangential 1-blocks over GF(4).

*Case 3.* $M$ contains $U_{3,5}$ as a subgeometry. There are three one-point extensions of $U_{3,5}$. These are obtained by adding the new point (a) in general position, so that one obtains $U_{3,6}$, (b) on one 2-point line, so that one obtains the geometry

$P_6$, or (c) on two 2-point lines, so that one obtains the geometry $Q_6$. The geometries $P_6$ and $Q_6$ are illustrated on p. 503 in Oxley [**106**]. The geometry $P_6$ is not GF(4)-representable. The geometries $U_{3,6}$ and $Q_6$ are GF(4)-representable, but both contain a 5-point line minor. Hence, none of these three extensions is a tangential 1-block over GF(4). Moreover, any geometry containing any one of these extensions is not a tangential 1-block over GF(4). Finally, the geometry $U_{3,5}$ is affine and it is not a 1-block over GF(4). We conclude that there are no rank-3 tangential 1-block over GF(4) containing $U_{3,5}$.

Our results are summarized in the following lemma.

8.10. LEMMA. *The following are all the 1-blocks over* GF(4) *with rank at most* 3: $U_{2,5}$, $F_7$, $T$, *and* AG(2,3).

There are two well-known tangential 1-blocks over GF(4) with rank exceeding 3 : $M(K_5)$ and $M^\perp(P_{10})$. These are both tangential 2-blocks over GF(2). We shall describe another (non-binary) tangential 1-blocks over GF(4) with rank greater than 3 in Section 8.8.

## 8.4. Blocks with modular copoints

All the classical tangential blocks have modular copoints, and, as we shall see in Section 8.7, there are others. Whittle [**156,157,158**] has made considerable progress towards finding all tangential $k$-blocks with modular copoints. In particular, he has proved that for given $k$ and $q$, there are only a finite number of tangential $k$-blocks over GF($q$) with modular copoints. With some changes, Whittle's argument yields similar results for minimal blocks. We shall present this generalization of Whittle's argument in this section.

We begin with a technical lemma about modular copoints. Recall that a copoint $X$ is modular in a geometry $G(S)$ if and only if for every line $L$ in $G$, the intersection $L \cap X$ is non-empty (Stanley [**125**]). A copoint $X$ is said to be *minimally modular* if $X$ is connected and for every point $x \in X$, the copoint $X \backslash \{x\}$ is not modular in the deletion $M \backslash x$. Note that because separators in the modular flat $X$ induce separators in the geometry $G$ (see Corollary 3.16 in Brylawski [**20**]), a geometry containing a minimally modular copoint is connected.[47]

8.11. LEMMA. *Let $X$ be a minimally modular copoint in a geometry $G(S)$. Then the complement $S \backslash X$ spans $G$.*

PROOF. It suffices to show that if $x$ is a point in $X$, then $x \in \overline{S \backslash X}$. Consider all the lines $L$ in $G(S)$ such that $L \cap X = \{x\}$. If every such line $L$ contains exactly two points, then deleting $x$ also removes all the lines $L$ such that $L \cap X = \{x\}$. Hence, $X \backslash \{x\}$ is modular in the deletion $G \backslash x$. $\qquad \square$

Note that our proof also shows the following result: *if a copoint $X$ in $G(S)$ is minimally modular, then the line-closure of $S \backslash X$ is $S$.* See Halsey [**56**] for the definition of line-closure.

Using Lemma 8.11, we prove the following characterizations of minimal and tangential blocks with modular copoints.

---

[47]The natural concept of being minimally modular has also appeared in Whittle's thesis [**156**].

8.12. THEOREM. *Let $M(S)$ be a geometry representable over* GF$(q)$ *containing a modular copoint $X$. Then $M(S)$ is a minimal $k$-block over* GF$(q)$ *if and only if it satisfies all of the following conditions:*

(MM1) *The complement $S\backslash X$ contains exactly $q^k$ points.*

(MM2) *The copoint $X$ is minimally modular.*

(MM3) $c(M|X; q) = k.$

(MM4) *For every point $x$ in the copoint $X$, $c((M|X)/x; q) \leq k$.*

8.13. THEOREM. *Let $M(S)$ be a geometry representable over* GF$(q)$ *containing a modular copoint $X$. Then, $M(S)$ is a tangential $k$-block over* GF$(q)$ *if and only if it satisfies conditions* (MM1), (MM2), (MM3), *and*

(TM4) *For every flat $Y$ in the copoint $X$, $c((M|X)/Y; q) \leq k$.*

We begin by proving the implication in Theorem 8.12. Let $M(S)$ be a rank-$n$ minimal $k$-block over GF$(q)$ with a modular copoint $X$. To prove (MM1), we adapt Whittle's method[48] in [**157**]. By the modular factorization theorem 5.6,

$$0 = \chi(M; q^k) = \chi(M|X; q^k)(q^k - t),$$

where $t = |S\backslash X|$. Because $M|X$ is a proper subgeometry of $M$, $c(M|X; q) \leq k$ and $\chi(M|X; q^k) \neq 0$. Hence, $q^k - t = 0$ or $|S\backslash X| = q^k$.

To prove (MM2), suppose that $X\backslash\{x\}$ is modular in the deletion $M\backslash x$. Then by the modular factorization theorem again,

$$\chi(M\backslash x; \lambda) = \chi(M|(X\backslash\{x\}); \lambda)(\lambda - q^k).$$

Hence, $\chi(M\backslash x; q^k) = 0$, contradicting the assumption that $M$ is a minimal $k$-block.

By Lemma 8.4, $M|X$ is a $(k-1)$-block. This proves (MM3). Finally, by condition (MB2′), $c(M/x; q) \leq k$. Because $(M|X)/x$ is a subgeometry of $M/x$, we conclude that $c((M|X)/x) \leq k$. This proves (MM4).

Because a tangential block is minimal, conditions (MM1), (MM2), and (MM3) also hold when $M(S)$ is a tangential $k$-block with a modular copoint $X$. By condition (TB2′), $c(M/Y; q) \leq k$ for any flat $Y \subseteq X$. Hence, we conclude, as earlier, that $c((M|X)/Y) \leq k$. This proves the implication in Theorem 8.13.

Next, we shall prove the converse implication in Theorem 8.12. Let $M(S)$ be a rank-$n$ geometry with a modular copoint $X$ satisfying the conditions in Theorem 8.12. By the modular factorization theorem and (MM1), $M$ is a $k$-block. Choose a representation of $M$ as a set of points in PG$(n-1, q)$. Let lin$(X)$ be the subspace of rank $n-1$ spanned by $X$ in PG$(n-1, q)$. We shall prove that $M$ is a minimal $k$-block by showing that every point $x$ in $S$ has a tangent of codimension $k$ in PG$(n-1, q)$. We distinguish two cases.

The first case is when $x \in S\backslash X$. By (MM3), there exists a subspace $U$ in lin$(X)$ having codimension $k$ relative to lin$(X)$ such that $U \cap X = \emptyset$. Because $X$ is a copoint, the subspace $U$ has rank $n - k - 1$ in PG$(n-1, q)$. Consider the rank-$(n-k)$ subspace $U'$ spanned by $U$ and $x$. If $U' \cap S$ contains another point $y$ in $S$, then the line $x \vee y$ intersects $X$ at a point in $U' \cap$ lin$(X)$. However, $U' \cap X$ is empty. Hence, $(x \vee y) \wedge X$ is empty, contradicting the assumption that $X$ is a

---

modular copoint in $M(S)$. We conclude that $U' \cap S = \{x\}$. Hence, $U'$ is a tangent of $x$.

The second case is when $x \in X$. Contracting $x$, we obtain the geometry $M/x$ on the set $S'$ of lines containing $x$. Let $X'$ be the set of lines in $S'$ contained in the copoint $X$. Then $X'$ is a modular copoint in $M/x$. By (MM2) and the argument in the proof of Lemma 8.11, there exist two points $y$ and $y'$ in $S \backslash X$ such that $x$ is on the line $y \vee y'$. In the contraction $M/x$, the points $y$ and $y'$ are identified. Hence, by (MM1), $t' = |S' \backslash X'| < q^k$ and

$$q^k - t' \neq 0.$$

Moreover, by (MM4), $\chi((M/x)|X'; q^k) \neq 0$. We conclude by the modular factorization theorem that

$$\chi(M/x; q^k) = \chi((M/x)|X'; q^k)(q^k - t') \neq 0.$$

Hence, there exists a codimension-$k$ tangent of $x$ in $\mathrm{PG}(n-1, q)$. This completes the proof of Theorem 8.12.

The proof of the converse implication in Theorem 8.13 is similar. We shall show that every non-empty flat $Y$ having rank at most $n-k$ has a tangent of codimension $k$ in $\mathrm{PG}(n-1, q)$. The first case is when $Y$ is a flat of $M$ not contained in $X$. Because $X$ is a modular copoint, the intersection $Y' = X \wedge Y$ is a flat with rank equal to $\mathrm{rank}(Y) - 1$. By (TM4), $c((M|X)/Y'; q) \leq k$ and there exists a subspace $U'$ of rank $n - k - 1$ in $\mathrm{PG}(n - 1, q)$ contained in $\mathrm{lin}(X)$ such that

$$U' \cap X = U' \cap S = Y'.$$

Let

$$U = \mathrm{lin}(U' \cup Y),$$

the subspace spanned by $U'$ and $Y$. Because $Y$ covers $Y'$, the subspace $U$ covers $U'$ and $\mathrm{rank}(U)$ equals $n - k$. Moreover,

$$U \cap X = U \cap (\mathrm{lin}(X) \cap S) = Y'.$$

Consider the intersection $U \cap S$. It is an $M$-flat containing $Y$. Using the fact that $X$ is a modular copoint, we obtain

$$\begin{aligned}
\mathrm{rank}(U \cap S) &= \mathrm{rank}((U \cap S) \cap X) + \mathrm{rank}((U \cap S) \cup X) - \mathrm{rank}(X) \\
&= \mathrm{rank}(Y') + n - (n - 1) \\
&= \mathrm{rank}(Y') + 1. \\
&= \mathrm{rank}(Y).
\end{aligned}$$

Because $U$ contains $Y$ (by construction), this implies that $U \cap S$ equals $Y$. We conclude that $U$ is a rank-$(n - k)$ tangent of $Y$ in $\mathrm{PG}(n - 1, q)$. The second case, when $Y$ is a flat contained in $X$, can be proved using the same argument as in the proof of Theorem 8.12. This concludes the proof of Theorem 8.13.

Combining Lemma 8.11 and Theorem 8.12, we conclude that a minimal $k$-block with a modular copoint has rank at most $q^k$. Because the rank-$q^k$ cycle matroid $M(K_m)$, where $m = q^k + 1$, is a tangential $k$-block, this rank is attained. Indeed, by Theorem 5.13, $M(K_m)$, where $m = q^k + 1$, is the *unique* tangential $k$-block with a modular copoint having rank $q^k$. Lemma 5.14, Lemma 8.11, Theorem 8.12 and Theorem 8.13 imply that every rank-$n$ minimal or tangential $k$-block with a modular copoint contains a subgeometry isomorphic to $M(K_{n+1})$.

If $q$ and $k$ are given, then $q^k$ is a fixed constant. As there are finitely many non-isomorphic geometries in $\mathcal{L}(q)$ having rank at most $q^k$, and the minimal $k$-blocks with modular copoints are amongst these geometries, one obtains the following generalization of a theorem proved by Whittle [157] for tangential blocks.

8.14. THEOREM. *A minimal $k$-block with modular copoints over* GF$(q)$ *has rank at most* $q^k$. *Hence, given $q$ and $k$, there are finitely many minimal $k$-blocks with modular copoints over* GF$(q)$. *In particular, there are finitely many tangential $k$-blocks with modular copoints over* GF$(q)$.

A natural question arising from Theorems 8.12 and 8.13 is whether there exist any minimal blocks with modular copoints which are not tangential blocks. Because a rank-3 minimal block is a tangential block, such minimal blocks must have rank exceeding 4. The following specialization of Theorem 8.13 gives a simpler description of rank-3 minimal or tangential 1-blocks with a modular line.

8.15. THEOREM. *Let $M(S)$ be a rank-3 geometry representable over* GF$(q)$ *containing a modular line $L$. Then, $M(S)$ is a tangential 1-block over* GF$(q)$ *if and only if $M(S)$ satisfies the following three conditions:*
(TM1′) *The complement $S \backslash L$ contains exactly $q$ points.*
(TM2′) *$L$ is minimally modular.*
(TM3′) *$L$ contains at most $q$ points.*

PROOF. It is easy to check that if $M(S)$ is a tangential 1-block, then the three conditions are satisfied. To prove the converse, observe that by (TM1′) and (TM2′), $M$ is a 1-block. To finish the proof, we show that every point has a line tangent to it. If $x$ is a point not on $L$, then (TM2′) and (TM3′) imply $x$ has a tangent line in PG$(2, q)$. If $x$ is on $L$, then by (TB1′) and (TB2′), the contraction $M/x$ is a line containing at most $q$ points. Hence, $M/x$ is affine over GF$(q)$. We conclude that there exists a line $L'$ in PG$(2, q)$ such that $L' \cap S = \{x\}$.                    □

Theorem 8.15 seems to give a way to construct many tangential 1-block with a modular line. However, the condition (TM2′) is quite difficult to check in general. For some examples of tangential 1-block with a modular line, see Whittle [157,158] and also Brylawski and Oxley [31], p. 198 and 199.

Using an identity of Oxley, Oxley and Whittle (see Whittle [157]) obtained the following "converse" to condition (MM1) in Theorem 8.13.

8.16. THEOREM. *Let $X$ be a copoint in a rank-$n$ tangential $k$-block $M(S)$ and let $S \backslash X$ be the bond associated with $X$. Then*

$$|S \backslash X| \geq q^k$$

*with equality if and only if $X$ is modular.*

To prove Theorem 8.16, suppose that $M(S)$ is a rank-$n$ tangential $k$-block with a copoint $X$. Since $c(M; q) > k$, we obtain, on setting $\lambda = q^k$ in Oxley's identity 5.1,

$$(8.2) \qquad 0 = \chi(M; q^k) = \chi(M|X; q^k)(q^k - t) + \sum_{N} \chi(N; q^k)$$

where $t$ is the number of points in the bond $S \backslash X$ and the sum is over certain proper minors $N$ of $M$. The sum is empty if and only if $X$ is modular. Because proper minors of $M$ have critical exponent $k$ or less, the sum is greater than or equal to 0. If $X$ is not modular, then the sum is strictly positive. Since $\chi(M|X; q^k) > 0$, we conclude that $q^k - t$ is negative, that is, $t > q^k$. If $X$ is modular, then the sum equals zero. Because $\chi(M|X; q^k) > 0$, it must be the case that $q^k - t = 0$ or $t = q^k$.

Theorem 8.16 can also be proved geometrically.[49] Let $M$ be a rank-$n$ tangential $k$-block represented as a set of points in $\mathrm{PG}(n-1, q^k)$ and let $X$ be a copoint of $M$. By (TB2), $c(M|X; q) \leq k$. Hence, $c(M|X; q^k) = 1$ and there exists a subspace $U$ of codimension 2 in $\mathrm{PG}(n-1, q^k)$ contained in the subspace $\mathrm{lin}(X)$ spanned by $X$ such that $U \cap X = \emptyset$. Consider the $q^k + 1$ hyperplanes covering $U$. One of these hyperplanes is $\mathrm{lin}(X)$. Because $M(S)$ is a $k$-block, the other $q^k$ hyperplanes have non-empty intersection with $S$. In addition, these hyperplanes have empty intersection with $X$. Hence, $|S \backslash X| \geq q^k$.

If $|S \backslash X| > q^k$, then there is a hyperplane not equal to $\mathrm{lin}(X)$ containing at least two points $x$ and $y$ in $M$. The intersection of the line $x \vee y$ with $\mathrm{lin}(X)$ is a point in $U$. Hence, $x \vee y$ does not intersect $X$. We conclude that $X$ is not modular.

If $|S \backslash X| = q^k$, then every hyperplane not equal to $\mathrm{lin}(X)$ covering $U$ contains exactly one point in $S$. In particular, if $x$ and $y$ are points in $S \backslash X$, then the line $x \vee y$ meets $\mathrm{lin}(X)$ at a point $z$ in $\mathrm{lin}(X) \backslash U$. If every such point $z$ is in $X$, then $X$ is modular. Otherwise, consider the quotient $(M|X)//z$. It is a subgeometry of the contraction $M/(x \vee y)$. Because $M$ is a tangential 1-block over $\mathrm{GF}(q^k)$, $M/(x \vee y)$, and hence $(M|X)//z$, is affine over $\mathrm{GF}(q^k)$. Hence, there exists a subspace $V$ of codimension 2 in $\mathrm{PG}(n-1, q^k)$ such that $z \in V$, $V \subseteq \mathrm{lin}(X)$, and $V \cap X = \emptyset$. Consider the $q^k + 1$ hyperplanes covering $V$. One of these hyperplane is $\mathrm{lin}(X)$. Another hyperplane contains the points $x$ and $y$. As there are exactly $q^k$ points in $S \backslash X$, there is a third hyperplane $W$ such that $W \cap S = \emptyset$. Hence, $M$ is not a 1-block over $\mathrm{GF}(q^k)$, contradicting the assumption that $M$ is a $k$-block over $\mathrm{GF}(q)$. This completes the geometric proof of Theorem 8.16.

Theorem 8.16 cannot be extended to minimal blocks because an odd circuit is a minimal 1-block over $\mathrm{GF}(2)$ without a modular copoint in which every bond has size 2. The algebraic proof of Theorem 8.16 depends strongly on Oxley's identity. One way to extend this theorem is to generalize Oxley's identity to modular flats of lower rank. Theorem 5.8 offers such an identity, but unfortunately the correction term contains positive and negative summands.

## 8.5. Jointless Dowling group geometries

By Theorems 8.13 and 8.14, for a given $k$ and $q$, there are finitely many tangential $k$-blocks over $\mathrm{GF}(q)$ with modular copoints and these tangential blocks have a reasonably predictable structure. The case of tangential blocks without modular copoints remains to be done. This case seems much more difficult and no general result is known. Following Whittle [161], we shall call such tangential blocks *nasty blocks*.

The first nasty block to be discovered is the cocycle geometry $M^{\perp}(P_{10})$ of the Petersen graph. This is a tangential 2-block over $\mathrm{GF}(2)$ and was discovered by Tutte in 1966 [136]. The second example is the affine ternary plane $\mathrm{AG}(2, 3)$. This is a tangential 1-block over $\mathrm{GF}(4)$.

---

[49]Another geometric proof involving a more complicated counting argument can be found in Whittle [155].

The geometry $AG(2,3)$ can be obtained from classical algebraic geometry by taking the nine points of inflexion of a non-singular cubic curve in complex projective space (see Ingleton [62]). It is also the geometric configuration associated with Pascal's theorem on a hexagon inscribed in a degenerate conic consisting of two lines (see Mac Lane [91]). Two questions arise from this. The first is whether there is a similar interpretation for $M^\perp(P_{10})$. The second is whether other configurations from algebraic or projective geometry yield tangential blocks. A more speculative idea is to find connections between the critical problem and algebraic geometry over finite fields. Such connections have proved to be very fruitful in coding theory (see, for example, Moreno [94]).[50]

In his paper [161], Whittle described an infinite family of nasty blocks containing $AG(2,3)$ as its smallest member.[51] The *jointless Dowling group geometry* $Q'_n(A)$ is the geometry obtained by deleting all the joints from the Dowling group geometry $Q_n(A)$.

8.17. THEOREM (WHITTLE). *Let $A$ be a subgroup of the multiplicative group* $\mathrm{GF}(q)^\times$ *and let*

$$(8.3) \qquad\qquad n = \frac{q^k - 1}{|A|} + 2.$$

*Then $Q'_n(A)$ is a tangential $k$-block over $\mathrm{GF}(q)$.*

PROOF. Because $A$ is a subgroup of $\mathrm{GF}(q)^\times$, $Q'_n(A)$ is representable over $\mathrm{GF}(q)$. From Section 5.4, the characteristic polynomial of $Q'_n(A)$ has integer roots:

$$(8.4) \quad (n-1)(|A|-1),\ (n-2)|A|+1,\ (n-3)|A|+1,\ \dots,\ 2|A|+1,\ |A|+1,\ 1.$$

By equation (8.3), $(n-2)|A|+1 = q^k$ and hence, $Q'_n(A)$ is a $k$-block over $\mathrm{GF}(q)$.

Next, observe that if $a \in Q'_n(A)$, then the contraction $Q'_n(A)/a$ is isomorphic to the geometry obtained by deleting all but one joint from $Q_{n-1}(A)$. Hence, any contraction $Q'_n(A)/X$ by a proper flat $X$ is a proper minor of $Q_{n-1}(A)$. Because $(n-2)|A|+1 = q^k$, $Q_{n-1}(A)$ is a tangential $k$-block over $\mathrm{GF}(q)$ and any proper minor of $Q_{n-1}(A)$ is not a $k$-block. We conclude that $Q'_n(A)/X$ is not a $k$-block. $\square$

8.18. THEOREM (WHITTLE). *Suppose that $|A| > 2$ and $n \geq 2$, or, $|A| = 2$ and $n > 2$. Then the jointless Dowling geometry $Q'_n(A)$ has no modular copoints.*

SKETCH OF PROOF. Observe that $Q'_n(A)$ is connected. Hence, any modular copoint is connected. The connected copoints in $Q_n(A)$ are known (Dowling [46], p. 69). They are isomorphic to $Q_{n-1}(A)$ or $M(K_n)$. From this, one concludes that the connected copoints in $Q'_n(A)$ are isomorphic to $Q'_{n-1}(A)$ or $M(K_n)$. It is not hard to show geometrically that copoints isomorphic to $Q'_{n-1}(A)$ or $M(K_n)$ are not modular in $Q'_{n-1}(A)$. An alternate method is to count the number of points in the complement of the copoint in question, observe that this number does not match any of the zeroes listed in (8.4), and use the modular factorization theorem 5.6. $\square$

---

[50]The ideas in this paragraph were inspired by discussions with Michael Falk about $AG(2,3)$ as a complex hyperplane arrangement.

[51]The cocycle geometry $M^\perp(P_{10})$ does not seem to be a member of an infinite family. In any case, by Jaeger's 8-flow theorem in Section 7.2, there are no cographic tangential $k$-blocks over $\mathrm{GF}(2)$ when $k \geq 3$.

Using the argument in the proof of Theorem 8.18, one can prove the stronger theorem: *Suppose $|A|$ and $n$ satisfy the condition in Theorem 8.18. If $X$ is a modular flat in $Q'_n(A)$, then $X$ is $\hat{0}$, $\hat{1}$, or a point.*

One can show that tangential blocks with modular copoints do not split, that is, they are not the union of two proper flats. The jointless Dowling geometries $Q'_n(A)$ are also non-splitting tangential blocks. Is there an analogue of Theorem 8.14 for non-splitting tangential blocks?

The jointless Dowling geometries $Q'_d(A)$ have "large" automorphism groups (Bonin [13]). Because the Petersen graph has an automorphism group isomorphic to the symmetric group $S_5$, the cocycle geometry $M^\perp(P_{10})$ also has a "large" automorphism group. Must all nasty blocks have "large" automorphism groups? Note that by Theorem 8.15, there are many rank-3 tangential 1-blocks with a modular line when $q$ is large. It seems plausible that some of them will have "small" automorphism groups.

It may also be relevant that when $A = \{+1, -1\}$, the Dowling geometry $Q_n(A)$ is the geometry of the root system $B_n$ and the jointless Dowling geometry $Q'_n(A)$ is the geometry of the root system $D_n$. Are the other root systems, especially the sporadic ones, related to tangential blocks?

A more precise question concerns rank-3 tangential blocks. By Theorem 8.15, a rank-3 tangential 1-block over $GF(q)$ with a modular line has at most $2q$ points. The jointless Dowling geometries $Q'_3(GF(q)^\times)$ are tangential 1-blocks over $GF(q)$ having $3q - 3$ points. Is there a constant $c$ not depending on $q$ such that every rank-3 tangential 1-block has at most $cq$ points?

### 8.6.  Lifting over $GF(q)$

Whittle found two ways of constructing new tangential blocks from known ones. The first construction is the $q$-lift, which appeared in [160]. (See also [159].) The $q$-lift construction has also appeared, under the name of "framing", in Kung [81], Section 4.5, where it is used to construct examples of minor-closed classes with quadratic size functions.[52] In this section, we shall give an account of the theory of $q$-lifts. In the first part, we shall describe the theory as presented in [160]. In the second part, we shall use an argument in [160] to obtain an explicit formula for the characteristic polynomial of the $q$-lift in terms of the characteristic of the base geometry. This formula yields an alternate proof of the main theorems.

Let $G(S)$ be a rank-$n$ geometry representable over $GF(q)$. Represent $G$ as a set $S$ of points in rank-$(n + 1)$ projective space $PG(n, q)$. Then $S$ spans a hyperplane $\text{lin}(S)$ in $PG(n, q)$. Choose a point $u$ in $PG(n, q)$ not in $\text{lin}(S)$. Let $T$ be the union of all the lines in $PG(n, q)$ of the form $u \vee x$, where $x$ is a point in $S$. Let $G^\#(T)$ be the geometry on the set $T$ given by linear dependence. A geometry $G^\#$ obtained in this way from $G(S)$ is called a $q$-lift of $G$. The set $S$ is called the *base* and the point $u$ is called the *apex* of the $q$-lift $G^\#$. A $q$-lift of $G(S)$ has rank $n + 1$ and $q|S| + 1$ points.

Given a representation of $G(S)$ in $PG(n, q)$, it is easy to see that if $u$ and $u'$ are two points outside $\text{lin}(S)$, then the $q$-lifts obtained from $u$ and $u'$ are projectively equivalent. It is also easy to see that if we take two projectively equivalent representations of $G$, then we obtain projectively equivalent $q$-lifts. However, it is an

---

[52]The definition on p. 36 of [81] should include the points $a$ in $G$ as well as points of the form $\omega + \alpha a$.

open problem whether one can obtain two $q$-lifts which are not matroid-isomorphic from two projectively inequivalent representations of $G$. This gap in our knowledge does not affect most of the applications of $q$-lifts to the theory of tangential blocks.

Let $G^{\#}(T)$ be a $q$-lift of $G(S)$. It is immediate from the definition that the contraction $G^{\#}/u$ of $G^{\#}$ by the apex $u$ is isomorphic to $G$. Let $U$ be any hyperplane in $\mathrm{PG}(n, q)$ not containing the apex $u$. If $x$ is a point in $S$, then the $(q+1)$-point line $u \vee x$ intersects $U$ at a (unique) point $x'$ in $T$. Thus, the points in $S$ (which all lie on the hyperplane $\mathrm{lin}(S)$) and the points in $U \cap T$ (which all lie on the hyperplane $U$) are perspective from the point $u$ and hence, the restrictions $G^{\#}|(U \cap T)$ and $G^{\#}|(\mathrm{lin}(S) \cap T)$ are isomorphic. Because the latter geometry is simply the base geometry $G$, the restriction $G^{\#}|(U \cap T)$ is isomorphic to $G$ for every hyperplane $U$ in $\mathrm{PG}(n, q)$ not containing $u$. From this, we conclude that if $a$ is a point in $G^{\#}$ not equal to the apex $u$, then the contraction $G^{\#}/a$ is isomorphic to the $q$-lift $(G/a')^{\#}$ of the contraction $G/a'$, where $a'$ is the (unique) point on the line $a \vee u$ in the base geometry $G$. Using this description of the one-point contractions of $G^{\#}$, we obtain the following lemma (Whittle [160]).

8.19. LEMMA. *Let $G^{\#}(T)$ be a $q$-lift of $G(S)$ and let $H$ be a minor of $G^{\#}(T)$. Then $H$ is isomorphic to a minor of $G$ or a minor of a $q$-lift of a minor of $G$.*

The next lemma can also be found in [160].

8.20. LEMMA. *Let $G^{\#}$ be a $q$-lift of $G$. Then*

$$c(G^{\#}; q) = c(G; q) + 1.$$

PROOF. Represent $G$ in $\mathrm{PG}(n, q)$ and let $G^{\#}(T)$ be a $q$-lift of $G$ in $\mathrm{PG}(n, q)$. Suppose that $c(G^{\#}; q) \leq k+1$. Then there exists a $(k+1)$-tuple $(H_1, H_2, \ldots, H_{k+1})$ of hyperplanes of $\mathrm{PG}(n, q)$ distinguishing $G^{\#}$. One of these hyperplanes, $H_{k+1}$, say, does not contain the apex $u$. Hence, the intersection $T \cap H_{k+1}$ is isomorphic to the base geometry $G$. Because the $k$-tuple $(H_1, H_2, \ldots, H_k)$ distinguishes the restriction $G^{\#}|(T \cap H_{k+1})$ and the base geometry $G$ is isomorphic to $G^{\#}|(T \cap H_{k+1})$, we conclude that $c(G; q) \leq k$. At this point, we have proved that if $c(G^{\#}; q) = c + 1$, then $c(G; q) \leq c$.

On the other hand, if $c(G; q) = c$, then there exists a subspace $U$ of codimension $c$ relative to the hyperplane $\mathrm{lin}(S)$ spanned by $S$ in $\mathrm{PG}(n, q)$ such that $U \cap S = \emptyset$. The subspace $U$ is a subspace of codimension $c+1$ in $\mathrm{PG}(n, q)$ such that $U \cap T = \emptyset$. Hence, if $c(G; q) = c$, then $c(G^{\#}; q) \leq c + 1$. $\square$

From Lemmas 8.19 and 8.20, we obtain the following theorem [160].

8.21. WHITTLE'S THEOREM FOR $q$-LIFTS. *A $q$-lift of a tangential $k$-block over $\mathrm{GF}(q)$ is a tangential $(k+1)$-block over $\mathrm{GF}(q)$.*

Whittle also showed that modularity is preserved under $q$-lifts.

8.22. PROPOSITION. *Let $G^{\#}$ be a $q$-lift of $G$ with apex $u$ and let $X$ be a flat of $G$. Then $X$ is a modular flat in $G$ if and only if the flat $X \vee u$ is a modular flat in $G^{\#}$. In addition, $G$ contains no modular copoints if and only if $G^{\#}$ contains no modular copoints.*

See [160] for the proof of this proposition.

Whittle concludes from Proposition 8.22 that a $q$-lift of a supersolvable geometry is supersolvable. Indeed, if $G$ is a rank-$n$ supersolvable geometry with modular flag $\hat{0} = X_0 < X_1 < X_2 < \ldots < X_n$, then a $q$-lift $G^{\#}$ with apex $u$ is supersolvable with modular flag

$$\hat{0} < u < X_1 \vee u < X_2 \vee u < \ldots < X_n \vee u.$$

From this, one concludes that if $\chi(G; \lambda) = \prod_{i=1}^{n}(\lambda - a_i)$, where $a_i = |X_i \backslash X_{i-1}|$, then

$$(8.5) \qquad \chi(G^{\#}; \lambda) = (\lambda - 1) \prod_{i=1}^{n}(\lambda - qa_i).$$

Equation (8.5) is a special case of the the following theorem.

8.23. THEOREM. *Let $G^{\#}$ be a $q$-lift of the rank-$n$ geometry $G$. Then*

$$\chi(G^{\#}; \lambda) = (\lambda - 1)q^n \chi(G; \frac{\lambda}{q}).$$

We shall prove Theorem 8.23 using a contraction-and-deletion argument. We first show that if $a$ is a point which is not an isthmus of $G$, then

$$(8.6) \qquad \chi(G^{\#}; \lambda) = \chi((G \backslash a)^{\#}; \lambda) - q\chi((G/a)^{\#}; \lambda).$$

Let $a$ be a point in $S$ which is not an isthmus and let $a = a_1, a_2, \ldots, a_q$ be the $q$ points on the line $u \vee a$ not equal to $u$. Then by the argument in the proof of Lemma 8.19, we have

$$G^{\#}/a_i \cong (G/a)^{\#}.$$

Moreover, in the contraction $G^{\#}/a$, the points $a_i$ are identified with the apex $u$. Hence,

$$((G^{\#} \backslash \{a_1, a_2, \ldots, a_{j-1}\})/a_j) \cong (G/a)^{\#}.$$

Applying the contraction-and-deletion argument $q$ times with the points $a_1, a_2, \ldots, a_q$, we obtain equation (8.6).

Next, suppose that $a \in S$ is an isthmus of $G$. Then

$$(8.7) \qquad \chi(G^{\#}; \lambda) = \chi((G \backslash a)^{\#}; \lambda)(\lambda - q).$$

There are several easy ways to show this. One way is to observe that if $a$ is an isthmus of $G$, then $G^{\#}$ is the parallel connection of $(G \backslash a)^{\#}$ and the line $u \vee a$ at the apex $u$. Hence, the set of points in $(G \backslash a)^{\#}$ is a modular copoint in $G^{\#}$. Using the modular factorization theorem 5.6, we obtain equation (8.7).

Finally, we observe that if $I$ is the rank-1 geometry (on one point), then $I^{\#}$ is a $(q + 1)$-point line. Hence,

$$(8.8) \qquad \chi(I^{\#}; \lambda) = (\lambda - 1)(\lambda - q).$$

Theorem 8.23 now follows by induction from the equations (8.6), (8.7), and (8.8). Note that although $\chi(G^{\#}; \lambda)$ satisfies a contraction-and-deletion relation, the initial condition is of the wrong kind to make it a generalized Tutte-Grothendieck invariant *as a function of the geometry $G$*. An interesting consequence of Theorem 8.23 is that if one can construct non-isomorphic $q$-lifts from projectively inequivalent representations, then they would have the same characteristic polynomial. Another consequence of Theorem 8.23 is the following identity between Möbius functions:

$$\mu_{G^\#}(\hat{0}, \hat{1}) = -q^{\mathrm{rank}(G)} \mu_G(\hat{0}, \hat{1}).$$

Whittle's theorem for $q$-lifts is an immediate consequence of Theorem 8.23. It is possible to prove Proposition 8.22 using the second part of Theorem 5.8 and the fact that taking principal truncations geometrically commutes with taking $q$-lifts, that is, if $X$ is a rank-$k$ flat of $G$ represented as a set of points in $\mathrm{PG}(n, q)$, and the principal truncations are obtained by adding and then contracting a subspace of rank $k - 1$ contained in $\mathrm{lin}(X)$ in general position in $G$, then

$$T_X(G)^\# = T_X(G^\#).$$

## 8.7. Quotients

The second method, also due to Whittle, of constructing new tangential blocks is to take quotients of tangential blocks with modular flats. A summary of the results we shall need from the theory of strong maps and quotients can be found in Section 1. Whittle's proofs are "algebraic" and are based on the modular factorization theorem 5.6. The proofs presented here are based on Whittle's proofs and an argument for producing tangents in quotients which first appeared in a paper [**39**] of Datta.

Following Whittle, we begin with the simplest construction, that of taking a (complete) principal truncation (Whittle [**157**]).

8.24. THEOREM. *Let $M(S)$ be a tangential $k$-block over $\mathrm{GF}(q)$ with a proper modular flat $X$ such that $c(M|X; q) = 1$. Then the geometry obtained by simplifying the principal truncation $T_X(M)$ is a tangential $k$-block over $\mathrm{GF}(q)$.*

The first condition to check in the proof of Theorem 8.24 is that $T_X(M)$ is representable over $\mathrm{GF}(q)$. Suppose that $M$ is represented as a set $S$ of points in $\mathrm{PG}(d-1, q)$. Let $X$ be a rank-$r$ flat of $M$. An $X$-*hyperplane* is a rank-$(r-1)$ subspace contained in the linear span $\mathrm{lin}(X)$ of $X$. Intuitively, the principal truncation $T_X(M)$ can be obtained geometrically by taking the quotient $M//Q$, where $Q$ is an $X$-hyperplane "in general position". While the notion of general position is vague, it is clear that if $Q$ is in general position, then none of the points in the flat $X$ is in $Q$, that is, $Q$ is an $X$-hyperplane distinguishing $M|X$. The next lemma[53] says that when $X$ is modular, this necessary condition is in fact sufficient.

8.25. LEMMA. *Let $M$ be a geometry represented as a set $S$ of points in $\mathrm{PG}(d-1, q)$, let $X$ be a modular flat of $M$, and let $Q$ be an $X$-hyperplane such that $Q \cap X = \emptyset$. Then the quotient $M//Q$ equals the principal truncation $T_X(M)$. In particular, if $Q$ and $R$ are two $X$-hyperplanes distinguishing $M|X$, then $M//Q = M//R$.*

PROOF. Suppose first that $Y$ is an $M$-flat containing $X$. Then its linear span $\mathrm{lin}(Y)$ contains $Q$, and $\mathrm{lin}(Y \cup Q) = \mathrm{lin}(Y)$. Hence, $Y$ is an $M//Q$-flat. Next, suppose that $X \nsubseteq Y$. If $Y \cap X \neq \emptyset$, then there exists a point in $Y \cap X$ not in $Q$. Hence, $X \subseteq \mathrm{lin}(Y \cup Q)$ and $Y$ is not closed in $M//Q$. If $Y \cap X = \emptyset$, then $Y \cap Q = \emptyset$,

$$\mathrm{rank}(\mathrm{lin}(Y \cup Q)) = \mathrm{rank}(Y) + \mathrm{rank}(Q),$$

---

[53]This lemma is basically Theorem 3.1 in Whittle [**157**] and Lemma 4.4 in Kung [**81**].

and $Y$ has the same rank in $M$ and $M//Q$. This implies that $Y$ is $M//Q$-closed, because if $Y$ is not $M//Q$-closed, then the $M//Q$-closure of $Y$ would be an $M$-flat with strictly higher rank in $M$, a contradiction.

We conclude that the flats of $M//Q$ consist of the $M$-flats $Y$ such that $X \subseteq Y$ or $Y \cap X = \emptyset$. Because $X$ is modular, the second condition is equivalent to the condition: $\mathrm{rank}(Y \vee X) = \mathrm{rank}(Y) + \mathrm{rank}(X)$. Therefore, $M//Q$ has the same flats as the principal truncation $T_X(M)$. $\qquad\square$

By the assumption that $c(M|X; q) = 1$, there exists an $X$-hyperplane $Q$ distinguishing $X$ in $\mathrm{PG}(d-1, q)$. Hence, $T_X(G)$ and its simplification can be represented in the contraction $\mathrm{PG}(d-1, q)/Q$.

The second condition to check is that the simplification of $T_X(M)$ is a $k$-block. To do this, we use the modular factorization identity 5.6 at $\lambda = q^k$ :

$$0 = (q^k - 1)\chi(M; q^k) = \chi(M|X; q^k)\chi(T_X(M); q^k).$$

Because $\chi(M|X; q^k)$ is non-zero, $\chi(T_X(M); q^k) = 0$, that is, $T_X(M)$ is a $k$-block.

The third and final condition to check is that for every flat $Y$ in the simplification of $T_X(M)$, the critical exponent $c(T_X(M)/Y; q)$ does not exceed $k$. Let $M$ be represented in $\mathrm{PG}(n-1, q)$ and let $Q$ be an $X$-hyperplane.

We shall consider the two types of flats in $T_X(M)$ separately. Suppose first that $Y$ is an $M$-flat containing $X$. Then $Q \subset \mathrm{lin}(X) \subseteq \mathrm{lin}(Y)$, and hence, $M/Y = (M//Q)/Y$. Because $c(M/Y; q) \leq k$, we conclude that $c((M//Q)/Y; q) \leq k$.

Next suppose that $Y$ is an $M$-flat such that $Y \cap X = \emptyset$. Then the set $X$ forms a modular flat in $M/Y$. In addition, $\mathrm{lin}(Y) \cap Q = \emptyset$ and the subspace $Q \vee \mathrm{lin}(Y)$ has codimension 1 relative to the subspace $\mathrm{lin}(X \vee Y)$. Hence, $Q \vee \mathrm{lin}(Y)$ is an $X$-hyperplane of the modular flat $X$ in the representation of $M/Y$ in $\mathrm{PG}(d-1, q)/Y$. We conclude that

(8.9) $T_X(M)/Y = (M//Q)/Y = M^+(S \cup Q)/(Q \cup Y) = (M/Y)//Q = T_X(M/Y),$

where $M^+$ is the extension of $M$ obtained by adding the points in the subspace $Q$ to $S$. By the modular factorization theorem,

$$(q^k - 1)\chi(M/Y; q^k) = \chi((M/Y)|X; q^k)\chi(T_X(M/Y); q^k).$$

Because $\chi(M/Y; q^k)$ is non-zero, $\chi(T_X(M/Y); q^k) \neq 0$. From this and equation (8.9), we conclude that $T_X(M)/Y$ has critical exponent at most $k$.

The second and third conditions can also be verified geometrically using the fact that $M$ and $T_X(M)$ can be simultaneously represented in $\mathrm{PG}(d-1, q^k)$. Let $M$ be represented in $\mathrm{PG}(d-1, q)$ and let $Q$ be an $X$-hyperplane distinguishing $X$, so that $T_X(M)$ is represented in $\mathrm{PG}(d-1, q)/Q$. We begin by checking that $T_X(M)$ is a 1-block over $\mathrm{GF}(q^k)$. Assume that $T_X(M)$ is not a 1-block. Then there exists a hyperplane $U$ in $\mathrm{PG}(d-1, q^k)/Q$ distinguishing $T_X(M)$. As a hyperplane in $\mathrm{PG}(d-1, q^k)$, $U$ contains none of the points in $S \backslash X$. In addition, $U \cap \mathrm{lin}(X) = Q$ and $U \cap X = \emptyset$. Hence, $U \cap S = \emptyset$, contradicting the assumption that $M$ is a 1-block over $\mathrm{GF}(q^k)$.

To finish the geometric verification, represent $T_X(M)$ as a quotient $M//Q$ in $\mathrm{PG}(n-1, q^k)$. We shall show that every non-empty flat $Y$ of $T_X(M)$ has a hyperplane tangent. To do this, we use the following observation:

*If $T$ is a hyperplane of $\mathrm{PG}(d-1, q^k)$ tangent to $Y$ as an $M$-flat and $T$ contains $Q$, then $T$, as a hyperplane of $\mathrm{PG}(d-1, q^k)/Q$, is a tangent of $Y$ as an $M//Q$-flat.*

As in the algebraic proof, there are two cases. If $Y$ contains $X$, then any hyperplane tangent to $Y$ contains $\mathrm{lin}(X)$ and hence $Q$. Therefore, any hyperplane $T$ tangent to $Y$ in $\mathrm{PG}(d-1, q^k)$ is also tangent to $Y$ in $\mathrm{PG}(d-1, q^k)/Q$.

Now suppose that $Y \cap X = \emptyset$. Let $T$ be a hyperplane in $\mathrm{PG}(d-1, q^k)$ tangent to $Y$ and let $T' = T \cap \mathrm{lin}(X)$. Then $T'$ is an $X$-hyperplane and $T' \cap X = \emptyset$. Hence, $Y$ has a hyperplane tangent to it as a flat in the quotient $M//T'$ and $\chi(M//T')/Y; q^k) \neq 0$. But by Lemma 8.25, $M//T' = T_X(M) = M//Q$. Hence, $\chi((M//Q)/Y; q^k) \neq 0$ and $Y$ has a hyperplane tangent in $\mathrm{PG}(d-1, q^k)/Q$. This completes the geometric verification. The modular factorization theorem has a counting proof based on counting distinguishing hyperplanes (see Kung [83]; a variation on this proof is sketched in Section 5.8). From the perspective of this counting proof, the algebraic and geometric proofs of Theorem 8.24 are essentially the same.

We remark that Lemma 8.25 has the following converse. *Let $M(S)$ be a rank-$n$ $\mathrm{GF}(q)$-representable geometry and let $X$ be a flat in $M$. Suppose that the following condition holds for at least $n$ distinct values of $t$: there exists a representation of $M$ as a set of points in a projective geometry $\mathrm{PG}(d-1, q^t)$ over an extension field of $\mathrm{GF}(q)$ of degree $t$ such that for every $X$-hyperplane $Q$ distinguishing the subgeometry $M|X$, the quotient $M//Q$ is isomorphic to the principal truncation $T_X(M)$. Then $X$ is modular in $M$.* This result can be proved using methods in Kung [83].

Theorem 8.24 was extended to quotients of a more general form in Whittle [158]. The following result is a geometric formulation of Whittle's main theorem in [158].

8.26. THEOREM. *Let $M(S)$ be a tangential $k$-block over $\mathrm{GF}(q)$ with a proper modular flat $X$. Suppose that $M$ is represented as a set $S$ of points in $\mathrm{PG}(d-1, q)$. Let $Q$ be a subspace in $\mathrm{PG}(d-1, q)$ contained in the linear span $\mathrm{lin}(X)$ of $X$ and let $M//Q$ be the quotient obtained by considering the points in $S$ as points in the contraction $\mathrm{PG}(d-1, q)/Q$. Suppose that*
(W1) *$Q \cap S = \emptyset$, and*
(W2) *for every $M//Q$-flat $Z$ properly contained in $X$,*

$$c([(M//Q)|X]/Z; q) \leq k.$$

*Then the simplification of the quotient $G//Q$ is a tangential $k$-block over $\mathrm{GF}(q)$.*

We shall prove Theorem 8.26 using a combination of algebraic and geometric methods. By construction, the quotient $M//Q$ is representable over $\mathrm{GF}(q)$. Because $Q \subseteq \mathrm{lin}(X)$ and $X$ is modular in $M$, the flat $X \cup Q$ is modular in the extension $M^+(S \cup Q)$. Hence, $X$ remains a modular flat when $Q$ is contracted to yield the quotient $M//Q$.

To check that $M//Q$ is a $k$-block, suppose that there exists a codimension-$k$ subspace $U$ disjoint from the set $\{x \vee Q : x \in S\}$ in $\mathrm{PG}(d-1, q)/Q$. Then $U$, as a subspace in $\mathrm{PG}(d-1, q)$, is disjoint from the set $S$, contradicting the assumption that $M$ is a $k$-block.

The major portion of the proof is to check that for every non-empty $M//Q$-flat $Y$, the critical exponent $c((M//Q)/Y; q)$ does not exceed $k$.

As in the proof of Theorem 8.24, there are two cases. The first case is when $Y$ is an $M//Q$-flat containing $X$. Then $Q \subset \mathrm{lin}(Y)$, and a codimension-$k$ subspace $T$ tangent to $Y$ contains $Q$. Hence, $T$ is also tangent to $Y$ as a subspace in $\mathrm{PG}(d - 1, q)/Q$. We conclude that $c((M//Q)/Y; q) \leq k$.

The second and more complicated case is when $X \not\subseteq Y$. Let $Z$ be the intersection $X \cap Y$. (The flat $Z$ may be empty.) Since both $X$ and $Y$ are $M//Q$-flats, $Z$ is also a $M//Q$-flat. Let $X' = X \backslash Z$. We shall first prove two technical lemmas.

8.27. LEMMA. *The set $X'$ has the same closure in $M/Y$ and $(M//Q)/Y$.*

PROOF. The closure of $X'$ in $M/Y$ equals

$$\mathrm{lin}(X' \cup Y) \cap (S \backslash Y).$$

But $X' \cup Y = X \cup Y$ and $Q \subset \mathrm{lin}(X)$. Hence,

(8.10)                $\mathrm{lin}(X' \cup Y) = \mathrm{lin}(X \cup Y) = \mathrm{lin}(X' \cup Q \cup Y).$

We conclude that $\mathrm{lin}(X' \cup Y) \cap (S \backslash Y)$ equals $\mathrm{lin}(X' \cup Q \cup Y) \cap (S \backslash Y)$, the closure of $X'$ in $(M//Q)/Y$.                ☐

We shall denote the closure of $X'$ in $M/Y$ or $(M//Q)/Y$ by $\overline{X'}$.

8.28. LEMMA.
(a) *The flat $\overline{X'}$ is modular in $M/Y$ and $(M//Q)/Y$.*
(b) *The simplifications of the two matroids $(M//Q)/Y)|\overline{X'}$ and $((M//Q)|X)/Z$ are isomorphic.*
(c) $T_{\overline{X'}}((M//Q)/Y) = T_{\overline{X'}}(M/Y).$

PROOF. Consider the flat $\overline{X'}$ in the lattice $L(M//Q)$ of flats. Then, by equation (8.10), $\overline{X'}$ equals the lattice join $X \vee Y$. Because $X$ is modular in $L(M//Q)$, $X \vee Y$ is modular in the upper interval $[Y, \hat{1}]$ in $L(M//Q)$. Hence, $\overline{X'}$ is a modular flat in $(M//Q)/Y$. A similar argument shows that $\overline{X'}$ is a modular flat in $M/Y$.

To prove part (b), we use the fact that $\overline{X'}$ equals $Y \vee X$ in the lattice $L(M//Q)$. Because $X$ is modular,

$$[Y, Y \vee X] \cong [Y \wedge X, X]$$

by the Dedekind transposition principle. Hence, the lattices of flats of the two matroids in part (b) are isomorphic, and hence, their simplifications are also isomorphic.

To prove part (c), observe that the matroid $(M//Q)/Y$ equals the contraction $M^+(S \cup Q)/(Q \cup Y)$, where $M^+(S \cup Q)$ is the extension of $M$ obtained by adding the points in $Q$ to $S$. By Lemma 8.25, the principal truncation $T_{\overline{X'}}((M//Q)/Y)$ equals $M//R$, where $R$ is an $\overline{X'}$-hyperplane such that $Q \cup Y \subseteq R$ and $R \cap \overline{X'} = \emptyset$. (Such an $X$-hyperplane exists in $\mathrm{PG}(d-1, q^t)$ for sufficiently large $t$.) Because $Y \subseteq R$ and $R \cap \overline{X'} = \emptyset$, we conclude from Lemma 8.25 that $M//R$ equals $T_{\overline{X'}}(M/Y)$. Hence, both matroids in part (c) equal $M//R$.                ☐

By the modular factorization theorem,

$$(q^k - 1)\chi((M//Q)/Y; q^k) = \chi(((M//Q)/Y)|\overline{X'}; q^k)\chi(T_{\overline{X'}}((M//Q)/Y); q^k).$$

We shall show that $\chi((M//Q)/Y; q^k) \neq 0$ by showing that both factors on the right hand side are non-zero. By Lemma 8.28(b), the first factor on the right hand side equals $\chi(((M//Q)|X)/Z; q^k)$. Hence, by condition (W2), the first factor is non-zero.

By Lemma 8.28(c), the second factor equals $\chi(T_{\overline{X'}}(M/Y); q^k)$. Because $M$ is a tangential $k$-block, $c(M/Y; q) \leq k$. Hence, applying the modular factorization theorem to the modular flat $\overline{X'}$ in $M/Y$, we obtain

$$0 \neq (q^k - 1)\chi(M/Y; q^k) = \chi((M/Y)|\overline{X'}; q^k)\chi(T_{\overline{X'}}(M/Y); q^k).$$

From this, we conclude that $\chi(T_{\overline{X'}}(M/Y); q^k)$, and hence $\chi(T_{\overline{X'}}((M//Q)/Y); q^k)$, is non-zero. This completes the proof of Theorem 8.26.

The abstract form of Whittle's theorem (Theorem 3.1 in [**158**]) is the following theorem: *Let $M'$ be a quotient of a tangential $k$-block over* $\mathrm{GF}(q)$. *Suppose that there exists an $M'$-flat $X$ satisfying the following conditions:*
(1) $M'$ *is* $\mathrm{GF}(q)$*-representable,*
(2) $M'$ *contains no loops,*
(3) $X$ *is modular as an $M$-flat,*
(4) $\mathrm{rank}_M(X) - \mathrm{rank}_{M'}(X) = \mathrm{rank}(M) - \mathrm{rank}(M')$, *and*
(5) *for every $M'$-flat $Z$ properly contained in $X$,* $c((M'|X)/Z; q) \leq k$.
*Then the simplification of $M'$ is a tangential $k$-block over* $\mathrm{GF}(q)$.

The only known way to obtain a quotient satisfying the five conditions given above is to take a quotient of the form $M//Q$ given in Theorem 8.26. The five conditions imply that there exists a major $M^+(S \cup E)$ of the quotient map $M \to M'$ on the disjoint union $S \cup E$ such that
(1) the rank of $E$ in the major $M^+$ equals $\mathrm{rank}(M) - \mathrm{rank}(M')$,
(2) $E$ is contained in the closure of $X$ in $M^+$, and
(3) $E$ is closed in $M^+$.
If Conjecture 1.1 holds, then there exists a major $M^+(S \cup E)$ satisfying these three conditions and the additional condition that it is $\mathrm{GF}(q)$-representable. In the major $M^+$, the set $E$ of added points spans a subspace $Q$ satisfying conditions (W1) and (W2) in Theorem 8.26. Hence, assuming Conjecture 1.1, the quotient $M'$ is of the form $M//Q$ and the abstract and geometric versions of Whittle's theorem are equivalent.

The method of taking quotients to produce new tangential blocks first appeared (in a somewhat disguised form) in papers of Datta [**38,39,40**]. Here is a generalization of one of his results.

8.29. THEOREM. *Let $M(S)$ be a rank-$n$ tangential $k$-block represented as a set of points in* $\mathrm{PG}(d-1, q)$. *Let $U$ be a rank-$(m+k)$ flat of $M$ and $Q$ be a rank-$m$ subspace of* $\mathrm{PG}(d-1, q)$ *contained in* $\mathrm{lin}(U)$. *Suppose that the following conditions hold.*
(D1) $Q \cap S = \emptyset$.
(D2) *If $Q'$ is a rank-$m$ subspace contained in* $\mathrm{lin}(U)$ *and $Q'$ does not equal $Q$, then* $Q' \cap S \neq \emptyset$.
(D3) *If $W$ is a rank-$(m+1)$ subspace in the interval* $[Q, \mathrm{lin}(U)]$ *in* $\mathrm{PG}(d-1, q)$, *then $S \cap W$ spans $W$, or, equivalently,* $\mathrm{rank}_G(W \cap S) = m+1$.
*Then the simplification of $M//Q$ is a tangential $k$-block over* $\mathrm{GF}(q)$.

To show that $M//Q$ is a tangential $k$-block, we need to check two conditions. The first condition, that $M//Q$ is a $k$-block, can be proved using the argument at the beginning of Theorem 8.26. The second condition, that every non-empty $M//Q$-flat $X$ has a codimension-$k$ tangent in the contraction $\mathrm{PG}(d-1, q)/Q$, is somewhat harder to verify. As in Theorem 8.26, it suffices to show that every non-empty $M//Q$-flat $X$ has a codimension-$k$ tangent in $\mathrm{PG}(d-1, q)$ containing the subspace $Q$.

Let $X$ be a non-empty $M//Q$-flat. Then $X$ is also an $M$-flat and there exists a codimension-$k$ subspace $T$ tangent to $X$ in $\mathrm{PG}(d-1, q)$. We shall prove the stronger result that every tangent $T$ of $X$ contains the subspace $Q$. Consider the intersection $T \cap \mathrm{lin}(U)$. By the submodular inequality,

$$m \leq \mathrm{rank}(T \cap \mathrm{lin}(U)) \leq m + k.$$

Hence, $T \cap \mathrm{lin}(U)$ contains a rank-$m$ subspace $Q'$ in the interval $[\hat{0}, \mathrm{lin}(U)]$. If $Q'$ equals $Q$, then we are done. Otherwise, consider the $M$-flat $Q' \cap S$. Its closure $\overline{Q' \cap S}$ in the quotient $M//Q$ equals

$$\mathrm{lin}((Q' \cap S) \vee Q) \cap S.$$

By (D2), the flat $Q' \cap S$ is non-empty. In particular, it contains a point outside $Q$. Hence, $\mathrm{lin}((Q' \cap S) \vee Q)$ is a subspace in $[Q, \mathrm{lin}(U)]$ with rank exceeding $m$ and it contains a subspace $W$ of rank-$(m+1)$ in $[Q, \mathrm{lin}(U)]$. Now observe that

$$W \cap S \subseteq \overline{Q' \cap S} \subseteq T \cap S = X.$$

Thus, by (D3),

$$Q \subseteq W = \mathrm{lin}(W \cap S) \subseteq \mathrm{lin}(X) \subseteq T.$$

We conclude that $Q \subseteq T$. This completes the proof of Theorem 8.29.

Theorem 8.29 is useful for proving that tangential blocks do not exist. For example, when $q = k = 2$, it follows from Theorem 8.29 that if there are no rank-$n$ tangential 2-blocks, then every plane in a rank-$(n+1)$ tangential 2-block can contain at most 5 points. Because there are no rank-5 tangential 2-blocks over $\mathrm{GF}(2)$ (Tutte [136]), this implies that the rank-6 tangential 2-block $M^{\perp}(P_{10})$ has no $M(K_4)$-subgeometry. Using results of this kind, Datta [38,40] showed that there are no tangential 2-blocks over $\mathrm{GF}(2)$ having rank 7 or 8.

## 8.8. Constructing tangential blocks

In this section, we shall construct tangential blocks by taking $q$-lifts and quotients. Most of the theorems and examples are derived from Whittle's papers [156,157,158,160].

Our first example is a tangential 1-block over $\mathrm{GF}(4)$ obtained by taking the principal truncation of $M^{\perp}(P_{10})$ at a 3-point line. This yields a non-binary 13-point rank-5 geometry $T_{M(K_3)}(M^{\perp}(P_{10}))$. By equation (6.2) in Section 6.5 and the modular factorization theorem 5.6, its characteristic polynomial equals

$$(\lambda - 1)(\lambda - 3)(\lambda - 4)(\lambda^2 - 10\lambda + 5).$$

Note that by Theorem 8.29 or by case-checking, $M^{\perp}(P_{10})$ has no subgeometry isomorphic to $M(K_4)$, and hence, no modular planes. From this, it is easy to deduce that there are no modular flats in $M^{\perp}(P_{10})$ having rank 3 or higher. Therefore, one cannot apply the principal truncation or quotient construction to $M^{\perp}(P_{10})$ to obtain another tangential 1-block. Note also that the principal truncation of $M(K_5)$ at a (modular) 3-point line is the rank-3 tangential 1-block $T$. The six examples in Section 8.3 and the principal truncation $T_{M(K_3)}(M^{\perp}(P_{10}))$ constitute all the currently known tangential 1-blocks over $\mathrm{GF}(4)$.

There are two general methods for producing tangential blocks with modular copoints. The first method produces tangential blocks by taking principal truncations of $M(K_{q^k+1})$, or, more generally, suitable Dowling group geometries.

8.30. COROLLARY.
*(a) Let $1 \leq m \leq q-1$ and let $X$ be a rank-m modular flat in $M(K_{q^k+1})$. Then the principal truncation $T_X(M(K_{q^k+1}))$ is a tangential k-block over $\mathrm{GF}(q)$.*
*(b) Let $A$ be a subgroup of the multiplicative group $\mathrm{GF}(q)^\times$, let $n = ((q^k-1)/|A|)+1$, and let $1 \leq m \leq ((q-2)/|A|)+1$. Let $X$ be a rank-m modular flat in $Q_n(A)$. Then the principal truncation $T_X(Q_n(A))$ is a tangential k-block over $\mathrm{GF}(q)$.*

PROOF. When $1 \leq m \leq q-1$, the characteristic polynomial $\chi((M(K_{m+1}); \lambda)$ has zeroes at $\lambda = 1, 2, \ldots, m$. Hence, $\chi((M(K_{m+1}); q) \neq 0$, $c(M(K_{m+1}); q) = 1$, and Theorem 8.24 can be applied. The proof of part (b) is similar.  $\square$

Note that a rank-$m$ modular flat in $M(K_{q^k+1})$ is isomorphic to $M(K_{m+1})$. Hence, for a given rank $m$, all the principal truncations $T_X(M(K_{q^k+1}))$ are isomorphic. A similar remark applies to $Q_n(A)$.

Corollary 8.30 and Theorem 8.14 imply that there are rank-$r$ tangential $k$-blocks with modular copoints over $\mathrm{GF}(q)$ if $q^k - q + 2 \leq r \leq q^k$. In particular, when $2 \leq r \leq q$, there are rank-$r$ tangential 1-blocks with modular copoints over $\mathrm{GF}(q)$.

The second method uses the method in the proof of Theorem 8.26 to produce supersolvable tangential $k$-blocks. To use Theorem 8.26, we have to verify condition (W2). In general, this is quite difficult. However, when we know that $\mathrm{rank}((M//Q)|X) \leq k$, verifying (W2) is automatic because a $k$-block has rank at least $k + 1$.

8.31. COROLLARY. *Let $M(S)$ be a supersolvable rank-n tangential k-block over $\mathrm{GF}(q)$. Suppose that $n > k+1$. Then there exists a proper elementary quotient, that is, a rank-$(n-1)$ quotient, of $M$ which is a supersolvable tangential k-block over $\mathrm{GF}(q)$.*

PROOF. Represent $M$ as a set $S$ of points in $\mathrm{PG}(n-1, q)$. Let $X_0 < X_1 < X_2 < \ldots < X_n$ be a modular flag in $M$. Let $j$ be the minimum index such that

$$\mathrm{lin}(X_j) \setminus X_j \neq \emptyset,$$

or, equivalently, $X_j$ is not a subspace in $\mathrm{PG}(n-1, q)$. Because the rank-$(k+1)$ projective geometry $\mathrm{PG}(k, q)$ is a tangential $k$-block, the index $j$ does not exceed $k+1$. Since $n > k+1$, $X_j$ is a proper flat. Let $z$ be a point in $\mathrm{lin}(X_j) \setminus X_j$. Consider the quotient $M//z$. Because $z \notin S$, (W1) is satisfied. Because $\mathrm{rank}(X_j) = j \leq k+1$,

$$\mathrm{rank}((M//z)|X_j) = \mathrm{rank}(X_j) - 1 \leq k.$$

Hence, (W2) is satisfied. We conclude that $M//z$ is a tangential $k$-block.

To finish the proof, let $\overline{X}$ be the closure of the $M$-flat $X$ in $M//z$. Consider the flag
$$\overline{X_0} < \overline{X_1} < \overline{X_2} < \ldots < \overline{X_{j-1}} < \overline{X_{j+1}} < \overline{X_{j+2}} < \ldots < \overline{X_n}$$
in $M//z$. The first $j$ flats $\overline{X_0}, \overline{X_1}, \ldots, \overline{X_{j-1}}$ are modular because that they are subspaces in $PG(n-1, q)/z$. The remaining flats are modular by the lattice-theoretic argument in the proof of Lemma 8.28(a). We conclude that $M//z$ is supersolvable.  $\square$

Corollary 8.31 and Theorem 8.14 imply that there are rank-$r$ supersolvable tangential $k$-blocks over $GF(q)$ if and only if $k + 1 \leq r \leq q^k$.

By analysing carefully where the points in $S$ are projected under contraction by $z$, we can derive the characteristic polynomial of $M//z$ from the characteristic polynomial of $M$. Let $\chi(M; \lambda) = \prod_{i=1}^{n}(\lambda - a_i)$, where $a_i = |X_i \setminus X_{i-1}|$. By the choice of $j$, the flats $X_0, X_1, X_2, \ldots, X_{j-1}$ are isomorphic to (full) projective geometries. Hence, $a_i = q^{i-1}$ for $1 \leq i \leq j - 1$ and

$$\chi(M; \lambda) = (\lambda - 1)(\lambda - q)(\lambda - q^2) \cdots (\lambda - q^{j-2})(\lambda - a_j)(\lambda - a_{j+1}) \cdots (\lambda - a_n).$$

Similarly, because $\overline{X_i}$ are subspaces,

$$|\overline{X_i} \setminus \overline{X_{i-1}}| = q^{i-1},$$

for $1 \leq i \leq j - 1$.

Next, let $x$ be a point in $|X_j \setminus X_{j-1}|$. Because $\mathrm{lin}(X_j) = X_{j-1} \vee z$ in $PG(n-1, q)$, the point $x$ is projected by $z$ onto a point in $X_{j-1}$. Therefore, every point in $|X_j \setminus X_{j-1}|$ is parallel to some point in $X_{j-1}$ in $M//z$ and is deleted when $M//z$ is simplified. In particular, points in $|X_j \setminus X_{j-1}|$ do not play a role in the calculation of the characteristic polynomial of $M//z$.

Finally, consider the points in $S \setminus X_j$. Let $x$ be a such a point. Because $X_j$ is modular in $M$ and $z$ is not a point in $X_j$, the line $x \vee z$ in $PG(n-1, q)$ contains $x$ and no other point in $S$. From this, we conclude that all the points in $S \setminus X_j$ remain distinct in the quotient $M//z$. Hence,

$$|\overline{X_{j+1}} \setminus \overline{X_{j-1}}| = |X_{j+1} \setminus X_j| = a_{j+1}$$

and for $j + 2 \leq i \leq n$,

$$|\overline{X_i} \setminus \overline{X_{i-1}}| = |X_i \setminus X_{i-1}| = a_i.$$

By Theorem 5.7, we conclude that

$$\chi(M//z; \lambda) = \chi(M; \lambda)/(\lambda - a_j)$$
$$= (\lambda - 1)(\lambda - q)(\lambda - q^2) \cdots (\lambda - q^{j-2})(\lambda - a_{j+1})(\lambda - a_{j+2}) \cdots (\lambda - a_n).$$

We are now ready for our second and third examples. In the second example, we consider the case of tangential 3-blocks over $GF(2)$. By Theorem 8.21, a 2-lift of a tangential 2-block over $GF(2)$ is a tangential 3-block. Thus, from the three known tangential 2-blocks over $GF(2)$, we obtain three tangential 3-blocks over $GF(2)$:

(1)  $PG(2,2)^{\#}$, which is isomorphic to $PG(3,2)$,
(2)  $M(K_5)^{\#}$, and
(3)  $M^{\perp}(P_{10})^{\#}$.

That we can obtain exactly three tangential 3-blocks by the 2-lift construction follows from the fact that any two representations of a binary matroid over $GF(2)$ are projectively equivalent. (See, for example, Oxley [106], Section 10.1.) The first two tangential 3-blocks are supersolvable. By equation (8.5),

$$\chi(M(K_5)^{\#}; \lambda) = (\lambda - 1)(\lambda - 2)(\lambda - 4)(\lambda - 6)(\lambda - 8).$$

By Theorem 8.23,

$$\chi(M^{\perp}(P_{10})^{\#}; \lambda) = (\lambda - 1)(\lambda - 2)(\lambda - 4)(\lambda - 6)(\lambda - 8)(\lambda^2 - 10\lambda + 40).$$

In addition to these tangential 3-blocks, there is the "classical" tangential 3-block $M(K_9)$. Taking quotients in $M(K_9)$ as in the proof of Corollary 8.31, we obtain tangential 3-blocks with the following rank and characteristic polynomials:

| Rank | Characteristic polynomial |
|------|---------------------------|
| 8 | $(\lambda - 1)(\lambda - 2)(\lambda - 3)(\lambda - 4)(\lambda - 5)(\lambda - 6)(\lambda - 7)(\lambda - 8)$ |
| 7 | $(\lambda - 1)(\lambda - 2)(\lambda - 4)(\lambda - 5)(\lambda - 6)(\lambda - 7)(\lambda - 8)$ |
| 6 | $(\lambda - 1)(\lambda - 2)(\lambda - 4)(\lambda - 6)(\lambda - 7)(\lambda - 8)$ |
| 5 | $(\lambda - 1)(\lambda - 2)(\lambda - 4)(\lambda - 7)(\lambda - 8)$ |

The rank-8 tangential 3-block is $M(K_9)$ as an improper quotient of itself. The rank-7 tangential 3-block $N_7$ is obtained by taking a rank-3 modular flat $X_3$ (which is necessarily isomorphic to $M(K_4)$), choosing the unique point $z$ in $\text{lin}(X_3) \setminus X_3$, and contracting that point.

The geometry $N_7$ can be represented in $PG(6, 2)$ in the following way. Let $e_1, e_2, e_3, e_4, e_5, e_6, e_7$ be a basis of $PG(6, 2)$ and let $L$ be the line $\{e_1, e_1 + e_2, e_2\}$. Then $N_7$ is represented by the set consisting of all the points in the planes $L \vee e_i$, $3 \leq i \leq 7$, together with the points $e_j + e_k$, $3 \leq j < k \leq 7$. The geometry $N_7$ is supersolvable and has a modular flag for which $X_0$ is the empty set, $X_1$ is the point $e_1$, $X_2$ is the line $L$, $X_3$ is the plane $L \vee e_3$ (which is isomorphic to the Fano plane), and $X_4$ is the subset of points in $N_7$ in the linear span of $e_1, e_2, e_3, e_4$. The flat $X_4$ contains 12 points and the three points in the subspace $\text{lin}(X_4)$ not in $X_4$ are $e_1 + e_2 + e_3 + e_4$, $e_1 + e_2 + e_4$, and $e_1 + e_3 + e_4$. It is easy to check that these three points are in the same orbit of the subgroup of automorphisms of $PG(6, 2)$ which fixes $N_7$ as a set. Hence, the three quotients obtained by adding and then contracting one of these points are isomorphic.

Taking the quotient $N_7 // e_1 + e_2 + e_3 + e_4$, we obtain a rank-6 tangential 3-block $N_6$. The geometry $N_6$ is supersolvable and has a modular flag in which the flats $X_1$, $X_2$, and $X_3$ are full projective geometries, and the flat $X_4$ is isomorphic to the geometry obtained from $PG(3, 2)$ by removing two points. This can be seen geometrically or from the characteristic polynomial. Using a variant of the argument in the previous case, we conclude that the quotients obtained by adding and contracting either of these points are isomorphic. This yields a rank-5 tangential 3-block $N_5$. In the modular flag in $N_5$, the flats $X_1$, $X_2$, and $X_3$ are full projective geometries. The flat $X_4$ is isomorphic to $PG(3, 2)$ with one point removed. If we take the quotient using this point, then we obtain $PG(3, 2)$.

Summarizing our analysis, the tangential 3-blocks $N_7$, $N_6$, and $N_5$ are all the tangential blocks obtainable by the construction given in Corollary 8.31. This confirms a statement in Whittle [158]. Explicit representations of these tangential blocks can be found in [158]. Note that the characteristic polynomial of $M(K_5)^\#$ does not equal the characteristic polynomial of the quotient $N_5$. Hence, they are not isomorphic. Note also that $M(K_r)$ is not affine over $GF(2)$ for $3 \leq r \leq 7$. Thus, the principal truncation construction cannot be used to obtain further tangential 3-blocks.

In our third and last example, we shall consider tangential 2-blocks over $GF(3)$. The 3-lift construction yields two tangential 2-blocks,

(1) $U_{2,4}^\#$, which is isomorphic to $PG(2, 3)$, and

(2) $M(K_4)^\#$.

Because any two representations of a ternary matroid over $GF(3)$ are projectively equivalent, the 3-lift construction yields precisely these two tangential 2-blocks.

From the tangential 2-block $M(K_{10})$, one obtains quotients having ranks 4 to 9 using the construction given in Corollary 8.31. Because there is "more space" in ternary projective geometries, it is plausible that there is more than one isomorphism class of quotients for some of these ranks, but this has not been verified rigorously. A list of the characteristic polynomials of these quotients can be found in [158].

In addition to these tangential 2-blocks, one can also take quotients of the rank-5 tangential 2-block $Q_5(GF(3)^\times)$ using the construction in Corollary 8.31. We obtain tangential 2-blocks with the following ranks and characteristic polynomials.

| Rank | Characteristic polynomial |
|------|---------------------------|
| 5 | $(\lambda - 1)(\lambda - 3)(\lambda - 5)(\lambda - 7)(\lambda - 9)$ |
| 4 | $(\lambda - 1)(\lambda - 3)(\lambda - 7)(\lambda - 9)$ |

The rank-5 tangential 2-block is $Q_5(GF(3)^\times)$ itself. To obtain the rank-4 tangential 2-block, we take a rank-3 modular flat $X_3$. The flat $X_3$ is isomorphic to $Q_3(GF(3)^\times)$ and there are four points outside $X_3$ in the plane $P$ spanned by $X_3$ in $PG(4,3)$. It is easy to check that all four points are intersections of two lines in $P$ obtained by taking the closure of a joint and an internal point in $X_3$. It follows from this that all four points are in the same orbit of the subgroup of automorphisms of $PG(4,3)$ which fixes a given $Q_5(GF(q)^\times)$-subgeometry as a subset. Therefore, all four quotients are isomorphic.

Most of the preceding examples are untypical. For larger prime powers $q$, non-isomorphic quotients can be obtained by different choices of the point $z$. Whittle has shown in [157] that there are three different rank-3 quotients of $M(K_6)$ which are tangential 1-blocks over $GF(5)$. Two of these are obtained from a construction of the type given in Corollary 8.31. Besides the construction given in Corollary 8.31, there are many other ways to obtain supersolvable tangential $k$-blocks by taking quotients of $M(K_{q^k+1})$. In fact, Whittle has conjectured[54] that every supersolvable tangential $k$-block is a quotient of $M(K_{q^k+1})$. As a difficult exercise, the reader can verify that if $A$ is a subgroup of $GF(q)^\times$, then the Dowling group geometry $Q_n(A)$, where $n$ is given by equation (8.1), is a quotient of $M(K_{q^k+1})$. Yet another plausible conjecture is that every tangential block with a modular copoint is supersolvable.

## 8.9. Maximum classes having a given critical exponent

Let $\mathcal{M}(k;q)$ be the minor-closed class obtained by excluding all the tangential $k$-blocks over $GF(q)$ from $\mathcal{L}(q)$, that is,

$$\mathcal{M}(k;q) = \mathcal{EX}(M_1, M_2, \dots) \cap \mathcal{L}(q),$$

where $M_1, M_2, \dots$ are all the tangential $k$-blocks over $GF(q)$. There are two other ways to describe $\mathcal{M}(k;q)$ :

(MC1)  $\mathcal{M}(k;q)$ is the class of all geometries $G$ in $\mathcal{L}(q)$ such that $G$ and *all* the minors of $G$ have critical exponent less than or equal to $k$.

---

[54]This conjecture appeared in Whittle's thesis [156]. An account can be found in Brylawski and Oxley [31], p. 175.

(MC2) $\mathcal{M}(k;q)$ is the union of all the minor-closed classes in $\mathcal{L}(q)$ having critical exponent $k$ or less. Thus, it is the *maximum* minor-closed class (under set-theoretic containment) in $\mathcal{L}(q)$ having critical exponent $k$.

We call $\mathcal{M}(k;q)$ the *maximum minor-closed class of* GF$(q)$-*representable geometries with critical exponent* $k$. It follows from (MC2) that if $\mathcal{C}$ is a minor-closed class in $\mathcal{L}(q)$, then $c(\mathcal{C};q) \leq k$ if and only if $\mathcal{C} \subseteq \mathcal{M}(k,q)$.

There are only two maximum minor-closed classes which have been completely described. These correspond to the cases described in Theorem 8.8: $\mathcal{M}(1;2)$ equals $\mathcal{U}(1)$ and $\mathcal{M}(1;3)$ equals $\mathcal{EX}(M(K_4)) \cap \mathcal{L}(2)$, the class of series-parallel graphic geometries. If the tangential 2-block conjecture holds, then

$$\mathcal{M}(2;2) = \mathcal{EX}(F_7, M(K_5), M^{\perp}(P_{10})) \cap \mathcal{L}(2).$$

A more explicit form of Conjecture 7.6 can be formulated using maximum classes.

8.32. CONJECTURE. *There exists a constant* $a(k,q)$ *depending on* $k$ *and* $q$ *such that*

$$h(\mathcal{M}(k;q);n) \leq a(k,q)n.$$

Note that when $n \geq q^k - 1$, generalized parallel connections of $n - q^k + 2$ copies of $M(K_{q^k})$ at modular copoints [which must be isomorphic to $M(K_{q^k-1})$] have rank $n$ and

$$(q^k - 1)(n - q^k - 1) + \binom{q^k}{2}$$

points. Because these parallel connections are in $\mathcal{M}(k;q)$,

(8.11) $$a(k,q) \geq q^k - 1.$$

Conjecture 8.32 is known for three cases. The first two cases are consequences of Theorem 8.8. Because $\mathcal{M}(1;2)$ equals $\mathcal{U}(1)$,

$$h(\mathcal{M}(1;2);n) = n.$$

Because $\mathcal{M}(1,3)$ is the class of series-parallel graphic geometries,

$$h(\mathcal{M}(1;3);n) = 2n - 1.$$

This formula can be deduced directly from the structure of series-parallel graphs or from Dirac's theorem [41] that a graph with $v$ vertices and no $K_4$-minor has at most $2v - 3$ edges. The last case is more complicated.

8.33. THEOREM.

$$h(\mathcal{M}(2;2);n) = 3n - 3.$$

PROOF. It is known that $F_7$ and $M(K_5)$ are tangential 2-blocks over GF(2). Hence,

$$\mathcal{M}(2;2) \subseteq \mathcal{EX}(F_7, M(K_5)) \cap \mathcal{L}(2).$$

Because

(8.12) $$h(\mathcal{EX}(F_7, M(K_5)) \cap \mathcal{L}(2);n) = 3n - 3,$$

(see Kung [75], p. 856), the size function $h(\mathcal{M}(2;2);n)$ is bounded above by $3n-3$. Hence, by equation (8.11), it is exactly $3n - 3$. $\qquad\square$

Equation (8.12) also yields the following theorem. This theorem shows how results about the size function yield results about the minor structure of tangential blocks.

8.34. THEOREM. *The critical exponent of the class* $\mathcal{EX}(F_7, M(K_5)) \cap \mathcal{L}(2)$ *equals* 3. *In particular, every tangential 3-block over* $\mathrm{GF}(2)$ *contains a minor isomorphic to* $F_7$ *or* $M(K_5)$.

Theorem 8.34 follows from equation (8.12), Lemma 7.5, and the fact that $M^{\perp}(P_{10})$ has critical exponent 3 but contains no minor isomorphic to $F_7$ or $M(K_5)$.

Theorem 8.33 may also be of relevance to the tangential 2-block conjecture 8.9. It says that a rank-$n$ tangential 2-block not isomorphic to $F_7$ or $M(K_5)$ can have at most $3n - 3$ points.

By Lemma 8.1,

$$\mathcal{M}(k; q) \subseteq \mathcal{M}(1; q^k).$$

Therefore, to prove Conjecture 8.32 it suffices to prove it for the cases when $k = 1$. Because $M(K_{q^k+1})$ is a tangential $k$-block over $\mathrm{GF}(q)$, Conjecture 8.32 is implied by and is strictly weaker than the growth rate conjecture 7.9. It seems that the size function of $\mathcal{M}(k; q)$ does not depend on nasty blocks. To be more precise, it is plausible that the two classes $\mathcal{M}(k; q)$ and $\mathcal{EX}(\mathcal{S}_k(q)) \cap \mathcal{L}(q)$, where $\mathcal{S}_k(q)$ is the (finite) set of supersolvable tangential $k$-blocks over $\mathrm{GF}(q)$, have the same size function. We note that when $q$ is a prime $p$, then it is known (Kung [**79**]) that

$$h(\mathcal{EX}(U_{2,p+1}) \cap \mathcal{L}(p); n) \le c_p \binom{n}{2}$$

where $c_p$ is a constant depending on $p$. Thus, excluding the smallest tangential 1-block $U_{2,p+1}$ over $\mathrm{GF}(p)$ reduces the size function of $\mathcal{L}(p)$ from an exponential function to a quadratic function.

## 8.10. Minors of tangential blocks

Motivated by the fact that in a tangential block with a modular copoint, the complement of the modular copoint spans, Whittle made the following conjecture[55] in his thesis [**156**].

8.35. CONJECTURE. *Let* $M(S)$ *be a tangential $k$-block over* $\mathrm{GF}(q)$. *Then there exists a copoint* $X$ *in* $M(S)$ *such that its complement* $S \backslash X$ *is spanning.*

Note that odd circuits with at least 5 points over $\mathrm{GF}(2)$ show that Conjecture 8.35 does not hold for minimal blocks.

If Conjecture 8.35 were true, then it would be a very useful tool for doing inductions. We shall demonstrate this by showing how Conjecture 8.35 could be used to improve the bound given in equation (7.4) in Section 7.3.

8.36. PROPOSITION. *Suppose that Conjecture 8.35 is true for $k = 4$ and $q = 2$. Then*

$$c(\mathcal{EX}(M(K_5)) \cap \mathcal{L}(2); 2) \le 4,$$

*or, equivalently, every tangential 4-block over* $\mathrm{GF}(2)$ *contains an* $M(K_5)$*-minor.*

---

[55] An account can be found on p. 175 of Brylawski and Oxley [**31**].

PROOF. We shall show that if $M(S)$ is a tangential 4-block over GF(2), then it contains an $M(K_5)$-minor. Assuming that Conjecture 8.35 holds, let $X$ be a copoint in $M(S)$ such that the complement $S\backslash X$ is spanning. By Lemma 8.4, the restriction $M|X$ is a 3-block. Hence, by Lemma 8.3 and Theorem 8.34, $M|X$ contains a minor isomorphic to $F_7$ or $M(K_5)$. If $M|X$ contains an $M(K_5)$-minor, then we are done. Otherwise, by the scum theorem,[56] there exists a flat $Y$ contained in $X$ such that
(1) rank$(Y) = $ rank$(X) - 3$, and
(2) the contraction $(M|X)/Y$ is isomorphic to $F_7$.
Consider the contraction $M/Y$. It contains a copoint $X'$ isomorphic to $F_7$. The copoint $X'$ is modular. Because $S\backslash X$ contains a basis of $M$, the complement of $X'$ contains a basis of $M/Y$. By Lemma 5.14, $M/Y$ contains an $M(K_5)$-subgeometry. $\square$

Using the same method, one can prove that Conjecture 8.35 implies Conjecture 7.8.

We remark that Conjectures 7.8 and 7.10 can be formulated in terms of minors of tangential blocks. For example, Conjecture 7.10 is equivalent to the following statement:

There exists a constant $\psi(m)$ such that every tangential $\psi(m)$-block (over any finite field) contains an $M(K_m)$-minor.

The smallest non-trivial case of this conjecture is Brylawski's conjecture [21] that every tangential 2-block contains an $M(K_4)$-minor. One way to approach Brylawski's conjecture inductively is to consider minors of tangential 1-blocks. Tugger [131] has made the following conjecture.

8.37. CONJECTURE. Every tangential 1-block over GF($q$) contains a minor isomorphic to the $(q+1)$-point line $U_{2,q+1}$, the cycle geometry $M(K_4)$, or the 3-whirl $\mathcal{W}_3$.

Tugger's conjecture holds for $q = 2$ and $q = 3$ by Theorem 8.8. Note that the jointless Dowling group geometry $Q'_3(\mathrm{GF}(2^t)^\times)$ is a tangential 1-block over GF($2^t$) with no minor isomorphic to $U_{2,q+1}$ or $M(K_4)$. Hence, the 3-whirl is necessary in Tugger's conjecture when $q$ is a power of 2. However, when $q$ is an odd prime power, it is plausible that the stronger conjecture, that every tangential 1-block over GF($q$) contains a minor isomorphic to $U_{2,q+1}$ or $M(K_4)$, is true.

## 8.11. Tangential blocks in $\mathcal{Z}(A)$

In this section, we give an account of what is currently known about tangential blocks in $\mathcal{Z}(A)$, the class of gain-graphic geometries over the finite group $A$. Tangential blocks in $\mathcal{Z}(A)$ were first studied in Whittle [161].

The critical problem in $\mathcal{Z}(A)$ can be defined using $s$-tuples of hyperplanes or copoints in $Q_d(A)$ (Section 4.4) or $s$-tuples of $d$-dimensional abstract linear functionals (Section 4.5). A geometry $M(S)$ in $\mathcal{Z}(A)$ is a $k$-block (in $\mathcal{Z}(A)$) if $c(M; A) > k$. A minimal $k$-block is a restriction-minimal $k$-block and a tangential $k$-block is a minor-minimal $k$-block.

There is a basic difference between projective geometries and Dowling group geometries. In a projective geometry, every subspace is modular and the intersection of $k$ hyperplanes is a subspace having codimension at most $k$. This is false in a

---

[56]See, for example, Kung [72].

Dowling group geometry. Much of the theory of blocks can be saved, however, by the following analogue of Lemma 8.1.

8.38. LEMMA. *Let $M(S)$ be a $k$-block in $\mathcal{Z}(A)$. Then $M(S)$ is a 1-block in $\mathcal{Z}(A')$, where $A'$ is a group of order $(|A| + 1)^k - 1$ containing $A$ as a subgroup. In particular, a geometry $M(S)$ in $\mathcal{Z}(A)$ is a minimal (respectively, tangential) $k$-block in $\mathcal{Z}(A)$ if and only if it is a minimal (respectively, tangential) 1-block in $\mathcal{Z}(A')$.*

Note that one can construct a group $A'$ satisfying the condition in Lemma 8.38 by taking the direct product of $A$ with a group, say, the cyclic group, of order $[(|A| + 1)^k - 1]/|A|$. By Lemma 8.38, the theory of tangential $k$-blocks can be reduced to the theory of tangential 1-blocks. The advantage with 1-blocks is that we need only consider hyperplanes and not intersections of hyperplanes.

Let $M$ be a rank-$n$ gain-graphic geometry represented as a set $S$ of points in $Q_d(A)$. Let $X$ be a flat of $M$. A hyperplane $U$ in $Q_d(A)$ is a *tangent* of $X$ if $U \cap S = X$. It is easy to see that $M(S)$ is a tangential 1-block in $\mathcal{Z}(A)$ if and only if $c(M; A) > 1$ and every non-empty flat of rank at most $n - 1$ has a hyperplane tangent to it. Using this, one concludes, as in Section 8.1, that $M(S)$ is a tangential $k$-block if and only if $M(S)$ is a $k$-block and for every proper flat $X$ of $M(S)$, the contraction $M/X$ has critical exponent at most $k$.

Most of the theorems in Section 8.1 have direct analogues in $\mathcal{Z}(A)$. For example, Lemma 8.5 holds in the following form. *Let $M(S)$ be a minimal $k$-block and let $X$ be a copoint in $M$. Then the bond $S \backslash X$ contains at least $(|A| + 1)^k$ points.* To prove this, use the argument in the geometric proof of Theorem 8.16.

Because Dowling group geometries are not modular, one result which has to be modified substantially is Lemma 8.4. The correct analogue is obtained by restricting intersections to intersections with modular flats. This results in the weaker lemma: *Let $M(S)$ be a $k$-block represented as a subset in $Q_d(A)$ and let $k'$ be a positive integer strictly less than $k$. Then the intersection of $S$ with any modular flat of corank $k'$ is a $(k - k')$-block.* Note that a rank-$r$ flat $X$ is modular in $Q_d(A)$ if and only if $X$ is isomorphic to $Q_r(A)$.

For the same reason, the proofs of Theorems 8.12, 8.13 and 8.15 require some modification. However, the portion of the proof showing that a minimal block satisfies (MM1) and (MM2) carries over directly. More precisely, one can prove, using basically the same argument, that if $M(S)$ is a minimal or tangential $k$-block in $\mathcal{Z}(A)$ with a modular copoint $X$, then

$$|S \backslash X| = (|A| + 1)^k,$$

and $X$ is minimally modular. From these facts and Lemma 8.11, one concludes that for a given finite group $|A|$ and a given positive integer $k$, there are finitely many minimal or tangential $k$-blocks with a modular copoint in $\mathcal{Z}(A)$. The argument using Oxley's identity in the proof of Theorem 8.16 also carries over directly. It gives an alternate proof that for given $|A|$ and $k$, there are finitely many tangential $k$-blocks with a modular copoint in $\mathcal{Z}(A)$.

As we have seen in Sections 7.4 and 7.5, the analogues of Conjectures 7.9 and 7.10 hold for $\mathcal{Z}(A)$.

There are two infinite families of tangential blocks (Whittle [161]): the (full) Dowling group geometries and the jointless Dowling geometries. For a given group $A$ and a given integer $k$, the following are tangential $k$-blocks in $\mathcal{Z}(A)$.

(1)  The Dowling geometries $Q_n(B)$, where $B$ is a subgroup of $A$ and

$$n = \frac{(|A| + 1)^k - 1}{|B|} + 1.$$

(2)  The jointless Dowling geometries $Q'_n(B)$, where $B$ is a subgroup of $A$ and

$$n = \frac{(|A| + 1)^k - 1}{|B|} + 2.$$

For example, the cycle geometry $M(K_{|A|+2})$, the Dowling geometry $Q_2(A)$ (which is isomorphic to the $(|A| + 2)$-point line $U_{2,|A|+2}$), and the jointless Dowling geometry $Q'_3(A)$ are tangential 1-blocks in $\mathcal{Z}(A)$.

Because $M^{\perp}(P_{10})$ is not gain-graphic, there are no known "sporadic" gain-graphic tangential blocks. In addition, there seems no natural way to define "$A$-lifts" of gain-graphic geometries. Quotients of the known gain-graphic tangential blocks are generally not gain-graphic. However, there is one important exception. Let $M(S)$ be a tangential $k$-block in $\mathcal{Z}(A)$ embedded as a set of points in $Q_d(A)$. Suppose that there is a line $L$ in $M$ which is modular in $M$ such that $L$ does not equal $\overline{L}$, where $\overline{L}$ is the closure of $L$ in $Q_d(A)$. Then, using the argument in the proof of Theorem 8.26, the simplification of the quotient $M//z$, where $z$ is a point in $\overline{L} \backslash L$, is a tangential $k$-block in $\mathcal{Z}(A)$. Because $L$ is modular, $M//z$ is isomorphic to the principal truncation $T_L(M)$. Figure 6 shows an example of this construction.

Just as for the classes $\mathcal{L}(q)$, the problem of determining all the tangential $k$-blocks in $\mathcal{Z}(A)$ for given $k$ and $A$ is very difficult in general. Two easy cases can be deduced from Theorem 8.8. The first is the graphic case when $k = 1$ and $A$ is the group $\{1\}$ of order 1. Then the only tangential 1-block in $\mathcal{Z}(\{1\})$ is the 3-point line $U_{2,3}$. The second is the sign-graphic case when $k = 1$ and $A$ is the "sign group" $\{+1, -1\}$ of order 2. There are precisely two tangential 1-blocks in $\mathcal{Z}(\{+1, -1\})$: the 4-point line $U_{2,4}$ and $M(K_4)$. One more case is known, the graphic case when $k = 2$ and $A$ is the group $\{1\}$. Because the case $m = 5$ of Hadwiger's conjecture is true,[57] the only tangential 2-block in $\mathcal{Z}(\{1\})$ is $M(K_5)$. If Hadwiger's conjecture holds at $m = 2^k + 1$, then the only tangential $k$-block in $\mathcal{Z}(\{1\})$ is $M(K_{2^k+1})$.

It may be possible to do the case $k = 1$ and $A = C_3$, the cyclic group of order 3, with currently known methods. A gain-graphic geometry in $\mathcal{Z}(C_3)$ is representable over GF(4). Hence, from results in Section 8.3, the following four geometries are tangential 1-blocks in $\mathcal{Z}(C_3)$: $U_{2,5}$, $T$, AG(2, 3), and $M(K_5)$. It seems feasible to obtain a decomposition theorem for gain-graphic geometries without any of these four geometries as minors, and, from this theorem, construct all tangential 1-blocks in $\mathcal{Z}(C_3)$.

We remark that minimal and tangential blocks can be defined for any minor-closed class with a critical problem. However, if we restrict our attention to critical problems defined *via* an embedding into an ambient space, then, because a result of Kahn and Kung [**67**] indicates that the only minor-closed classes with "natural" ambient spaces are $\mathcal{L}(q)$ and $\mathcal{Z}(A)$, these classes are the only minor-closed classes with "natural" critical problems.

---

[57]This follows from the 4-color theorem and the theorem of Wagner that the 4-color theorem and Hadwiger's conjecture for $m = 5$ are equivalent. See Ore [**98**] for an expository account.

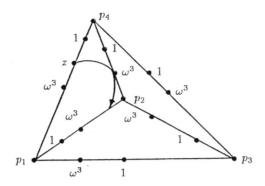

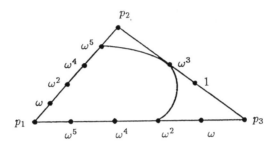

FIGURE 6. Two tangential 1-blocks in $\mathcal{Z}(C_6)$. The gain group $C_6$ is the cyclic group $\{1, \omega, \omega^2, \omega^3, \omega^4, \omega^5\}$ of order 6. The set $\{1, \omega^3\}$ forms a subgroup of order 2. In the figure, the point $(\omega^k)_{ij}$ on the coordinate line $p_i \vee p_j$ is labelled simply by $\omega^k$. The upper tangential 1-block is the rank-4 geometry $Q_4(\{1, \omega^3\})$. The point $z$ on the line $p_1 \vee p_4$ is the point $(\omega^2)_{14}$ and is *not* a point in $Q_4(\{1, \omega^3\})$. The lower tangential 1-block is the rank-3 geometry obtained by simplifying the quotient $Q_4(\{1, \omega^3\})//z$ obtained by adding and then contracting the point $z$. Contraction by the point $z$ projects two new points onto each of the coordinate lines $p_1 \vee p_2$ and $p_1 \vee p_3$. Not all the 3-point lines are shown.

### 8.12. The finite forbidden minor conjecture

It is appropriate to end this paper with what is perhaps the most difficult and significant conjecture in the theory of critical problems. In a somewhat different form, this conjecture was made by Rota [118].

8.39. THE FINITE FORBIDDEN MINOR CONJECTURE. *For any prime power $q$ and positive integer $k$, there are finitely many tangential $k$-blocks in $\mathcal{L}(q)$. Equivalently, the maximum class $\mathcal{M}(k; q)$ can be characterized by a finite set of forbidden minors.*

To prove Conjecture 8.39, it suffices to prove the cases when $k = 1$ and $q$ is an arbitrary prime power. Note that by the $q$-lift construction described in Section

8.6, if Conjecture 8.39 fails at the positive integer $k$ for $\text{GF}(q)$, then it fails for all integers greater than $k$ for $\text{GF}(q)$.

The following theorem, which follows from difficult results of Robertson and Seymour and is implicit in Seymour [124], provides some evidence that the conjecture is true.

8.40. THEOREM. *There are finitely many tangential 2-blocks over* $\text{GF}(2)$.

SKETCH OF PROOF. Because $F_7$ is a tangential 2-block, any other tangential 2-block is contained in $\mathcal{EX}(F_7) \cap \mathcal{U}(2)$. By Seymour's decomposition theorem, this class is "slightly bigger" than the class of regular geometries (Seymour [122,124]). The class of regular geometries is well-quasi-ordered by the Robertson-Seymour theorem.[58] Since the collection of tangential 2-blocks is an antichain in the minor order, it is a finite set. $\qquad\square$

In particular, this theorem says that even if the tangential 2-block conjecture is false, there are only finitely many tangential 2-blocks over $\text{GF}(2)$.

One may also gain perspective by considering an analogous situation in the development of invariant theory. A central problem in nineteenth-century invariant theory is to decide whether the set of covariants of a form of a given degree can be finitely generated. Much of the early work, by Cayley, Sylvester, and others, consisted of finding explicit finite sets of generators. Such an approach involved long calculations and complicated algebraic arguments. This approach was superseded by finiteness principles due to Gordan and Hilbert. Their finite basis theorems produced extremely simple *conceptual* proofs. Of course, the ideas behind these theorems also produced a revolution in mathematics. To find a conceptual proof of the finite forbidden minor conjecture is perhaps the most important and difficult problem in matroid theory today.

## Appendix: Corrections to "Extremal matroid theory."

In this appendix, we take the opportunity to correct a technical error in our earlier paper "Extremal matroid theory" [81].

Theorem 6.2 in that paper is only "asymptotically" correct. What follows is perhaps the easiest way to correct the statement.

(6.2) THEOREM. *Let $\mathcal{C}$ be a minor-closed class in $\mathcal{U}(q)$.*
(a) *The case $k \geq 2$. Let $k$ be a positive integer greater than 1. Suppose that for some integer $n$,*

$$g(\mathcal{C}; n) > \sum_{j=0}^{k} q^{k-j}(q-1)^j \binom{n}{j}$$

$$= (q-1)^k \binom{n}{j} + q(q-1)^{k-1} \binom{n}{k-1} + \cdots + q^{k-1}(q-1)\binom{n}{1} + q^k.$$

*Then $\mathcal{C}$ contains a matroid of rank $k + 2$ containing at least $2^{k+2} - 1$ points.*
(b) *The case $k = 1$. Suppose that for some integer $n$,*

$$g(\mathcal{C}; n) > (q-1)n.$$

---

[58]Reference [116] is the latest in the series of papers proving this result to appear.

*Then $\mathcal{C}$ contains a matroid of rank 3 containing at least 7 points.*

The problem with the upper bound of $(q-1)^k \binom{n}{k}$ stated in the paper is that it is vacuously satisfied when $n \leq k$. Adding the extra terms ensures that the number of points in the cone $C$ in the proof exceeds

$$\frac{q^k - 1}{q - 1}.$$

Corollary 6.6 also needs to be corrected.

(6.6) POLYNOMIAL OR EXPONENTIAL GROWTH. *Let $\mathcal{C}$ be a minor-closed class in $\mathcal{U}(q)$. Either there exists a positive integer $k$ such that, for all $n$,*

$$h(\mathcal{C}; n) \leq \sum_{j=1}^{k} q^{k-j}(q-1)^j \binom{n+1}{j+1}$$

*and $h(\mathcal{C}; n)$ is bounded above by a polynomial in $n$, or, for all $n$,*

$$h(\mathcal{C}; n) \geq 2^n - 1$$

*and $h(\mathcal{C}; n)$ is bounded below by a function exponential in $n$.*

## Acknowledgements

I would like to thank Joseph Bonin, first, for inviting me to give a survey lecture at this conference, thereby motivating me think about the critical problem at a more basic level than I would otherwise have done, and second, for his many comments and suggestions on successive drafts of this paper. Geoff Whittle has also given me invaluable advice on polymatroids and tangential blocks. In addition, I would like to thank Michael Falk for many discussions about Orlik-Solomon algebras and other algebraic matters, James Oxley for information about minimal blocks and series connections, and Dirk Vertigan for information about complexity issues. I would also like to thank the National Security Agency for its support of my research under grants MDA904-91-0030 and MDA904-93-H-3023.

## References

1. M. Aigner, *Uniformität des verbandes der Partitionen*, Math. Ann. **207** (1974), 1–22.

2. M. Aigner, *Uniform binary geometries*, Aequationes Math. **16** (1977), 37–50.

3. T. Asano, T. Nishizeki, J. G. Oxley and N. Saito, *A note on the critical problem for matroids*, European J. Combin. **5** (1984), 93–97.

4. R. Baer, *A unified theory of projective spaces and finite abelian groups*, Trans. Amer. Math. Soc. **52** (1942), 283–343.

5. R. D. Baker, J. E. Bonin, F. Lazebnik, and E. Shustin, *On the number of nowhere zero points in linear mappings*, Combinatorica **14** (1994), 149–157.

6. L. W. Beineke and R. J. Wilson, eds., Selected topics in graph theory 3, Academic Press, London and San Diego, 1988.

7. M. K. Bennett, K. P. Bogart and J. E. Bonin, *The geometry of Dowling lattices*, Adv. Math. **103** (1994), 131–161.

8. N. L. Biggs, E. K. Lloyd and R. J. Wilson, Graph theory: 1736-1936, Oxford Univ. Press, Oxford, 1976.

9. G. D. Birkhoff and D. C. Lewis, *Chromatic polynomials*, Trans. Amer. Math. Soc. **60** (1946), 355–451.

10. A. Björner and G. Ziegler, *Broken circuit complexes: factorizations and generalizations*, J. Combin. Theory Ser. B **51** (1991), 96–126.

11. K. P. Bogart and J. R. Stonesifer, *Characterizations of partition lattices*, Algebra Universalis **19** (1984), 92–98.

12. J. E. Bonin, *Modular elements of higher-weight Dowling lattices*, Discrete Math. **119** (1993), 3–11.

13. J. E. Bonin, *Automorphisms of Dowling lattices and related geometries*, Combin. Probab. Comput. **4** (1995), 1–9.

14. J. E. Bonin, *Matroids with no $(q+2)$-point-line minors*, Adv. Appl. Math., to appear.

15. J. E. Bonin, *Private communication*, 1995 and 1996.

16. A. Brini, *Some remarks on the critical problem*, in *Matroid theory and its applications*, A. Barlotti, ed., Liguori, Naples, 1982, pp. 113–124.

17. T. Brown, *Transversal theory and F-products*, J. Combin. Theory Ser. A **17** (1974), 290–298.

18. T. H. Brylawski, *A combinatorial model for series-parallel networks*, Trans. Amer. Math. Soc. **154** (1971), 1–22.

19. T. H. Brylawski, *A decomposition for combinatorial geometries*, Trans. Amer. Math. Soc. **171** (1972), 235–282.

20. T. Brylawski, *Modular constructions for combinatorial geometries*, Trans. Amer. Math. Soc. **203** (1975), 1–44.

21. T. H. Brylawski, *An affine representation for transversal geometries*, Stud. Appl. Math. **54** (1975), 143–160.

22. T. Brylawski, *The broken-circuit complex*, Trans. Amer. Math. Soc. **234** (1977), 417–433.

23. T. H. Brylawski, *Intersection theory for embeddings of matroids into uniform geometries*, Stud. Appl. Math. **61** (1979), 211–244.

24. T. H. Brylawski, *Alcune applicazioni della teorie dell'intersezione alle geometrie di Galois*, Ricerche di Matematica **29** (1980), 65–84.

25. T. H. Brylawski, *Intersection theory for graphs*, J. Combin. Theory Ser. B **30** (1981), 233–246.

26. T. Brylawski, *Coordinatizing the Dilworth truncation*, in *Matroid theory (Szeged, 1982)*, Colloq. Math. János Bolyai, Vol. 40, North-Holland, Amsterdam, 1985, pp. 61–95.

27. T. Brylawski, *Blocking sets and Möbius functions*, in *Symposia Mathematica Vol. 28 (Rome, 1983)*, Academic Press, London and New York, 1986, pp. 231–249.

28. T. Brylawski, *Constructions*, in [**150**], pp. 127–223.

29. T. Brylawski and J. G. Oxley, *Several identities for the characteristic polynomial of a combinatorial geometry*, Discrete Math. **31** (1980), 161–170.

30. T. Brylawski and J. G. Oxley, *The broken-circuit complex: its structure and factorization*, European J. Combin. **2** (1981), 107–121.

31. T. Brylawski and J. G. Oxley, *The Tutte polynomial and its applications*, in [**152**], pp. 123–225.

32. H. H. Crapo, *The joining of exchange geometries*, J. Math. Mech. **17** (1967/68), 837–852.

33. H. H. Crapo, *Möbius inversion in lattices*, Archiv der Math. **19** (1968), 595–607.

34. H. H. Crapo, *The Tutte polynomial*, Aequationes Math. **3** (1969), 211–229.

35. H. H. Crapo, *Orthogonality*, in [**150**], pp. 76–96.

36. H. H. Crapo and G.-C. Rota, *On the foundations of combinatorial theory: Combinatorial geometries*, Preliminary edition, M. I. T. Press, Cambridge, Massachusetts, 1970.

37. P. Crawley and R. P. Dilworth, *Algebraic theory of lattices*, Prentice-Hall, Englewood Cliffs, New Jersey, 1973.

38. B. T. Datta, *Non-existence of six-dimensional tangential 2-blocks*, J. Combin. Theory **21** (1976), 171–193.

39. B. T. Datta, *On tangential 2-blocks*, Discrete Math. **15** (1976), 1–22.

40. B. T. Datta, *Non-existence of seven-dimensional tangential 2-blocks*, Discrete Math. **36** (1981), 1–32.

41. G. A. Dirac, *In abstrakten Graphen vorhandene vollständige 4-Graphen und ihre Unterteilungen*, Math. Nachr. **22** (1960), 61–85.

42. P. Doubilet, G.-C. Rota and R. Stanley, *On the foundations of combinatorial theory. VI. The idea of generating function*, in *Proceedings of the Sixth Berkeley Symposium on Mathematical Statistics and its Applications, Vol. II (Probability theory)*, Univ. California Press, Berkeley, 1972, pp. 267–318.

43. P. Doubilet, G.-C. Rota and J. Stein, *On the foundations of combinatorial theory. IX. Combinatorial methods in invariant theory*, Stud. Appl. Math. **53** (1974), 185–216.

44. T. A. Dowling, *Codes, packing and the critical problem*, in *Atti del Convegno di Geometria Combinatoria e sue Applicazioni*, Instituto di Matematica, Univ. di Perugia, Perugia, 1971, pp. 209–224.

45. T. A. Dowling, *A q-analog of the partition lattice*, in *A survey of combinatorial theory*, J. N. Srivastava, ed., North-Holland, Amsterdam, 1973, pp. 101–115.

46. T. A. Dowling, *A class of geometric lattices based on finite groups*, J. Combin. Theory Ser. B **14** (1973), 61–86; *erratum, ibid.* **15** (1973), 211.

47. J. Edmonds, *Minimal partition of a matroid into independent sets*, J. Res. Nat. Bur. Standards Sect. B **69B** (1965), 67–77.

48. M. J. Falk, *On the algebra associated with a geometric lattice*, Adv. Math. **80** (1990), 152–163.

49. G. E. Farr, *A generalization of the Whitney rank generating function*, Math. Proc. Cambridge Philos. Soc. **113** (1993), 267–280.

50. G. Frattini, *Intorno alla generazione dei gruppi di operazioni*, Rend. Atti Accad. Lincei (4) **1** (1885), 281–285, 455-457.

51. G. Frobenius and L. Stickelberger, *Ueber Gruppen von vertauschbaren Elementen*, J. Reine Angew. Math. **86** (1879), 217–262.

52. W. Gaschütz, *Die Eulersche Funcktion endlicher auflösbarer Gruppen*, Illinois J. Math. **3** (1959), 469–476.

53. C. Greene, *Weight enumeration and the geometry of linear codes*, Stud. Appl. Math. **55** (1976), 119–128.

54. G. Hajós, *Über einfache und mehrfache Bedeckung des n-dimensionalen Raumes mit einem Wurfelgitter*, Math. Z. **47** (1942), 427–467.

55. P. Hall, *The Eulerian functions of a group*, Quart. J. Math. Oxford Ser. **7** (1936), 134–151.

56. M. Halsey, *Line-closed combinatorial geometries*, Discrete Math. **65** (1987), 245–248.

57. T. Helgason, *On hypergraphs and hypergeometries*, Ph. D. thesis, M. I. T., Cambridge, Massachusetts, 1971.

58. T. Helgason, *On geometric hypergraphs*, in *Proceedings of the Second Chapel Hill Conference on Combinatorial Mathematics and its Applications*, Univ. of North Carolina, Chapel Hill, North Carolina, 1970.

59. T. Helgason, *Aspects of the theory of hypermatroids*, in *Hypergraph seminar*, C. Berge and D. K. Ray-Chaudhuri, eds., Lecture Notes in Math. No. 411, Springer, Berlin and New York, 1974, pp. 191–214.

60. I. Heller, *On linear systems with integral valued solutions*, Pacific J. Math. **7** (1957), 1351–1364.

61. D. A. Higgs, *Strong maps of geometries*, J. Combin. Theory **5** (1968), 185–191.

62. A. W. Ingleton, *Representations of matroids*, in *Combinatorial mathematics and its applications*, D. J. A. Welsh, ed., Academic Press, London and New York, 1971, pp. 149–169.

63. F. Jaeger, *Flows and generalized coloring theorems in graphs*, J. Combin. Theory Ser. B **26** (1979), 205–216.

64. F. Jaeger, *A constructive approach to the critical problem for matroids*, European J. Combin. **2** (1981), 137–144.

65. F. Jaeger, *Nowhere-zero flow problems*, in [**6**], pp. 71–95.

66. F. Jaeger, D. Vertigan and D. J. A. Welsh, *On the computational complexity of the Jones and Tutte polynomials*, Math. Proc. Cambridge Philos. Soc. **108** (1990), 35–53.

67. J. Kahn and J. P. S. Kung, *Varieties of combinatorial geometries*, Trans. Amer. Math. Soc. **271** (1982), 485–499.

68. D. G. Kelly and G.-C. Rota, *Some problems in combinatorial geometry*, in *A survey of combinatorial theory*, J. N. Srivastava, ed., North-Holland, Amsterdam, 1973, pp. 309–312.

69. J. P. S. Kung, *An Erlanger program for combinatorial geometries*, Ph. D. thesis, M. I. T., Cambridge, Massachusetts, 1978.

70. J. P. S. Kung, *Bimatroids and invariants*, Adv. Math. **30** (1978), 238–249.

71. J. P. S. Kung, *The Rédei function of a relation*, J. Combin. Theory Ser. A **29** (1980), 287–296.

72. J. P. S. Kung, *Strong maps*, in [**150**], pp. 224–253.

73. J. P. S. Kung, *A factorization for comaps of geometric lattices*, J. Combin. Theory Ser. B **34** (1983), 40–47.

74. J. P. S. Kung, *Numerically regular hereditary classes of combinatorial geometries*, Geom. Dedicata **21** (1986), 85–105.

75. J. P. S. Kung, *Growth rates and critical exponents of minor-closed classes of binary geometries*, Trans. Amer. Math. Soc. **293** (1986), 837–857.

76. J. P. S. Kung, ed., *A sourcebook in matroid theory*, Birkhäuser, Boston and Basel, 1986.

77. J. P. S. Kung, *Excluding the cycle geometries of the Kuratowski graphs from binary geometries*, Proc. London Math. Soc. **55** (1987), 209–242.

78. J. P. S. Kung, *The long-line graph of a combinatorial geometry. I. Excluding $M(K_4)$ and the $(q+2)$-point line as minors*, Quart. J. Math. Oxford (2) **39** (1988), 223–234.

79. J. P. S. Kung, *The long-line graph of a combinatorial geometry. II. Geometries representable over two fields of different characteristics*, J. Combin. Theory Ser. B **50** (1990), 41–53.

80. J. P. S. Kung, *Combinatorial geometries representable over GF(3) and GF(q). I. The number of points*, Discrete Comput. Geom. **5** (1990), 84–95.

81. J. P. S. Kung, *Extremal matroid theory*, in *Graph structure theory*, N. Robertson and P. D. Seymour, eds., Amer. Math. Soc., Providence, Rhode Island, 1993, pp. 21–62.

82. J. P. S. Kung, *Flags and Whitney numbers of matroids*, J. Combin. Theory Ser. B **59** (1993), 85–88.

83. J. P. S. Kung, *Sign-coherent identities for characteristic polynomials of matroids*, Combin. Probab. Comput. **2** (1993), 33–51.

84. J. P. S. Kung, *The geometric approach to matroid theory*, in *Gian-Carlo Rota on combinatorics: Introductory papers and commentaries*, J. P. S. Kung, ed., Birkhäuser, Boston and Basel, 1995, pp. 604–622.

85. J. P. S. Kung, *A critical problem for points in a finite symplectic space*, in preparation.

86. J. P. S. Kung, M. R. Murty and G.-C. Rota, *On the Rédei zeta function*, J. Number Theory **12** (1981), 421–436.

87. J. P. S. Kung and J. G. Oxley, *Combinatorial geometries representable over GF(3) and GF(q). II. Dowling geometries*, Graphs and Combin. **4** (1988), 323–332.

88. B. Lindström, *On the chromatic number of regular matroids*, J. Combin. Theory Ser. B **24** (1978), 367–369.

89. L. Lovász, *Graphs and set systems*, in *Beiträge zur Graphentheorie*, H. Sachs *et al.*, ed., Tuebner, Leipzig, 1968, pp. 99–106.

90. D. Lucas, *Weak maps of combinatorial geometries*, Trans. Amer. Math. Soc. **206** (1975), 247–279.

91. S. Mac Lane, *Some interpretation of abstract linear dependence in terms of projective geometry*, Amer. J. Math. **58** (1936), 236–240.

92. W. Mader, *Homomorphieeigenschaften und mittlere Kantendichte von Graphen*, Math. Ann. **174** (1967), 265–268.

93. K. R. Matthews, *An example from power residues of the critical problem of Crapo and Rota*, J. Number Theory **9** (1977), 203–208.

94. C. Moreno, *Algebraic curves over finite fields*, Cambridge Univ. Press, Cambridge, 1991.

95. R. C. Mullin and R. G. Stanton, *An covering problem in binary spaces of finite dimension*, in *Graph theory and related topics*, Academic Press, New York, 1979, pp. 315–327.

96. C. St. J. Nash-Williams, *Edge-disjoint spanning trees of finite graphs*, J. London Math. Soc. **36** (1961), 445–450.

97. C. St. J. Nash-Williams, *An application of matroids to graph theory*, in *Theory of graphs international symposium (Rome)*, Dunod, Paris, 1966, pp. 263–265.

98. O. Ore, *The four-color problem*, Academic Press, New York, 1967.

99. P. Orlik and L. Solomon, *Combinatorics and topology of complements of hyperplanes*, Inventiones Math. **56** (1980), 167–189.

100. P. Orlik and H. Terao, *Arrangements of hyperplanes*, Springer, Berlin and New York, 1992.

101. J. G. Oxley, *Colouring, packing and the critical problem*, Quart. J. Math. Oxford (2) **29** (1978), 11–22.

102. J. G. Oxley, *A generalization of a problem of Mullin and Stanton for matroids*, in *Combinatorial mathematics VI*, Lecture Notes in Mathematics, No. 748, Springer, Berlin and New York, 1979, pp. 92–97.

103. J. G. Oxley, *On a covering problem of Mullin and Stanton for binary matroids*, Aequationes Math. **20** (1980), 104–112.

104. J. G. Oxley, *On a matroid identity*, Discrete Math. **44** (1983), 55–60.

105. J. G. Oxley, *A characterization of the ternary matroids with no $M(K_4)$-minor*, J. Combin. Theory Ser. B **42** (1987), 212–249.

106. J. G. Oxley, *Matroid theory*, Oxford Univ. Press, Oxford, 1992.

107. J. G. Oxley and G. P. Whittle, *A characterization of Tutte invariants of 2-polymatroids*, J. Combin. Theory Ser. B **59** (1993), 210–244.

108. R. Rado, *A theorem on independence relations*, Quart. J. Math. (Oxford) **13** (1942), 83–89.

109. R. C. Read, *An introduction to chromatic polynomials*, J. Combin. Theory **4** (1968), 52–71.

110. R. C. Read and W. T. Tutte, *Chromatic polynomials*, in [**6**], pp. 15–42.

111. L. Rédei, *Zetafunktionen in der Algebra*, Acta Math. Acad. Sci. Hungar. **6** (1955), 5–25.

112. L. Rédei, *Neuer Beweis des Hajósschen Satzes über die endlichen Abelschen Gruppen*, Acta Math. Acad. Sci. Hungar. **6** (1955), 27–40.

113. L. Rédei, *Die gruppentheoretischen Zetafunktionen und der Satz von Hajós*, Acta Math. Acad. Sci. Hungar. **6** (1955), 271–279.

114. L. Rédei, *Die neue Theorie der endlichen Abelschen Gruppen und Verallgemeinerung des Hauptsatzes von Hajós*, Acta Math. Acad. Sci. Hungar. **16** (1965), 329–373.

115. L. Rédei, *Algebra, Volume 1*, translated from the Hungarian, Pergamon, Oxford, 1967.

116. N. Robertson and P. D. Seymour, *Graph minors. XII. Distance on a surface*, J. Combin. Theory Ser. B **64** (1995), 240–272.

117. G.-C. Rota, *On the foundations of combinatorial theory. I. Theory of Möbius functions*, Z. Wahrsch. Verw. Gebeite **2** (1964), 340–368.

118. G.-C. Rota, *Combinatorial theory, old and new*, in *Proceedings of the International Congress of Mathematicians (Nice, 1971)*, Gauthier-Villars, Paris, 1971, pp. 229–233.

119. G.-C. Rota, *Combinatorial theory and invariant theory*, Notes taken by L. Guibas from the National Science Foundation Seminar in Combinatorial Theory, Bowdoin College, Maine, unpublished typescript, 1971.

120. G.-C. Rota, *Théorie combinatoire des invariants classiques*, Seminar notes by J. Désarménien, IRMA, Strasbourg, 1977.

121. G.-C. Rota, *Private communication*, 1974 to 1996.

122. P. D. Seymour, *Decomposition of regular matroids*, J. Combin. Theory Ser. B **28** (1980), 305–359.

123. P. D. Seymour, *Nowhere-zero 6-flows*, J. Combin. Theory Ser. B **30** (1981), 130–135.

124. P. D. Seymour, *On Tutte's extension of the four-colour problem*, J. Combin. Theory Ser. B **31** (1981), 82–94.

125. R. P. Stanley, *Modular elements of geometric lattices*, Algebra Universalis **1** (1971), 214–217.

126. R. P. Stanley, *Supersolvable lattices*, Algebra Universalis **2** (1972), 197–217.

127. S. K. Stein and R. S. Szabó, *Algebra and tiling*, Carus Mathematical Monographs Number 25, Math. Assoc. Amer., Washington, D. C., 1994.

128. C. Thomassen, *Paths, circuits and subdivisions*, in [**6**], pp. 97–131.

129. H. Terao, *Modular elements of lattices and topological fibrations*, Adv. Math. **62** (1986), 135–154.

130. H. Terao, *Factorization of the Orlik-Solomon algebra*, Adv. Math. **92** (1992), 45–53.

131. R. T. Tugger, *Private communication*, 1991.

132. W. T. Tutte, *A ring in graph theory*, Proc. Cambridge Philos. Soc. **43** (1947), 26–40.

133. W. T. Tutte, *A contribution to the theory of chromatic polynomials*, Canad. J. Math. **6** (1954), 80–91.

134. W. T. Tutte, *A homotopy theorem for matroids, I.*, Trans. Amer. Math. Soc. **88** (1958), 144–160; *II.*, *ibid.* **88** (1958), 161–174.

135. W. T. Tutte, *Matroids and graphs*, Trans. Amer. Math. Soc. **90** (1959), 527–552.

136. W. T. Tutte, *On the algebraic theory of graph colourings*, J. Combin. Theory **1** (1966), 15–50.

137. W. T. Tutte, *On dichromatic polynomials*, J. Combin. Theory **2** (1967), 301–320.

138. W. T. Tutte, *Projective geometry and the 4-colour problem*, in *Recent progress in combinatorics*, W. T. Tutte, ed., Academic Press, London and New York, 1969, pp. 199–207.

139. P. Ungar, *2N noncollinear points determine at least 2N directions*, J. Combin. Theory Ser. A **33** (1982), 343–347.

140. O. Veblen, *An application of modular equations in analysis situs*, Ann. Math. (2) **14** (1912), 86–94.

141. K. Wagner, *Beweis einer Abschwächung der Hadwiger-Vermutung*, Math. Ann. **153** (1964), 139–141.

142. P. N. Walton, *Some topics in combinatorial theory*, D. Phil. thesis, Oxford University, Oxford, 1981.

143. P. N. Walton and D. J. A. Welsh, *On the chromatic number of binary matroids*, Mathematika **27** (1980), 1–9.

144. P. N. Walton and D. J. A. Welsh, *Tangential 1-blocks over* GF(3), Discrete Math. **40** (1982), 319–320.

145. D. J. A. Welsh, *Matroid theory*, Academic Press, London and New York, 1976.

146. D. J. A. Welsh, *Colouring problems and matroids*, in *Surveys in combinatorics (Proceedings of the Seventh British Combinatorial Conference, Cambridge 1979)*, Cambridge Univ. Press, Cambridge, 1979, pp. 229–257.

147. D. J. A. Welsh, *Colourings, flows, and projective geometry*, Nieuw Arch. Wisk. (3) **28** (1980), 159–176.

148. D. J. A. Welsh, *Matroids and combinatorial optimisation*, in *Matroid theory and its applications*, A. Barlotti, ed., Liguori, Naples, 1982, pp. 323–416.

149. D. J. A. Welsh, *Matroids and their applications*, in [**6**], pp. 43–70.

150. N. L. White, ed., *Theory of matroids*, Cambridge University Press, Cambridge, 1986.

151. N. L. White, ed., *Combinatorial geometries*, Cambridge University Press, Cambridge, 1987.

152. N. L. White, ed., *Matroid applications*, Cambridge University Press, Cambridge, 1992.

153. H. Whitney, *The coloring of graphs*, Ann. of Math. (2) **33** (1932), 688–718.

154. H. Whitney, *On the abstract properties of linear dependence*, Amer. J. Math. **57** (1935), 509–533.

155. G. P. Whittle, *On the critical exponent of transversal matroids*, J. Combin. Theory Ser. B **37** (1984), 94–95.

156. G. P. Whittle, *Some aspects of the critical problem for matroids*, Ph. D. thesis, University of Tasmania, Hobart, Australia, 1985.

157. G. P. Whittle, *Modularity in tangential k-blocks*, J. Combin. Theory Ser. B **42** (1987), 24–35.

158. G. P. Whittle, *Quotients of tangential k-blocks*, Proc. Amer. Math. Soc. **102** (1988), 1088–1098.

159. G. P. Whittle, *A generalization of the matroid lift construction*, Trans. Amer. Math. Soc. **316** (1989), 141–159.

160. G. P. Whittle, *q-lifts of tangential k-blocks*, J. London Math. Soc. (2) **39** (1989), 9–15.

161. G. P. Whittle, *Dowling group geometries and the critical problem*, J. Combin. Theory Ser. B **47** (1989), 80–92.

162. G. P. Whittle, *A geometric theory of hypergraph colourings*, Aequationes Math. **42** (1992), 45–58.

163. G. P. Whittle, *Characteristic polynomials of weighted lattices*, Adv. Math. **99** (1993), 125–151.

164. G. P. Whittle, *The critical problem for polymatroids*, Quart. J. Math. Oxford (2) **45** (1994), 117–125.

165. G. P. Whittle, *Private communication*, 1995 to 1996.

166. Y.-J. Yoon, *Characterizations of some combinatorial geometries*, Ph. D. thesis, University of North Texas, Denton, Texas, 1992.

167. Y.-J. Yoon, *Characterizations of partition lattices*, Bull. Korean Math. Soc. **31** (1994), 237–242.

168. T. Zaslavsky, *Signed graphs*, Discrete Appl. Math. **4** (1982), 47–74.

169. T. Zaslavsky, *The Möbius function and the characteristic polynomial*, in [**151**], pp. 114–138.

170. T. Zaslavsky, *Biased graphs. III. Chromatic and dichromatic invariants*, J. Combin. Theory Ser. B **64** (1995), 17–88.

Contemporary Mathematics
Volume **197**, 1996

# Structure Theory and Connectivity for Matroids

## James Oxley

ABSTRACT. The concept of 3–connectedness for graphs was generalized to matroids by Tutte in 1966. Tutte identified wheels and whirls as being the only 3–connected matroids for which no single-element deletion or contraction remains 3–connected. This Wheels and Whirls Theorem has played a foundational role in the establishment of a coherent theory for 3–connected matroids. The Splitter Theorem, a powerful generalization of the Wheels and Whirls Theorem, was proved by Seymour in 1980. This survey of structure theory and connectivity results for matroids focuses particularly on how profoundly the Wheels and Whirls and Splitter Theorems have influenced the development of these areas.

## 1. Introduction

Throughout mathematics, there is widespread interest in breaking large objects into smaller, more easily understood, pieces. For matroids, the first such decomposition result was proved by Whitney [**106**] when he showed that every matroid can be uniquely written as the direct sum of its connected components. This transfers attention from arbitrary matroids to connected matroids. For such matroids, a decomposition theorem was established by Cunningham and Edmonds [**22**]. In particular, their result proved that every connected matroid can be built up from some of its 3–connected minors by a sequence of 2–sums. The attention is thus transferred from connected matroids to 3–connected matroids. These are the matroids that will be the focus of this paper. One important reason for stopping with 3–connected matroids and not looking at, say, 4–connected matroids is that, although there has been some work done for graphs in the latter case [**19, 73**], there is no known decomposition theorem for arbitrary 4–connected matroids.

## 2. Preliminaries

Any unexplained matroid terminology used here will follow Oxley [**62**]. For a matroid $M$, the simple matroid and the cosimple matroid associated with $M$ will be denoted by $\widetilde{M}$ and $\underline{M}$, respectively. We call these matroids the *simplification* and the *cosimplification* of $M$. The basic matroid property that a circuit and a cocircuit cannot have exactly one common element will be referred to as *orthogonality*.

---

1991 *Mathematics Subject Classification*. Primary 05B35; Secondary 05C40, 05C99.
The author was supported in part by the National Security Agency.

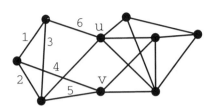

FIGURE 1. $G$.

The notion of a *connected* or *non-separable* matroid as one in which every pair of distinct elements is in a circuit was introduced by Whitney [**106**]. But it was Tutte [**99**] who originated the concept of higher connectivity for matroids. His motivation appears to derive from a desire to generalize the notion of $n$–connectedness for graphs and a wish to incorporate duality into the theory.

Consider the graph $G$ shown in Figure 1. Evidently, $G$ is not 3–connected. The 2–vertex cut $\{u, v\}$ of $G$ induces a natural partition of $E(G)$. Letting $X = \{1, 2, 3, 4, 5, 6\}$, we have

$$r(X) + r(E(G) - X) - r(M(G)) = 1.$$

In general, for a positive integer $k$ and a matroid $M$, a partition $\{X, Y\}$ of $E(M)$ is a $k$–*separation* if

$$min\{|X|, |Y|\} \geq k;$$

and

$$r(X) + r(Y) - r(M) \leq k - 1.$$

If equality holds in the last inequality, then the $k$–separation is *exact*. For $n \geq 2$, the matroid $M$ is $n$–*connected* provided that, for all $k$ in $\{1, 2, \ldots, n - 1\}$, $M$ has no $k$–separation. Hence $M$ is 2–connected exactly when it is connected. Moreover, a routine rank argument establishes that a matroid is $n$–connected if and only if its dual is $n$–connected. The link between the graph and matroid concepts of $n$–connectedness is contained in the following result.

PROPOSITION 2.1. *For $n \geq 2$, let $G$ be a graph without isolated vertices and suppose that $|V(G)| \geq n + 1$. Then $M(G)$ is $n$–connected if and only if $G$ is $n$–connected and has no cycles with fewer than $n$ edges.*

In particular, if $|V(G)| \geq 4$ and $G$ has no isolated vertices, then $M(G)$ is 3–connected if and only if $G$ is 3–connected and simple. Indeed, every 3–connected matroid with at least four elements is both simple and cosimple. It is straightforward to check that the only 3–connected matroids with fewer than four elements are $U_{0,0}, U_{0,1}, U_{1,1}, U_{1,2}, U_{1,3}$, and $U_{2,3}$. We shall frequently follow the common practice of restricting attention to 3–connected matroids with at least four elements.

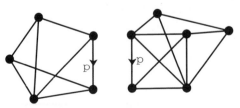

FIGURE 2. $G$ is the 2–sum of $G_1$ and $G_2$ across the edge $p$.

FIGURE 3. A wheel.

The graph $G$ in Figure 1 is the 2–sum across the edge $p$ of the graphs $G_1$ and $G_2$ in Figure 2, that is, $G$ is obtained from $G_1$ and $G_2$ by identifying the (directed) edges labeled $p$, respecting their directions, and then deleting this composite edge. This graph operation has a natural matroid generalization because the cycles in $G$ can be specified in terms of those of $G_1$ and $G_2$. Let $M_1$ and $M_2$ be 2–connected matroids each having at least three elements such that $E(M_1) \cap E(M_2) = \{p\}$. The 2–*sum* of $M_1$ and $M_2$ (with respect to $p$) is the matroid $M_1 \oplus_2 M_2$ with ground set $[E(M_1) \cup E(M_2)] - \{p\}$ for which the circuits are the following: all circuits of $M_1$ avoiding $p$; all circuits of $M_2$ avoiding $p$; and all sets of the form $(C_1 \cup C_2) - \{p\}$, where $C_i$ is a circuit of $M_i$ containing $p$.

The following basic link between 2–sum and 3–connectedness was proved by several authors [8, 20, 82].

THEOREM 2.2. *A 2–connected matroid $M$ is not 3–connected if and only if $M = M_1 \oplus_2 M_2$ for some matroids $M_1$ and $M_2$ each of which is isomorphic to a proper minor of $M$.*

A complete decomposition of a 2–connected matroid into 3–connected pieces was determined by Cunningham and Edmonds [22]. The details of this decomposition together with an example may be found on pp. 290–291 of [62].

We now know that a matroid that is not 3–connected can be built up by direct sums and 2–sums from 3–connected matroids, each of which is isomorphic to a minor of the original matroid. It is straightforward to show that many basic matroid properties are preserved under both direct sum and 2–sum. Hence it is natural to focus on 3–connected matroids. Two particularly important families of 3–connected matroids are the wheels and the whirls. For $r \geq 2$, the *wheel* $\mathcal{W}_r$ *of rank* $r$ is a graph having $r + 1$ vertices, $r$ of which lie on a cycle (the *rim*); the remaining vertex is joined by a single edge (a *spoke*) to each of the other vertices (see Figure 3). The *rank-$r$ whirl* $\mathcal{W}^r$ is the matroid on $E(\mathcal{W}_r)$ that has as its circuits all cycles of $\mathcal{W}_r$ other than the rim as well as all sets of edges formed by adding a single spoke to the edges of the rim. The terms "rim" and "spoke" will be applied in the obvious way in $M(\mathcal{W}_r)$ with the following warning. The case $r = 3$ differs from all other cases in that one cannot distinguish rim elements from spokes by looking just at the matroid. In that case, we arbitrarily designate one of the 3–element circuits of $M(\mathcal{W}_3)$ to be the rim. We shall usually refer to the cycle matroid of a wheel as just a wheel. The smallest 3–connected whirl is $\mathcal{W}^2$, which is isomorphic to $U_{2,4}$; the smallest 3–connected wheel is $M(\mathcal{W}_3)$, which is isomorphic to $M(K_4)$ (see Figure 4).

Every element of a wheel or whirl is in both a *triangle*, a 3–element circuit, and a *triad*, a 3–element cocircuit. Thus if $M$ is a wheel or whirl with at least six elements,

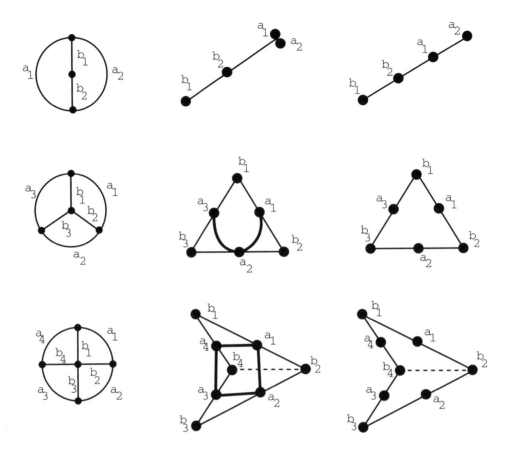

FIGURE 4. Three wheel graphs with geometric representations of
their cycle matroids and of the corresponding whirls.

then $M$ has no single-element deletion or contraction that is 3–connected. Tutte's
Wheels and Whirls Theorem [**99**], which we state next, asserts that the wheels and
whirls are the only matroids with this property. The usefulness of such a result in
induction arguments is clear and, indeed, this theorem has had a profound influence
on the development of results for 3–connected matroids.

THEOREM 2.3 (The Wheels and Whirls Theorem). *The following statements
are equivalent for a 3–connected matroid $M$ having at least one element.*

   (i) *For every element $e$ of $M$, neither $M \backslash e$ nor $M/e$ is 3–connected.*
   (ii) *$M$ has rank at least three and is isomorphic to a wheel or a whirl.*

The fact that no corresponding result is known for arbitrary $n$–connected matroids when $n \geq 4$ goes a long way towards explaining the relative lack of development of results for such matroids. Evidently Theorem 2.3 distinguishes a prominent
role for wheels and whirls within the class of 3–connected matroids. Indeed, using
the elementary observation that the only 4–element 3–connected matroid is $U_{2,4}$,
which is isomorphic to the rank–2 whirl, we deduce the following consequence of
the last theorem.

COROLLARY 2.4. *Let $M$ be a 3–connected matroid having at least four elements. Then there is a sequence $M_0, M_1, \ldots, M_n$ of 3–connected matroids such that $M_0 = M$; $M_n$ is a wheel of rank at least three, or a whirl of rank at least two; and, for all $i$ in $\{1, 2, \ldots, n\}$, the matroid $M_i$ is a single-element deletion or a single-element contraction of $M_{i-1}$.*

The Wheels and Whirls Theorem and the corollary just noted have served as the foundation upon which the theory of 3–connected matroids has been built. The importance of this foundation will be apparent throughout this paper. The next section gives some examples of well-known structural results for graphs. Section 4 presents a powerful extension of Corollary 2.4 known as the Splitter Theorem. This theorem is then used to derive some structural results for matroids that are similar to the graph results in Section 3. In particular, these results describe the structure of certain excluded-minor classes of matroids with much of the attention focusing on cases where a small wheel or a small whirl is among the excluded minors.

The Splitter Theorem was originally used to prove an important decomposition theorem for the class of regular matroids, and this theorem is discussed in Section 5. Section 6 considers the problem of characterizing the 3–connected matroids for which every sequence of the type discussed in Corollary 2.4 ends in an isomorphic copy of the same matroid. In Section 7, some examples are given of other structural results that have been obtained by using the technique that arises naturally from the Splitter Theorem.

In Section 8, the concern is with identifying partial wheels in 3–connected matroids and then breaking these off to leave smaller 3–connected matroids. The results from that section are used in Section 9 to obtain another extension of the Wheels and Whirls Theorem in which the extremal connectivity hypothesis of the latter result is weakened slightly. This result is an example of a number of such extremal results that are known for matroids. Many of these results mimic corresponding results for graphs or have played important roles as lemmas in the derivation of other matroid theorems. Sections 10 and 11 discuss these results for 2– and 3–connected matroids, respectively.

Section 12 examines an alternative definition of $n$–connectedness for matroids that exactly generalizes the familiar graph concept. Finally, Section 13 looks at some further questions that arise naturally from the Splitter Theorem and also discusses some of the other directions of research in this area. Many of the topics treated in this survey are examined in more detail in Seymour's survey [84], the author's book [62] (see particularly Chapters 8 and 11), or Truemper's book [95]. Both [62] and [95] have long lists of references that should be used to supplement the list of references for this paper. In particular, each chapter of [95] concludes with a section containing historical notes and references to further readings.

## 3. Some structural results for graphs

The structural results for matroids that will be presented later in the paper were foreshaddowed by certain results for graphs. We now briefly discuss these graph results.

One of the best-known theorems in graph theory is the Kuratowski-Wagner characterization of planar graphs [38, 102].

THEOREM 3.1. *A graph $G$ has no $K_{3,3}$-minor and no $K_5$-minor if and only if $G$ is planar.*

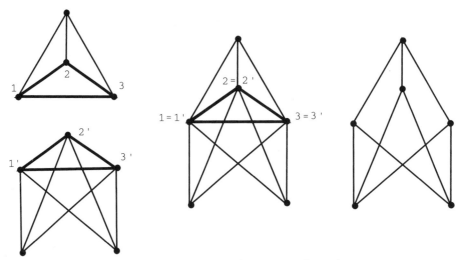

FIGURE 5. An example of a 3–sum of graphs.

Stated in this form, the theorem raises the questions as to whether one can specify all graphs with no $K_{3,3}$-minor and all graphs with no $K_5$-minor. These questions were answered by D.W. Hall [**31**] and by Wagner [**103**]. Before presenting their answers, we recall the definition of the graph operation of $n$–sum. An example of a 2–sum was given in Figure 2. More generally, let $G_1$ and $G_2$ be graphs each of which has a distinguished $K_n$-subgraph. To form an $n$–*sum* of $G_1$ and $G_2$, one first pairs the vertices of the chosen $K_n$-subgraph of $G_1$ with distinct vertices of the chosen $K_n$-subgraph of $G_2$. The paired vertices are then identified, as are the corresponding pairs of edges. Finally, all identified edges are deleted. In Figure 5, for example, it is shown how $K_{3,3}$ can be obtained as a 3–sum of $K_4$ and $K_5 \backslash e$, the last graph being the unique graph that is obtained from $K_5$ by deleting a single edge. The operation of 0–sum is just disjoint union, while 1–sum involves sticking two graphs together at a vertex. Clearly the 0–sum and all the 1–sums of graphs $G_1$ and $G_2$ have identical cycle matroids, namely $M(G_1) \oplus M(G_2)$.

THEOREM 3.2 (D.W. Hall). *A graph $G$ has no $K_{3,3}$-minor if and only if $G$ can be obtained from planar graphs and copies of $K_5$ by repeatedly applying the operations of* 0–*sum,* 1–*sum, and* 2–*sum.*

The graph $V_8$ that features in the next theorem is the 4–rung Möbius ladder. It is drawn in two different ways in Figure 6. For comparison, we note that $K_{3,3}$ is the 3–rung Möbius ladder.

THEOREM 3.3 (Wagner). *A graph $G$ has no $K_5$-minor if and only if $G$ can be obtained from planar graphs and copies of $V_8$ by repeatedly applying the operations of* 0–*sum,* 1–*sum,* 2–*sum, and* 3–*sum.*

The last two theorems distinguish prominent roles for the graphs $K_5$ and $V_8$. Indeed, $M(K_5)$ is a maximal 3–connected member of the class of graphic matroids with no $M(K_{3,3})$-minor, and $M(V_8)$ is a maximal 3–connected member of the class of graphic matroids with no $M(K_5)$-minor. In general, for a minor-closed class $\mathcal{M}$ of matroids, a *splitter* is a member $N$ of $\mathcal{M}$ such that no 3–connected member of $\mathcal{M}$ has $N$ as a proper minor. The last two assertions are that $M(K_5)$ is a splitter

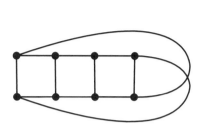
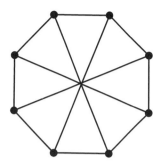

FIGURE 6. Two drawings of the graph $V_8$.

for the class of graphic matroids with no $M(K_{3,3})$-minor, and $M(V_8)$ is a splitter for the class of graphic matroids with no $M(K_5)$-minor. The task of checking these assertions is potentially immense. The main result of the next section is Seymour's Splitter Theorem, a consequence of which is that, in order to check whether a 3–connected member $M$ is a splitter for a minor-closed class $\mathcal{M}$ of matroids, one needs only to show that $M$ has no 3–connected single-element extensions or coextensions in $\mathcal{M}$. If we accept this assertion, it is easy to see that $M(K_5)$ is a splitter for the class of graphic matroids with no $M(K_{3,3})$-minor. Certainly $M(K_5)$ has no simple graphic single-element extension, and so $M(K_5)$ has no 3–connected such extension. Moreover, the unique graphic coextension of $M(K_5)$ is $M(H_6)$ where $H_6$ is the graph shown in Figure 7. Since $M(H_6)\backslash e, f \cong M(K_{3,3})$, it follows that every 3–connected single-element graphic coextension of $M(K_5)$ has an $M(K_{3,3})$-minor.

To see that $M(V_8)$ is a splitter for the class of graphic matroids with no $M(K_5)$-minor, we note first that, as $V_8$ is a cubic graph, $M(V_8)$ has no 3–connected graphic single-element coextension. Moreover, by symmetry, $M(V_8)$ has exactly two non-isomorphic 3–connected graphic single-element extensions, and each of these is easily shown to have an $M(K_5)$-minor.

## 4. The Splitter Theorem and some applications

A far-reaching extension of Corollary 2.4 is Seymour's Splitter Theorem [**82**], which he proved on the way to his regular matroids decomposition theorem.

THEOREM 4.1 (The Splitter Theorem). *Let $M$ and $N$ be 3–connected matroids such that $N$ is a minor of $M$, $|E(N)| \geq 4$, and if $N$ is a wheel, then $M$ has no larger wheel as a minor, while if $N$ is a whirl, then $M$ has no larger whirl as a minor. Then there is a sequence $M_0, M_1, \ldots, M_n$ of 3–connected matroids such*

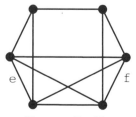

FIGURE 7. $H_6$.

*that $M_0 = M$; $M_n \cong N$; and, for all $i$ in $\{1, 2, \ldots, n\}$, $M_i$ is a single-element deletion or a single-element contraction of $M_{i-1}$.*

The crux of this theorem is that, while removing elements one at a time in going from $M$ to an isomorphic copy of $N$, one is able to maintain 3–connectedness. It should also be noted here that $M_n$, while it is isomorphic to $N$, cannot be guaranteed to be equal to $N$. The Splitter Theorem was also proved independently by Tan [85] for matroids and by Negami [46] for graphs. A proof of the theorem, due to C.R. Coullard and L.L. Gardner, may be found in Section 11.1 of [62].

Two examples of splitters within classes of graphic matroids were given in the last section. The next proposition gives another example of a splitter. Two matroids that are important in this example are the vector matroids of the following matrices over $GF(2)$:

$$\left[ \begin{array}{c} I_4 \end{array} \left| \begin{array}{cccc} 0 & 1 & 1 & 1 \\ 1 & 0 & 1 & 1 \\ 1 & 1 & 0 & 1 \\ 1 & 1 & 1 & 0 \end{array} \right] \right. \quad \text{and} \quad \left[ \begin{array}{c} I_4 \end{array} \left| \begin{array}{cccc} 0 & 1 & 1 & 1 \\ 1 & 0 & 1 & 1 \\ 1 & 1 & 0 & 1 \\ 1 & 1 & 1 & 1 \end{array} \right] \right. .$$

The first of these matroids is the affine geometry $AG(3, 2)$; the second is denoted by $S_8$.

PROPOSITION 4.2 (Seymour [82]). *Let $\mathcal{M}$ be the class of binary matroids having no minor isomorphic to the Fano matroid, $F_7$. Then $F_7^*$ is a splitter for $\mathcal{M}$.*

PROOF. Evidently $F_7^* \in \mathcal{M}$. Moreover, since $F_7 \cong PG(2, 2)$, there is no simple binary single-element extension of $F_7$. Hence $F_7^*$ has no 3–connected single-element coextension in $\mathcal{M}$. Now $F_7^*$ is represented by the matrix $A$ over $GF(2)$ where

$$A = \left[ \begin{array}{cccc} & & & \\ & I_4 & & \end{array} \left| \begin{array}{ccc} \overset{1\ \ 2\ \ 3\ \ 4\ \ 5\ \ 6\ \ 7}{0} & 1 & 1 \\ 1 & 0 & 1 \\ 1 & 1 & 0 \\ 1 & 1 & 1 \end{array} \right] \right. .$$

A 3–connected binary single-element extension $M$ of $F_7^*$ can be represented by the matrix that is obtained from $A$ by adjoining the column $(x_1, x_2, x_3, x_4)^T$ where each of $x_1$, $x_2$, $x_3$, and $x_4$ is in $\{0, 1\}$. As $M$ is 3–connected and therefore simple, at least two of $x_1$, $x_2$, $x_3$, and $x_4$ are non-zero. By symmetry, we may assume that $(x_1, x_2, x_3, x_4)^T$ is one of $(1, 1, 1, 0)^T$, $(1, 1, 1, 1)^T$, $(1, 1, 0, 0)^T$, and $(1, 0, 0, 1)^T$. Adjoining the first of these columns to $A$ gives a representation for $AG(3, 2)$. Adjoining the second of the columns to $A$ gives a representation for $S_8$. Moreover, it is straightforward to check that adjoining any one of the two remaining columns to $A$ also gives a representation for a matroid isomorphic to $S_8$. Since each of $AG(3, 2)$ and $S_8$ has a representation of the form $[I_4 | D]$ where $D$ is symmetric, each is isomorphic to its dual. As each has $F_7^*$ as a minor, each also has $F_7$ as a minor, and so $F_7^*$ has no 3–connected binary single-element extension in $\mathcal{M}$. Hence $F_7^*$ is a splitter for $\mathcal{M}$. $\qquad\square$

The last result can be used in conjunction with Tutte's excluded-minor characterization of regular matroids [97] to give the following structural result [82].

COROLLARY 4.3. *Every binary matroid that has no $F_7$-minor can be obtained from regular matroids and copies of $F_7^*$ by a sequence of direct sums and 2–sums.*

The last result used a relatively straightforward application of the Splitter Theorem. Before presenting a more complicated example, we motivate this example. The fundamental role played by wheels and whirls within the class of 3–connected matroids prompts consideration of the structure of a minor-closed class of matroids which avoids some small wheel or some small whirl. The class of matroids for which the smallest whirl $\mathcal{W}^2$ is the unique excluded minor is precisely the class of binary matroids. If we exclude as minors both the smallest whirl $\mathcal{W}^2$ and the smallest 3–connected wheel $M(\mathcal{W}_3)$, then the only non-empty matroids we get are direct sums of series-parallel networks. Here a *series-parallel network* is the cycle matroid of a graph that can be obtained from one of the two connected single-edge graphs by a sequence of the operations of replacing an edge by either two edges in parallel or two edges in series.

Next we shall describe the structure of the class of matroids that have no minor isomorphic to $\mathcal{W}^2$ or $M(\mathcal{W}_4)$, or equivalently, the class of binary matroids with no 4–wheel minor. Since every member of this class that is not 3–connected can be constructed from 3–connected members of the class by direct sums and 2–sums, it suffices to specify the 3–connected members of the class. In general, for a set $\{M_1, M_2, \dots\}$ of matroids, $EX(M_1, M_2, \dots)$ will denote the class of matroids having no minor isomorphic to any of $M_1, M_2, \dots$ .

The strategy that will be used to find the 3–connected members of $EX(\mathcal{W}^2, M(\mathcal{W}_4))$ is as follows. First we note that all 3–connected matroids with fewer than four elements are trivially in the class. Next we let $M$ be a 3–connected member of the class having four or more elements. Then, by Corollary 2.4, $M$ has an $M(\mathcal{W}_3)$-minor. Moreover, since $M$ has no $M(\mathcal{W}_4)$-minor, it has no minor isomorphic to $M(\mathcal{W}_r)$ for any $r \geq 4$. Thus, by Corollary 2.4, there is a sequence $M_0, M_1, \dots, M_n$ of 3–connected matroids such that $M_n \cong M(\mathcal{W}_3)$; $M_0 = M$; and, for all $i$ in $\{1, 2, \dots, n\}$, $M_{i-1}$ is a single-element extension or a single-element coextension of $M_i$. Clearly each of $M_0, M_1, \dots, M_n$ is binary. The unique 3–connected binary extension of $M(\mathcal{W}_3)$ is $F_7$; by duality, the unique 3–connected binary coextension of $M(\mathcal{W}_3)$ is $F_7^*$. Thus $M_{n-1}$ is $F_7$ or $F_7^*$. It now follows, by the proof of Proposition 4.2, that $M_2$ is $AG(3, 2)$ or $S_8$. The fact that each of $\mathcal{W}^2$ and $M(\mathcal{W}_4)$ is self-dual means that $EX(\mathcal{W}^2, M(\mathcal{W}_4))$ is closed under duality. Moreover, as both $AG(3, 2)$ and $S_8$ are self-dual, either $M_{n-2}$ or $M_{n-2}^*$ is a binary 3–connected extension of $S_8$ or $AG(3, 2)$. To determine the possible such extensions, we take matrices representing $S_8$ and $AG(3, 2)$ over $GF(2)$ and consider what columns can be added to these matrices so as to avoid creating an $M(\mathcal{W}_4)$-minor. We are relying here on the unique representability of binary matroids. Continuing to analyze the sequence $M_0, M_1, \dots, M_n$ in this way, a pattern emerges and, from this, one can formulate and then prove the structure theorem stated below. The details of this proof can be found in [**56**].

Let $r$ be an integer exceeding two and $Z_r$ be the vector matroid of the following matrix over $GF(2)$:

$$
\begin{array}{cccccccc}
a_1 & a_2 & \dots & a_r & b_1 & b_2 & b_3 & \dots & b_r & c_r \\
\end{array}
$$

$$
\left[
\begin{array}{c|ccccc|c}
 & & & & 0 & 1 & 1 & \cdots & 1 & 1 \\
 & & & & 1 & 0 & 1 & \cdots & 1 & 1 \\
 & I_r & & & 1 & 1 & 0 & \cdots & 1 & 1 \\
 & & & & \vdots & \vdots & \vdots & \ddots & \vdots & \vdots \\
 & & & & 1 & 1 & 1 & \cdots & 0 & 1 \\
\end{array}
\right].
$$

FIGURE 8. The graphs $H_6$, $Q_3$, $K_{2,2,2}$, and $H_7$.

Then $Z_r$ and its minors have the following properties:

(i) $Z_3 \cong F_7$; $Z_4 \backslash c_4 \cong AG(3,2)$; and $Z_4 \backslash b_4 \cong S_8$;

(ii) $Z_r^* \cong Z_{r+1} \backslash b_{r+1}, c_{r+1}$ for all $r \geq 3$;

(iii) $Z_r \backslash e \cong Z_r \backslash b_r$ for all $e \neq c_r$;

(iv) $Z_r \backslash b_r$ and $Z_r \backslash c_r$ are isomorphic to their duals.

THEOREM 4.4. *Let $M$ be a binary matroid with at least four elements. Then $M$ is 3–connected and has no $M(\mathcal{W}_4)$-minor if and only if $M \cong Z_r$, $Z_r^*$, $Z_r \backslash b_r$, or $Z_r \backslash c_r$ for some $r \geq 3$.*

Theoretically, the technique used above of building up, an element at a time, from a wheel or a whirl could be applied to find the structure of $EX(\mathcal{W}^2, M(\mathcal{W}_r))$ for any $r \geq 5$. But, even when $r = 5$, the number of possibilities to be considered is large. This makes it much more difficult to detect the patterns in the building-up process, and the class of binary matroids with no $M(\mathcal{W}_5)$-minor has so far defied analysis. However, if one confines attention to the class of graphic matroids with no $M(\mathcal{W}_5)$-minor, the case analysis becomes manageable [**59**].

For $k \geq 3$, consider the graph $K_{3,k}$, labeling its vertex classes $V_1$ and $V_2$ where $|V_1| = 3$. Let $K'_{3,k}$, $K''_{3,k}$, and $K'''_{3,k}$ be obtained from $K_{3,k}$ by adding one, two, and three pairwise non-parallel edges joining vertices in $V_1$. It is straightforward to check that $K'''_{3,k}$ has no $\mathcal{W}_5$-minor. Hence none of $K'''_{3,k}$, $K''_{3,k}$, $K'_{3,k}$, and $K_{3,k}$ has a $\mathcal{W}_5$-minor. Similarly, none of the graphs $H_6$, $Q_3$, $K_{2,2,2}$, and $H_7$ shown in Figure 8 has a $\mathcal{W}_5$-minor.

THEOREM 4.5. *Let $G$ be a graph. Then $G$ is simple and 3–connected having no $\mathcal{W}_5$-minor if and only if*

(i) *$G$ is isomorphic to a simple 3–connected minor of one of $H_6$, $Q_3$, $K_{2,2,2}$, and $H_7$; or*

(ii) *for some $k \geq 3$, $G$ is isomorphic to one of $K_{3,k}$, $K'_{3,k}$, $K''_{3,k}$, and $K'''_{3,k}$.*

When one turns to excluding $M(\mathcal{W}_6)$ as a minor, the number of cases seems unmanageable even in the graphic case. This prompts consideration of the planar graphs with no 6–wheel minor. Gubser [**28**] proved the following structural theorem for this class.

THEOREM 4.6. *Let $\mathcal{G}$ be the class of planar graphs having no $\mathcal{W}_6$-minor. Then every simple 3–connected member of $\mathcal{G}$ is a minor of one of the thirty-eight splitters for $\mathcal{G}$, thirty-six of which have seventeen edges and two of which have sixteen edges.*

The increasing complexity of the case analyses needed in the last three results suggests that a general result concerning exclusion of a wheel minor will not be able to provide such specific structural information as in these three results. The last result provides a hint at what can be proved in general by showing that, for $r = 6$, there are only finitely many simple 3–connected planar graphs with no $\mathcal{W}_r$-minor. A proof that the last assertion is true for all $r$ initiated work of Oporowski, Oxley, and Thomas [47] that lead to the following result and the corresponding result for 4–connected graphs.

THEOREM 4.7. *For every integer $n \geq 3$, there is an integer $N$ such that every 3–connected graph with at least $N$ vertices has a minor isomorphic to $\mathcal{W}_n$ or $K_{3,n}$.*

The argument used to prove this theorem relies on results and techniques [76, 86] from Robertson and Seymour's graph minors project (see, for example, [74, 75]). The reader who is familiar with this work will not be surprised to learn that the bounds obtained on the number $N$ are huge.

Theorem 4.7 gives information about unavoidable minors in large 3–connected graphs. It raises the question as to what can be said for binary matroids or, indeed, for matroids in general. For binary matroids, Ding, Oporowski, Oxley, and Vertigan [24] proved the following result.

THEOREM 4.8. *For every integer $n \geq 3$, there is an integer $N$ such that every 3–connected binary matroid with at least $N$ elements has a minor isomorphic to $M(K_{3,n})$, $M^*(K_{3,n})$, $M(\mathcal{W}_n)$, or $Z_n \backslash c_n$.*

The proof of this result treats binary matroids via their matrix representations and depends heavily on certain Ramsey-theoretic results for matrices. Very recently, using new techniques, Ding, Oporowski, Oxley, and Vertigan [25] have extended the last result to matroids in general. Before stating this result, we make some observations concerning $Z_n$. This matroid has the following properties:

(i) the ground set is the union of $n$ lines, $L_1, L_2, \ldots, L_n$, all having three points and passing through a common point, $p$;
(ii) for all $k$ in $\{1, 2, \ldots, n - 1\}$, the union of any $k$ of $L_1, L_2, \ldots, L_n$ has rank $k + 1$;
(iii) $r(L_1 \cup L_2 \cup \ldots \cup L_n) = n$.

An arbitrary matroid satisfying these conditions will be called an *n-spike* with *tip* $p$. It is not difficult to see that $Z_n$ is the unique *binary* $n$–spike. But it is certainly not the only $n$–spike. In general, if $M$ is an $n$–spike with tip $p$, then

(i) $L_i$ is a circuit of $M$ for all $i$;
(ii) $(L_i \cup L_j) - p$ is a circuit of $M$ for all distinct $i$ and $j$;
(iii) every non-spanning circuit of $M$ other than those listed in (i) and (ii) avoids $p$ and contains a unique element from each of $L_1 - p, L_2 - p, \ldots, L_n - p$;
(iv) $M/p$ can be obtained from an $n$–element circuit by replacing each element by two elements in parallel; and
(v) if $L_i = \{p, x_i, y_i\}$, then each of $M\backslash p/x_i$ and $(M\backslash p\backslash x_i)^*$ is an $(n - 1)$-spike with tip $y_i$.

We are now ready to state the generalization of the last theorem to arbitrary matroids.

THEOREM 4.9. *For every integer $n \geq 3$, there is an integer $N$ such that every 3–connected matroid with at least $N$ elements has a minor isomorphic to $U_{2,n}$, $U_{n-2,n}$, $M(K_{3,n})$, $M^*(K_{3,n})$, $M(\mathcal{W}_n)$, $\mathcal{W}^n$, or an $n$–spike.*

When one is unable to obtain specific structural information for a minor-closed class of matroids, one can often bound the size of a simple rank-$r$ member of the class. Kung has proved numerous such results and these are surveyed in [**37**]. The following is a result of this type that relates specifically to the problem of excluding wheels from binary matroids.

THEOREM 4.10. *Let $g(r)$ be the maximum number of elements in a simple rank-$r$ member of $EX(\mathcal{W}^2, M(\mathcal{W}_k))$. Then*

$$g(r) - g(r - 1) \leq 2^{2k-3} \text{for all } r.$$

Kung observed that, since both $PG(k - 2, 2)$ and $PG(k - 3, 2)$ are members of $EX(\mathcal{W}^2, M(\mathcal{W}_k))$, it follows that $g(k - 1) - g(k - 2) = 2^{k-2}$. Kung also remarked that it is probable that the bound in Theorem 4.10 can be sharpened to $2^{k-2}$ for all $r$.

## 5. The decomposition of regular matroids

The most significant application of the Splitter Theorem remains its original use in the proof of a decomposition theorem for regular matroids. That result differs from the matroid structural results stated so far in that it allows, in addition to the operations of direct sum and 2–sum, the operation of 3–sum for matroids. An example of the 3–sum operation for graphs is given in Figure 5. For another example of this operation, we refer to Figure 8. In that figure, consider the central triangle in the drawing of $K_{2,2,2}$. The 3–sum of $K_{2,2,2}$ and $K_4$ across this triangle produces the last graph $H_7$ in Figure 8. A 3–sum of this type where one of the graphs involved is $K_4$ is often called a $\Delta - Y$ *exchange*.

The operation that Seymour [**82**] called 3–sum of binary matroids can be derived from a more general matroid operation that involves sticking two matroids together across a common restriction. To ensure that such an operation is well-defined, one needs some additional conditions. Let $M_1$ and $M_2$ be matroids such that $M_1|T = M_2|T$ where $T = E(M_1) \cap E(M_2)$. Assume that $T$ is a triangle $\Delta$ and that $\Delta$ is a modular flat in $\widetilde{M_1}$. This last condition is always satisfied if $M_1$ is binary. The *generalized parallel connection* $P_\Delta(M_1, M_2)$ of $M_1$ and $M_2$ across $\Delta$ is the matroid on $E(M_1) \cup E(M_2)$ whose flats are those subsets $X$ of $E(M_1) \cup E(M_2)$ such that $X \cap E(M_1)$ is a flat of $M_1$, and $X \cap E(M_2)$ is a flat of $M_2$. This operation is a special case of an operation introduced by Brylawski [**15**]. For our particular interests here, it is sufficient to note that if $M_1$ is binary, then $P_\Delta(M_1, M_2)$ is certainly well-defined. If we delete $\Delta$ from $P_\Delta(M_1, M_2)$, we have completed a matroid operation that generalizes the graph operation of 3–sum. If $M_1$ and $M_2$ are both binary having more than six elements and $\Delta$ does not contain a cocircuit of $M_1$ or of $M_2$, then $P_\Delta(M_1, M_2)\backslash\Delta$ is what Seymour called the 3–*sum* of $M_1$ and $M_2$. Seymour actually used an equivalent definition of 3–sum taking it to be the matroid on $[E(M_1) \cup E(M_2)] - \Delta$ whose circuits are the minimal non-empty sets of the form $(X_1 \cup X_2) - (X_1 \cap X_2)$ where $X_i$ is a disjoint union of circuits of $M_i$. We remark that Truemper [**95**] uses the name $\Delta$–*sum* for this operation and uses "3–sum" for a somewhat different operation. It is also interesting to observe that

$$P_\Delta(M(K_4), F_7)\backslash\Delta = F_7^* \text{ and } P_\Delta(M(K_4), F_7^-)\backslash\Delta = (F_7^-)^*.$$

The first of these constructions is illustrated in Figure 9.

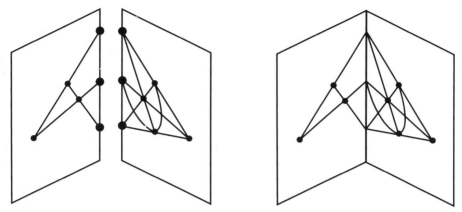

FIGURE 9. A $\Delta - Y$ exchange on $F_7$ produces $F_7^*$.

Two matroids that play an important role in the proof of the regular matroids decomposition theorem are $R_{10}$ and $R_{12}$, which are represented over $GF(2)$ by the matrices $A_{10}$ and $A_{12}$.

$$A_{10} = \left[ \begin{array}{c|ccccc} & 1 & 1 & 0 & 0 & 1 \\ & 1 & 1 & 1 & 0 & 0 \\ I_5 & 0 & 1 & 1 & 1 & 0 \\ & 0 & 0 & 1 & 1 & 1 \\ & 1 & 0 & 0 & 1 & 1 \end{array} \right] \quad A_{12} = \left[ \begin{array}{c|cccccc} & 1 & 1 & 1 & 0 & 0 & 0 \\ & 1 & 1 & 0 & 1 & 0 & 0 \\ I_6 & 1 & 0 & 0 & 0 & 1 & 0 \\ & 0 & 1 & 0 & 0 & 0 & 1 \\ & 0 & 0 & 1 & 0 & 1 & 1 \\ & 0 & 0 & 0 & 1 & 1 & 1 \end{array} \right]$$

We are now able to state Seymour's theorem [**82**].

THEOREM 5.1. *Every regular matroid $M$ can be constructed by means of direct sums, 2–sums, and 3–sums starting with matroids each of which is isomorphic to a minor of $M$, and each of which is either graphic, cographic, or isomorphic to $R_{10}$.*

A key step in the proof of this theorem is the following:

THEOREM 5.2. *Let $M$ be a 3–connected regular matroid. Then either $M$ is graphic or cographic, or $M$ has a minor isomorphic to one of $R_{10}$ and $R_{12}$.*

This results breaks the rest of the proof of the theorem into two cases: (i) $M$ has an $R_{10}$–minor; and (ii) $M$ has an $R_{12}$–minor. The first case is disposed of by showing that $R_{10}$ is a splitter for the class of regular matroids. This is achieved by checking that every simple binary extension of $R_{10}$ has an $F_7$- or $F_7^*$-minor. In case (ii), the rest of the argument begins with the observation that $R_{12}$ has an exact 3–separation $(Y_1, Y_2)$ in which $Y_1$ is the 6–element set that is the union of the only two triangles in $R_{12}$. The argument proceeds by showing that this exact 3–separation of $R_{12}$ *induces* an exact 3–separation of every regular matroid $M$ with an $R_{12}$-minor, that is, every such matroid $M$ has an exact 3–separation $(Z_1, Z_2)$ in which $Z_1 \supseteq Y_1$ and $Z_2 \supseteq Y_2$. This exact 3–separation of $M$ implies that $M$ can be decomposed as the 3–sum of two smaller matroids, $M_1$ and $M_2$, each of which is isomorphic to a minor of $M$. To describe the construction of $M_1$ and $M_2$, we shall assume that $M$ is simple, for the general case follows easily from this case. We may view $M$ as a restriction of the binary projective geometry $PG(r - 1, 2)$ where $r = r(M)$. Then, as $r(Z_1) + r(Z_2) = r + 2$, modularity in the projective geometry implies that the closures of $Z_1$ and $Z_2$ in $PG(r-1,2)$ meet in a line $L$ of $PG(r-1,2)$. Now let $M_i = PG(r-1,2)|(Z_i \cup L)$. Then $M$ is the 3–sum of $M_1$ and $M_2$ unless $L$ meets $Z_1$ or $Z_2$. In the exceptional case, $M$ is again the 3–sum of $M_1$ and $M_2$ if we modify $M_i$ by replacing each element of $L \cap Z_i$ by two elements in parallel.

As an example of the process just described, we note that $R_{12}$ itself is the 3–sum of $M^*(K_{3,3})$ and $M(K_5 \backslash e)$ where the distinguished triangle in the latter is the one whose vertices are disjoint from the endpoints of $e$. To show that each of the matroids $M_1$ and $M_2$ constructed above is a minor of $M$ requires some effort and we omit the details, which may be found in Seymour's original paper [82].

The above discussion allows us to rewrite Theorem 5.2 as follows.

THEOREM 5.3. *Let $M$ be a 3–connected regular matroid. Then*

(i) *$M$ is graphic or cographic; or*

(ii) *$M \cong R_{10}$; or*

(iii) *$M$ has an $R_{12}$–minor, this minor has an exact 3–separation, and this 3–separation induces an exact 3–separation of $M$.*

The last theorem provided the model for a general theory of matroid decomposition developed in a sequence of papers by Truemper [88]–[94] and described in his book [95]. The most significant difference between this scheme and the method used in Section 4 is that it incorporates a separation algorithm that efficiently decides whether or not a given $k$–separation of a minor $N$ of a matroid $M$ induces a $k$–separation of $M$.

Among the numerous applications of the regular matroids decomposition theorem is an algorithm that tests in polynomial time whether or not a given real matrix is totally unimodular. For the details of this, the reader is referred to [77]; other applications of Theorem 5.1 may also be found in [84]. One relatively easy application of the theorem is in extending Theorem 4.5 to describe the structure of all *regular* matroids with no $M(\mathcal{W}_5)$-minor. Indeed, if the columns of the matrix $A_{12}$ representing $R_{12}$ are labeled $1, 2, \ldots, 12$, it is easy to check that $R_{12}/3 \backslash 10 \cong M(\mathcal{W}_5)$. The next theorem [59] now follows immediately from combining Theorems 4.5 and 5.2.

THEOREM 5.4. *Let $M$ be a regular matroid. Then $M$ is 3–connected and has no $M(\mathcal{W}_5)$-minor if and only if*

(i) *for some $k \geq 3$, $M$ is isomorphic to one of $M(K_{3,k})$, $M(K'_{3,k})$, $M(K''_{3,k})$, or $M(K'''_{3,k})$, or their duals; or*

(ii) *$M$ is isomorphic to a 3–connected minor of one of $R_{10}$, $M(Q_3)$, $M(K_{2,2,2})$, $M(H_7)$, $M(H_6)$, or $M^*(H_6)$.*

## 6. Reductions to wheels and whirls

By Corollary 2.4, for every 3–connected matroid $M$ with at least four elements, there is a sequence $M_0, M_1, \ldots, M_n$ of 3–connected matroids such that $M_0 = M$; for all $i$ in $\{1, 2, \ldots, n\}$, $M_i$ is a single-element deletion or a single-element contraction of $M_{i-1}$; and the *end*, $M_n$, of the sequence is a wheel or a whirl. Indeed, for a given matroid $M$, there are potentially several such sequences having possibly different ends. We shall call such a sequence a *reduction* of $M$ and say that $M$ has a *unique reduction* if there is just one matroid $N$ such that the end of every reduction of $M$ is isomorphic to $N$.

For the cycle matroid $M$ of the first graph in Figure 10, one obvious reduction is the sequence $M, M \backslash e$ since the last matroid is isomorphic to $M(\mathcal{W}_5)$. Another reduction, shown in the figure, is $M, M \backslash f, M \backslash f \backslash g, M \backslash f \backslash g / h$. In this case, the last matroid is isomorphic to $M(\mathcal{W}_4)$. Thus the matroid $M$ does not have a unique reduction. A natural problem here is to determine all the 3–connected matroids that do have a unique reduction. This problem was raised for graphic matroids by Hamza Ahmad in a private communication. In this section, we present the answer to this problem which, in light of the theorems presented in the last section, is intriguing.

We begin by noting an extension of the Splitter Theorem due to Coullard [17]. This theorem weakens the restriction on how the Splitter Theorem applies to wheels and whirls. A proof of this result may be found in Coullard and Oxley [18].

THEOREM 6.1. *Let $M$ and $N$ be 3–connected matroids such that $N$ is a minor of $M$, $|E(N)| \geq 4$, $M$ is not a wheel or whirl, and if $N \cong \mathcal{W}^2$, then $M$ has no larger whirl as a minor, while if $N \cong M(\mathcal{W}_3)$, then $M$ has no larger wheel as a minor. Then there is a sequence $M_0, M_1, \ldots, M_n$ of 3–connected matroids such that $M_0 = M$; $M_n \cong N$; and, for all $i$ in $\{1, 2, \ldots, n\}$, $M_i$ is a single-element deletion or a single-element contraction of $M_{i-1}$.*

The next theorem determines all the matroids having a unique reduction.

THEOREM 6.2. *Let $M$ be a 3–connected matroid. Then $M$ has a unique reduction if and only if*
 (i) *$M$ is a wheel or a whirl;*
 (ii) *$M$ is a binary matroid having no $M(\mathcal{W}_4)$-minor;*
 (iii) *$M$ is a regular matroid having no $M(\mathcal{W}_5)$-minor;*
 (iv) *$M$ is a ternary matroid having no $M(\mathcal{W}_3)$-minor; or*
 (v) *$M$ has no $M(\mathcal{W}_3)$-minor and no $\mathcal{W}^3$-minor.*

The proof of this theorem will use the following extension of Theorem 4.4 [56]. The matroid $M(\mathcal{W}_4)$ has exactly three non-isomorphic binary 3–connected single-element extensions, namely $M^*(K_{3,3})$, $M(K_5 \backslash e)$, and a matroid denoted $P_9$. A geometric representation for the last matroid is shown in Figure 11. Evidently $P_9$ is isomorphic to $P_\Delta(M(K_4), F_7) \backslash p$ where $p$ is an arbitrary element of $\Delta$.

THEOREM 6.3. *Let $M$ be a binary matroid. Then $M$ is 3–connected having no minor isomorphic to $P_9$ or $P_9^*$ if and only if*
 (i) *$M$ is regular and 3–connected; or*
 (ii) *for some $r \geq 3$, $M \cong Z_r, Z_r^*, Z_r \backslash b_r$, or $Z_r \backslash c_r$.*

PROOF OF THEOREM 6.2. We distinguish three cases:
 (I) $M$ is a wheel or a whirl;

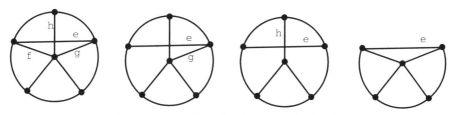

FIGURE 10. A reduction to a 4–wheel.

(II) $M$ is not a wheel or a whirl and has $M(\mathcal{W}_5)$ or $\mathcal{W}^4$ as a minor;

(III) $M$ is not a wheel or a whirl and has neither $M(\mathcal{W}_5)$ nor $\mathcal{W}^4$ as a minor.

In case (I), $M$ clearly has a unique reduction. In case (II), if $M$ has an $M(\mathcal{W}_5)$-minor, then $M$ also has an $M(\mathcal{W}_4)$-minor. Thus, by Theorem 6.1, $M$ has a reduction whose end is isomorphic to $M(\mathcal{W}_5)$ and another whose end is isomorphic to $M(\mathcal{W}_4)$. Hence if $M$ has an $M(\mathcal{W}_5)$-minor, it does not have a unique reduction. Similarly, if $M$ has a $\mathcal{W}^4$-minor, it has reductions to both $\mathcal{W}^3$ and $\mathcal{W}^4$. Thus, in case (II), $M$ does not have a unique reduction.

In case (III), suppose first that $M$ has no $\mathcal{W}^2$-minor. Then $M$ is binary having no $M(\mathcal{W}_5)$-minor. If $M$ has no $M(\mathcal{W}_4)$-minor, then clearly $M$ has a unique reduction. Suppose now that $M$ has an $M(\mathcal{W}_4)$-minor. Then either (a) $M$ has $P_9$ or $P_9^*$ as a minor; or (b) $M$ has no minor isomorphic to $P_9$ or $P_9^*$. In case (a), we may assume, by duality, that $M$ has a $P_9$-minor. Theorem 4.1 implies that there is a sequence of 3–connected matroids, $M_0, M_1, \ldots, M_n$, with each member being a single-element deletion or contraction of its predecessor, $M_0 = M$, and $M_n \cong P_9$. But $P_9$ is a single-element extension of both $M(\mathcal{W}_4)$ and $S_8$, the latter is a single-element extension of $F_7^*$ which, in turn, is a single-element coextension of $M(\mathcal{W}_3)$. Thus $P_9$, and hence $M$, has reductions to both $M(\mathcal{W}_4)$ and $M(\mathcal{W}_3)$. Therefore, in case (a), $M$ does not have a unique reduction. On the other hand, in case (b), Theorem 6.3 implies that $M$ is regular. Thus $M$ is regular having an $M(\mathcal{W}_4)$-minor but no $M(\mathcal{W}_5)$-minor. Because $M(\mathcal{W}_3)$ has no 3–connected regular single-element extension or coextension, it follows that $M$ has a unique reduction.

To complete the proof in case (III), we need to consider the case when $M$ has a $\mathcal{W}^2$-minor. If $M$ has no $M(\mathcal{W}_3)$-minor and no $\mathcal{W}^3$-minor, then every reduction of $M$ must have its end isomorphic to $\mathcal{W}^2$. Thus, in this case, $M$ has a unique reduction. We may now assume that $M$ has $M(\mathcal{W}_3)$ or $\mathcal{W}^3$ as a minor. In the first case, $M$ has reductions that end in both the largest wheel minor of $M$ and the largest whirl minor of $M$, so $M$ does not have a unique reduction. Thus we may assume that $M$ has no $M(\mathcal{W}_3)$-minor. Hence $M$ has a $\mathcal{W}^3$-minor. If $M$ has a $U_{2,5}$- or $U_{3,5}$-minor, then $M$ has a reduction to $\mathcal{W}^2$ that goes through such a minor, and $M$ has another reduction to $\mathcal{W}^3$. Thus if $M$ has a $U_{2,5}$- or $U_{3,5}$-minor, then $M$ does not have a unique reduction. We may now suppose that $M$ has no $U_{2,5}$-

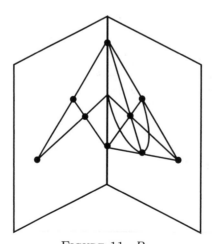

FIGURE 11. $P_9$.

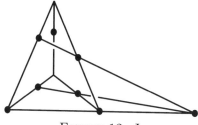

FIGURE 12. J.

or $U_{3,5}$-minor. Since $M$ also has no $M(\mathcal{W}_3)$-minor, $M$ has no $F_7$- or $F_7^*$-minor. We conclude that $M$ is a ternary matroid having no $M(\mathcal{W}_3)$-minor and that such matroids have a unique reduction.                                                       □

The feature of Theorem 6.2 that seems particularly striking is that, even before the problem was raised, the matroids listed under (ii), (iii), and (iv) had been explicitly described. Moreover, those results were essentially the only known structural results involving exclusion of wheels or whirls. The theorems that specify the matroids listed under (ii) and (iii) were stated above. The matroids listed under (iv) were determined in [**57**]. Before stating that result, we observe that it means that all the matroids having a unique reduction are known explicitly except for those that have no $M(\mathcal{W}_3)$-minor and no $\mathcal{W}^3$-minor. Hence we have the following:

PROBLEM 6.4. *Determine all the matroids that have no $M(\mathcal{W}_3)$-minor and no $\mathcal{W}^3$-minor.*

The class of matroids with no $M(\mathcal{W}_3)$-minor and no $\mathcal{W}^3$-minor includes, for example, all rank-3 matroids in which there are at most two elements that are on more than one non-trivial line. The task of determining all the matroids in this class seems difficult, although it should be noted that the quaternary members of that class were listed in [**57**]. Moreover, Hipp [**32**] proved the following theorem, a proof of which may also be found in [**37**].

THEOREM 6.5. *A rank-r simple matroid $M$ in $EX(\mathcal{W}^3, M(\mathcal{W}_3), U_{2,q+2})$ has at most $q(r-1)+1$ elements. Moreover, equality is attained if and only if $M$ can be formed from $r-1$ copies of $U_{2,q+1}$ by using $r-2$ parallel connections.*

Two special matroids appear in the next result, namely the splitters for the class of ternary matroids with no $M(\mathcal{W}_3)$-minor. One of these matroids is $J$, the rank-4 self-dual matroid for which a geometric representation is shown in Figure 12. The second such matroid is the vector matroid of the matrix $D_{12}$ over $GF(3)$ where $D_{12}$ is

$$\left[ \quad I_6 \quad \begin{array}{|cccccc} 0 & 1 & 1 & 1 & 1 & 1 \\ 1 & 0 & 1 & -1 & -1 & 1 \\ 1 & 1 & 0 & 1 & -1 & -1 \\ 1 & -1 & 1 & 0 & 1 & -1 \\ 1 & -1 & -1 & 1 & 0 & 1 \\ 1 & 1 & -1 & -1 & 1 & 0 \end{array} \right].$$

The last matrix and its associated matroid are actually very well known in a slightly different context. The matrix $D_{12}$ is a generator matrix for the ternary Golay code, this being a member of the special class of *perfect codes* (see, for

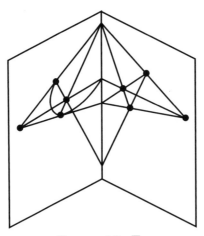

FIGURE 13. $T_8$.

example, Chapter 20 of [**41**]). Moreover, if $E$ is the set of elements of $M[D_{12}]$ and $\mathcal{H}$ is its set of hyperplanes, then the pair $(E, \mathcal{H})$ is the unique Steiner system $S(5, 6, 12)$; that is, every member of $\mathcal{H}$ contains exactly six elements and every 5–element subset of $E$ is contained in a unique member of $\mathcal{H}$. The matroid $M[D_{12}]$ has many attractive properties. For instance, both the set of circuits and the set of cocircuits of this matroid equal $\mathcal{H}$. Hence $M[D_{12}]$ is identically self-dual. Moreover, $M[D_{12}]$ has as its automorphism group the Mathieu group, $M_{12}$, which is 5–transitive; that is, if $(e_1, e_2, \ldots, e_5)$ and $(f_1, f_2, \ldots, f_5)$ are ordered 5–tuples of distinct elements of $M[D_{12}]$, then there is an automorphism of $M[D_{12}]$ that, for all $i$, maps $e_i$ to $f_i$. In particular, if $|X| = 3$, then $M[D_{12}]/X$ is isomorphic to the ternary affine plane, $AG(2, 3)$. We shall follow convention in denoting the matroid $M[D_{12}]$ by $S(5, 6, 12)$.

THEOREM 6.6. *A matroid $M$ is 3–connected, ternary, and has no $M(\mathcal{W}_3)$-minor if and only if $M$ is isomorphic to $J$, to $\mathcal{W}^r$ for some $r \geq 2$, or to a 3–connected minor of $S(5, 6, 12)$.*

## 7. More applications of the Splitter Theorem

The technique that was used to derive Theorems 4.4, 4.5, and 6.5 has also been successfully employed to prove numerous other results. Many of these are noted in Chapter 11 of [**62**]. In this section, we give some examples of such results concentrating on newer results not noted in [**62**].

A matroid is called *paving* if it has no circuits of size less than its rank. For comparison, a matroid is uniform if and only if it has no circuits of size less than or equal to its rank. It is straightforward to show that the class of paving matroids is minor-closed and that the unique excluded minor for the class is $U_{2,2} \oplus U_{0,1}$ [**61**]. It is not difficult to determine all paving matroids that are not 3–connected and these are listed in [**61**]. The following result was proved directly by Acketa [**1**].

THEOREM 7.1. *The 3–connected binary paving matroids are precisely the 3–connected minors of $AG(3, 2)$.*

It is straightforward to prove this result using the building-up technique exemplified in Section 4. The same technique can also be used to determine all

3–connected ternary paving matroids although more work is needed for this. Some of the matroids that arise here are familiar or have appeared earlier. Two that we have not yet seen here are $R_8$ and $T_8$. The first of these is the real affine cube; the second has the geometric representation shown in Figure 13. These matroids are represented over $GF(3)$ by the matrices

$$
\left[\begin{array}{c|cccc}
 & 0 & 1 & 1 & 1 \\
I_4 & 1 & 0 & 1 & 1 \\
 & 1 & 1 & 0 & 1 \\
 & 1 & 1 & 1 & 0
\end{array}\right]
\quad\text{and}\quad
\left[\begin{array}{c|cccc}
 & -1 & 1 & 1 & 1 \\
I_4 & 1 & -1 & 1 & 1 \\
 & 1 & 1 & -1 & 1 \\
 & 1 & 1 & 1 & -1
\end{array}\right],
$$

respectively. Evidently both $R_8$ and $T_8$ are isomorphic to their duals.

THEOREM 7.2. *The 3–connected ternary paving matroids are precisely the 3–connected minors of $PG(2,3)$, $S(5,6,12)$, $R_8$, and $T_8$.*

Evidently there are relatively few 3–connected $GF(q)$-representable paving matroids for $q \in \{2,3\}$. Rajpal [**70**] proved that, in general, there are only finitely many 3–connected $GF(q)$-representable paving matroids by establishing the following result.

PROPOSITION 7.3. *Let $M$ be a rank-$r$ $GF(q)$-representable paving matroid with $1 < r < |E(M)|$. If $r > q$, then*

(i) *$M^*$ is a paving matroid; and*
(ii) *$|E(M)| \le 4q$ and $r \le 2q$.*

By using the same technique that was used to prove Theorem 7.2, Rajpal [**71**] was able to determine all quaternary paving matroids. The case-checking required here is considerable and needed the aid of a computer.

THEOREM 7.4. *Every 3–connected quaternary paving matroid is a minor of one of the fifteen splitters for the class of such matroids. These splitters consist of*

(i) *$PG(2,4)$;*
(ii) *eight matroids of rank four of which five have twelve elements and one each have thirteen, fourteen, and sixteen elements;*
(iii) *three matroids of rank five all having ten elements; and*
(iv) *the dual of the Pappus matroid and two other matroids of rank six having ten and twelve elements, respectively.*

One of the graph results that motivated the matroid structural results that we have discussed here is D.W. Hall's Theorem (3.2). A restatement of that result is that every simple 3–connected graph with a $K_5$-minor must have a $K_{3,3}$-minor, the only exception being $K_5$ itself. Kingan [**36**] proved an attractive generalization of this result to binary matroids. We denote by $T_{12}$ the vector matroid of the following matrix over $GF(2)$:

$$
\left[\begin{array}{c|cccccc}
 & 1 & 1 & 0 & 0 & 0 & 1 \\
 & 1 & 0 & 0 & 0 & 1 & 1 \\
I_6 & 0 & 0 & 0 & 1 & 1 & 1 \\
 & 0 & 0 & 1 & 1 & 1 & 0 \\
 & 0 & 1 & 1 & 1 & 0 & 0 \\
 & 1 & 1 & 1 & 0 & 0 & 0
\end{array}\right].
$$

This matroid has a transitive automorphism group, and $T_{12}/e$ will denote the unique single-element contraction of $T_{12}$.

THEOREM 7.5. *Let $M$ be a 3–connected binary matroid with an $M(K_5)$-minor. Then either $M$ has an $M(K_{3,3})$- or $M^*(K_{3,3})$-minor, or $M$ is isomorphic to $M(K_5)$, $T_{12}$, or $T_{12}/e$.*

The matroid $T_{12}$ has an interesting link with the Petersen graph, $P_{10}$. Take the $15 \times 12$ binary matrix whose rows are indexed by the edges of $P_{10}$ and whose columns are indexed by the 5–cycles of $P_{10}$ with each column being the incidence vector of the corresponding 5–cycle. Then the vector matroid of this matrix is $T_{12}$.

The matroid $T_{12}$ arises in another interesting context. The classes of binary and ternary matroids are relatively well understood, as is their intersection, the class of regular matroids. The union of the classes of binary and ternary matroids is also minor-closed, but it not known whether the set of excluded minors for this union is finite. The following conjecture is due to Oporowski, Oxley, and Whittle (private communication).

CONJECTURE 7.6. *Let $\mathcal{M}$ be the class of matroids that are binary or ternary. Then the excluded minors for $\mathcal{M}$ are $U_{2,4} \oplus F_7$, $U_{2,4} \oplus F_7^*$, $U_{2,4} \oplus_2 F_7$, $U_{2,4} \oplus_2 F_7^*$, $U_{2,5}$, $U_{3,5}$, and the unique matroids that are obtained by relaxing a circuit-hyperplane in each of $AG(3,2)$ and $T_{12}$.*

Oporowski, Oxley, and Whittle have proved that the above list contains all the excluded minors for $\mathcal{M}$ with at most twenty-three elements. Moreover, they have shown that, for every remaining excluded minor $N$, there is a 3–connected binary matroid $M$ whose ground set is the union of two disjoint circuit-hyperplanes such that relaxing one of these produces $N$ and relaxing both produces a ternary matroid. This implies, in particular, that $|E(N)|$ is divisible by 4.

The finiteness problem considered above is a special case of the general question: If $\mathcal{M}_1$ and $\mathcal{M}_2$ are minor-closed classes of matroids, each characterized by a finite set of excluded minors, is $\mathcal{M}_1 \cup \mathcal{M}_2$ also characterized by a finite set of excluded minors? This problem, the *intertwining problem* for matroids, was posed by Brylawski [16] and, independently, by several others. It appears as Problem 14.1.8 in [62] and was recently answered in the negative by Vertigan [101]. While Vertigan gave a large collection of examples of classes $\mathcal{M}_1$ and $\mathcal{M}_2$ for which $\mathcal{M}_1 \cup \mathcal{M}_2$ does not have a finite set of excluded minors yet $\mathcal{M}_1$ and $\mathcal{M}_2$ do, it appears to be very difficult to characterize precisely when this occurs.

In Section 4, we considered sets of unavoidable minors in large 3–connected matroids. The next result, which is much easier to prove, identifies another collection of small unavoidable matroids [54, 104]. Geometric representations for the matroids $Q_6$ and $P_6$ are shown in Figure 14.

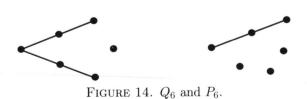

FIGURE 14. $Q_6$ and $P_6$.

PROPOSITION 7.7. *Let $M$ be a 3–connected matroid having rank and corank at least three. Then $M$ has a minor isomorphic to one of the matroids $M(\mathcal{W}_3)$, $\mathcal{W}^3$, $Q_6$, $P_6$, or $U_{3,6}$.*

This list of five small matroids raises the question of describing the structure of the classes that arise when one excludes certain of these as minors. For instance, it is not difficult to see that $EX(\mathcal{W}^3, Q_6, P_6, U_{3,6})$ consists of those matroids that can be constructed from binary matroids and uniform matroids of rank or corank two by direct sums and 2–sums. We noted above that the problem of describing the members of the class $EX(M(\mathcal{W}_3), \mathcal{W}^3)$ is unsolved. But we should certainly expect to be able to describe those classes that arise when four of $M(\mathcal{W}_3)$, $\mathcal{W}^3$, $Q_6$, $P_6$, and $U_{3,6}$ are excluded as minors [**58**]. However, there is one problematic case: the structure of $EX(M(\mathcal{W}_3), \mathcal{W}^3, Q_6, U_{3,6})$ has yet to be determined, whereas, by contrast, the members of $EX(\mathcal{W}^3, P_6)$ have been specified [**60**]. This raises a general issue that looms over all results of this type, namely its unpredictability. With current methods, it seems impossible to foretell when one is likely to be able to determine the structure of a certain class. One applies the building-up method and hopes that a pattern can be detected before the number of cases explodes. Another interesting feature of this process is that, even when the method produces an answer, knowing the answer helps little in verifying that this answer is correct.

## 8. Essential elements and fans

An element $e$ in a 3–connected matroid $M$ is *essential* if neither $M \backslash e$ nor $M/e$ is 3–connected. The Wheels and Whirls Theorem identified wheels and whirls of rank at least three as being precisely those 3–connected matroids in which every element is essential. In this section, we consider what can be said concerning the local structure about an essential element in a 3–connected matroid. Since a 3–connected matroid with at least four elements is both simple and cosimple, one way for an element to be essential is for it to be in both a triangle and a triad. Indeed, Tutte [**99**] proved the following:

THEOREM 8.1. *An essential element in a 3–connected matroid is in either a triangle or a triad.*

In both wheels and whirls, we have sequences of interlocking triangles and triads. We shall be interested in such sequences in arbitrary 3–connected matroids. For instance, in the cycle matroid of the graph $G$ in Figure 15, the members of the sequence $\{a_1, a_2, a_3\}, \{a_2, a_3, a_4\}, \ldots, \{a_5, a_6, a_7\}$ are alternately triangles and triads. In general, a non-empty sequence $T_1, T_2, \ldots, T_k$ of triangles and triads is a *chain* of *length* $k$ in a matroid $M$ if, for all $i$ in $\{1, 2, \ldots, k-1\}$,

(i) exactly one of $T_i$ and $T_{i+1}$ is a triangle;

(ii) $|T_i \cap T_{i+1}| = 2$; and

(iii) $(T_{i+1} - T_i) \cap (T_1 \cup T_2 \cup \ldots \cup T_i)$ is empty.

Since the only 3–connected matroid with a triangle that is also a triad is $U_{2,4}$, condition (i) here is redundant if $M$ is 3–connected having at least five elements. Evidently $T_1, T_2, \ldots, T_k$ is a chain in $M$ if and only if it is a chain in $M^*$. Moreover, a straightforward induction argument using orthogonality establishes that if $T_1, T_2, \ldots, T_k$ is a chain in $M$, then $M$ has $k+2$ distinct elements $a_1, a_2, \ldots, a_{k+2}$ such that $T_i = \{a_i, a_{i+1}, a_{i+2}\}$ for all $i$ in $\{1, 2, \ldots, k\}$. The sets $T_1, T_2, \ldots, T_k$ are called *links* in the chain.

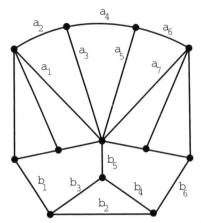

FIGURE 15. A graph $G$ containing several chains.

Although chains can certainly occur in both non-graphic and graphic matroids, we follow Tutte [99] in keeping track of the triangles and triads in a chain by using graphs as in Figure 16(a)–(c). In each case, the chain is $T_1, T_2, \ldots, T_k$ where $T_i = \{a_i, a_{i+1}, a_{i+2}\}$, and every triangle in the graph is a triangle in the chain, while the triads in the chain correspond to circled vertices.

The following result, known as Tutte's Triangle Lemma [99], is an important tool in dealing with chains particularly in extending a given chain.

THEOREM 8.2. *Let $\{x, y, z\}$ be a triangle in a 3–connected matroid $M$. If neither $M\backslash x$ nor $M\backslash y$ is 3–connected, then $x$ is in a triad with exactly one of $y$ and $z$.*

Much of our interest is in maximal chains in 3–connected matroids. By extending Tutte's proof of the Wheels and Whirls Theorem, one can show that such a chain has non-essential elements at both ends [65].

THEOREM 8.3. *Let $M$ be a 3–connected matroid with at least four elements and suppose that $M$ is not a wheel or a whirl. Let $T_1, T_2, \ldots, T_k$ be a maximal chain in $M$. Then the elements of $T_1 \cup T_2 \cup \ldots \cup T_k$ can be labeled so that neither $a_1$ nor $a_{k+2}$ is essential where $T_i = \{a_i, a_{i+1}, a_{i+2}\}$ for all $i$.*

As an immediate consequence of this, we have the following result [65].

COROLLARY 8.4. *Let $M$ be a 3–connected matroid with at least four elements. Then either $M$ is a wheel or a whirl, or $M$ has at least two non-essential elements.*

A maximal chain $T_1, T_2, \ldots, T_k$ in a 3–connected matroid $M$ other than a wheel or a whirl is called a *fan*. Type–1, type–2, and *type–3 fans* correspond to the chains shown in (a), (b), and (c), respectively, in Figure 16. In that figure, the non-essential elements of the fans have been marked in bold.

Theorem 8.1 established that every essential element $e$ in a 3–connected matroid $M$ is in some chain. Thus, provided $M$ is neither a wheel nor a whirl, $e$ is in some fan. The next result [65] specifies exactly when this fan is unique.

THEOREM 8.5. *Let $M$ be a 3–connected matroid that is not a wheel or a whirl. Suppose that $e$ is an essential element of $M$. Then $e$ is in a fan. Moreover, this fan is unique unless*

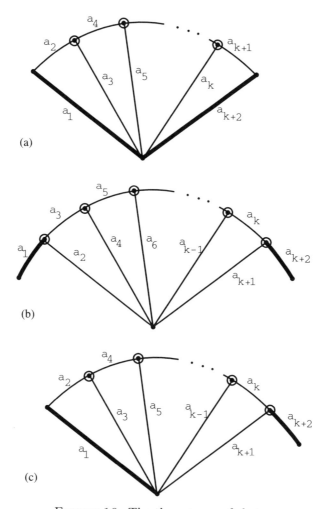

FIGURE 16. The three types of chains.

(a) *every fan containing e consists of a single triangle and any two such triangles meet in $\{e\}$;*

(b) *every fan containing e consists of a single triad and any two such triads meet in $\{e\}$;*

(c) *e is in exactly three fans; these three fans are of the same type, each has five elements, together they contain a total of six elements; and, depending on whether these fans are of type-1 or type-2, the restriction or contraction, respectively, of M to this set of six elements is isomorphic to $M(K_4)$.*

An example of the third possibility above may be found in Figure 15. There, each of $b_2, b_3$, and $b_4$ is essential and is in the three fans of the form $T_1, \{b_2, b_3, b_4\}, T_3$ where $T_1$ and $T_3$ are any two of $\{b_1, b_2, b_3\}, \{b_3, b_4, b_5\}$, and $\{b_2, b_4, b_6\}$.

When $M$ is graphic, case (b) in Theorem 8.5 can be strengthened to the assertion that $e$ is in exactly two fans each of which is a single triad corresponding to a vertex of degree three. The proof of this fact relies on the following strengthening

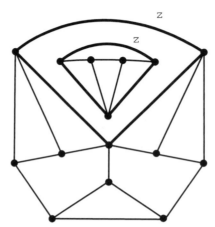

FIGURE 17. Breaking off a wheel; the outer graph is $G_1$.

of Theorem 8.1 due to Tutte [**98**]: In a 3–connected graphic matroid $M(G)$, every essential element that is not in a triangle meets a degree–3 vertex of $G$.

Theorem 8.5 implies that the fans in a 3–connected matroid other than a wheel or a whirl induce a partition of the set of essential elements.

COROLLARY 8.6. *Let $M$ be a 3–connected matroid that is not a wheel or a whirl. Then there is a partition of the set of essential elements of $M$ such that two elements are in the same class if and only if there is a fan whose ground set contains both.*

Returning to the cycle matroid $M$ of the graph $G$ in Figure 15, we observe that the fan with ground set $\{a_1, a_2, \ldots, a_7\}$ can be viewed as a partial wheel. Indeed, we can break off a wheel from the original matroid leaving a 3–connected matroid. Figure 17 shows two disjoint graphs with one, a 4–wheel, drawn inside the other $G_1$. If the bold edges are identified in the natural way and then the identified edge $z$ is deleted, we recover the original graph. On the other hand, the graph $G_1$ can be obtained from $G$ by deleting the edges $a_3$ and $a_5$, contracting the edges $a_2$ and $a_4$, and then relabeling $a_6$ as $z$. The next theorem [**65**] asserts that any 3–connected matroid $M$ having a chain of odd length exceeding two can be constructed by sticking together a wheel and a certain 3–connected minor of $M$, just as in this example.

THEOREM 8.7. *Let $M$ be a 3–connected matroid and suppose that, for some non-negative integer $n$, the sequence*

$$\{y_0, x_0, y_1\}, \{x_0, y_1, x_1\}, \{y_1, x_1, y_2\}, \ldots, \{y_n, x_n, y_{n+1}\}$$

*is a chain in $M$ in which $\{y_0, x_0, y_1\}$ is a triangle. Then*

$$M = P_{\Delta_1}(M(\mathcal{W}_{n+2}), M_1) \backslash z$$

*where $\Delta_1 = \{y_0, y_{n+1}, z\}$; $\mathcal{W}_{n+2}$ is labeled as in Figure 18; and $M_1$ is obtained from the matroid $M/x_0, x_1, \ldots, x_{n-1} \backslash y_1, y_2, \ldots, y_n$ by relabeling $x_n$ as $z$. Moreover, $\widetilde{M_1}$ is 3–connected. More precisely, either*

(i) *$M_1$ is 3–connected; or*
(ii) *$z$ is in a unique 2–circuit $\{z, h\}$ of $M_1$, and $M_1 \backslash z$ is 3–connected.*

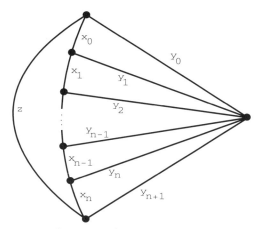

FIGURE 18. A labeled $(n+2)$–wheel.

*In the latter case,*

$$M = P_{\Delta_2}(M(\mathcal{W}_{n+2}), M_2)$$

*where $\Delta_2 = \{y_0, y_{n+1}, h\}$; $\mathcal{W}_{n+2}$ is labeled as in Figure 18 with $z$ relabeled as $h$; and $M_2$ is $M_1 \backslash z$, which equals $M \backslash x_0, x_1, \ldots, x_n, y_1, y_2, \ldots, y_n$.*

An immediate consequence of this theorem is that the restriction of $M$ to $\{x_0, x_1, \ldots, x_n, y_0, y_1, \ldots, y_{n+1}\}$, the ground set of the chain, is equal to the cycle matroid of the graph shown in Figure 18 with the edge $z$ deleted. Thus our view of a chain as a partial wheel is validated.

The behavior of essential elements when a wheel is broken off as above is determined in [**65**]. In particular, it is shown that, for $i$ in $\{1, 2\}$, if $M_i$ is 3–connected, then an element of $M_i$ that is essential in $M$ remains essential in $M_i$. Non-essential elements behave somewhat less straightforwardly but still predictably.

Theorem 8.7 indicates how one can break off a wheel from a 3–connected matroid having a chain of odd length exceeding two. In fact, that theorem explicitly describes this break off when the chain has a triangle as its first link and hence has a triangle as its last link. If the chain has triads as its first and last links, then one can reduce to the case described in Theorem 8.7 by taking duals. A similar result [**65**] holds for chains of even length although, in this case, it is slightly more difficult to recover a 3–connected matroid in what is left after the break off.

THEOREM 8.8. *Let $M$ be a 3–connected matroid that is not a wheel or a whirl. Suppose that, for some non-negative integer $n$, the sequence*

$$\{y_0, x_0, y_1\}, \{x_0, y_1, x_1\}, \ldots, \{y_n, x_n, y_{n+1}\}, \{x_n, y_{n+1}, x_{n+1}\}$$

*is a chain in $M$ in which $\{y_0, x_0, y_1\}$ is a triangle. Then*

$$M = P_\Delta(M(\mathcal{W}_{n+3}), M_3) \backslash \{z', y'_{n+1}\}$$

*where $\Delta = \{y_0, z', y'_{n+1}\}$; $\mathcal{W}_{n+3}$ is labeled as in Figure 19; and $M_3$ is obtained from the matroid $M/x_0, x_1, \ldots, x_{n-1} \backslash y_1, y_2, \ldots, y_n / x_{n+1}$ by relabeling $x_n$ and $y_{n+1}$ as $z'$ and $y'_{n+1}$. Moreover, $\widetilde{M_3}$ is 3–connected. More precisely,*

(i) *$M_3$ is 3–connected; or*

(ii) *$z'$ is in a unique 2–circuit of $M_3$, and $M_3 \backslash z'$ is 3–connected; or*

(iii) *$y'_{n+1}$ is in a unique 2–circuit of $M_3$, and $M_3 \backslash y'_{n+1}$ is 3–connected; or*

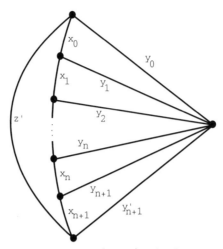

FIGURE 19. A labeled $(n+3)$–wheel.

(iv) *each of $z'$ and $y'_{n+1}$ is in a unique 2–circuit of $M_3$, and $M_3 \backslash z', y'_{n+1}$ is 3–connected.*

By breaking off wheels in the manner described above, one is able to reduce the size of the 3–connected matroid being considered by removing a piece of the matroid whose behavior is well-understood. The reader may be curious that, in the general matroid case, one is always breaking off wheels rather than wheels *or* whirls. This can be explained relatively simply. If $\Delta$ is a triangle in a wheel and $z$ is a rim element in this triangle, then the matroid $P_\Delta(M(\mathcal{W}_{n+2}), U_{2,4}) \backslash z$ is precisely $\mathcal{W}^{n+2}$. Thus, loosely speaking, attaching wheels and attaching whirls are really the same process with only the points of attachment altering.

## 9. Matroids with few non-essential elements

A 3–connected matroid with no non-essential elements is a wheel or a whirl. Moreover, by Corollary 8.4, there are no 3–connected matroids with exactly one non-essential element. In this section, following [**66**], we describe the 3–connected matroids that have exactly two non-essential elements.

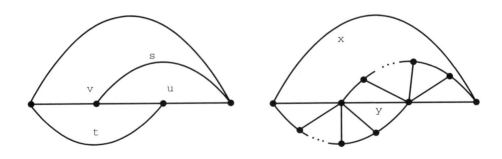

FIGURE 20. Construction of a twisted wheel from $K_4$.

We know from Theorem 8.3 that if $M$ is a 3–connected matroid other than a wheel or a whirl, then every essential element of $M$ is in a fan the ends of which are non-essential. Thus if $M$ has exactly two non-essential elements, these two elements must occur as the ends of every fan. Therefore $M$ is formed by somehow attaching these fans together across the two non-essential elements. In what follows, we shall describe precisely how these attachments are done. If $M$ is graphic, it is not difficult to find some examples of such attachments. The graph in Figure 20(b) is called a *twisted wheel*. It can be obtained from $K_4$, drawn as in Figure 20(a), by subdividing each of the edges $s$ and $t$ into at least two edges and then joining each of the newly created vertices to one of $u$ and $v$ as shown. Evidently $x$ and $y$ are the only non-essential elements in the cycle matroid of such a graph. It is clear that a twisted wheel can also be constructed by appropriately joining two type-3 fans with ends $x$ and $y$.

The graph in Figure 21(b) is an example of a 3–dimensional wheel. In general, a *multidimensional wheel* is constructed as follows: begin with the 3–vertex graph in Figure 21(a) in which $u$ and $v$ are joined by a path $u, h, v$ of length two and by $k$ parallel edges $x_1, x_2, \dots, x_k$, for some $k \geq 3$. Subdivide each of these parallel edges into at least two edges and, finally, join each newly created vertex to $h$. Evidently the cycle matroid of the resulting graph has $x$ and $y$ as its only non-essential elements. Moreover, this matroid can be obtained by appropriately joining $k$ type-1 fans with ends $x$ and $y$. Observe that if each of $x_1, x_2, \dots, x_k$ is subdivided into exactly two edges, the resulting $k$–dimensional wheel is isomorphic to $K''_{3,k}$.

Based on Theorem 8.5, it is fairly straightforward to prove that the only graphic matroids with exactly two non-essential elements are those described above.

THEOREM 9.1. *Let $M$ be a 3–connected graphic matroid. Then $M$ has exactly two non-essential elements if and only if $M$ is the cycle matroid of a twisted wheel or a multidimensional wheel.*

There are many non-graphic 3–connected matroids that have exactly two non-essential elements and we now proceed to describe them. Theorem 8.7, which specifies how to break off a wheel, is crucial in deriving this description.

Let $M$ be a 3–connected matroid with exactly two non-essential elements. Then every element of $M$ is in a fan so every element is in a triangle or a triad. Hence,

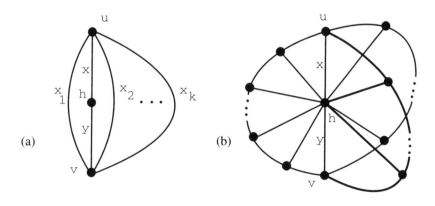

FIGURE 21. Construction of a multidimensional wheel.

for every element $x$ of $M$, at least one of $M \backslash x$ and $M/x$ fails to be 3–connected. We call an element $e$ of a 3–connected matroid $N$ *deletable* if $N \backslash e$ is 3–connected; $e$ is *contractible* if $N/e$ is 3–connected. In $M$, we must have one of the following:

(i) both non-essential elements are deletable but not contractible;
(ii) both non-essential elements are contractible but not deletable;
(iii) one non-essential element is deletable but not contractible and the other is contractible but not deletable.

Hence, for example, the cycle matroid of a multidimensional wheel satisfies (i), whereas the cycle matroid of a twisted wheel satisfies (iii). Evidently, in cases (i), (ii), and (iii), every fan of $M$ is of type-1, type-2, or type-3, respectively. Accordingly, in these three cases, we shall refer to $M$ itself as being of *type*-1, *type*-2, or *type*-3. Clearly the class of type-2 matroids coincides with the class of duals of type-1 matroids, so it will suffice to specify the matroids of type-1 and those of type-3.

To see how to construct all type-1 matroids, it is instructive to consider a geometric construction for the cycle matroid of a multidimensional wheel. Begin with a 3–point line $\{x, y, z\}$ and $k$ wheels for some $k \geq 3$. Let $\{x, y, z\}$ also label a triangle in each of these wheels with $x$ and $y$ being spokes. Attach the wheels to the line, one at a time, via generalized parallel connection. Finally, delete the element $z$ to obtain the desired matroid.

THEOREM 9.2. *The class of 3–connected matroids that have exactly two non-essential elements each of which is deletable coincides with the class of matroids $M$ that are constructed as follows.*

(i) *Let $L$ be an $n$–point line for some $n \geq 3$, and $x$ and $y$ be two elements of $L$.*
(ii) *Let $N_1, N_2, \ldots, N_k$ be a collection of wheels of rank at least three such that $E(L), E(N_1), E(N_2), \ldots, E(N_k)$ are disjoint and $k \geq 3$.*
(iii) *Let $\Delta_1, \Delta_2, \ldots, \Delta_k$ be a collection of triangles in $L$ each containing $\{x, y\}$, and $\Delta'_1, \Delta'_2, \ldots, \Delta'_k$ be triangles in $N_1, N_2, \ldots, N_k$, respectively.*
(iv) *For each $i$ in $\{1, 2, \ldots, k\}$, identify the elements of $\Delta'_i$ with the elements of $\Delta_i$ so that $x$ and $y$ are identified with spokes of $N_i$.*
(v) *Let $A_0 = L$ and, for all $i$ in $\{1, 2, \ldots, k\}$, let $A_i = P_{\Delta_i}(N_i, A_{i-1})$.*
(vi) *Let $M = A_k \backslash (L - \{x, y\})$.*

It should be noted here that the triangles $\Delta_1, \Delta_2, \ldots, \Delta_k$ in the above construction need not be distinct. We also remark that if (vi) is modified so that one deletes some subset of $L - \{x, y\}$ rather than the whole set, then (i)–(vi) describe the construction for all 3–connected matroids in which every non-essential element is deletable and the set of such elements has rank two.

Like the type-1 matroids, the type-3 matroids are obtained by attaching wheels to a certain root matroid. This root matroid is again a familiar one.

LEMMA 9.3. *For some $n \geq 3$, let $N$ be an $n$–spike with tip $y$ and let $\{x, y, z\}$ be a triangle of $N$. Then $N \backslash z$ is a 3–connected matroid whose set of non-essential elements is contained in $\{x, y\}$. Indeed, $y$ is deletable and $x$ is contractible in $N \backslash z$ unless $n = 3$ and $N \backslash z$ is a wheel or a whirl.*

PROOF. Clearly each element of $E(N \backslash z) - \{x, y\}$ is in both a triangle and a triad. Moreover, $y$ is in a triangle and $x$ is in a triad. It is not difficult to check that $N \backslash z$ is 3–connected, and so the lemma follows.                               □

THEOREM 9.4. *The class of 3–connected matroids that have exactly two non-essential elements one of which is deletable and one of which is contractible coincides with the non-wheels and non-whirls that are in the class of matroids M that are constructed as follows.*

(i) *Let $\Delta, \Delta_1, \Delta_2, \ldots, \Delta_{n-1}$ be the triangles of an n–spike N that contain the tip y of N where $\Delta = \{y, x, z\}$ and $\Delta_i = \{y, x_i, z_i\}$ for all i.*

(ii) *Let $N_0 = N \backslash z$ and, for some $t \leq n-1$, let $N_1, N_2, \ldots, N_t$ be a collection of wheels of rank at least three such that $E(N_0), E(N_1), E(N_2), \ldots, E(N_t)$ are disjoint.*

(iii) *Let $\Delta_1', \Delta_2', \ldots, \Delta_t'$ be triangles in $N_1, N_2, \ldots, N_t$, respectively.*

(iv) *For each i in $\{1, 2, \ldots, t\}$, identify the elements of $\Delta_i'$ with the elements of $\Delta_i$ so that y is identified with a spoke and $z_i$ with a rim element of $N_i$.*

(v) *Let $R_0 = N_0$ and, for all i in $\{1, 2, \ldots, t\}$, let $R_i = P_{\Delta_i}(N_i, R_{i-1})$.*

(vi) *Let $M = R_t \backslash z_1, z_2, \ldots, z_t$.*

By using the last result together with the modification of Theorem 9.2 discussed immediately following it, it is not difficult to deduce a description of all 3–connected matroids in which the set of non-essential elements is collinear. Moreover, in [**67**], all 3–connected *graphic* matroids with exactly three non-essential elements are determined.

## 10. Extremal results for 2–connected matroids

The Wheels and Whirls Theorem characterizes the 3–connected matroids $M$ that are extremal in the sense that, for every element $e$, neither $M \backslash e$ nor $M/e$ is 3–connected. As we have seen, this result is particularly useful in the development of matroid structure theory. It is one of a number of extremal connectivity results that are not only interesting in their own right but have also been used as valuable tools in other areas of matroid theory. In this section and the next, we review such results. Since so many of the results for 3–connected matroids mimic corresponding results for 2–connected matroids, our discussion in this section will focus on the latter results. The matroid results obtained here were strongly influenced by a well-established body of extremal connectivity results for graphs that includes work of Dirac [**26**], Plummer [**68**], Halin [**29, 30**], and Mader [**42, 43, 44**].

One of the most powerful tools in induction arguments for 2–connected matroids is the following result of Tutte [**99**].

THEOREM 10.1. *Let e be an element of a 2–connected matroid M. Then $M \backslash e$ or $M/e$ is 2–connected.*

The following useful extension of this result was proved independently by Brylawski [**14**] and Seymour [**78**].

THEOREM 10.2. *Let N be a 2–connected minor of a 2–connected matroid M and suppose that $e \in E(M) - E(N)$. Then $M \backslash e$ or $M/e$ is 2–connected and has N as a minor.*

Let $N$ be a $k$–connected minor of a $k$–connected matroid $M$. The Splitter Theorem told us that, when $k = 3$, provided $N$ satisfies some very weak restrictions, we can remove elements from $M$ one at a time in *some* order staying $k$–connected until we arrive at an isomorphic copy of $N$. The last result tells us that, for $k = 2$ and an *arbitrary* ordering of the elements of $E(M) - E(N)$, we can remove these elements in the specified order staying $k$–connected until we arrive at $N$ itself. The only aspect of the last process that we do not control is how each element is removed, that is, whether it is deleted or contracted.

For $n \geq 2$, an $n$–connected graph $G$ is *minimally $n$–connected* if, for all edges $e$ of $G$, the deletion $G \backslash e$ is not $n$–connected. One obvious way for the deletion of an edge to destroy $n$–connectedness is if the edge meets a degree-$n$ vertex. In fact, a minimally $n$–connected graph must have many vertices of degree $n$. The following result was proved by Dirac [26] for $n = 2$, by Halin [30] for $n = 3$, and by Mader [43] in general.

THEOREM 10.3. *Let $G$ be a minimally $n$–connected graph where $n \geq 2$. Then the number of degree-n vertices in $G$ is at least*

$$\frac{(n-1)|V(G)| + 2n}{2n - 1}.$$

An $n$–connected matroid $M$ is *minimally $n$–connected* if, for all elements $e$ of $M$, the matroid $M \backslash e$ is not $n$–connected. One potential matroid analogue of the last theorem would be that a minimally $n$–connected matroid has a lot of $n$–element cocircuits. For $n \geq 4$, it is not known whether such a result is true. But, if $n$ is 2 or 3, such a result does hold. First we describe what is known for $n = 2$. Murty [45], White [105], and Seymour [80] independently proved that every minimally 2–connected matroid with at least two elements has a 2–cocircuit. This result was later strengthened by Seymour [81] when he proved the following result.

PROPOSITION 10.4. *Let $M$ be a 2–connected matroid having at least two elements and let $C$ be a circuit of $M$ such that $M \backslash e$ is not 2–connected for all $e$ in $C$. Then $C$ contains some 2–cocircuit of $M$.*

A slight improvement on this result was obtained by Oxley [51].

PROPOSITION 10.5. *Let $M$ be a 2–connected matroid having at least two elements. Let $f$ be an element of a circuit $C$ of $M$ such that $M \backslash e$ is not 2–connected for all $e$ in $C - f$. Then $C - f$ contains a 2–cocircuit of $M$.*

The last result was used to prove the following:

THEOREM 10.6. *Let $M$ be a 2–connected matroid other than a single circuit. Suppose that $A \subseteq E(M)$ and $M \backslash a$ is not 2–connected for all $a$ in $A$. Then either $A$ is independent in $M$, or $A$ contains at least $|A| - r(A) + 1$ non-trivial series classes of $M$.*

As a consequence of this, we are able to show that a minimally 2–connected matroid has a lot of 2–cocircuits [51].

COROLLARY 10.7. *Let $M$ be a minimally 2–connected matroid. Then either $M$ is a circuit, or $M$ has at least $r^*(M) + 1$ non-trivial series classes and so has at least $r^*(M) + 1$ pairwise disjoint 2–cocircuits.*

The minimally 2–connected matroids $M$ for which the number of 2–cocircuits is exactly $r^*(M) + 1$ were determined in [52]. While the last result maintains the spirit of Theorem 10.3 in the case $n = 2$, the bound obtained is not analogous to the graph bound. The fact that the analogous bound does hold was proved by a different method in [53].

THEOREM 10.8. *Let $M$ be a minimally 2–connected matroid having at least four elements. Then the number of pairwise disjoint 2–cocircuits of $M$ is at least $\frac{1}{3}(r(M) + 2)$.*

The matroids attaining equality in this theorem were determined in [52]. The last result is a matroid theorem that was motivated by a graph result. The next two results [51] are graph analogues of two matroid results, Theorem 10.6 and Corollary 10.7. The number of connected components of a graph $G$ is denoted by $\omega(G)$.

THEOREM 10.9. *Let $G$ be a 2–connected loopless graph other than a cycle. Suppose that $A$ is a set of edges of $G$ such that $G \backslash a$ is not 2–connected for all $a$ in $A$. Then either $A$ is a forest, or $V(A)$ contains at least $|A| - |V(A)| + \omega(G[A]) + 1$ pairwise non-adjacent vertices having degree two in $G$.*

COROLLARY 10.10. *A minimally 2–connected graph $G$ having at least four edges has at least $|E(G)| - |V(G)| + 2$ pairwise non-adjacent vertices of degree two.*

By combining the last result with Theorem 10.3 in the case $n = 2$, one obtains the following result [51] after a little additional argument.

THEOREM 10.11. *Let $G$ be a minimally 2–connected graph with at least four edges. Then the number $\nu_2$ of degree-two vertices in $G$ satisfies*

$$\nu_2 \geq \begin{cases} \frac{1}{3}(|V(G)| + 5) & \text{for } |E(G)| < \frac{1}{3}(4|V(G)| - 2); \\ |E(G)| - |V(G)| + 2 & \text{for } \frac{1}{3}(4|V(G)| - 2) \leq |E(G)|. \end{cases}$$

The next result [53] is obtained by combining Corollary 10.7 and Theorem 10.8.

THEOREM 10.12. *Let $M$ be a minimally 2–connected matroid. Then the number $d_2^*$ of pairwise disjoint 2–cocircuits in $M$ satisfies*

$$d_2^* \geq \begin{cases} \frac{1}{3}(r(M) + 2) & \text{for } |E(M)| < \frac{1}{3}(4r(M) - 1); \\ r^*(M) + 1 & \text{for } \frac{1}{3}(4r(M) - 1) \leq |E(M)|. \end{cases}$$

Brylawski [13] showed that if a single-element deletion of a 2–connected matroid $M$ is not 2–connected, then $M$ can be written as a series connection of two of its minors. Building on this, we have the following decomposition result [51] for minimally 2–connected matroids.

THEOREM 10.13. *A matroid $M$ is minimally 2–connected if and only if $M$ has at least three elements, and either $M$ is 2–connected having every element in a 2–cocircuit, or $M = S((M_1/q_1; p_1), (M_2/q_2; p_2))$ where $M_1$ and $M_2$ are minimally 2–connected matroids each of which is isomorphic to a minor of $M$ and has at least five elements, and $\{p_1, q_1\}$ and $\{p_2, q_2\}$ are 2–cocircuits of $M_1$ and $M_2$, respectively.*

As one of several applications of the last theorem, we note that it can be used to prove the following result of Murty [45].

COROLLARY 10.14. *For $r \geq 3$, a minimally 2–connected matroid $M$ of rank $r$ has at most $2r - 2$ elements, the upper bound being attained if and only if $M \cong M(K_{2,r-1})$.*

The next result is another extremal connectivity result of Seymour [80]. He used it as a tool in his proof of the excluded-minor characterization of the class of ternary matroids.

PROPOSITION 10.15. $U_{2,4}$ *is the only 2–connected matroid with more than one element in which no 2–element deletion and no 2–element contraction is 2–connected, but every 1–element deletion and every 1–element contraction is 2–connected.*

Another extremal connectivity lemma is used in Kahn and Seymour's short proof of the excluded-minor theorem for ternary matroids (see [**62**],10.2.4). In [**53**], minor-minimally-connected matroids are considered, these being those 2–connected matroids $M$ such that, for all elements $e$, either $M \backslash e$ or $M/e$ is not 2–connected. A characterization of such matroids similar to Theorem 10.13 is proved and it is shown that every such matroid must contain a number of 2–element sets that are circuits or cocircuits.

## 11. Extremal results for 3–connected matroids

In this section, we turn our attention to 3–connected matroids with much of our focus being on which of the results for 2–connected matroids noted in the last section can be generalized. Some examples of extremal connectivity results for $n$–connected matroids for arbitrary values of $n$ may be found in [**3**, **4**].

Although Theorem 10.1 certainly fails if one replaces "2–connected" by "3–connected", the following useful analogue of the theorem was proved by Bixby [**10**].

THEOREM 11.1. *Let $e$ be an element of a 3–connected matroid $M$. Then $\widetilde{M \backslash e}$ or $\widetilde{M/e}$ is 3–connected.*

It is well known that if $X$ and $Y$ are subsets of the ground set of a matroid $M$ and both $M|X$ and $M|Y$ are 2–connected, then, provided $X \cap Y$ is non-empty, $M|(X \cup Y)$ is also 2–connected. The following useful generalization of this fact was proved by Oxley and Wu [**64**].

THEOREM 11.2. *Let $n$ be an integer exceeding one and $M$ be a matroid having no circuits with fewer than $n$ elements. If $M|X$ and $M|Y$ are $n$–connected and the closures of $X$ and $Y$ have at least $n - 1$ common elements, then $M|(X \cup Y)$ is $n$–connected.*

Halin [**30**] made crucial use of the next lemma in his proof that a minimally 3–connected graph $G$ has at least $\frac{1}{5}(2|V(G)| + 6)$ vertices of degree three.

LEMMA 11.3. *Every cycle in a minimally 3–connected graph meets at least two vertices of degree three.*

By using the fact that the minimal sets meeting every cycle in a graph $G$ are the cobases of $M(G)$, one can also use this lemma to obtain a second bound on the number of degree-3 vertices in a minimally 3–connected graph. The next result combines these two bounds, identifies the intervals on which each is sharper, and slightly improves Halin's bound on the specified interval.

THEOREM 11.4. *Let $G$ be a minimally 3–connected graph. Then the number $\nu_3$ of degree-three vertices in $G$ satisfies*

$$\nu_3 \geq \begin{cases} \frac{1}{5}(2|V(G)| + 7) & \text{for } |E(G)| < \frac{1}{5}(9|V(G)| - 3); \\ \frac{1}{2}(|E(G)| - |V(G)| + 3) & \text{for } \frac{1}{5}(9|V(G)| - 3) \leq |E(G)|. \end{cases}$$

The following matroid analogue of Lemma 11.3 was proved by Oxley [51].

LEMMA 11.5. *Let $C$ be a circuit in a minimally 3–connected matroid $M$ where $|E(M)| \geq 4$. Then $M$ has at least two distinct triads meeting $C$.*

Using this, one can prove the following analogue of the second bound in Theorem 11.4.

THEOREM 11.6. *A minimally 3–connected matroid $M$ with at least four elements has at least $\frac{1}{2}r^*(M) + 1$ triads.*

A 3–connected matroid $M$ for which every 2–element deletion fails to be 2–connected is easily seen to be minimally 3–connected as long as $|E(M)| \geq 5$. The last result guarantees that such a matroid has many triads but, as Akkari and Oxley [3] showed, one can say considerably more.

THEOREM 11.7. *The following statements are equivalent for a matroid $M$ having at least four elements.*

  (i) *$M$ is 3–connected and no 2–element deletion from $M$ is 2–connected.*
 (ii) *Every pair of elements of $M$ is in a triad.*
(iii) *$M$ and all its 1–element deletions are 2–connected but no 2–element deletion from $M$ is 2–connected.*

Proposition 10.15 follows easily by combining the last result with its dual.

The first bound on $\nu_3$ in Theorem 11.4 and the corresponding results for minimally 2–connected graphs suggest that one may be able to show that a minimally 3–connected matroid $M$ has at least $\frac{2}{5}r(M) + c$ triads for some constant $c$. However, John Leo (private communication) has found an infinite family of minimally 3–connected non-binary matroids $M$ each of which has only $\frac{1}{4}(r(M) + 6)$ triads.

The next theorem, which was proved by Lemos [39], answers a question of Oxley [51]. It is a generalization of Proposition 10.5 and shows that the conclusion to Lemma 11.5 holds under a weaker hypothesis.

THEOREM 11.8. *Let $C$ be a circuit in a 3–connected matroid $M$ such that, for all $e$ in $C$, the matroid $M\backslash e$ is not 3–connected. Then $C$ meets at least two triads of $M$.*

The last result played a crucial role in the proofs of Theorems 4.8 and 4.9. Using it, one can show that a 3–connected matroid with a $k$–element circuit has a 3–connected minor of rank at least $k - 1$ that has a spanning circuit. Lemos also noted that the following graph-theoretic analogue of his result is true, and this graph result was also independently proved by Mader [44].

THEOREM 11.9. *Let $C$ be a cycle of a simple 3–connected graph $G$. If $G\backslash e$ is not 3–connected for all $e$ in $C$, then $C$ meets at least two degree-3 vertices of $G$.*

Leo [40] noted that by combining Theorem 11.8 with the proof technique used to give Theorem 10.6, one can obtain the following analogue of that result.

THEOREM 11.10. *Let $M$ be a 3–connected matroid. Suppose that $A \subseteq E(M)$ and $M\backslash a$ is not 3–connected for all $a$ in $A$. Then either $A$ is independent, or $A$ meets at least $\frac{1}{2}(|A| - r(A)) + 1$ distinct triads of $M$.*

Theorems 11.7 and 11.8 suggest consideration of those 3–connected matroids having a circuit such that the deletion of any pair of elements from this circuit produces a matroid that is not 2–connected. The following attractive generalization of Theorem 11.7 was proved by Akkari [**2**].

THEOREM 11.11. *Let $C$ be a circuit in a 3–connected matroid $M$ such that, for all pairs $\{e, f\}$ of distinct elements of $C$, the matroid $M \backslash e, f$ is not 2–connected. Then either every pair of elements of $C$ is in a triad, or $M$ is a wheel of rank at least four and $C$ is its rim.*

In view of Proposition 10.5 for 2–connected matroids, it is natural to ask whether the corresponding result is true for 3–connected matroids. Leo [**40**] answered this question affirmatively.

THEOREM 11.12. *Let $C$ be a circuit in a 3–connected matroid $M$ and $f$ be an element of $C$. If $M \backslash e$ is not 3–connected for all $e$ in $C - f$, then $M$ has a triad meeting $C - f$.*

Halin [**29**] proved the following upper bound on the number of edges in a minimally 3–connected graph.

THEOREM 11.13. *Let $G$ be a minimally 3–connected graph. Then*

$$|E(G)| \leq \begin{cases} 2|V(G)| - 2 & \text{if } |V(G)| \leq 6; \\ 3|V(G)| - 9 & \text{if } |V(G)| \geq 7. \end{cases}$$

*Moreover, the only graphs attaining equality in these bounds are $\mathcal{W}_m$ for $3 \leq m \leq 6$ and $K_{3,n}$ for $n \geq 4$.*

The next result [**49**] shows that precisely the same bounds hold for arbitrary minimally 3–connected matroids.

THEOREM 11.14. *Let $M$ be a minimally 3–connected matroid having at least four elements. Then*

$$|E(M)| \leq \begin{cases} 2r(M) & \text{if } r(M) \leq 5; \\ 3r(M) - 6 & \text{if } r(M) \geq 6. \end{cases}$$

A characterization of the matroids that attain equality in these bounds is given in [**49**]. The only binary matroids attaining equality are the cycle matroids of the graphs that attain equality in the bounds in Theorem 11.13.

In Section 9, we discussed the 3–connected matroids with a small number of non-essential elements. The following result of Wu [**109**] gives interesting information about how the non-essential elements are arranged in a minimally 3–connected matroid.

THEOREM 11.15. *Let $M$ be a minimally 3–connected matroid that is not a wheel or a whirl. Then every largest circuit of $M$ contains a non-essential element of $M$.*

## 12. Vertical connectivity

It was noted in Section 2 that the notions of $n$–connectedness for graphs and matroids, while similar, do not coincide precisely. One difference lies in the fact that, whereas a circuit of size less than $n$ does not prevent a graph from being $n$–connected, it does prevent its cycle matroid from being $n$–connected unless the graph has fewer than $2n - 2$ edges. In this section, we shall see that this is the fundamental difference between the graph and matroid concepts. We shall present a slight modification of the definition of $n$–connectedness which produces a matroid notion that exactly generalizes the graph concept. The cost of making this modification is that one loses invariance under duality with this alternate concept.

For a positive integer $k$ and a matroid $M$, a partition $\{X, Y\}$ of $E(M)$ is a *vertical k–separation* if

$$min\{r(X), r(Y)\} \geq k;$$

and

$$r(X) + r(Y) - r(M) \leq k - 1.$$

For $2 \leq n \leq r(M)$, the matroid $M$ is *vertically n–connected* provided that, for all $k$ in $\{1, 2, \dots, n - 1\}$, $M$ has no vertical $k$–separation. Hence $M$ is vertically 2–connected exactly when the matroid obtained by deleting all loops from $M$ is 2–connected. Here "vertical" is used as the adjective corresponding to "vertex". This usage, which was originated by Tutte [100], is justified by the following result [21, 33, 48].

THEOREM 12.1. *Let $G$ be a connected graph and $n$ be an integer exceeding one. Then $G$ is an n–connected graph if and only if $M(G)$ is a vertically n–connected matroid.*

The next result, a generalization of Proposition 2.1, describes the link between vertical $n$–connectedness and $n$–connectedness as defined in Section 2. The latter concept is sometimes called *Tutte n–connectedness*.

THEOREM 12.2. *Let $M$ be a matroid that is not isomorphic to any uniform matroid $U_{r,m}$ with $m \geq 2r - 1$. For all integers $n$ exceeding one, $M$ is n–connected if and only if $M$ is vertically n–connected and has no circuits with fewer than $n$ elements.*

If the dual of a matroid is vertically $n$–connected, then the matroid itself is called *cyclically n–connected*. The next result notes that Tutte $n$–connectedness is basically the conjunction of vertical $n$–connectedness and cyclic $n$–connectedness.

PROPOSITION 12.3. *Let $M$ be a matroid that is not isomorphic to any uniform matroid $U_{r,m}$ with $2r - 1 \leq m \leq 2r + 1$. For all integers $n$ exceeding one, $M$ is n–connected if and only if $M$ is both vertically and cyclically n–connected.*

Although a wheel $M(\mathcal{W}_r)$ with $r \geq 4$ has no element $e$ such that $M(\mathcal{W}_r)/e$ is 3–connected, for every rim edge $f$ of $\mathcal{W}_r$, the matroid $M(\mathcal{W}_r)/f$ is vertically 3–connected. In general, Cunningham [21], and independently Seymour, proved the following result.

PROPOSITION 12.4. *Let $M$ be a non-empty 3–connected matroid. Then $M$ has an element $e$ such that $M/e$ is vertically 3–connected.*

If $M$ is the cycle matroid of a 3–connected graph $G$, then, by Theorem 12.1, $M$ is vertically 3–connected. Moreover, for every edge $e$ of $G$, the matroid $M/e$ is vertically 3–connected if and only if the graph $G/e$ is 3–connected. An edge $x$ in a 3–connected graph $G$ is *contractible* if $G/x$ remains 3–connected. Several papers over the last decade (see, for example, [6, 27, 23, 5]) have studied the number of contractible edges in 3–connected graphs. Recently Wu [109] considered the corresponding problem for matroids. An element $x$ in a 3–connected matroid $M$ is *vertically contractible* if $M/x$ is vertically 3–connected. Proposition 12.4 asserts

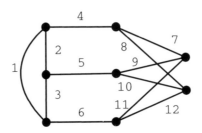

FIGURE 22. $G$.

that every non-empty 3–connected matroid has at least one vertically contractible element. Wu [**109**] sharpened this result.

PROPOSITION 12.5. *Every 3–connected matroid with at least three elements has at least three vertically contractible elements.*

Wu [**109**] deduced the last result from the following theorem. It is interesting to observe the presence of a familiar class of matroids in this result.

THEOREM 12.6. *Let $M$ be a minimally 3–connected matroid with at least four elements. Then $M$ has at least $\max\{\frac{2}{3}|E(M)| - r(M) + 2, 3\}$ vertically contractible elements. Moreover, $M$ has exactly three vertically contractible elements if and only $M \cong M^*(K_{3,k}''')$ for some $k \geq 2$.*

## 13. Isomorphism versus equality, and roundedness

Let $M$ be the cycle matroid of the graph $G$ in Figure 22, and let $M/\{1, 2, 3\} = N$. Evidently $N$ is a 3–connected minor of $M$, which is also 3–connected. The Splitter Theorem guarantees the existence of a sequence $M_0, M_1, M_2, M_3$ of 3–connected matroids each a single-element deletion or contraction of its predecessor such that $M_0 = M$ and $M_3 \cong N$. Indeed, such a sequence is $M, M/5, M/5/4, M/5/4\backslash 2$. The point that we wish to note here is that $M/5/4\backslash 2$, while it is *isomorphic* to $N$ is not *equal* to $N$. Moreover, the reader can easily check that there is no sequence $M_0, M_1, M_2, M_3$ of the required type in which $M_3 = N$. In fact, $M$ has no proper 3–connected minor that has $N$ itself as a proper minor.

One is often interested in maintaining a specific minor rather than just a copy of that minor. Suppose that $N_1$ is a $k$–connected minor of a $k$–connected matroid $M_1$. If we seek a $k$–connected minor $N_2$ of $M_1$ that has $N_1$ as a proper minor so that the gap, $|E(N_2) - E(N_1)|$, is as small as possible, then, when $k = 2$, Theorem 10.2 guarantees that $N_2$ can be found so that $|E(N_2) - E(N_1)| = 1$. Rajan [**69**] gave a family of examples to show that, when $k = 4$, arbitrarily large gaps exist between $N_1$ and a next largest $k$–connected minor $N_2$ of $M_1$ having $N_1$ as a minor. But Truemper [**87**] showed that, when $k = 3$, this gap has size at most three. Truemper's result was strengthened slightly by Bixby and Coullard [**11**] who proved the following result.

THEOREM 13.1. *Let $N$ be a 3–connected proper minor of a 3–connected matroid $M$. Then $M$ has a 3–connected minor $M_1$ and an element $e$ such that $N$ is a cosimple matroid associated with $M_1\backslash e$ or a simple matroid associated with $M_1/e$, and $|E(M_1) - E(N)| \leq 3$.*

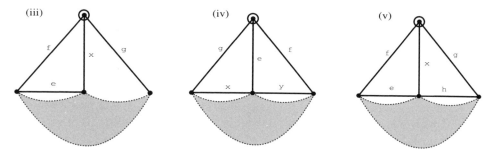

FIGURE 23. A graphic depiction of (iii)–(v) of Theorem 11.2.

Bixby and Coullard [11] strengthened the last result when $N$ has no circuits or cocircuits with fewer than four elements. The details of this and many of the other results considered in this section may be found in Section 11.3 of [62]. Another very useful result of Bixby and Coullard [12] considers a variant of Theorem 13.1 in which one seeks a 3–connected minor $M_1$ of $M$ that not only has $N$ as a minor but also contains some nominated element $e$ of $E(M) - E(N)$. They show that such a matroid $M_1$ can be found so that $|E(M_1) - E(N)| \leq 4$. Moreover, their result also contains much very helpful structural information.

THEOREM 13.2. *Let $N$ be a 3–connected minor of a 3–connected matroid $M$. Suppose that $|E(N)| \geq 4$, $e \in E(M) - E(N)$, and $M$ has no 3–connected proper minor that both uses $e$ and has $N$ as a minor. Then, for some $(N_1, M_1)$ in $\{(N, M), (N^*, M^*)\}$, one of the following holds where $|E(M) - E(N)| = n$.*

(i) *$n = 1$ and $N_1 = M_1 \backslash e$.*

(ii) *$n = 2$, $N_1 = M_1 \backslash e / f$, and $N_1$ has an element $x$ such that $\{e, f, x\}$ is a triangle of $M_1$.*

(iii) *$n = 3$, $N_1 = M_1 \backslash e, g/f$, and $N_1$ has an element $x$ such that $\{e, f, x\}$ is a triangle of $M_1$ and $\{f, g, x\}$ is a triad of $M_1$. Moreover, $M_1 \backslash e$ is 3–connected.*

(iv) *$n = 3$, $N_1 = M_1 \backslash e, g/f = M_1 \backslash e, f/g = M_1 \backslash f, g/e = M_1 \backslash e, f, g$, and $\{e, f, g\}$ is a triad of $M_1$. Moreover, $N_1$ has distinct elements $x$ and $y$ such that $\{e, g, x\}$ and $\{e, f, y\}$ are triangles of $M_1$.*

(v) *$n = 4$, $N_1 = M_1 \backslash e, g/f, h$ and $N_1$ has an element $x$ such that $\{e, f, x\}$ and $\{g, h, x\}$ are triangles of $M_1$, and $\{f, g, x\}$ is a triad of $M_1$. Moreover, $M_1 \backslash e$ and $M_1 \backslash e/f$ are 3–connected.*

Although the last result applies to all matroids and not just graphic ones, Bixby and Coullard use graphs to depict what happens in (iii)–(v) (see Figure 23). Note that a vertex is circled if it corresponds to a known triad in the matroid; all cycles shown are indeed circuits of the matroid; and the shaded part of the diagram corresponds to the rest of the matroid.

Theorem 13.2 has a number of applications that relate to what is called "roundedness" in matroid theory. This subject is concerned with relating certain minors of a matroid to particular elements of the matroid. An example of one of the many such results is the following theorem of Seymour [83]. This result, which extends an earlier result of Bixby [9] for 2–connected matroids, played an important role in the proof of Kahn's theorem [34] that determines precisely when a quaternary matroid is uniquely $GF(4)$–representable.

THEOREM 13.3. *Let $M$ be a 3–connected matroid having a $U_{2,4}$-minor and suppose that $e$ and $f$ are distinct elements of $M$. Then $M$ has a $U_{2,4}$-minor using $\{e, f\}$.*

The last result, a statement about 3–connected non-binary matroids, was extended to non-graphic matroids by Asano, Nishizeki, and Seymour [7] when they proved the following result, a further extension of which was later obtained by Reid [72].

THEOREM 13.4. *Let $T$ be a triangle in a 3–connected non-graphic matroid $M$. Then $M$ has a minor $N$ using $T$ such that $N$ is isomorphic to*

(i) $M^*(K_{3,3})$ *if $M$ is regular;*
(ii) $F_7$ *if $M$ is binary and non-regular; and*
(iii) $U_{2,4}$ *if $M$ is non-binary.*

A more recent result of the same type is the following theorem [63]. The matroid $F_7^+$ is obtained from the Fano matroid by freely adding an element to one of the lines.

THEOREM 13.5. *Let $M$ be a 3–connected matroid having a $U_{2,5}$-minor and a subset $X$ such that $M|X \cong U_{2,4}$. Then $M$ has a minor $N$ using $X$ such that $N$ is isomorphic to $U_{2,5}$ or $F_7^+$.*

This theorem is of crucial importance in Oxley, Vertigan, and Whittle's [63] proof that, when $q = 5$, a 3–connected $GF(q)$–representable matroid has a bounded number of inequivalent $GF(q)$–representations. The best-possible bound here is six since, for instance, $U_{3,5}$ has six inequivalent $GF(5)$–representations. The existence of inequivalent representations is a major difficulty that arises when dealing with matroid representations. The above result verifies a conjecture of Kahn [34] in the case $q = 5$. Kahn had conjectured that the same result holds for all prime powers $q$, but examples in [63] show that this conjecture is false for all $q > 5$.

A 3–connected matroid $M$ is *internally 4–connected* if $min\{|X|, |Y|\} = 3$ for every 3–separation $\{X, Y\}$ of $M$. Loosely speaking, such a matroid $M$ is 4–connected except that it may have triangles and triads. The following structural result of Tseng and Truemper [96] can be used to prove a matroid extension of the edge form of Menger's Theorem, which was originally derived by Seymour [79]. A formal statement of the last result and its relationship to Menger's Theorem are described in [84] and Section 11.3 of [62]. Tseng and Truemper's result is stated here as an example of another matroid structural result that has interesting consequences elsewhere.

THEOREM 13.6. *Let $e$ be an element of a 3–connected, internally 4–connected binary matroid $M$ and suppose that $e \in E(M)$. Then exactly one of the following holds.*

(i) *There is an $F_7^*$-minor of $M$ using $e$.*
(ii) *$M$ is regular.*
(iii) *$M \cong F_7$.*

To conclude this section, we note yet another connectivity result that has played a vital role in the proof of a result from another area of matroid theory. The following result is due to Whittle [107] and is of central importance in the proofs of his very attractive recent theorems [107, 108] that characterize the ternary matroids that are representable over some other field. The result has a more intricate hypothesis than most of the connectivity results noted earlier, so it is probably not surprising that the proof is very difficult.

THEOREM 13.7. *Let $M$ be a 3–connected non-binary matroid having rank at least four. Then $M$ has an independent set $\{a, b, c\}$ such that the simplifications of all of the matroids $M/a, M/b, M/c, M/a, b,$ and $M/a, c$ are 3–connected and non-binary.*

## References

[1] D.M. Acketa, *On binary paving matroids*, Discrete Math. **70** (1988), 109–110.

[2] S. Akkari, *A minimal 3–connectedness result for matroids*, Discrete Math. **103** (1992), 221–232.

[3] S. Akkari and J. Oxley, *Some extremal connectivity results for matroids*, J. Combin. Theory Ser. B **52** (1991), 301–320.

[4] S. Akkari and J. Oxley, *Some local extremal connectivity results for matroids*, Combin., Probab. and Comput. **2** (1993), 367–384.

[5] R.E.L. Aldred, R.L. Hemminger, and K. Ota, *The 3–connected graphs having a longest cycle containing only three contractible edges*, J. Graph Theory **17** (1993), 361–371.

[6] K. Ando, H. Enomoto, and A. Saito, *Contractible edges in 3–connected graphs*, J. Combin. Theory Ser. B **42** (1987), 87–93.

[7] T. Asano, T. Nishizeki, and P.D. Seymour, *A note on nongraphic matroids*, J. Combin. Theory Ser. B **37** (1984), 290–293.

[8] R.E. Bixby, *Composition and decomposition of matroids and related topics*, Ph.D. thesis, Cornell University, 1972.

[9] R.E. Bixby, *l–matrices and a characterization of non-binary matroids*, Discrete Math. **8** (1974), 139–145.

[10] R.E. Bixby, *A simple theorem on 3–connectivity*, Linear Algebra Appl. **45** (1982), 123–126.

[11] R.E. Bixby and C.R. Coullard, *On chains of 3–connected matroids*, Discrete Appl. Math. **15** (1986), 155–166.

[12] R.E. Bixby and C.R. Coullard, *Finding a smallest 3–connected minor maintaining a fixed minor and a fixed element*, Combinatorica **7** (1987), 231–242.

[13] T.H. Brylawski, *A combinatorial model for series–parallel networks*, Trans. Amer. Math. Soc. **154** (1971), 1–22.

[14] T.H. Brylawski, *A decomposition for combinatorial geometries*, Trans. Amer. Math. Soc. **171** (1972), 235–282.

[15] T.H. Brylawski, *Modular constructions for combinatorial geometries*, Trans. Amer. Math. Soc. **203** (1975), 1–44.

[16] T.H. Brylawski, *Constructions*, Theory of Matroids (ed. N. White), Cambridge University Press, Cambridge, 1986, pp. 127–223.

[17] C.R. Coullard, *Minors of 3–connected matroids and adjoints of binary matroids*, Ph.D. thesis, Northwestern University, 1985.

[18] C.R. Coullard and J.G. Oxley, *Extensions of Tutte's Wheels-and-Whirls Theorem*, J. Combin. Theory Ser. B **56** (1992), 130–140.

[19] C.R. Coullard, L.L. Gardner, and D.K. Wagner, *Decomposition of 3–connected graphs*, Combinatorica **13** (1993), 7–30.

[20] W.H. Cunningham, *A combinatorial decomposition theory*, Ph.D. thesis, University of Waterloo, 1973.

[21] W.H. Cunningham, *On matroid connectivity*, J. Combin. Theory Ser. B **30** (1981), 94–99.

[22] W.H. Cunningham and J. Edmonds, *A combinatorial decomposition theory*, Canad. J. Math. **32** (1980), 734–765.

[23] N. Dean, R.L. Hemminger, and K. Ota, *Longest cycles in 3–connected graphs contain three contractible edges*, J. Graph Theory **12** (1989), 17–21.

[24] G. Ding, B. Oporowski, J. Oxley, and D. Vertigan, *Unavoidable minors of large 3–connected binary matroids*, J. Combin. Theory Ser. B **66** (1996), 334–360.

[25] G. Ding, B. Oporowski, J. Oxley, and D. Vertigan, *Unavoidable minors of large 3–connected matroids*, in preparation.

[26] G.A. Dirac, *Minimally 2–connected graphs*, J. Reine Angew. Math. **228** (1967), 204–216.

[27] Y. Egawa, H. Enomoto, and A. Saito, *Contactible edges in triangle-free graphs*, Combinatorica **6** (1986), 269–274.

[28] B.S. Gubser, *Planar graphs with no 6–wheel minor*, Discrete Math. **120** (1993), 59–73.

[29] R. Halin, *Zur Theorie der n-fach zusammenhängenden Graphen*, Abh. Math. Sem. Univ. Hamburg **33** (1969), 133-164.

[30] R. Halin, *Untersuchungen über minimale n-fach zusammenhängende Graphen*, Math. Ann. **182** (1969), 175-188.

[31] D.W. Hall, *A note on primitive skew curves*, Bull. Amer. Math. Soc. **49** (1943), 935–937.

[32] J.W. Hipp, *The maximum size of combinatorial geometries excluding wheels and whirls as minors*, Ph.D. thesis, University of North Texas, 1989.

[33] T. Inukai and L. Weinberg, *Whitney connectivity of matroids*, SIAM J. Alg. Disc. Methods **2** (1981), 108–120.

[34] J. Kahn, *On the uniqueness of matroid representations over GF(4)*, Bull. London Math. Soc. **20** (1988), 5–10.

[35] J. Kahn and P. Seymour, *On forbidden minors for GF(3)*, Proc. Amer. Math. Soc. **102** (1988), 437–440.

[36] S.R. Kingan, *A generalization of a graph result by D.W. Hall*, Discrete Math., to appear.

[37] J.P.S. Kung, *Extremal matroid theory*, Graph Structure Theory (eds. N. Robertson and P. Seymour), Contemporary Mathematics **147** (1993), 21–61.

[38] K. Kuratowski, *Sur le problème des courbes gauches en topologie*, Fund. Math. **15** (1930), 271–283.

[39] M. Lemos, *On 3–connected matroids*, Discrete Math. **73** (1989), 273–283.

[40] J.W. Leo, *Triads and triangles in 3–connected matroids*, submitted.

[41] F.J. MacWilliams and N.J.A. Sloane, *The Theory of Error-Correcting Codes*, North-Holland, Amsterdam, 1977.

[42] W. Mader, *Ecken vom Grad n in minimalen n–fach zusammenhängenden Graphen*, Arch. Math. (Basel) **23** (1972), 219–224.

[43] W. Mader, *Connectivity and edge-connectivity in finite graphs*, Surveys in Combinatorics (ed. B. Bollobás), London Math. Soc. Lecture Notes **38**, Cambridge University Press, 1979, pp. 66-95.

[44] W. Mader, *On vertices of degree n in minimally n–connected graphs and digraphs*, Combinatorics, Paul Erdős is Eighty, Volume 2 (eds. D. Miklós, V.T. Sós, T. Szőnyi), János Bolyai Math. Soc., Budapest, 1996, pp. 423–449.

[45] U.S.R. Murty, *Extremal critically connected matroids*, Discrete Math. **8** (1974), 49–58.

[46] S. Negami, *A characterization of 3–connected graphs containing a given graph*, J. Combin. Theory Ser. B **32** (1982), 69–74.

[47] B. Oporowski, J. Oxley, and R. Thomas, *Typical subgraphs of 3– and 4–connected graphs*, J. Combin. Theory Ser. B **57** (1993), 239–257.

[48] J.G. Oxley, *On a matroid generalization of graph connectivity*, Math. Proc. Camb. Phil. Soc. **90** (1981), 207–214.

[49] J.G. Oxley, *On matroid connectivity*, Quart. J. Math. Oxford Ser. (2) **32** (1981), 193–208.

[50] J.G. Oxley, *On 3–connected matroids*, Canad. J. Math. **33** (1981), 20–27.

[51] J.G. Oxley, *On connectivity in matroids and graphs*, Trans. Amer. Math. Soc. **265** (1981), 47-58.

[52] J.G. Oxley, *On some extremal connectivity results for graphs and matroids*, Discrete Math. **41** (1982), 181–198.

[53] J.G. Oxley, *On minor-minimally-connected matroids*, Discrete Math. **51** (1984), 63–72.

[54] J.G. Oxley, *On the intersections of circuits and cocircuits in matroids*, Combinatorica **4** (1984), 187–195.

[55] J.G. Oxley, *On nonbinary 3–connected matroids*, Trans. Amer. Math. Soc. **300** (1987), 663–679.

[56] J.G. Oxley, *The binary matroids with no 4–wheel minor*, Trans. Amer. Math. Soc. **301** (1987), 63–75.

[57] J.G. Oxley, *A characterization of the ternary matroids with no $M(K_4)$–minor*, J. Combin. Theory Ser. B **42** (1987), 212–249.

[58] J.G. Oxley, *A characterization of certain excluded-minor classes of matroids*, Europ. J. Combin. **10** (1989), 275–279.

[59] J.G. Oxley, *The regular matroids with no 5–wheel minor*, J. Combin. Theory Ser. B **46** (1989), 292–305.

[60] J.G. Oxley, *On an excluded-minor class of matroids*, Discrete Math. **82** (1990), 35–52.

[61] J.G. Oxley, *Ternary paving matroids*, Discrete Math. **91** (1991), 77–86.

[62] J.G. Oxley, *Matroid Theory*, Oxford University Press, New York, 1992.

[63] J. Oxley, D. Vertigan, and G. Whittle, *On inequivalent representations of matroids over finite fields*, J. Combin. Theory Ser. B, to appear.

[64] J. Oxley and H. Wu, *A note on matroid connectivity*, Discrete Math. **146** (1995), 321–324.

[65] J. Oxley and H. Wu, *On the structure of 3–connected matroids and graphs*, submitted.

[66] J. Oxley and H. Wu, *Matroids and graphs with few non-essential elements*, in preparation.

[67] J. Oxley and H. Wu, *The 3–connected graphs with three non-essential edges*, in preparation.

[68] M.D. Plummer, *On minimal blocks*, Trans. Amer. Math. Soc. **134** (1968), 85–94.

[69] A. Rajan, *Algorithmic applications of connectivity and related topics in matroid theory*, Ph.D. thesis, Northwestern University, 1987.

[70] S. Rajpal, *On paving matroids and a generalization of M.D.S. codes*, Discrete Appl. Math. **60** (1995), 343–347.

[71] S. Rajpal, *Quaternary paving matroids*, J. Combin. Theory Ser. B, to appear.

[72] T.J. Reid, *Triangles in 3–connected matroids*, Discrete Math. **90** (1991), 281–296.

[73] N. Robertson, *Minimal cyclic-4-connected graphs*, Trans. Amer. Math. Soc. **284** (1984), 665–687.

[74] N. Robertson and P.D. Seymour, *Generalizing Kuratowski's Theorem*, Congressus Numerantium **45** (1984), 129–138.

[75] N. Robertson and P.D. Seymour, *Graph minors – a survey*, Surveys in combinatorics 1985 (ed. I. Anderson), London Math. Soc. Lecture Notes **103**, Cambridge University Press, Cambridge, 1985, pp. 155–171.

[76] N. Robertson, P.D. Seymour, and R. Thomas, *Quickly excluding a planar graph*, J. Combin. Theory Ser. B **62** (1994), 323–348.

[77] A. Schrijver, *Theory of Linear and Integer Programming*, Wiley, Chichester, 1986.

[78] P.D. Seymour, *A note on the production of matroid minors*, J. Combin. Theory Ser. B **22** (1977), 289–295.

[79] P.D. Seymour, *The matroids with the max-flow min-cut property*, J. Combin. Theory Ser. B **23** (1977), 189–222.

[80] P.D. Seymour, *Matroid representation over GF(3)*, J. Combin. Theory Ser. B **26** (1979), 159–173.

[81] P.D. Seymour, *Packing and covering with matroid circuits*, J. Combin. Theory Ser. B **28** (1980), 237–242.

[82] P.D. Seymour, *Decomposition of regular matroids*, J. Combin. Theory Ser. B **28** (1980), 305–359.

[83] P.D. Seymour, *On minors of non-binary matroids*, Combinatorica **1** (1981), 387–394.

[84] P.D. Seymour, *Matroid minors*, Handbook of Combinatorics (eds. R. Graham, M. Grötschel, L. Lovász), Elsevier, Amsterdam; MIT Press, Cambridge, Mass., 1995, pp. 527–550.

[85] J.J.-M. Tan, *Matroid 3–connectivity*, Ph. D. thesis, Carleton University, 1981.

[86] R. Thomas, *A Menger-like property of tree-width. The finite case*, J. Combin. Theory Ser. B **48** (1990), 67–76.

[87] K. Truemper, *Partial matroid representations*, Europ. J. Combin. **5** (1984), 377–394.

[88] K. Truemper, *A decomposition theory for matroids. I. General results*, J. Combin. Theory Ser. B **39** (1985), 43–76.

[89] K. Truemper, *A decomposition theory for matroids. II. Minimal violation matroids*, J. Combin. Theory Ser. B **39** (1985), 282–297.

[90] K. Truemper, *A decomposition theory for matroids. III. Decomposition conditions*, J. Combin. Theory Ser. B **41** (1986), 275–305.

[91] K. Truemper, *A decomposition theory for matroids. IV. Graph decomposition*, J. Combin. Theory Ser. B **45** (1988), 259–292.

[92] K. Truemper, *A decomposition theory for matroids. V. Testing of matrix total unimodularity*, J. Combin. Theory Ser. B **49** (1990), 241–281.

[93] K. Truemper, *A decomposition theory for matroids. VI. Almost regular matroids*, J. Combin. Theory Ser. B **55** (1992), 253–301.

[94] K. Truemper, *A decomposition theory for matroids. VII. Analysis of minimal violation matroids*, J. Combin. Theory Ser. B **55** (1992), 302–335.

[95] K. Truemper, *Matroid Decomposition,* Academic Press, New York, 1992.

[96] F.T. Tseng and K. Truemper, *A decomposition of the matroids with the max-flow min-cut property*, Discrete Appl. Math. **15** (1986), 329–364.

[97] W.T. Tutte, *A homotopy theorem for matroids, I, II*, Trans. Amer. Math. Soc. **88** (1958), 144–174.

[98] W.T. Tutte, *A theory of 3–connected graphs*, Nederl. Akad. Wetensch. Proc. Ser. A **64** (1961), 441–455.

[99] W.T. Tutte, *Connectivity in matroids*, Canad. J. Math. **18** (1966), 1301–1324.

[100] W.T. Tutte, *Selected Papers of W.T. Tutte, Volume II* (eds. D. McCarthy and R.G. Stanton), Charles Babbage Research Centre, Winnipeg, 1979.

[101] D.L. Vertigan, *On the intertwining conjecture for matroids*, in preparation.

[102] K. Wagner, *Über eine Erweiterung eines Satzes von Kuratowski*, Deut. Math. **2** (1937), 280–285.

[103] K. Wagner, *Bermerkungen zu Hadwigers Vermutung*, Math. Ann. **141** (1960), 433–451.

[104] P. Walton, *Some topics in combinatorial theory*, D.Phil. thesis, University of Oxford, 1981.

[105] N.L. White, *The bracket ring of a combinatorial geometry. II: Unimodular geometries*, Trans. Amer. Math. Soc. **214** (1975), 233–248.

[106] H. Whitney, *On the abstract properties of linear dependence*, Amer. J. Math. **57** (1935), 509-533.

[107] G. Whittle, *A characterisation of the matroids representable over $GF(3)$ and the rationals*, J. Combin. Theory Ser. B **65** (1995), 222–261.

[108] G. Whittle, *On matroids representable over $GF(3)$ and other fields*, Trans. Amer. Math. Soc., to appear.

[109] H. Wu, On contractible and vertically contractible elements in 3–connected matroids and graphs, Discrete Math., to appear.

DEPARTMENT OF MATHEMATICS, LOUISIANA STATE UNIVERSITY, BATON ROUGE, LOUISIANA 70803-4918

*E-mail address*: oxley@math.lsu.edu

Contemporary Mathematics
Volume **197**, 1996

# Some Matroids from Discrete Applied Geometry

WALTER WHITELEY

June 6, 1996

*Dedicated to Janos Baracs and Henry Crapo on the occasions of their 64th birthdays*

ABSTRACT. We present an array of matroids drawn from three sources in discrete applied geometry: (i) static (or first-order) rigidity of frameworks and higher skeletal rigidity; (ii) parallel drawings (or equivalently polyhedral pictures); and (iii) $C_r^{r-1}$-cofactors abstracted from multivariate splines in all dimensions. The strong analogies (sometimes isomorphisms) between generic rigidity matroids and generic cofactor matroids is one central theme of the chapter. We emphasize matroidal results for the combinatorial 'generic' situations, with geometric techniques used when they contribute combinatorial insights. A second basic theme is the analysis of represented matroids using the duality of row and column dependencies of the representing matrix (generalizing statics and kinematics in rigidity).

Parts I and II concentrate on matroids for geometric graphs (or frameworks) and the role of submodular counts on the edges and vertices. The specific structure of such counts, which generalize the graphic matroid (rigidity on the line), is explored in an Appendix. For matroids based on geometric realizations of higher simplices, Part III emphasizes the intimate role of the homology (statics) of resulting geometric chain complexes and cohomology (kinematics) of the associated cochain complexes. We include a re-presentation of the simplicial homology matroid as the starting point for the geometric complexes and new results on orthogonal homology matroids. A number of unsolved problems and conjectures, both old and new, are presented.

## Contents

1991 *Mathematics Subject Classification.* Primary 05B35, 52C25; Secondary 05C75, 05C65, 52B05, 55U15, 65D07, 68U07.

*Key words and phrases.* first-order rigidity, parallel drawings, $C_1^0$-cofactors, generic rigidity matroids, simplicial matroids, geometric homology and cohomology, skeletal rigidity complex, multivariate spline complex, orthogonal matroids.

Work supported by grants from NSERC (Canada).

## 1. Introduction

Within the spirit of Gian-Carlo Rota's 'geometric approach to matroid theory' [**Ku**], I offer several related arrays of matroids: matroids for geometric graphs which generalize the graphic matroid (Figure 1.1); and matroids from geometric chain complexes which generalize the simplicial matroids of ordinary homology (Figure 13.1), themselves a generalization of graphic matroids. I am a geometer and the underlying work on these objects has been driven by geometric questions. The work draws heavily on problems and examples from true applications of discrete geometry and matroidal thinking has contributed significant insights to this work. We present these patterns in the hope that they will also contribute to the geometric side of 'combinatorial geometries'.

**1.1. The broad themes.** A number of problems in discrete applied geometry lead to matrices with rows indexed by the edges of a graph and columns indexed by the vertices. With these matrices, we naturally have matroids on the index sets (edges) given by the independence of the rows. Some of these matroids, such as that for first-order rigidity of frameworks, have been around for at least 150 years. Other matroids, such as parallel drawing, scene analysis and cofactor matroids for splines, have arisen in the last few decades, within research on processing geometry on computers (Computer Aided Geometric Design, computer graphics, robotic vision, ...).

These matrices from applied geometry have an inherent 'sensual' content. For rigidity, the dependence and rank of a set of edges may be modeled with bars and joints and sensed through the hands and through the eyes. Explicit visual and geometric constructions can verify the rank or dependence of sets (constructions such as dynamic parallel drawings on The Geometer's Sketchpad or Maxwell's reciprocal diagrams). Unfortunately, this sensual character will be absent in our text. We encourage the readers to turn to other writing [**CoW,RW,CrW5**] and other media, such as physical models and computer programs (Geometer's Sketchpad, Cabri, Structures) for that more complete experience.

Not all matrices produce interesting matroids, nor are all aspects of a large field like first-order rigidity of frameworks matroidal. We focus on those aspects which have basic matroidal content and which generalize to wider families of matroids for which these core examples serve as an introduction. Over two decades, these core matroids have been studied by a number of matroid theorists including: Henry Crapo, Jack Graver, Andras Recski, Brigitte Servatius and Neil White; and specific matroidal features have been identified and developed [**GSS,Re4**]. Within the larger theories, we select topics to illustrate some central themes:

1. Matroid theory offers important insights into these structures.

   Techniques such as matroid union, Dilworth truncation, matroid partition, submodular functions, etc. have contributed to the theory and the algorithms (Part I and Appendix §A).

2. Many of the techniques developed for the core examples generalize to other matroids arising from other settings.

   This body of matrix / matroid techniques on graphs has wider applications and has a more unified whole (Parts I, II, III). Already, inductive techniques have been moved from rigidity of frameworks to multivariate splines and related techniques have been moved back, based on the common structure of the matrices (see §10, §11, and §16.5).

3. These matroids raises interesting, unsolved problems and conjectures within matroid theory.

   We will describe several of these conjectures in Part II.

4. These matroids on geometric graphs are a first layer in a rich array of matroids derived from geometric chain complexes (Part III) [**Wh15**].

   We want to promote an investigation this broad family of matroids. Some of these are intimately related to the core areas of matroid theory, such as orthogonality and homology of surfaces (§14), others are related to fields such as multivariate splines (§15) and still others drawn from core combinatorial and geometric properties of polytopes (§16).

5. For graphs and for homologies we emphasize a 'two sided' analysis of the matrix of a represented matroid – the row rank and row dependencies as the circuits of the matroid (statics of frameworks and homology), and the column rank and kernel (kinematics of frameworks and cohomology).

   The interplay of these two complementary or dual approaches to a single matroid is a central theme of this chapter. This duality is implicit in the homology and cohomology of the underlying chain complexes.

**1.2.  A pattern of matroids on graphs.** Part I concentrates on alternate forms of a single matroid: the core example in the white box of Figure 1.1, referred to as plane rigidity, plane parallel drawing and $C_1^0$-cofactors. On complete graphs (for points affinely spanning the plane), these have bases $E$ with $|E| = 2|V| - 3$. We give such space to this well-studied matroid (and the even simpler matroid on the line – the graphic matroid of the lowest white box) because the three versions have distinct, independently interesting, extensions to higher geometric dimensions (or, for cofactors, higher algebraic powers) in Part II. The exploration of this matroid also establishes the pattern of results and techniques which we strive to approximate in these extensions.

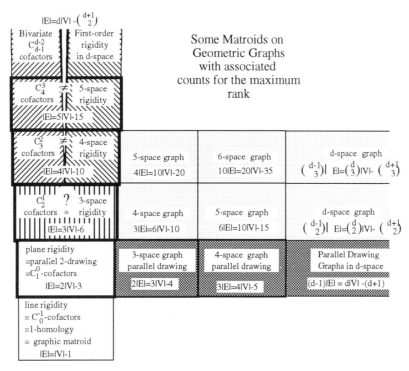

FIGURE. 1.1. *Some connected families of matroids on graphs realized in $d$-space.*

Part II describes three strips of Figure 1.1 which extend out for this core example: the parallel drawing hypermatroids (or polymatroids) for geometric graphs in dimensions $d \geq 3$ (and more general parallel drawing and polyhedral picture matroids) (§8), the first-order rigidity matroids for dimensions $d \geq 3$ (§9,§11), and the bivariate $C_s^{s-1}$-cofactor matroids for graphs in the plane (§10,§11).

Part III describes two related families of matroids on higher skeleta of simplicial complexes in $d$-space – families spreading in layers 'above' the initial layer of Figure 1.1 (see Figure 13.1). These families generalize the usual matroids for simplicial homology of the underlying complex (§14) in precisely the sense that the rigidity and cofactor matroids generalize the usual graphic matroid.

Parts I and II record a number of examples of matroids for which the rank is calculated by explicit 'counts' on the edges and vertices of a graph, multigraph or hypergraph. In the Appendix §A, we extract a particular pattern of submodular functions and induced matroids on hypergraphs which corresponds to these 'counts' of the edges and vertices.

It is our goal to paint a picture of larger patterns within this range of examples, connections which are easily lost in the detailed presentation of a single part. We hope that this broader picture will contribute to the evolution of these areas and the resolution of the large collection of conjectures which are scattered through the chapter.

It has been difficult to resist many aesthetically pleasing digressions: examples or twists of the theory. I trust the reader will forgive some wandering from the central path to give a richer flavour to the results, the connections, and the problems. In spite of appearances, I have left out more of these 'added remarks' than I have retained!

**1.3. Acknowledgments.** I owe a large debt to Henry Crapo and Neil White for over two decades of joint projects and informal conversations on areas implicitly and explicitly related to this chapter. In particular, the Appendix records previously unpublished joint work with Neil White. I owe a less obvious, but very deep debt to Janos Baracs for sharing his rich geometric insights, his provocative conjectures and his stimulating examples. Within the Structural Topology Research Group, I shared with Janos and Henry a program to understand the geometry and combinatorics of frameworks in 3-space.

15 years of exchanges, conjectures and conversations with Bob Connelly have also contributed to Parts I and II. Several projects with Tiong-Seng Tay contributed to Parts II and III (particularly §16 which includes results of a joint project with Tiong-Seng and Neil White on 'skeletal rigidity'). Conversations with Luis Billera and joint work with Peter Alfeld on multivariate splines also contributed to §10 and §15 in essential ways.

Finally, I owe a longstanding debt to Gian-Carlo Rota who introduced me to matroid theory and to the attractions of a good analogy. Since my days as a graduate student I have continued to learn both from his particular insights and from his broader vision: his search for patterns and analogies which connect diverse areas of mathematics – and his love of a digression!

All of this material has evolved through many hands and many minds. The community of workers in this field has been an important source of support over the last 25 years. In the end, however, the larger patterns and connections claimed here are my responsibility.

## Part I: The Core Plane Matroid

We present a single matroid on the edges of a geometric graph in the Euclidean plane from four points of view. Each of the points of view has its own historical roots and its own applications. These approaches also lead to three distinct 'higher' families of matroids.

1. Statics and stresses of bar frameworks (§2). This is a well-developed theory, with roots in structural engineering of pin-jointed iron trusses and more general frameworks. The key structure is the rigidity matrix, for a graph $G$ and a configuration $\mathbf{p}$ of the points, and the corresponding matroid of the rows. This theory has a combinatorial aspect (what happens for almost all configurations for the vertices) and a geometric aspect: the projective geometry of the algebraic variety of special configurations for the vertices which reduce the rank of the matroid. In keeping with the combinatorial tone of this chapter, we will concentrate on the generic aspects. However, in an interesting twist of proving the general through single special examples, certain generic results are best derived from very special configurations.

2. First-order rigidity of bar frameworks (§3). We will follow the lead of the classical engineers and also analyze the rank of the rigidity matrix in terms of its column rank (instantaneous kinematics). While this two sided 'dual' approach (in the sense of linear algebra) is not common in matroid theory, it is an essential feature of this field. In Part III, we will see that this two sided approach reflects the more general duality of homology and cohomology for chain complexes over fields [**Wh15**].

3. Parallel drawings (and scene analysis) (§4). For graphical analysis of instantaneous kinematics in the last century, engineers developed a geometrically equivalent representation called parallel drawing (or parallel redrawing). For modern studies, this theory has three roles:

   a. It remains easier to handle graphically (with programs such as Sketchpad) because the failures in rank then occur on a large scale as well as an 'infinitesimal scale'.

   b. Parallel drawings are natural geometric objects for certain modern geometric theories, such as Minkowski decomposition of polytopes, reciprocal diagrams, etc. and they have the simplest generalizations to all higher dimensions.

   c. Parallel drawings are the projective polar of the 'projection and lifting' problems for scene analysis of polyhedral objects (see §4, §8).

4. $C_1^0$-cofactors from bivariate splines (§5). This is a matroid extracted from approximation theory and CAGD. However, it records a far older connection which is implicit in Maxwell's Theorem of 1864 [**Max,CrW2,3,4**]:

   *A realization of a planar graph in the plane is dependent in the static rigidity matroid if, and only if, it is the projection of the edges of a spatial polyhedron (on the faces identified by some planar drawing) with at least two distinct planes for faces.*

We will close Part I with some other 'plane' matroids from CAD (§6) which highlight further extensions and related unsolved problems and wrap up with a summary of plane results to prepare for the step up to Part II (§7).

The broad theory of rigidity of frameworks includes many other mathematical components, some of them clearly not matroidal (see Remark 3.2.6 and Figure 3.4). We encourage the interested reader to look further into the wider literature in the references [**CoW,RW,Wh14**].

## 2.  The Plane Rigidity Matroid: Statics

Unlike many presentations of rigidity [**GSS,Wh11**], we will begin with the statics (the basic dependencies of the matroid) then follow with the more traditional first-order kinematics in §3. While this approach has less immediate physical motivation, it leads us from the more traditional approach in matroid theory (dependencies) to a dual approach typical of rigidity.

**2.1. The matroid from self-stresses.** A *plane bar-and-joint framework*, or *plane framework* for short, is a standard graph $G = (V, E)$ (no loops or multiple edges) and a *plane configuration* $\mathbf{p} : V \to \mathbb{R}^2$, with $\mathbf{p}(i) = \mathbf{p}_i$. The framework is also written $G(\mathbf{p})$ and the configuration $\mathbf{p}$ can be treated as a point in $\mathbb{R}^{2|V|}$.

A *dependence* on the plane framework $G(\mathbf{p})$ is an assignment $\omega : E \to \mathbb{R}$, with $\omega\{i,j\} = \omega_{i,j} = \omega_{j,i}$, such that, for each vertex $i$:

$$\sum_{j|\{i,j\}\in E} \omega_{i,j}(\mathbf{p}_i - \mathbf{p}_j) = \mathbf{0}.$$

A dependence is also called a *self-stress*, and a *non-trivial self-stress* is a dependence with $\omega_{i,j} \neq 0$ for some $\{i,j\} \in E$. These self-stresses are the row dependencies of the *rigidity matrix* of the framework, $R_G(\mathbf{p})$:

$$[\ldots \quad \omega_{i,j} \quad \ldots] \begin{bmatrix} \vdots & \ddots & \vdots & \cdots & \vdots & \ddots & \vdots \\ \mathbf{0} & \cdots & (\mathbf{p}_i - \mathbf{p}_j) & \cdots & (\mathbf{p}_j - \mathbf{p}_i) & \cdots & \mathbf{0} \\ \vdots & \ddots & \vdots & \cdots & \vdots & \ddots & \vdots \end{bmatrix} = [\mathbf{0} \quad \cdots \quad \mathbf{0}].$$

The corresponding *plane rigidity matroid* on the edges, $\mathcal{R}_2(G; \mathbf{p})$, defines independence of sets by independence of rows of the rigidity matrix. A framework $G(\mathbf{p})$ is *independent* if its edge set is independent in $\mathcal{R}_2(G; \mathbf{p})$, and the *rank of* $G(\mathbf{p})$ is the rank of $\mathcal{R}_2(G; \mathbf{p})$. For the complete graph on $n$ vertices, $K_n$, we write $\mathcal{R}_2(n; \mathbf{p})$.

EXAMPLE 2.1.1. Consider the framework $G(\mathbf{p})$ of Figure 2.1A. This has a rigidity matrix as follows, with a column for a dependence $\omega$ (which is guaranteed to exist, as we will see below).

| $R_G(\mathbf{p})$ | $\omega$ | $v_1$ | $v_2$ | $v_3$ | $v_4$ |
|---|---|---|---|---|---|
| $\{1,2\}$ | $\omega_{12}$ | $\mathbf{p}_1 - \mathbf{p}_2$ | $\mathbf{p}_2 - \mathbf{p}_1$ | $\mathbf{0}$ | $\mathbf{0}$ |
| $\{1,3\}$ | $\omega_{13}$ | $\mathbf{p}_1 - \mathbf{p}_3$ | $\mathbf{0}$ | $\mathbf{p}_3 - \mathbf{p}_1$ | $\mathbf{0}$ |
| $\{1,4\}$ | $\omega_{14}$ | $\mathbf{p}_1 - \mathbf{p}_4$ | $\mathbf{0}$ | $\mathbf{0}$ | $\mathbf{p}_4 - \mathbf{p}_1$ |
| $\{2,3\}$ | $\omega_{23}$ | $\mathbf{0}$ | $\mathbf{p}_2 - \mathbf{p}_3$ | $\mathbf{p}_3 - \mathbf{p}_2$ | $\mathbf{0}$ |
| $\{2,4\}$ | $\omega_{24}$ | $\mathbf{0}$ | $\mathbf{p}_2 - \mathbf{p}_4$ | $\mathbf{0}$ | $\mathbf{p}_2 - \mathbf{p}_4$ |
| $\{3,4\}$ | $\omega_{34}$ | $\mathbf{0}$ | $\mathbf{0}$ | $\mathbf{p}_3 - \mathbf{p}_4$ | $\mathbf{p}_3 - \mathbf{p}_4$ |

The dependence, or self-stress, can be visualized as a set of forces, equal in magnitude and opposite in direction, in the bars (Figure 2.1B,D) which represent tension ($\omega_{i,j} < 0$) or compression ($\omega_{i,j} > 0$) pushing or pulling on the vertex. The equations $\sum_{j|\{i,j\}\in E} \omega_{i,j}(\mathbf{p}_i - \mathbf{p}_j) = \mathbf{0}$ says these forces are in *equilibrium* at vertex $i$ – an equilibrium verified graphically for the four vertices through the four small vector polygons in Figure 2.1C.

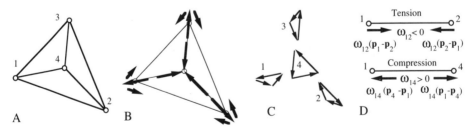

FIGURE. 2.1. *A dependent framework (A), with forces of a self-stress (B) and their vector equilibria at each vertex (C).*

If we consider a particular configuration $\mathbf{p}_1 = (0,0)$, $\mathbf{p}_2 = (3,0)$, $\mathbf{p}_3 = (0,3)$, and $\mathbf{p}_4 = (1,1)$, then we can verify that the assignment $\omega$ given in the second column is a row dependence.

| $R_G(\mathbf{p})$ | $\omega$ | $v_1$ | | $v_2$ | | $v_3$ | | $v_4$ | |
|---|---|---|---|---|---|---|---|---|---|
| $\{1,2\}$ | $1$ | $-3$ | $0$ | $3$ | $0$ | $0$ | $0$ | $0$ | $0$ |
| $\{1,3\}$ | $1$ | $0$ | $-3$ | $0$ | $0$ | $0$ | $3$ | $0$ | $0$ |
| $\{1,4\}$ | $-3$ | $-1$ | $-1$ | $0$ | $0$ | $0$ | $0$ | $1$ | $1$ |
| $\{2,3\}$ | $1$ | $0$ | $0$ | $3$ | $-3$ | $-3$ | $3$ | $0$ | $0$ |
| $\{2,4\}$ | $-3$ | $0$ | $0$ | $2$ | $-1$ | $0$ | $0$ | $-2$ | $1$ |
| $\{3,4\}$ | $-3$ | $0$ | $0$ | $0$ | $0$ | $-1$ | $2$ | $1$ | $-2$ |

| | | | | | | | | | |
|---|---|---|---|---|---|---|---|---|---|
| $T_x$ | | $1$ | $0$ | $1$ | $0$ | $1$ | $0$ | $1$ | $0$ |
| $T_y$ | | $0$ | $1$ | $0$ | $1$ | $0$ | $1$ | $0$ | $1$ |
| $T_r$ | | $0$ | $0$ | $0$ | $3$ | $-3$ | $0$ | $-1$ | $1$ |

Up to a single scalar multiplier, this self-stress is unique. In fact, looking at the equation for any vertex, there is a unique linear combination of the three distinct vectors (up to a single scalar). This matrix has rank 5 and the matroid has a single circuit.

The lower box shows three independent solutions to the equations $R_G(\mathbf{p})\mathbf{x} = \mathbf{0}$ (that is, three rows orthogonal to the rows of $R_G(\mathbf{p})$). These 'equilibrium coefficients' (see Remark 2.1.5) also indicate that the matrix has column rank $\leq 8-3 = 5$. Since the row rank is 5, these added vectors must span the solution space.

What is the rank of the matrix $R_G(\mathbf{p})$, and the matroid $\mathcal{R}(G;\mathbf{p})$, for the complete graph on $n$ vertices, $K_n$, realized with at least two distinct points? In Example 2.1 and in subsets of these edges, we see that the ranks follow a pattern:

$$n = 4, \text{rank} = 5, \quad n = 3, \text{rank} = 3, \quad n = 2, \text{rank} = 1, \quad n = 1, \text{rank} = 0.$$

In general, for $n > 1$, the rank of $R_{K_n}(\mathbf{p})$ is $2n - 3$. Notice that removing vertices and restricting the configuration does not change the rank of a set of edges on the remaining vertices, nor does changing the labels of the vertices and the corresponding points in the configuration: the matroid is 'symmetric' [Ka2]. We can speak of the independence and dependence of a set $E'$ of edges at any configuration $\mathbf{p}$ for at least the vertices $V(E')$ of these edges.

We can prove that the rank of a framework $G(\mathbf{p})$, such that $\mathbf{p}$ contains at least two distinct points, is at most $2|V| - 3$, by considering the equilibrium coefficients illustrated in Example 2.1.

$$
\begin{aligned}
T_x &= [ & 1 & \ 0 & \ldots & 1 & 0 & \ldots & 1 & 0 & ] \\
T_y &= [ & 0 & \ 1 & \ldots & 0 & 1 & \ldots & 0 & 1 & ] \\
T_r &= [ & -x_1 & \ y_1 & \ldots & -x_i & y_i & \ldots & -x_{|V|} & y_{|V|} & ]
\end{aligned}
$$

It is easy to check that these are solutions to the linear equations $R_G(\mathbf{p})\mathbf{x} = \mathbf{0}$, for any graph on these vertices. For $T_x$ and $T_y$, this is the observation that $(\mathbf{p}_i - \mathbf{p}_j) + (\mathbf{p}_j - \mathbf{p}_i) = \mathbf{0}$. For $T_r$, we have:

$$(\mathbf{p}_i - \mathbf{p}_j) \cdot (\mathbf{p}_i)^\perp + (\mathbf{p}_j - \mathbf{p}_i) \cdot (\mathbf{p}_j)^\perp = (\mathbf{p}_i - \mathbf{p}_j) \cdot (\mathbf{p}_i^\perp - \mathbf{p}_j^\perp) = (\mathbf{p}_i - \mathbf{p}_j) \cdot (\mathbf{p}_i - \mathbf{p}_j)^\perp = 0.$$

where $\mathbf{p}_i^\perp$ represents a counterclockwise rotation of $\mathbf{p}_i$ by $90°$. (See Remark 2.1.5 for a static interpretation of these solutions and §3 for a kinematic interpretation.)

$T_x, T_y, T_r$ are three independent vectors, for at least two distinct points (check the first four columns in Example 2.1). If we do not have two distinct points, then the rank of $G(\mathbf{p})$ will be 0 for all sets of edges. We have shown the following simple sufficient condition for dependence.

COUNTING LEMMA 2.1.2. *Any non-empty set of edges $E$ with $|E| > 2|V(E)| - 3$ is dependent for every plane configuration $\mathbf{p}$. Equivalently, a set $E$ is independent only if, for all non-empty subsets $E''$, $|E''| \leq 2|V(E'')| - 3$.*

By induction, we can also demonstrate that some independent graphs have this maximal rank $2|V| - 3$, at general position configurations $\mathbf{p}$ – i.e. they are bases of the matroid $\mathcal{R}_2(|V|; \mathbf{p})$. Given a graph $G = (V, E)$, a *vertex 2-addition of* 0 is the addition of one new vertex, 0, and two new edges $(0, i), (0, j)$ creating the graph $G' = (V', E')$.

A graph $G = (V, E)$, with at least two vertices, is *2-simple* if there is an ordering of the vertices $\sigma(1), \sigma(2), \ldots, \sigma(|V|)$ such that:
  (i)   $G_2$ is the single edge $\{\sigma(1), \sigma(2)\}$;
  (ii)  for $2 \leq i < |V|$, $G_{i+1}$ is a vertex 2-addition of $\sigma(i+1)$ to $G_i$;
  (iii) $G_{|V|}$ is $G$.

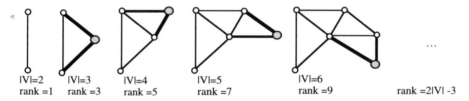

|V|=2     |V|=3     |V|=4     |V|=5     |V|=6
rank =1   rank =3   rank =5   rank =7   rank =9          rank =2|V| -3

FIGURE. 2.2. *Building a 2-simple graph as a basis for the plane rigidity matroid $\mathcal{R}_2(n; \mathbf{p})$.*

VERTEX 2-ADDITION LEMMA 2.1.3. *Given a framework $G(\mathbf{p})$ and a vertex 2-addition of 0 creating the framework $G'(\mathbf{p}_0, \mathbf{p})$, with $\mathbf{p}_0, \mathbf{p}_i, \mathbf{p}_j$ not collinear, then*
  1. *$G'(\mathbf{p}_0, \mathbf{p})$ is independent if and only if $G(\mathbf{p})$ is independent;*
  2. *rank $R_{G'}(\mathbf{p}_0, \mathbf{p}) =$ rank $R_G(\mathbf{p}) + 2$.*

PROOF. Consider the rigidity matrix for $R_{G'}(\mathbf{p}_0, \mathbf{p})$:

| $R_{G'}(\mathbf{p}_0, \mathbf{p})$ | 0 | 1 | $\ldots$ | $|V|$ |
|---|---|---|---|---|
| $e_1$ | **0** | | | |
| $\vdots$ | $\vdots$ | | $R_G(\mathbf{p})$ | |
| $e_{|E|}$ | **0** | | | |
| $\{0, i\}$ | $\mathbf{p}_0 - \mathbf{p}_i$ $\ldots$ | $\ldots$ | $\ldots$ | |
| $\{0, j\}$ | $\mathbf{p}_0 - \mathbf{p}_j$ $\ldots$ | $\ldots$ | $\ldots$ | |

Part 1. The vertex 2-addition requires that $G$ has at least two vertices. Assume there is a dependence in $R_{G'}(\mathbf{p}_0, \mathbf{p})$. For the first two columns, the equilibrium equations are:

$$\omega_{0,i}(\mathbf{p}_0 - \mathbf{p}_i) + \omega_{0,j}(\mathbf{p}_0 - \mathbf{p}_j) = \mathbf{0}.$$

Now $(\mathbf{p}_0 - \mathbf{p}_i)$ and $(\mathbf{p}_0 - \mathbf{p}_j)$ are linearly independent if and only if $\mathbf{p}_0, \mathbf{p}_i, \mathbf{p}_j$ are not collinear, in which case $\omega_{0,i} = \omega_{0,j} = 0$. $\omega$ is a non-trivial dependence if and only if this is a non-trivial dependence on $R_G(\mathbf{p})$.

Part 2. As noted above the two added rows are independent of any basis for $R_G(\mathbf{p})$. Thus the rank has increased by 2.

A *general position* plane configuration $\mathbf{p}$ has any set of at most 3 points affinely independent (i.e., no three points are collinear and any two points are distinct).

STATIC 2-RIGIDITY THEOREM 2.1.4. *For any $n \geq 2$ and any general position configuration $\mathbf{p}$ on $n$ vertices, the edges $E$ of any 2-simple graph $G$ on $n$ vertices are a basis of $\mathcal{R}_2(n; \mathbf{p})$ of rank $2n - 3$.*

PROOF. If $n = 2$, $K_n$ is a single edge which has rank $1 = 2 \times 2 - 3$. This graph is both 2-simple and a basis of the matroid.

If $n > 2$, we prove by induction that there is a 2-simple graph $G$ whose edges are a basis for $K_n$ of size $2n - 3$. Assume $G_k$ is a 2-simple graph for $n = k$, which is a basis for $\mathcal{R}_2(k; \mathbf{p}|_k)$ of rank $2k - 3$. Let $G_{k+1}$ be a vertex 2-addition of $k + 1$ with edges $(1, k + 1), (2, k + 1)$. Since $\mathbf{p}$ is in general position, $\mathbf{p}_1, \mathbf{p}_2, \mathbf{p}_{k+1}$ are not collinear, and $E_{k+1}$ is independent of rank $2k - 3 + 2 = 2(k + 1) - 3$ by Lemma 2.1.3. By Lemma 2.1.2, this is a maximal independent set in $K_{k+1}$, so $E_{k+1}$ is a basis. This completes the induction step.

Any framework $G(\mathbf{p})$ for which $R_G(\mathbf{p})$ has rank $2|V| - 3$ (or for which $|V| \leq 1$) is *statically 2-rigid*. We also say that the edge set $E$ is *statically 2-rigid* on $V(E)$ at $\mathbf{p}$. There are other edge sets which are not 2-simple but which satisfy the condition of Lemma 2.1.2 to be independent for some configurations (Figure 2.3A,B). We will see below that these are also statically 2-rigid for some choices of $\mathbf{p}$, including the illustrated configurations.

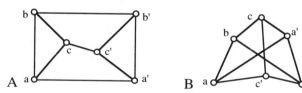

FIGURE. 2.3. *Graphs which are not 2-simple, but are bases for the 2-rigidity matroid.*

REMARK 2.1.5. For a civil engineer, static rigidity of a framework means that the framework will 'resolve all the permitted external loads'. We can interpret our definition in precisely these terms.

The vocabulary describes the the row space of the rigidity matrix. An *equilibrium load* is an assignment $\mathbf{L} : V \to \mathbf{IR}^2$ of vectors $\mathbf{L}_i$ to the vertices satisfying the equilibrium equations:

$$(i) \quad \sum_{i \in V} \mathbf{L}_i = \mathbf{0} \quad \text{and} \quad (ii) \quad \sum_{i \in V} \mathbf{L}_i \cdot (\mathbf{p}_i)^\perp = 0.$$

These equations say that the forces of the load have: (i) no net translational component; and (ii) no net rotational component. Equivalently, an equilibrium load is any vector orthogonal to the three vectors $T_x, T_y, T_r$ defined above. In particular, the entries of any row of the rigidity matrix for $K_{|V|}(\mathbf{p})$ form an equilibrium load on these vertices. The row space of $R_G(\mathbf{p})$ is a subset of the space of equilibrium loads.

We have already seen that the equilibrium equations have rank 3, for frameworks with at least two distinct vertices. Therefore the space of equilibrium loads has dimension $2|V| - 3$. The only equilibrium load with $|V| = 1$ is the zero load. The only equilibrium loads on two distinct vertices have the form $\lambda(\mathbf{p}_1 - \mathbf{p}_2)$ at 1 and $\lambda(\mathbf{p}_2 - \mathbf{p}_1)$ at 2. Notice that the definition of an equilibrium load depends on the vertices and the configuration, not on the edges of the framework.

A *resolution* of the equilibrium load $\mathbf{L}$ on the framework $G(\mathbf{p})$ is a *stress*: an assignment of scalars $\omega : E \to \mathbf{R}$, such that, for each vertex $i$:

$$\mathbf{L}_i + \sum_{j|\{i,j\}\in E} \omega_{i,j}(\mathbf{p}_i - \mathbf{p}_j) = \mathbf{0}.$$

This resolution achieves an equilibrium of the internal forces (tensions and compressions) and the external load at each vertex (Figure 2.4). A self-stress is a resolution of the zero equilibrium load.

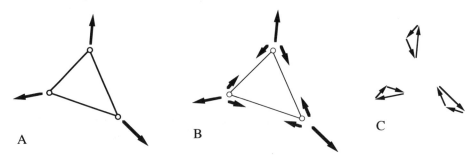

FIGURE. 2.4. *An equilibrium load on a statically 2-rigid framework (A), with its resolution (B) and the visual check of equilibria at the vertices (C).*

For each edge $\{i,,j\} \in E$, we write the corresponding row of the rigidity matrix as $R_{i,j}(\mathbf{p})$. The resolution of an equilibrium load $\mathbf{L}$ is a linear combination of these rows:

$$\mathbf{L} + \sum_{\{i,j\}\in E} \omega_{i,j} R_{i,j}(\mathbf{p}) = \mathbf{0}.$$

By definition, a framework $G(\mathbf{p})$ is statically 2-rigid if the dimension of the row space equals the dimension of the equilibrium loads. Since the row space is contained in the space of equilibrium loads, the two spaces are the same.

COROLLARY 2.1.6. *A framework $G(\mathbf{p})$ is statically 2-rigid if and only if each equilibrium load has a resolution by a stress in the edges of the framework.*

This does correspond to the civil engineer's concept of static rigidity. If the framework is independent then the resolution of an external equilibrium load is unique. However, if the framework is dependent then we can add any multiple of a self-stress to a given resolution to get another resolution. Which resolution actually appears in a physical loaded framework will depend on the elasticity of the materials and any prestress (self-stress) built into the structure [**CoW**].

REMARK 2.1.7. If we choose a configuration $\mathbf{p}$ consisting of distinct collinear points then the matrix and the matroid take on a familiar form.

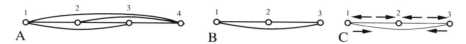

FIGURE. 2.5. *In a collinear framework (A), every polygon (B) has a dependence (C).*

Consider the framework of Figure 2.5A with all vertices collinear on a line with unit direction $\mathbf{u}$. All entries have the form $\mathbf{p}_i - \mathbf{p}_j = l_{i,j}\mathbf{u}$, where $l_{i,j}$ is a signed length for $i < j$. The rigidity matrix now looks like:

| $R_G(\mathbf{p})$ | $\omega$ | 1 | 2 | 3 | 4 |
|---|---|---|---|---|---|
| $\{1,2\}$ | $\frac{1}{l_{1,2}}$ | $l_{1,2}\mathbf{u}$ | $-l_{1,2}\mathbf{u}$ | $\mathbf{0}$ | $\mathbf{0}$ |
| $\{1,3\}$ | $-\frac{1}{l_{1,3}}$ | $l_{1,3}\mathbf{u}$ | $\mathbf{0}$ | $-l_{1,3}\mathbf{u}$ | $\mathbf{0}$ |
| $\{1,4\}$ | $0$ | $l_{1,4}\mathbf{u}$ | $\mathbf{0}$ | $\mathbf{0}$ | $-l_{1,4}\mathbf{u}$ |
| $\{2,3\}$ | $\frac{1}{l_{2,3}}$ | $\mathbf{0}$ | $l_{2,3}\mathbf{u}$ | $-l_{2,3}\mathbf{u}$ | $\mathbf{0}$ |
| $\{2,4\}$ | $0$ | $\mathbf{0}$ | $l_{2,4}\mathbf{u}$ | $\mathbf{0}$ | $-l_{2,4}\mathbf{u}$ |
| $\{3,4\}$ | $0$ | $\mathbf{0}$ | $\mathbf{0}$ | $l_{3,4}\mathbf{u}$ | $-l_{3,4}\mathbf{u}$ |

After dividing each row $R_{i,j}$ by the non-zero scalar $l_{i,j}$, all entries are $\mathbf{0}$ or $\pm\mathbf{u}$, and the pattern of the $\mathbf{u}$ entries is the pattern of the usual matrix representation of the cycle matroid of the graph $G$, as the rows of a matrix over $\mathbb{R}$ [**Wh11**]. In particular, every polygon has a dependence (self-stress), as illustrated by the coefficients for the polygon $(1,2),(2,3),(3,1)$ (Figure 2.5B,C) above.

PROPOSITION 2.1.8. *For a configuration $\mathbf{p}$ of distinct collinear points on the vertices of a graph $G$, the matroid $\mathcal{R}_2(G;\mathbf{p})$ is the cycle matroid of the graph $G$. In particular:*

1. *A set $E'$ of edges is independent if and only if it is a forest;*
2. *A set $E'$ of edges is independent if and only if, for all nonempty subsets $E''$, $|E''| \le |V(E'')| - 1$;*
3. *A set $E'$ has rank $|V(E')| - 1$ if and only if $G' = (V(E'), E')$ is a connected graph;*
4. *A set $E'$ is a basis for the 2-rigidity matroid on $K_n(\mathbf{p})$ if and only if it is a spanning tree on the $n$ vertices;*
5. *A set $E'$ is a basis for the 2-rigidity matroid on $K_n(\mathbf{p})$ if and only if $|E'| = n - 1$ and for all subsets $E''$, $|E''| \le |V(E'')| - 1$.*

Our goal in the next section is a similar characterization of the bases of $\mathcal{R}_2(n;\mathbf{p})$ for the most general or 'generic' plane configurations $\mathbf{p}$. From Remark 2.1.7, we already see that the rank of the matroid depends on the geometric placement of the configuration $\mathbf{p}$. However, for any given graph there is a maximal rank over all plane configurations. Consider the rigidity matrix $R_{K_n}(\mathbf{x})$, where the positions $\mathbf{p}_i$ are replaced by indeterminates $(x_i, y_i)$. The rank of any subset of edges can be determined by maximal non-zero minors on these rows – which are polynomials in these indeterminates. Such polynomials are either zero for all reals or they define an algebraic variety of *singular positions* for which they are zero and are non-zero on the complement – an open dense subset of $\mathbb{R}^{2|V|}$. The union of these singular varieties over the finite number of such non-zero minors in $R_{K_n}(\mathbf{x})$ defines the *singular configurations* on $n$-vertices. The open dense complement of the singular configurations for $n$-vertices is the set of *generic configurations for $n$-vertices.*

If the coordinates of a configuration are algebraically independent reals then the configuration will be generic. Any generic configuration on $n$-vertices has an extension to a generic configuration on $n + k$ vertices – adding points with coordinates algebraically independent of the existing coordinates – and any restriction of a generic configuration on $n + k$ vertices is a generic configuration on $n$ vertices. We will suppress discussion of these extensions and restrictions of generic configurations.

Each of these generic configurations gives a set of edges on at most $n$ vertices its maximal possible rank and defines the same *generic 2-rigidity matroid* on the complete graph on these vertices, $\mathcal{R}_2(n)$. A set $E$ of edges is *generically 2-independent* or *independent in* $\mathcal{R}_2(n)$ if $E$ is independent in the framework $(V(E), E)(\mathbf{p})$ for some generic configuration $\mathbf{p}$ (therefore all generic configurations). A set of edges $E$ is *generically 2-rigid* if $E$ if the framework $(V(E), E)(\mathbf{p})$ is statically 2-rigid for some generic plane configuration $\mathbf{p}$. A graph $G$ is generically 2-independent (generically 2-rigid) if its edge set $E$ is generically 2-independent (generically 2-rigid).

Notice that an edge set $E$ is generically 2-rigid if and only if the $\mathcal{R}_2(V(E))$-matroid closure of $E$, written $\langle E \rangle$, is the complete graph on its vertices. Similarly, at any non-collinear configuration $\mathbf{p}$, an edge set is statically 2-rigid if and only if closure of $E$ in $\mathcal{R}_2(V(E); \mathbf{p})$ is the complete graph. However, at a collinear configuration $\mathbf{p}$ on at least 3-vertices, a graph $G = (V, E)$ is *never statically 2-rigid*, though a spanning tree $E$ will have $K_{V(E)}$ as its $\mathcal{R}_2(V; \mathbf{p})$ matroid closure.

**2.2. Bases of the generic 2-rigidity matroid.** In the Counting Lemma 2.1.2, we gave a necessary condition for independent sets $E'$ in the generic 2-rigidity matroid:

$$\text{for all non-empty subsets } E'', \ |E''| \leq 2|V(E'')| - 3.$$

This is also a sufficient condition for independence.

We begin with an inductive construction for bases of the generic 2-rigidity matroid on $K_n$. One basic technical 'trick' for establishing independence or rank results for generic 2-rigidity is the following.

SPECIAL POSITION LEMMA 2.2.1. *For any set of edges $E$, the following are equivalent:*

1. *$E$ is independent in the generic 2-rigidity matroid;*
2. *$E$ is independent in $\mathcal{R}_2(V(E); \mathbf{p})$ for one configuration $\mathbf{p}$.*

PROOF. This follows from the fact that if a polynomial in $2n$ variables is non-zero at one point (or configuration), then it is non-zero at almost all configurations.

A graph $G'$ is an *edge 2-split* of the graph $G$ on $a, b; c$, if $\{a, b\}$ is an edge of $G$ and $G'$ is formed from $G$ by adding a new vertex $0$, removing the edge $\{a, b\}$, and adding three new edges $\{0, a\}, \{0, b\}, \{0, c\}$.

EDGE 2-SPLIT THEOREM 2.2.2. *Assume $G'$ is an edge 2-split of $G = (V, E)$ on $a, b; c$, and $\mathbf{p}$ is a plane configuration with $\mathbf{p}_a, \mathbf{p}_b, \mathbf{p}_c$ not collinear.*

*If $G(\mathbf{p})$ is 2-independent (statically 2-rigid), then $G'(\mathbf{p}_0, \mathbf{p})$ is 2-independent (statically 2-rigid) for almost all choices of $\mathbf{p}_0$, including $\mathbf{p}_0$ a distinct point on $\mathbf{p}_a, \mathbf{p}_b$ (Figure 2.6B).*

*Conversely, if $G'(\mathbf{p}_0, \mathbf{p})$ is 2-independent (statically 2-rigid) for some choice of $\mathbf{p}_0$, with vertex $0$ connected to exactly vertices $a, b, c$ at three non-collinear points then, for some edge $e$ of with endpoints in $a, b, c$, $E' = E \cup \{e\} - \{(0, a), (0, b), (0, c)\}$ is independent (statically 2-rigid) at $\mathbf{p}$ and $G'$ is an edge 2-split of $G = (V' - 0, E)$.*

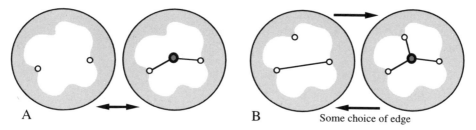

FIGURE. 2.6. *Two inductive steps which preserve static 2-rigidity and are sufficient for Henneberg 2-constructions for bases: (A) vertex 2-addition; (B) edge 2-split.*

PROOF. We first verify the implications for independence. We choose to place $\mathbf{p}_0$ at a distinct point on the line $\mathbf{p}_a, \mathbf{p}_b$. Up to reordering the vertices and edges, the rigidity matrix for $G'$ has the form:

| $R_{G'}(\mathbf{p}_0, \mathbf{p})$ | $0$ | $a$ | $b$ | $\ldots$ |
|---|---|---|---|---|
| $e_1$ | $\mathbf{0}$ | $\ldots$ | $\ldots$ | $\ldots$ |
| $\vdots$ | $\vdots$ | $\vdots$ | $\vdots$ | $\ddots$ |
| $e_{|V|}$ | $\mathbf{0}$ | $\ldots$ | $\ldots$ | $\ldots$ |
| $\{0, a\}$ | $\mathbf{p}_0 - \mathbf{p}_a$ | $\mathbf{p}_a - \mathbf{p}_0$ | $\mathbf{0}$ | $\ldots$ |
| $\{0, b\}$ | $\mathbf{p}_0 - \mathbf{p}_b$ | $\mathbf{0}$ | $\mathbf{p}_b - \mathbf{p}_0$ | $\ldots$ |
| $\{0, c\}$ | $\mathbf{p}_0 - \mathbf{p}_c$ | $\mathbf{0}$ | $\mathbf{0}$ | $\ldots$ |

Assume there is a non-trivial dependence in $G(\mathbf{p})$. The equations for vertex 0 read:

$$\omega_{0,a}(\mathbf{p}_0 - \mathbf{p}_a) + \omega_{0,b}(\mathbf{p}_0 - \mathbf{p}_b) + \omega_{0,c}(\mathbf{p}_0 - \mathbf{p}_c) = \mathbf{0}.$$

Since $\omega_{0,a}(\mathbf{p}_0 - \mathbf{p}_a)$ and $\omega_{0,b}(\mathbf{p}_0 - \mathbf{p}_b)$ are parallel, and $\omega_{0,c}(\mathbf{p}_0 - \mathbf{p}_c)$ is in a distinct direction, we conclude that $\omega_{0,c} = 0$ and $\omega_{0,a}(\mathbf{p}_0 - \mathbf{p}_a) = -\omega_{0,b}(\mathbf{p}_0 - \mathbf{p}_b) = \omega_{a,b}(\mathbf{p}_a - \mathbf{p}_b)$ for some scalar $\omega_{a,b}$. ($\omega_{a,b} \neq 0$ if $\omega_{0,b} \neq 0$.) If we transfer $\omega_{a,b}$ to $\{a, b\}$, and transfer the scalars on all edges $E' \cap E$ from $G'$ to $G$, we must have a non-trivial dependence on $E$. We conclude that if $G(\mathbf{p})$ is independent, then $G'(\mathbf{p}_0, \mathbf{p})$ is independent. Since this works for the special positions of $\mathbf{p}_0$, the same independence will hold for almost all positions $\mathbf{p}_0$ by the Special Position Lemma.

Conversely, assume that $G'(\mathbf{p}_0, \mathbf{p})$ is independent for some choice of $\mathbf{p}_0$, with vertex 0 connected to exactly vertices $a, b, c$ at three non-collinear points. Consider the graphs $G_{a,b}$, $G_{b,c}$ and $G_{a,c}$, formed by deleting vertex 0 and its edges, to create $E^*$ and adding the subscripted edge. (If this edge is already present, we 'double' the edge to get the dependence needed below.) If any one of these is independent at $\mathbf{p}$, we are finished.

Otherwise, assume that these have dependencies, $\alpha, \beta, \gamma$. We have:

$$\alpha_{a,b} R_{a,b} = \sum_{e \in E^*} -\alpha_e R_e \quad \text{with} \quad \alpha_{a,b} \neq 0$$

$$\beta_{b,c} R_{b,c} = \sum_{e \in E^*} -\beta_e R_e \quad \text{with} \quad \beta_{b,c} \neq 0$$

$$\gamma_{a,c} R_{a,c} = \sum_{e \in E^*} -\gamma_e R_e \quad \text{with} \quad \gamma_{b,c} \neq 0$$

In the graph $K_4$ on $\{0, a, b, c\}$ at $\mathbf{p}'$ which has $E'' = 6 > 2|V| - 3$, we have a dependence $\omega$, which must be non-zero on at least one of the edges at $0$, since the noncollinear triangle $a, b, c$ is independent. This gives

$$\omega_{0,a} R_{0,a} + \omega_{0,b} R_{0,b} + \omega_{0,c} R_{0,c} + \omega_{a,b} R_{a,b} + \omega_{b,c} R_{b,c} + \omega_{a,c} R_{a,c} = \mathbf{0}.$$

Substituting from above, we have:

$$\omega_{0,a} R_{0,a} + \omega_{0,b} R_{0,b} + \omega_{0,c} R_{0,c} + \sum_{e \in E^*} -(\alpha_e + \beta_e + \gamma_e) R_e = \mathbf{0}.$$

This is a non-trivial dependence on $R_{G'}(\mathbf{p})$, contradicting our assumption. We conclude that one of $G_{a,b}$, $G_{b,c}$ and $G_{a,c}$ is independent at $\mathbf{p}$, as required.

We now check the static 2-rigidity. An edge 2-split adds one vertex and adds a net of two edges. This exchanges the count $|E| = 2n - 3$ on $G$ with the count $|E'| = 2(n + 1) - 3$ on $G'$. Since the edge 2-split (or the converse) preserves independence, we conclude that this takes a basis for $K_n$ to a basis for $K_{n+1}$.

For a graph $G = (V, E)$ with at least two vertices, a *Henneberg 2-construction* is an ordering of the vertices $\sigma(1), \sigma(2), \ldots, \sigma(|V|)$ and a sequence of graphs $G_2, \ldots,$ $G_{|V|}$ such that:
   (i)  $G_2$ is the single edge $\{\sigma(1), \sigma(2)\}$;
  (ii)  for $2 \le i < |V|$, $G_{i+1}$ is a 2-addition of vertex $\sigma(i + 1)$ to $G_i$
      or $G_{i+1}$ is an edge 2-split on $G_i$ which adds a vertex $\sigma(i + 1)$;
 (iii)  $G_{|V|}$ is $G$.

HENNEBERG'S THEOREM 2.2.3 [**He,TW2**]. *A graph $G$ with at least two vertices is a basis for $\mathcal{R}_2(n)$ if and only if $G$ has a Henneberg 2-construction.*

PROOF. Assume that $G$ has a Henneberg 2-construction:

$$G_2, \ldots, G_k, G_{k+1}, \ldots, G_{|V|} = G.$$

$G_2$ is a a single edge on two vertices – a basis for $K_2$ at any generic configuration. Assume that $G_k$ is a basis for $K_k(\mathbf{p})$ for some generic $\mathbf{p}$. $G_{k+1}$ is constructed from $G_k$ by either (i) vertex 2-addition or (ii) an edge 2-split. By the Vertex 2-Addition Theorem or the Edge 2-Split Theorem, these make $G_{k+1}(\mathbf{p}')$ generically 2-independent and generically 2-rigid.

Conversely, assume $G$ is a basis for $\mathcal{R}_2(|V|)$. We prove there is a Henneberg 2-construction by induction on the number of vertices. If $|V| = 2$, we are finished with $G_2 = G$.

Otherwise, assume that all basic graphs on $|V| - 1$ vertices have a Henneberg 2-construction and $G$ has $|V|$ vertices with $|V| > 2$. Since $|E| = 2|V| - 3$, we have $2|E| = 4|V| - 6$. Therefore there is a vertex of valence $\le 3$. If any vertex $i$ has valence $< 2$ then deleting $i$ leaves $G'$ with $|E'| \ge |E| - 1 = 2|V| - 4 = 2|V'| - 2$. We conclude that $G'$ is dependent, which contradicts the independence of $G$. Therefore, there is a vertex $\sigma(|V|) = 0$ of valence 2 or 3.

Assume $0$ has valence 2. $G$ is now a vertex 2-addition of the graph $G'$ obtained by deleting $0$. $G$ is basic on $|V| - 1$ vertices. This gives the last step of a Henneberg 2-construction, which turns the 2-construction of $G'$ (guaranteed by induction) into a Henneberg 2-construction of $G$.

Assume $0$ has valence 3. Then, by the Edge 2-Split Theorem, $G$ is an edge 2-split of some basic $G'$, on $|V| - 1$ vertices. Again, this gives the last step of a

Henneberg 2-construction which turns the guaranteed 2-construction of $G'$ into a Henneberg 2-construction of $G$.

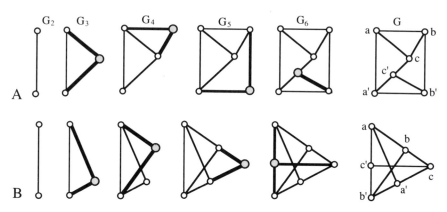

FIGURE. 2.7. *Henneberg 2-construction for two bases of the generic 2-rigidity matroid on* $K_6$.

REMARK 2.2.4. While we will concentrate on the generic configurations, we note that the geometry of special configurations of these graphs belongs to projective geometry [**CrW1,RW,WW1**]. For example:

A. For the graph of Figure 2.7A (and Figure 2.3A), the framework $G(\mathbf{p})$ is dependent if and only if, either one of the triangles $a, b, c$ or $a', b', c'$ is collinear or the three lines $aa'$, $bb'$, $cc'$ are concurrent. Equivalently, by Desargues' Theorem of projective geometry, the framework $G(\mathbf{p})$ is dependent if and only if the three points of intersection $ab \wedge a'b'$, $bc \wedge b'c'$, $ac \wedge a'c'$ are collinear [**WW1**].

B. For the bipartite graph $K_{3,3}$ of Figure 2.7B, the framework $G(\mathbf{p})$ is dependent if and only if the six vertices lie on a conic section. Equivalently, by Pascal's Theorem of projective geometry, the framework $G(\mathbf{p})$ is dependent if and only if the three points $ab \wedge a'b'$, $bc \wedge b'c'$, $ac' \wedge a'c$ are collinear [**WW1**].

LAMAN'S THEOREM 2.2.5 [**La**]. *A non-empty set of edges* $E'$ *on* $\{1, \ldots, n\}$ *is a basis for the generic 2-rigidity matroid on* $K_n$ *if and only if* $|E'| = 2n - 3$ *and for all proper subsets* $E''$, $|E''| \leq 2|V(E'')| - 3$.

PROOF. The Counting Lemma proves the counting condition is necessary for 2-independence.

We prove the sufficiency by induction on $n$. If $n = 2$ then $|E'| = 2 \times 2 - 3 = 1$ means we have a single edge, which is a generic basis. Assume the sufficiency is true for all $n \leq k$ and that $|E'| = 2(k + 1) - 3$. By the same argument used in the proof of Henneberg's Theorem, we have a vertex 0 of valence 2 or 3.

Assume 0 has valence 2. It is simple to check that $D$, formed by deleting this vertex and its edges, satisfies $|D| = 2k - 3$ and for all nonempty subsets $|D'| \leq 2|V(D')| - 3$, since these are subsets of $E'$. We conclude that $D$ is a basis for $K_k$ and, by vertex 2-addition, $E'$ is an independent set of rank $2(k + 1) - 3$ – a basis for $K_{k+1}$.

Assume 0 has valence 3, attached to $a, b, c$. Consider the sets $D_{a,b}, D_{b,c}, D_{a,c}$ formed by deleting 0, and adding the subscripted edge. (If the edge already lies in $E'$, then we work with a double edge.) By a simple count, $|D_e| = 2|V(D_e)| - 3$, for each pair $e$. If one of these sets satisfies $|D'| \leq 2|V(D')| - 3$, for all non-empty subsets $D'$, then this $D_e$ will satisfy the induction hypothesis. Therefore, this $D_e$ will be a basis for $K_k$. By the Edge 2-Split Theorem, $E'$ will be a basis for $K_{k+1}$.

We now seek a contradiction from the assumption that each of $D_{a,b}, D_{b,c}, D_{a,c}$ contains a (minimal) non-empty subset $D'_{a,b}, D'_{b,c}, D'_{a,c}$ with $|D'_e| \geq 2|V(D'_e)| - 2$, and $|D''_e| = 2|V(D''_e)| - 3$ for non-empty subsets. By the induction hypothesis, each of these is a *circuit* in the generic 2-rigidity matroid (removing any one edge leaves an independent set, but the whole set is dependent). (If we have doubled an edge $e$, this doubled edge will be the circuit – and we have the 'dependence' with opposite scalars on the two copies of the edge, in any configuration with distinct vertices.) Working at a generic configuration $\mathbf{p}$ for $k$ vertices, we have the three row dependencies, with $D$ formed by deleting 0 and its edges:

$$\alpha_{a,b} R_{a,b} = -\sum_{e \in D} \alpha_e R_e \quad \alpha_{a,b} \neq 0;$$

$$\beta_{b,c} R_{b,c} = -\sum_{e \in D} \beta_e R_e \quad \beta_{b,c} \neq 0;$$

$$\gamma_{a,c} R_{a,c} = -\sum_{e \in D} \gamma_e R_e \quad \gamma_{a,c} \neq 0.$$

As in the proof of the Edge 2-Split Theorem, adding in the 3-valent vertex 0 gives a non-trivial dependence on $E'$ – the required contradiction.

A simple observation on these counts shows that a circuit for the generic 2-rigidity matroid has $|E'| = 2|V(E')| - 2$ and $|E''| \leq 2|V(E'')| - 3$ for all proper subsets. This implies the following result.

2-RIGID CIRCUITS COROLLARY 2.2.6. *If $E$ is a circuit in the generic 2-rigidity matroid, then $E$ is generically 2-rigid.*

The Henneberg 2-constructions give inductive constructions for all bases of the generic 2-rigidity matroid. They can be easily adapted to construct either independent sets (add fewer edges in the construction) or generically 2-rigid sets (add extra edges in the construction). There are other inductive techniques which will reappear as results and conjectures for generic 3-rigidity [**TW2,Wh9**]. We give two of these results in visual form in Figures 2.8, 2.9.

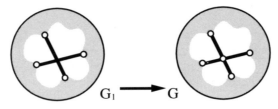

FIGURE. 2.8. *X-replacement - an inductive technique which replaces two edges by a 4-valent vertex and preserves generic 2-independence and 2-rigidity.*

We close this section with a conjecture about circuits in the generic 2-rigidity matroid [**GSS** Exercise 4.17].

CONNELLY'S CONJECTURE 2.2.7. *For the generic 2-rigidity matroid, every vertex 3-connected circuit has an inductive construction from $K_4$ using edge 2-splits.*

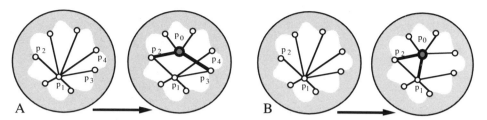

FIGURE. 2.9. *Two forms of vertex 2-splits – in which a given vertex 1 is split into two copies* 0, 1, *with the original edges at 1 partitioned between them (plus the heavy added or doubled lines). This inductive step preserves generic 2-independence and 2-rigidity.*

The results of §2 depend on a mixture of arguments based the counts $|E| \le 2|V(E)| - 3$ and arguments based on the form of the rigidity matrix. In Appendix §A, we will see that these counts alone define a matroid on the edges of a complete graph. (This analysis is based on standard matroid constructions from submodular functions, non-negative on non-empty sets.) A number of the results of this section also depend only on these counts. For example, the existence of a Henneberg 2-construction for each 'count basis' of $K_n$ could be proven directly from the counts. These counting techniques will break down for generic rigidity in 3-space.

The matrix-based techniques, such as vertex 2-addition, edge 2-splits and vertex 2-splits will generalize to higher dimensions, but will prove insufficient to characterize the generic 3-rigidity matroid.

## 3.   The Plane Rigidity Matroid: Kinematics

Since our matroid is defined in terms of the row rank of the rigidity matrix, we can also analyze the matroid through the column rank or kernels of this matrix. In engineering, these solutions are called 'infinitesimal motions' and their study is called infinitesimal or first-order kinematics.

**3.1. First-order rigidity in the plane.** A *first-order flex* or *infinitesimal motion* of a plane framework $G(\mathbf{p})$ is an assignment of *velocities* to the vertices $\mathbf{u} : V \to \mathbf{IR}^2$, such that for each edge $\{i, j\} \in E$ we have $(\mathbf{p}_i - \mathbf{p}_j) \cdot (\mathbf{u}_i - \mathbf{u}_j) = 0$ (Figure 3.1). Equivalently, a first-order motion is a solution to the system of linear equations: $R_G(\mathbf{p})\mathbf{x} = \mathbf{0}$. The equation can also be written as $(\mathbf{p}_i - \mathbf{p}_j) \cdot \mathbf{u}_i = (\mathbf{p}_i - \mathbf{p}_j) \cdot \mathbf{u}_j$, and visualized as: the two velocities $\mathbf{u}_i, \mathbf{u}_j$ have the same orthogonal projections onto the edge $\mathbf{p}_i - \mathbf{p}_j$ (Figure 3.1A).

A first-order flex $\mathbf{u}$ is a *trivial first-order flex* if it is a linear combination of the generating first-order flexes:

$$
\begin{array}{lllllllll}
T_x & = & [ & 1 & 0 & \dots & 1 & 0 & \dots & 1 & 0 & ] \\
T_y & = & [ & 0 & 1 & \dots & 0 & 1 & \dots & 0 & 1 & ] \\
T_r & = & [ & -x_1 & y_1 & \dots & -x_i & y_i & \dots & -x_{|V|} & y_{|V|} & ]
\end{array}
$$

In this interpretation, $\alpha T_x + \beta T_y$ is a translation with velocity $\mathbf{u}_i = (\alpha, \beta)$ at each vertex. Similarly, $\mathbf{u}_i = (\mathbf{p}_i)^\perp$ is the velocity of a counterclockwise rotation about the origin. The trivial first-order motions are the velocities of a general congruence of the configuration (Figure 3.1A,B).

A plane framework $G(\mathbf{p})$ is *first-order rigid* if every first-order flex is trivial (Figures 2.2, 2.3). Otherwise it is *first-order flexible* (Figure 3.1C,D). In §2.1 we checked that the trivial first-order flexes form a space of dimension 3 on at least two

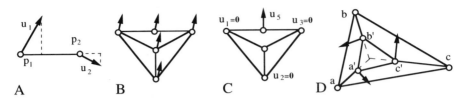

FIGURE. 3.1. *The arrows indicate the non-zero velocities of trivial first-order motions (A,B) and non-trivial motion (C,D ) of frameworks.*

distinct points, and dimension 2 (the translations) on one point. With the Static 2-Rigidity Theorem 2.1.4, this proves the following basic equivalence [**RW,Wh4**]:

2-RIGIDITY EQUIVALENCE 3.1.1. *For a plane framework $G(\mathbf{p})$ with at least two vertices, the following are equivalent:*
1. *$G(\mathbf{p})$ is first-order rigid;*
2. *$G(\mathbf{p})$ is statically 2-rigid;*
3. *the rigidity matrix $R_G(\mathbf{p})$ has rank $2|V| - 3$.*

COROLLARY 3.1.2. *For a framework $G(\mathbf{p})$, with the points of $\mathbf{p}$ in general position, a first-order motion is non-trivial if and only if for some pair of vertices $h, k$ (not an edge) $(\mathbf{p}_h - \mathbf{p}_k) \cdot (\mathbf{u}_h - \mathbf{u}_k) \neq 0$.*

PROOF. In §2.1, we checked that the generators for the trivial motions satisfy

$$(\mathbf{p}_h - \mathbf{p}_k) \cdot (\mathbf{u}_h - \mathbf{u}_k) = (\mathbf{p}_h - \mathbf{p}_k) \cdot \mathbf{u}_h + (\mathbf{p}_k - \mathbf{p}_h) \cdot \mathbf{u}_k = 0$$

for each pair $h, k$ (Figure 3.1 A). This same orthogonality now applies to the entire space of trivial first-order motions. Therefore, any first-order flex with $(\mathbf{p}_h - \mathbf{p}_k) \cdot (\mathbf{u}_h - \mathbf{u}_k) \neq 0$ is not trivial.

Conversely, if $(\mathbf{p}_h - \mathbf{p}_k) \cdot (\mathbf{u}_h - \mathbf{u}_k) = 0$ for each pair $h, k$, then $\mathbf{u}$ is a first-order flex of the complete framework $K_{|V|}(\mathbf{p})$. By the Static 2-Rigidity Theorem 2.1.4, $K_{|V|}(\mathbf{p})$ is statically (therefore first-order) 2-rigid and $\mathbf{u}$ must be trivial.

For any framework $G(\mathbf{p})$, the set of pairs $h, k$ for which $(\mathbf{p}_h - \mathbf{p}_k) \cdot (\mathbf{u}_h - \mathbf{u}_k) = 0$ for all first-order flexes will be $\langle E \rangle$, the closure of $E$ in the matroid $\mathcal{R}_2(K_V; \mathbf{p})$.

FIRST-ORDER FLEX TEST 3.1.3. *For any plane configuration $\mathbf{p}$ for the graph $K_n$, the following are equivalent:*
1. *the edge $\{h, k\}$ is not in the closure of the set $E$ in $\mathcal{R}_2(n; \mathbf{p})$;*
2. *every self-stress $\omega$ on $E \cup \{h, k\}$ is zero on $\{h, k\}$;*
3. *there is a first-order flex $\mathbf{u}$ on $G(\mathbf{p})$, such that $(\mathbf{p}_h - \mathbf{p}_k) \cdot (\mathbf{u}_h - \mathbf{u}_k) \neq 0$.*

PROOF. The equivalence of 1. and 2. is the definition of of the matroid closure. $2. \Rightarrow 3.$ If $\{h, k\}$ is independent, then adding the row $R_{h,k}$ to the rigidity matrix for $E$ must increase the rank by one or equivalently the nullity is reduced by one. Let $\mathbf{u}$ be one of the first-order flexes removed. Therefore

$$(\mathbf{p}_h - \mathbf{p}_k) \cdot \mathbf{u} = R_{h,k} \cdot \mathbf{u} \neq 0.$$

$3. \Rightarrow 2.$ We prove the contrapositive. If there is a self-stress $\omega$ on $E' = E \cup \{h, k\}$, then $\omega_{h,k} R_{h,k} = - \sum_{\{i,j\} \in E} \omega_{i,j} R_{i,j}$. Therefore, for any first-order flex $\mathbf{u}$ of $E$:

$$\omega_{h,k} (\mathbf{p}_h - \mathbf{p}_k) \cdot \mathbf{u} = \omega_{h,k} R_{h,k} \cdot \mathbf{u} = - \sum_{\{i,j\} \in E} \omega_{i,j} R_{i,j} \cdot \mathbf{u} = - \sum_{\{i,j\} \in E} 0 = 0.$$

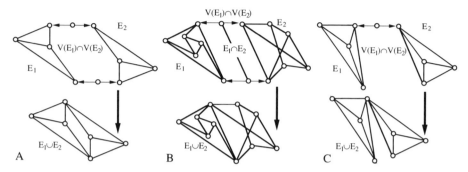

FIGURE. 3.2. *Gluing 2-rigid sets on two or more points gives a 2-rigid set (A), gluing independent sets on an 2-rigid set gives an independent set (B) and gluing rigid sets on a single point gives a flexible set (C).*

GENERIC PLANE GLUING LEMMA 3.1.4. *For two edge sets $E_1$, $E_2$,*

1. *if $E_1$ and $E_2$ are generically 2-rigid sets and $|V(E_1) \cap V(E_2)| \geq 2$, then the set $E_1 \cup E_2$ is generically 2-rigid (Figure 3.2A);*
2. *if $E_1$ and $E_2$ are generically 2-independent sets and the intersection graph $G = (V(E_1) \cap V(E_2), E_1 \cap E_2)$ is generically 2-rigid, then the set $E_1 \cup E_2$ is generically 2-independent (Figure 3.2B);*
3. *if $|V(E_1) \cap V(E_2)| < 2$, then the closure $\langle E_1 \cup E_2 \rangle$ in $\mathcal{R}_2(V(E_1) \cup V(E_2))$ is contained in $K_{V(E_1)} \cup K_{V(E_2)}$ (Figure 3.2C).*

PROOF. 1. Assume that $E_1$ and $E_2$ are 2-rigid sets at a generic point $\mathbf{p}$ and that $|V(E_1) \cap V(E_2)| \geq 2$. Assume $\mathbf{u}$ is a first-order flex on $G = (V(E_1 \cup E_2); E_1 \cup E_2)$. By assumption,

$$\mathbf{u}|_{V(E_1)} = \alpha_1 T_x + \beta_1 T_y + \gamma_1 T_r \quad \text{and} \quad \mathbf{u}|_{V(E_2)} = \alpha_2 T_x + \beta_2 T_y + \gamma_2 T_r.$$

However, since these agree on at least two shared vertices at distinct points, these coefficients $\alpha_i, \beta_i, \gamma_i$ are equal and $\mathbf{u}$ is this single combination – a trivial first-order flex. We conclude that $E_1 \cup E_2$ is generically 2-rigid.

2. Assume that $E_1$ and $E_2$ are generically 2-independent sets and that $G = (V(E_1) \cap V(E_2); E_1 \cap E_2)$ is generically 2-rigid. We prove, by contradiction, that there is no non-empty subset $D$ with $|D| \geq 2|V(D)| - 2$.

Assume there is such a subset $D$. Consider the sets $D_1 = D \cap E_1$ and $D_2 = D \cap E_2$. If one of these is empty, then $D$ is contained in one side (say $E_1$) and $|D| \leq 2|V(D)| - 3$ which is a contradiction. If $D_1$ and $D_2$ are disjoint then:

$$|D| = |D \cap E_1| + |D \cap E_2| \leq 2|V(D_1)| - 3 + 2|V(D_2)| - 3 \leq 2|V(D)| - 4 < 2|V| - 3.$$

This is also a contradiction.

Therefore $D_{12} = D_1 \cap D_2 \subseteq E_1 \cap E_2$ is nonempty and $E_1 \cap E_2$ is generically 2-independent and 2-rigid on $V(E_1) \cap V(E_2)$, with at least two vertices. We conclude that $|E_1 \cap E_2| = 2|V(E_1) \cap V(E_2)| - 3$. With this property in mind, we extend the nonempty $D_{12}$ to $E_1 \cap E_2$ which may add vertices $V'$ to $V(D)$ and edges $E'$ to $D$. Since $|D_{12}| \leq 2|V(D_{12})| - 3 \leq 2|V(D) \cap V(E_1 \cap E_2)| - 3$, and

$$|D_{12}| + |E'| = |E_1 \cap E_2| = 2|V(E_1 \cup E_2| - 3 = 2|V(D) \cap V(E_1 \cap E_2)| - 3 + 2|V'|,$$

the net changes satisfy $E' \geq 2|V'|$. This addition to $D$ creates $C$ with

$$|C| = |D| + |E'| \geq 2|V(D)| - 2 + 2|V'| = 2|V(C)| - 2.$$

We find our contradiction in $C$, using $C_1 = C \cap E_1$ and $C_2 = C \cap E_2$, which are independent subsets of $E_1$ and $E_2$ respectively. Note that $C_1 \cap C_2 = E_1 \cap E_2$ so $|C_1 \cap C_2| = 2|V(C_1) \cap V(C_2)| - 3$. We now have

$$
\begin{aligned}
|C| &= |C_1| + |C_2| - |C_1 \cap C_2| \\
&\leq 2|V(C_1)| - 3 + 2|V(C_2)| - 3 - [2|V(C_1) \cap V(C_2)| - 3] \\
&= 2|V(C)| - 3.
\end{aligned}
$$

This is the desired contradiction.

3. Assume $|V(E_1) \cap V(E_2)| < 2$ and take a generic plane configuration $\mathbf{p}$. Let $\mathbf{r}$ represent the rotation about the vertex $V(E_1) \cap V(E_2)$ (or a new general position point, if $V(E_1) \cap V(E_2) = \emptyset$). Consider the first-order flex $\mathbf{u}$ which assigns velocity $\mathbf{0}$ to points in $V(E_1)$ and $\mathbf{r}(j)$ to points in $V(E_2)$. For any $\{h, j\} \notin K_{V(E_1)} \cup K_{V(E_2)}$, we have:

$$
(\mathbf{p}_h - \mathbf{p}_j) \cdot (\mathbf{u}_h - \mathbf{u}_j) = (\mathbf{p}_h - \mathbf{p}_j) \cdot \mathbf{0} - (\mathbf{p}_h - \mathbf{p}_j) \cdot \mathbf{r}(j) = 0 + (\mathbf{p}_h - \mathbf{p}_j) \cdot \mathbf{r}(j) \neq 0
$$

where $(\mathbf{p}_h - \mathbf{p}_j) \cdot \mathbf{r}(j) \neq 0$ because the center of $\mathbf{r}$ is not collinear with any other two points by our assumption of a generic configuration. By the First-Order Flex Test 3.1.3, $\{h, j\}$ is not in $\langle E_1 \cup E_2 \rangle$. We conclude that $\langle E_1 \cup E_2 \rangle \subseteq K_{V(E_1)} \cup K_{V(E_2)}$.

REMARK 3.1.5. Properties 1 and 3, like property 2, can be proven directly from the counts, rather than by the 'matrix related' kinematic arguments used here. They can also be proven at any general position configuration $\mathbf{p}$. For any matroid on the edges of a complete graph, Properties 1 and 3 are the defining properties of an *abstract 2-rigidity matroid* [**GSS**] (see also §9.3). A number of properties of rigidity matroids at general position plane configurations, such as vertex 2-addition and the necessity of the counting properties for independent sets, can be proven from these properties and the usual properties of closure, rank etc. in a matroid [**GSS**, pages 86 -ff]. We recommend this reference for an extensive, matroidal analysis of these rigidity-like matroids on graphs. We will give some new related conjectures in Part II.

**3.2. Connections to finite rigidity.** Alongside static rigidity, with its roots in civil engineering, first-order rigidity has roots in mechanical engineering and in the study of linkages. We briefly describe this connection to indicate another source for this matroid. Published sources for this include [**AR,CoW,Gl,RW**]. This section will *not* give any additional matroidal results.

Given a plane framework $G(\mathbf{p})$, consider other 'equivalent' configurations $\mathbf{q}$ for which the edges of $G(\mathbf{q})$ have the same length as $G(\mathbf{p})$. These are captured by the *rigidity map*: $f_G : \mathbb{R}^{2|V|} \to \mathbb{R}^E$, with:

$$
f_G(\mathbf{p}_1, \ldots, \mathbf{p}_{|V|}) = (\ldots, |\mathbf{p}_i - \mathbf{p}_j|, \ldots).
$$

The inverse image $B(G, \mathbf{p}) = f_G^{-1}(f_G(\mathbf{p}))$ is the set of all *bar equivalent* frameworks $G(\mathbf{q})$ with $|\mathbf{p}_i - \mathbf{p}_j| = |\mathbf{q}_i - \mathbf{q}_j|$ for all bars $\{i, j\} \in E$. Of course, if the configuration $\mathbf{q}$ is *congruent to* $\mathbf{p}$, that is, there is an isometry $T$ of $\mathbb{R}^2$ with $T(\mathbf{p}_i) = \mathbf{q}_i$ for all $i \in V$, then $G(\mathbf{q})$ is bar equivalent to $G(\mathbf{q})$.

An *analytic flex* of $G(\mathbf{p})$ is an analytic function $\mathbf{p}(t) : [0, 1) \to B(G, \mathbf{p})$ such that $\mathbf{p} = \mathbf{p}(0)$. A plane framework $G(\mathbf{p})$ is *flexible* if there is a *non-trivial* analytic flex $\mathbf{p}(t)$ of $\mathbf{p}$ with $\mathbf{p}(t)$ not congruent to $\mathbf{p}$ for all $t > 0$ (Figure 3.3B,C). Otherwise all flexes are *trivial* and the framework is *rigid*.

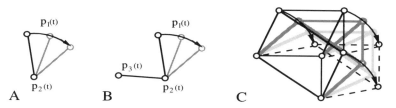

FIGURE. 3.3. *Shaded versions of a trivial analytic flex (A) and non-trivial flexes (B,C).*

ALTERNATE RIGIDITY DEFINITIONS 3.2.1 [Gl]. *For a plane framework $G(\mathbf{p})$ the following conditions are equivalent:*
  1. *the framework $G(\mathbf{p})$ is rigid;*
  2. *for every continuous path $\mathbf{p}(t) \in \mathbb{R}^{2|V|}$, $0 \le t < 1$ and $\mathbf{p}(0) = \mathbf{p}$, such that $G(\mathbf{p}(t))$ is bar equivalent to $G(\mathbf{p})$ for all $t$, $\mathbf{p}(t)$ is congruent to $\mathbf{p}$ for all $t$;*
  3. *there is an $\varepsilon > 0$ such that, if $G(\mathbf{p})$ and $G(\mathbf{q})$ are bar equivalent and $|\mathbf{p}-\mathbf{q}| < \varepsilon$ then $\mathbf{p}$ is congruent to $\mathbf{q}$.*

The rigidity matrix $R_G(\mathbf{p})$ is the Jacobian of the rigidity map $f_G$, at $\mathbf{p}$, which indicates the connection between rigidity and first-order rigidity. Equivalently, the derivative of an analytic path $\mathbf{p}(t)$ is a first-order flex $\mathbf{p}'$:

$$D_t\big[(\mathbf{p}_i(t) - \mathbf{p}_j(t))^2 = c_{ij}\big]|_{t=0} \quad \Rightarrow \quad 2(\mathbf{p}_j - \mathbf{p}_i) \cdot (\mathbf{p}'_j - \mathbf{p}'_i) = 0.$$

If $\mathbf{p}(t)$ is non-trivial, its derivative is usually a non-trivial first-order flex. (If $\mathbf{p}'$ is trivial, the second derivative will also be a first-order flex. Continue this process until a non-trivial first-order flex is found [Co2].) This process gives one proof of:

FIRST-ORDER RIGID TO RIGID THEOREM 3.2.2. *If a bar framework $G(\mathbf{p})$ is first-order rigid then $G(\mathbf{p})$ is rigid.*

The converse implication from rigidity to first-order rigidity also holds for generic configurations.

GENERIC 2-RIGIDITY THEOREM 3.2.3. *For a graph $G$ the following are equivalent:*
  1. *$G$ is generically 2-rigid;*
  2. *for all configurations $\mathbf{q}$ in some non-empty open set $U$ in $\mathbb{R}^{2|V|}$, the frameworks $G(\mathbf{q})$ are rigid;*
  3. *for all $\mathbf{q}$ in an open dense subset of configurations in $\mathbb{R}^{2|V|}$, $G(\mathbf{q})$ is first-order rigid (and rigid);*
  4. *$G(\mathbf{p})$ is first-order rigid for some configuration $\mathbf{p}$ in the plane.*
  5. *$G(\mathbf{p})$ is rigid for some generic configuration $\mathbf{p}$ in the plane.*

REMARK 3.2.4. Generic 2-rigidity, and therefore rigidity at a generic plane configuration $\mathbf{p}$, directly defines a matroid by the condition:
  *A set of edges $E$ is a basis for $K_{V(E)}$ if, and only if, $(V(E), E)(\mathbf{p})$ is a rigid framework, and is minimal among such frameworks.*
The comparable definition for a special position $\mathbf{p}$ may not produce a matroid. Consider the configurations in Figure 3.4A,B. Both of these are minimal rigid frameworks, but they have different sizes. They cannot be bases of the same matroid.

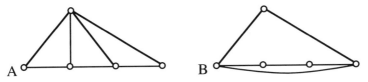

FIGURE. 3.4. *Two minimal rigid plane frameworks of different sizes on the same non-generic plane configuration* **p**.

**3.3. Counts and trees for generic 2-rigidity.** In Remark 2.1.7 we saw that the rigidity matroid on a collinear configuration **p**, or equivalently, rigidity on the line (1-rigidity), is the cycle matroid of the graph, with independence characterized by

(i) $|E'| \leq |V(E')| - 1$  *for all non-empty subsets* $E'$;

(ii) $|E|$ *is a forest.*

There are important traces of this pattern in the 2-rigidity matroid count:

$$|E| = 2|V| - 3 = 2(\ |V| - 1\ )\ - 1.$$

This numerical break-down of the count corresponds to a matroidal construction:

*the generic 2-rigidity matroid is the matroid union of two copies of the graphic matroid on G, followed by a Dilworth truncation* (see [**LY**,**Wh7**] and §A).

We will not prove this result here. However, the following example brings out the way in which 'trees and forests' arise in the rigidity matrix of a graph.

EXAMPLE 3.3.1. Consider the rigidity matrix for a triangle at **p**:

$$
\begin{array}{c}
\phantom{\{1,2\}} \\
\{1,2\} \\
\{2,3\} \\
\{1,3\}
\end{array}
\begin{array}{cccccc}
1_x & 1_y & 2_x & 2_y & 3_x & 3_y \\
\left(\begin{array}{cccccc}
(x_1 - x_2) & (y_1 - y_2) & (x_2 - x_1) & (y_2 - y_1) & 0 & 0 \\
0 & 0 & (x_2 - x_3) & (y_2 - y_3) & (x_3 - x_2) & (y_3 - y_2) \\
(x_1 - x_3) & (y_1 - y_3) & 0 & 0 & (x_3 - x_1) & (y_3 - y_1)
\end{array}\right)
\end{array}
$$

We permute the columns, placing first columns of each vertex together, then second columns together:

$$
\begin{array}{c}
\{1,2\} \\
\\
\{2,3\} \\
\\
\{1,3\}
\end{array}
\begin{array}{cccc}
1_x & 2_x & 3_x \\
\left(\begin{array}{ccc}
(x_1 - x_2) & (x_2 - x_1) & 0 \\
\\
0 & (x_2 - x_3) & (x_3 - x_2) \\
\\
(x_1 - x_3) & 0 & (x_3 - x_1)
\end{array}\right)
\end{array}
\begin{array}{ccc}
1_y & 2_y & 3_y \\
\left(\begin{array}{ccc}
(y_1 - y_2) & (y_2 - y_1) & 0 \\
\\
0 & (y_2 - y_3) & (y_3 - y_2) \\
\\
(y_1 - y_3) & 0 & (y_3 - y_1)
\end{array}\right)
\end{array}
$$

Dividing each non-zero row of a block by a scalar, we have two copies of the matrix for the cycle matroid of the graph:

$$
\begin{array}{c}
\{1,2\} \\
\\
\{2,3\} \\
\\
\{1,3\}
\end{array}
\begin{array}{c}
(x_1 - x_2) \\
\\
(x_2 - x_3) \\
\\
(x_1 - x_3)
\end{array}
\begin{array}{ccc}
1_x & 2_x & 3_x \\
\left(\begin{array}{ccc}
1 & -1 & 0 \\
\\
0 & 1 & -1 \\
\\
1 & 0 & -1
\end{array}\right)
\end{array}
\begin{array}{c}
(y_1 - y_2) \\
\\
(y_2 - y_3) \\
\\
(y_1 - y_3)
\end{array}
\begin{array}{ccc}
1_y & 2_y & 3_y \\
\left(\begin{array}{ccc}
1 & -1 & 0 \\
\\
0 & 1 & -1 \\
\\
1 & 0 & -1
\end{array}\right)
\end{array}
$$

To check whether a general graph with $|E| = 2|V| - 3$ is generically 2-rigid (or a basis of $\mathcal{R}_2(V)$), we can delete three columns from the rigidity matrix (at least one from each of the blocks as above), and take a determinant. For such a determinant to be non-zero, there must be two minors on disjoint edge sets $E_x$ for $x$ and $E_y$ for $y$, each with non-zero determinant. Since these blocks are copies of the graphic matroid on $G$ (with $|V| - 1$ columns for one side, say $x$, and $|V| - 2$ columns for the other) these minors will be non-zero only if we have three edge-disjoint trees: $T_1$ from the $x$-side (with $|V| - 1$ rows), and $T_2, T_3$ from the $y$-side (with $|V| - 2$ rows). The deleted 'columns' will also be connected to edges whose rows have only one non-zero entry left in a block.

For this decomposition, any vertex will touch exactly two of the trees ($T_1$ and one of $T_2$ or $T_3$). In addition, no two non-empty subtrees have the same span, because of our counts: a subset spanned by two trees has $|E'| = |T_1'| + |T_2'| = 2(|V| - 1) > 2|V| - 3$. These three properties define a $3\,Tree2$ partition of the edges (see Figure 3.5A) [**Cr5,Ta5**]: (i) three trees; (ii) exactly two at each vertex; and (iii) no two non-empty subtrees spanning the same set of vertices. The following theorem records (without proof) standard connections between trees and bases for the matroid $\mathcal{R}_2(n)$.

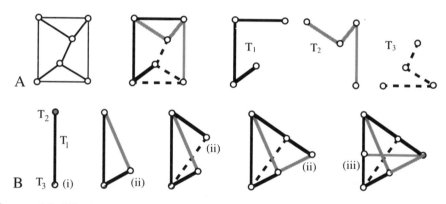

FIGURE. 3.5. $3\,Tree2$ partitions for two bases of the generic 2-rigidity matroid on 6 vertices.

GENERIC 2-BASIS THEOREM 3.3.2. *An edge set $E$ is a basis of the generic 2-rigidity matroid on $K_{V(E)}$ if and only if:*
1. $|E| = 2|V| - 3$ *and for every nonempty subset $E'$, $|E'| \leq 2|V(E')| - 3$ (Laman's Theorem);*
2. $G = (V(E), E)$ *has a Henneberg 2-construction (Henneberg's Theorem);*
3. $E$ *has a proper $3\,Tree2$ partition (Crapo's Theorem [**Cr5**]);*
4. *for each $\{i, j\} \in E$, the multigraph obtained by doubling the edge $\{i, j\}$ is the union of two spanning trees (Recski's Theorem [**Re2**]).*

REMARK 3.3.3. Each of these combinatorial characterizations for bases has an associated algorithm for verifying whether a graph is a basis for the generic 2-rigidity matroid on $K_V$:
1. Counts: this can be checked by an $O(|V|^2)$ algorithm based on bipartite matchings on an associated graph [**Im,Su2,3**].
2. 2-construction: existence of a 2-construction can be checked by an $O(2^{|V|})$ algorithm, but a proposed 2-construction can be verified in $O(|V|)$ time.
3. 3Tree2 covering: existence is checked by an $O(|V|^2)$ matroid algorithm [**Cr5**].

4. Double tree partition: all required double-tree partitions can be found by a matroidal algorithm of order $O(|V|^3)$ [**Re2**].

What is the complexity of moving between tree coverings and Henneberg 2-constructions? It is a simple (linear time) process to create a 3Tree2 partition of the edges of a basis directly from any Henneberg 2-construction (Figure 3.5B):

(i)   for a single edge, the edge is one tree and the two vertices are the second and third trees;

(ii)  for a 2-valent vertex, choose one tree covering each of the attachments (there must be two distinct choices) and place the new edge in the chosen tree;

(iii) for a 3-valent vertex replacing an edge, we add two edges in the same tree as the removed edge (preserving the counts at those ends) and add the third edge, in a different tree but extending some tree at the third vertex.

Notice that this construction allows us to choose one tree as a spanning tree. Unfortunately,we believe there is no direct (polynomial time) extraction of a Henneberg 2-construction from a 3Tree2 decomposition. (There is the exponential process, through the Generic 2-Basis Theorem 3.3.2: for each step removing a 3-valent vertex, we test all three possible insertions of an edge.) Henneberg 2-constructions are harder to find, easier to verify and easier to use than 3Tree2 decompositions.

A final thread for the generic 2-rigidity matroid is connectivity. It is clear that any graph which is 2-rigid is at least vertex 2-connected. If we remove one vertex and the attached edges, the remaining graph is connected (recall Figure 3.2C). On the other hand, the graph in Figure 3.6 is 5-connected but not generically 2-rigid. This failure is verified by a formula for the rank of the matroid adapted from submodular functions.

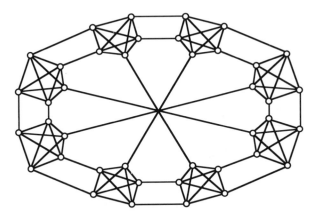

FIGURE. 3.6. *A 5-connected graph which is not generically 2-rigid.*

THEOREM 3.3.4 [**GSS**, Theorem 4.4.3]. *The rank of an edge set $E$ in the generic 2-rigidity matroid is:*

$$r(E) = \min\left\{ \sum_{i=1}^{k} \left(2|V(E_i)| - 3\right) \right\}$$

*where the minimum is taken over all partitions $\{E_i\}_{i=1}^{k}$ of $E$.*

The minimum occurs for blocks which are maximal generically 2-rigid components of the graph. In particular, if we partition the graph of Figure 3.6 into 8 blocks for the $K_5$ subgraphs and leave all other edges in separate blocks, we have

$$r(E) = 8 \times 7 + 20 = 76 < 2 \times 40 - 3 = 2|V| - 3,$$

which verifies that this is not 2-rigid. The following positive result is best possible.

SUFFICIENT CONNECTIVITY 3.3.5 [**LY**]. *If a graph $G$ is vertex 6-connected then $G$ is generically 2-rigid.*

## 4. Parallel Drawings in the Plane

We now introduce a second geometric form for the matroid of §2 and §3. For a graph $G$ at a plane configuration **p** we consider an alternate constraint matrix based on maintaining the directions of the edges (§4.1), then show this is isomorphic to the plane rigidity matroid.

This matroid for a 'direction graph' has an immediate generalization to a matroid on the vertex-face incidences on hypergraphs realized as point and line configurations in the plane (§4.2). This form, in turn, has a simple generalization to parallel scenes of point and hyperplane configurations in arbitrary dimensions (§8). Of all the matroids we will describe in higher dimensions and on larger hypergraphs, these parallel drawing matroids (and their projective duals, the polyhedral picture matroids) have the cleanest theory, with analogs of all the geometric and combinatorial results for 2-rigidity.

**4.1. Basic concepts of parallel designs.** We begin again with a graph $G$ and a plane configuration **p** for the vertices. For each edge, the new constraint on configurations **q** is 'this edge must retain its direction' rather than 'this edge must retain its length'. For a new configuration **q**, the constraint for an edge $\{i, j\}$ is :

$$(\mathbf{p}_i - \mathbf{p}_j)^\perp \cdot (\mathbf{q}_i - \mathbf{q}_j) = 0.$$

The solutions of this homogeneous linear system are the *parallel designs* $G(\mathbf{q})$ of the original *plane design* $G(\mathbf{p})$.

A parallel design $G(\mathbf{q})$ for $G(\mathbf{p})$ is *trivial* if **q** is a translation or dilation of **p** (Figure 4.1 A). Otherwise, the parallel design is non-trivial (Figure 4.1B).

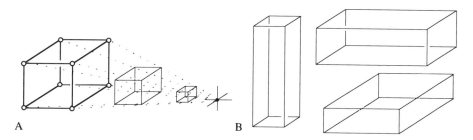

FIGURE. 4.1. *Some trivial (A) and non-trivial (B) parallel designs for a plane design.*

EXAMPLE 4.1.1. The constraints for parallel designs create an analog to the rigidity matrix. For the design in Figure 4.2A, the *parallel design matrix* is $P(G, \mathbf{p})$:

|            | $a$ | $b$ | $c$ | $d$ | $e$ | $f$ |
|------------|-----|-----|-----|-----|-----|-----|
| $\{a,b\}$  | $(\mathbf{a}-\mathbf{b})^\perp$ | $(\mathbf{b}-\mathbf{a})^\perp$ | $\mathbf{0}$ | $\mathbf{0}$ | $\mathbf{0}$ | $\mathbf{0}$ |
| $\{a,c\}$  | $(\mathbf{a}-\mathbf{c})^\perp$ | $\mathbf{0}$ | $(\mathbf{c}-\mathbf{a})^\perp$ | $\mathbf{0}$ | $\mathbf{0}$ | $\mathbf{0}$ |
| $\{a,d\}$  | $(\mathbf{a}-\mathbf{d})^\perp$ | $\mathbf{0}$ | $\mathbf{0}$ | $(\mathbf{d}-\mathbf{a})^\perp$ | $\mathbf{0}$ | $\mathbf{0}$ |
| $\{b,c\}$  | $\mathbf{0}$ | $(\mathbf{b}-\mathbf{c})^\perp$ | $(\mathbf{c}-\mathbf{b})^\perp$ | $\mathbf{0}$ | $\mathbf{0}$ | $\mathbf{0}$ |
| $\{c,f\}$  | $\mathbf{0}$ | $\mathbf{0}$ | $(\mathbf{c}-\mathbf{f})^\perp$ | $\mathbf{0}$ | $\mathbf{0}$ | $(\mathbf{f}-\mathbf{c})^\perp$ |
| $\{d,e\}$  | $\mathbf{0}$ | $\mathbf{0}$ | $\mathbf{0}$ | $(\mathbf{d}-\mathbf{e})^\perp$ | $(\mathbf{e}-\mathbf{d})^\perp$ | $\mathbf{0}$ |
| $\{d,f\}$  | $\mathbf{0}$ | $\mathbf{0}$ | $\mathbf{0}$ | $(\mathbf{d}-\mathbf{f})^\perp$ | $\mathbf{0}$ | $(\mathbf{f}-\mathbf{d})^\perp$ |
| $\{e,f\}$  | $\mathbf{0}$ | $\mathbf{0}$ | $\mathbf{0}$ | $\mathbf{0}$ | $(\mathbf{e}-\mathbf{f})^\perp$ | $(\mathbf{f}-\mathbf{e})^\perp$ |

| | $a$ | $b$ | $c$ | $d$ | $e$ | $f$ |
|------------|-----|-----|-----|-----|-----|-----|
| $T_\mathbf{t}$ | $\mathbf{a}+\mathbf{t}$ | $\mathbf{b}+\mathbf{t}$ | $\mathbf{c}+\mathbf{t}$ | $\mathbf{d}+\mathbf{t}$ | $\mathbf{e}+\mathbf{t}$ | $\mathbf{f}+\mathbf{t}$ |
| $T_D$ | $\frac{\mathbf{a}}{2}$ | $\frac{\mathbf{b}}{2}$ | $\frac{\mathbf{c}}{2}$ | $\frac{\mathbf{d}}{2}$ | $\frac{\mathbf{e}}{2}$ | $\frac{\mathbf{f}}{2}$ |
| $\mathbf{q}$ | $\mathbf{0}$ | $\mathbf{0}$ | $\mathbf{0}$ | $\frac{\mathbf{x}+\mathbf{d}}{2}$ | $\frac{\mathbf{x}+\mathbf{e}}{2}$ | $\frac{\mathbf{x}+\mathbf{f}}{2}$ |

The lower box gives a translation $T_\mathbf{t}$, a dilation $T_D$ towards the origin (Figure 4.2A), and a non-trivial parallel design $\mathbf{q}$, where $\mathbf{x}$ is the point of intersection of $ad, cf$ (Figure 4.2B). For most configurations (Figure 4.2B), this parallel drawing would be blocked by the addition of an edge $\{b,e\}$. However for the special position of Figure 4.2C, this parallel design will work on the extended design.

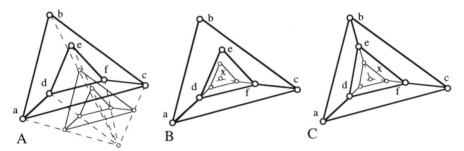

FIGURE. 4.2. *Trivial (A) and non-trivial (B) parallel designs for a plane design and a special position in which the non-trivial parallel design also exists for the extended object (C).*

We have defined a parallel design matrix $P(G, \mathbf{p})$ and a corresponding matroid. The resemblance to the rigidity matroid is striking – just a small twist in the entries, from $\mathbf{p}_i - \mathbf{p}_j$ to $(\mathbf{p}_i - \mathbf{p}_j)^\perp$.

LEMMA 4.1.2. *For a graph $G$ and a plane configuration $\mathbf{p}$, an assignment $\omega$ of scalars to the edges is a row dependence of the rigidity matrix if and only if $\omega$ is a row dependence of the parallel design matrix.*

PROOF. Compare the conditions for a row dependence of the rigidity matrix and the parallel design matrix for $G(\mathbf{p})$. For each vertex $i$:

$$\sum_{j\mid\{i,j\}\in E} \omega_{i,j}(\mathbf{p}_i - \mathbf{p}_j) = \mathbf{0} \qquad \Leftrightarrow \qquad \sum_{j\mid\{i,j\}\in E} \omega_{i,j}(\mathbf{p}_i - \mathbf{p}_j)^\perp = \mathbf{0}^\perp = \mathbf{0}$$

This equivalence of conditions gives the desired equivalence of dependencies.

COROLLARY 4.1.3. *For any graph $G$ and plane configuration $\mathbf{p}$, the 2-rigidity matroid and the parallel 2-design matroid are the same.*

For kinematics, the connection is almost as easy:

$$(\mathbf{p}_i - \mathbf{p}_j) \cdot \mathbf{u}_i + (\mathbf{p}_j - \mathbf{p}_i) \cdot \mathbf{u}_j = 0$$
$$\Leftrightarrow \quad (\mathbf{p}_i - \mathbf{p}_j)^\perp \cdot \mathbf{u}_i{}^\perp + (\mathbf{p}_j - \mathbf{p}_i)^\perp \cdot \mathbf{u}_j{}^\perp = 0$$
$$\Leftrightarrow \quad (\mathbf{p}_i - \mathbf{p}_j)^\perp \cdot \mathbf{q}_i + (\mathbf{p}_j - \mathbf{p}_i)^\perp \cdot \mathbf{q}_j = 0$$

Since $\mathbf{p}$ is itself a (trivial) solution to the system, we can replace $(\mathbf{u}_i)^\perp$ by $\mathbf{q} = (\mathbf{u}_i)^\perp + \mathbf{p}_i$ as the new parallel design. Visually in Figure 4.3, this means $(\mathbf{u}_i)^\perp$ is the change in the configurations: $\mathbf{q}_i - \mathbf{p}_i$. In this translation,
   1. the trivial first-order motions correspond to trivial parallel designs;
   2. the zero first-order motion corresponds to the parallel design $\mathbf{p}$;
   3. a translation by $\mathbf{t}$ corresponds to a translation by $\mathbf{t}^\perp$;
   4. a rotation about the origin corresponds to a dilation towards the origin;
   5. a non-trivial first-order motion corresponds to a non-trivial parallel design.
This correspondence between first-order flexes and parallel designs has its roots in drafting techniques during the last century. Today, we find these parallel drawings are also simpler to construct and detect with dynamic geometry programs, such as The Geometer's Sketchpad or Cabri, than first-order motions.

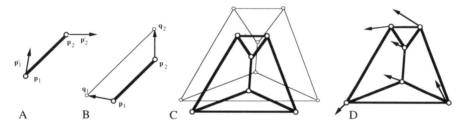

FIGURE. 4.3. *Turning the velocities of a first-order motion of a framework by 90° gives a parallel drawing (A,B) (D,C).*

THEOREM 4.1.4. *A plane framework $G(\mathbf{p})$ has a non-trivial first-order flex if and only if the configuration $G(\mathbf{p})$ has a non-trivial parallel design $G(\mathbf{q})$.*

Because of these correspondences, all the combinatorial and geometric results for plane first-order rigidity translate to plane parallel designs.

REMARK 4.1.5. If we consider an analytic path $\mathbf{p}(t)$ of parallel designs, and take derivatives at time $t = 0$, we have $(\mathbf{p}_i - \mathbf{p}_j)^\perp \cdot (\mathbf{p}_i'(0) - \mathbf{p}_j'(0)) = 0$. These are the equations we have given. Conversely, given any parallel design $\mathbf{q}$, we can take the affine combinations $\mathbf{p}(t) = (1 - t)\mathbf{p} + t\mathbf{q}$ as an analytic path of parallel designs. If $\mathbf{q}$ is non-trivial, then $\mathbf{p}(t)$ is a non-trivial drawing of $\mathbf{p}$ for all $t > 0$. Here there is no distinction between first-order and full 'motions'.

### 4.2. Parallel 2-scenes

It is a simple matter to generalize the process of parallel drawings from the plane designs in which each edge has only two vertices, to structures of points and longer lines with fixed directions. We introduce a general vocabulary which will extend easily to all dimensions. There are certain arbitrary conventions for writing the equations of lines (and planes in higher dimensions), because we are not using the underlying affine or projective coordinates.

We replace the abstract structure of a graph with a *polyhedral incidence structure* $S = (V, F; I)$: an abstract set of *vertices* $V$, an abstract set of *faces* $F$ and a set of *incidences* $I \subset V \times F$. The incidence structure can also be viewed as a bipartite *incidence graph* with two set of vertices $V, F$ and the incidences $I$ as edges.

We replace the configuration of points for the vertices of a graph with a *2-scene* for an incidence structure $S = (V, F; I)$: a pair of location maps, $\mathbf{p} : V \to \mathbb{R}^2$, $\mathbf{p}_i = (x_i, y_i)$ and $\mathbf{P} : F \to \mathbb{R}^3$, $\mathbf{P}^j = (A^j, 1, D^j)$, such that, for each incidence $(i, j) \in I$: $A^j x_i + y_i + D^j = 0$. Notice that the normal to the face $j$ is now $\mathbf{n}^j = (A^j, 1)$. As a convention, we assume that no face is 'vertical' – parallel to the vector $(0, 1)$. Up to a rotation of the original drawing, this will be valid.

A *parallel 2-scene* to $S(\mathbf{p}, \mathbf{P})$ is a 2-scene $S(\mathbf{q}, \mathbf{Q})$ such that for each face $j$, the normals are equal: that is, the $(P_1^j, 1) = (Q_1^j, 1)$ (Figure 4.4B). A *non-trivial parallel 2-scene* for $S(\mathbf{p}, \mathbf{P})$ is a parallel 2-scene $S(\mathbf{q}, \mathbf{Q})$, such that the point configuration $\mathbf{q}$ is not a translation or dilation of the configuration $\mathbf{p}$ (Figure 4.4B).

Instead of giving a 2-scene and asking about parallel scenes with the same normals, we can begin directly with an assignment $\mathbf{n}$ of *normals* for the faces: a 2-vector $\mathbf{n}^j = (A^j, 1)$ to each face $j \in F$. A 2-scene $S(\mathbf{p}, \mathbf{P})$ *realizes the normals* $\mathbf{n}$ if for each face $j \in F$ and vertex $i$, with $\mathbf{P}^j = (A^j, 1, D^j) = (\mathbf{n}^j, D^j)$

$$\mathbf{n}^j \cdot (x_i, y_i) + D^j = A^j x_i + y_i + D^j = 0.$$

Given the normal $\mathbf{n}^j$, this is a homogeneous linear equation in the unknowns $x_i, y_i, D^j$. The polyhedral incidence structure and the given directions create a linear system of $|I|$ equations in $|F| + 2|V|$ variables. This system is recorded in the $|I|$-by-$(|F| + 2|V|)$ *parallel 2-scene matrix* for plane normals $\mathbf{n}$, where the variables are ordered: $[\dots, D^j, \dots ; \dots, x_i, y_i, \dots]$.

EXAMPLE 4.2.1. For the configuration in Figure 4.4A, the parallel 2-scene matrix $M(S, \mathbf{n})$ is:

|          | $a$ | $b$ | $c$ | $d$ | $1$   |   | $2$   |   | $3$   |   | $4$   |   | $5$   |   | $6$   |   |
|----------|-----|-----|-----|-----|-------|---|-------|---|-------|---|-------|---|-------|---|-------|---|
| $(a,2)$  | 1 | 0 | 0 | 0 | 0 | 0 | $A^a$ | 1 | 0 | 0 | 0 | 0 | 0 | 0 | 0 | 0 |
| $(a,3)$  | 1 | 0 | 0 | 0 | 0 | 0 | 0 | 0 | $A^a$ | 1 | 0 | 0 | 0 | 0 | 0 | 0 |
| $(a,4)$  | 1 | 0 | 0 | 0 | 0 | 0 | 0 | 0 | 0 | 0 | $A^a$ | 1 | 0 | 0 | 0 | 0 |
| $(b,1)$  | 0 | 1 | 0 | 0 | $A^b$ | 1 | 0 | 0 | 0 | 0 | 0 | 0 | 0 | 0 | 0 | 0 |
| $(b,3)$  | 0 | 1 | 0 | 0 | 0 | 0 | 0 | 0 | $A^b$ | 1 | 0 | 0 | 0 | 0 | 0 | 0 |
| $(b,5)$  | 0 | 1 | 0 | 0 | 0 | 0 | 0 | 0 | 0 | 0 | 0 | 0 | $A^b$ | 1 | 0 | 0 |
| $(c,4)$  | 0 | 0 | 1 | 0 | 0 | 0 | 0 | 0 | 0 | 0 | $A^c$ | 1 | 0 | 0 | 0 | 0 |
| $(c,5)$  | 0 | 0 | 1 | 0 | 0 | 0 | 0 | 0 | 0 | 0 | 0 | 0 | $A^c$ | 1 | 0 | 0 |
| $(c,6)$  | 0 | 0 | 1 | 0 | 0 | 0 | 0 | 0 | 0 | 0 | 0 | 0 | 0 | 0 | $A^c$ | 1 |
| $(d,1)$  | 0 | 0 | 0 | 1 | $A^d$ | 1 | 0 | 0 | 0 | 0 | 0 | 0 | 0 | 0 | 0 | 0 |
| $(d,2)$  | 0 | 0 | 0 | 1 | 0 | 0 | $A^d$ | 1 | 0 | 0 | 0 | 0 | 0 | 0 | 0 | 0 |
| $(d,6)$  | 0 | 0 | 0 | 1 | 0 | 0 | 0 | 0 | 0 | 0 | 0 | 0 | 0 | 0 | $A^d$ | 1 |

It is clear there is a 2-space of trivial solutions to $M(S, \mathbf{n})\mathbf{x} = \mathbf{0}$:

$$[-\mathbf{p}_0 \cdot \mathbf{n}^a, -\mathbf{p}_0 \cdot \mathbf{n}^b, -\mathbf{p}_0 \cdot \mathbf{n}^c, -\mathbf{p}_0 \cdot \mathbf{n}^d; \ \mathbf{p}_0, \ \mathbf{p}_0, \ \mathbf{p}_0, \ \mathbf{p}_0, \ \mathbf{p}_0, \ \mathbf{p}_0]$$

in which all points lie at the same spot $\mathbf{p}_0$. However a count of columns minus rows (variables minus maximum possible rank) indicates we must have a solution space of dimension at least $|F| + 2|V| - |I| = 4 + 2 \times 6 - 12 = 4$. The configurations for Figure 4.4A,B indicate that, for general directions there is indeed a four space of solutions: (i) pick $\mathbf{p}_1$ (2 choices); (ii) pick $\mathbf{p}_2$ arbitrarily on the line $\mathbf{P}^d$ which is now fixed (1 choice); (iii) pick $\mathbf{p}_6$ arbitrarily on the same line (1 choice). The remaining points and lines can be constructed uniquely from the preassigned directions and these points.

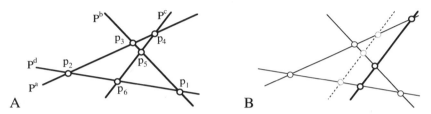

FIGURE. 4.4. *A 2-scene of incidences of points and lines (A) with a non-trivial parallel 2-scene (B).*

For a generic choice of directions on a general incidence structure, there is a 2-space of trivial parallel 2-scenes with all vertices at the same spot. If the directions were taken from an existing 2-scene $(\mathbf{p}, \mathbf{P})$ with at least two distinct points, then this space will have dimension at least 3: generated by these trivial 2-scenes and dilations of the given configuration, or equivalently, generated by translations and dilations of the the given configuration. These counts give some necessary conditions for independent sets of incidences on (1) a generic set of directions; (2) a generic set of directions with a non-trivial 2-scene. These conditions turn out to be necessary and sufficient [**Wh8**].

A set $I'$ of incidences is *independent* at set of normals $\mathbf{n}$ if the corresponding rows of the parallel 2-scene matrix $M(S, \mathbf{n})$ are linearly independent.

PARALLEL 2-SCENE THEOREM 4.2.2. *For a generic set of plane normals* $\mathbf{n}$ *and an incidence structure* $S = (V, F; I)$, *the following are equivalent:*

1. *the set* $I$ *of incidences is independent at* $\mathbf{n}$;
2. *for all non-empty subsets* $I'$ *of incidences,* $|I'| \leq 2|V(I')| + |F(I')| - 2$.

*The following are also equivalent:*

3. *the set of incidences is a circuit at* $\mathbf{n}$;
4. $|I| = 2|V| + |F| - 1$ *and for all non-empty subsets* $I'$ *of incidences* $|I'| \leq 2|V(I')| + |F(I')| - 2$.

This characterization of independence in terms of counts has strong similarities to the characterization of the generic 2-rigidity matroid. The *generic 2-parallel matroid* on the complete incidence structure $I = V \times F$ is defined by the independence of rows of the parallel 2-scene matrix at a generic set of directions.

A set of incidences is *2-tight* if its closure in the 2-parallel matroid is the complete incidence matroid on its vertices and faces. Many results from generic 2-rigidity extend directly:

1. all circuits in the generic 2-parallel matroid are 2-tight (analogous to 2-rigidity of circuits);

2. the Gluing Lemma will have an analog for combining 2-tight or independent sets of the 2-parallel matroid to create new 2-tight or independent sets on the combined vertices and faces;

3. there are inductive constructions for bases on a given set of vertices and faces to add an additional face (attached to one existing vertex), or an additional vertex (attached to two existing faces). [A counting argument confirms that each basis must have either a face of valence 1 or a vertex of valence 2 or valence 3. The replacement principles leading to vertices of valence 3 have not been investigated.]

We *conjecture* that a set of incidences will be 2-tight if the bipartite incidence graph is 4-connected (the analog of the Sufficient Connectivity Theorem 3.3.5). One aspect of this analogy to plane rigidity is explored further in appendix §A.

These results primarily apply to configurations with all vertices coincident. For a direct correspondence with the results on parallel drawings of plane graphs in the next section, we state a corollary for configurations with distinct vertices.

COROLLARY 4.2.3. *For a generic set of plane normals* **n** *and an incidence structure* $S = (V, F; I)$, *the following are equivalent:*

1. *the structure has an independent realization with all vertices distinct, unique up to translation and dilation;*

2. $|I| = 2|V| + |F| - 3$ *and for all subsets with at least two incidences* $|I'| \leq 2|V(I')| + |F(I')| - 3$.

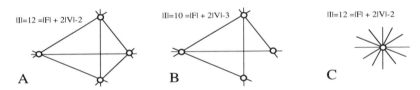

FIGURE. 4.5. *A 2-scene on a graph which a circuit at a generic configuration (A); independent with one edge removed (B), and also independent with all lines concurrent, for generic directions (C).*

EXAMPLE 4.2.4. Consider the incidence structure of a complete quadrangle (Figure 4.5A). [As a visual convention, we extend the lines of 2-scene to indicate their normals and distinguish it from a parallel design on a graph.] If the normals for all but one of the edges are assigned, the reader can check that the entire configuration can be constructed from two distinct vertices (Figure 4.5B). The last normal is not generic – it is determined by the previous normals in this position. Equivalently, the last incidence is dependent on the previous incidences for the given normals.

For generic normals, the realizations have all vertices coincident (Figure 4.5C).

**4.3. Reduction to plane graphs.** Graphs are a very special type of incidence structure, in which each face is incident with exactly two vertices. In this special case, the Parallel 2-Scene Theorem 4.2.2 reduces to a familiar result: Laman's Theorem 2.2.5.

Consider the counts. With $F' = E'$ and $|I'| = 2|E'|$ for all nonempty subsets $E'$, we have:

$$|I'| \leq 2|V(I')| + |F(I')| - 3 \Leftrightarrow 2|E'| \leq 2|V(I')| + |E'| - 3 \Leftrightarrow |E'| \leq 2|V(I')| - 3.$$

If we have generic directions $D$, the counts in the Parallel 2-scene Theorem guarantee a plane graph $G(\mathbf{p})$ with distinct vertices which is unique up to trivial parallel drawings and independent. This, in turn, guarantees that generic configurations $\mathbf{p}$ give independence and uniqueness, up to trivial parallel 2-scenes. In fact, generic directions and generic configurations are equivalent for these counts.

This equivalence fails for a generic circuit of the generic 2-rigidity matroid, with $|E| = 2|V| - 2$ and $|E| \leq 2|V| - 3$ on proper subsets. Realized at a generic configuration $\mathbf{p}$, the induced directions will *not* be generic directions (see Figure 4.5A)! The Parallel 2-Scene Theorem guarantees that generic directions will have only trivial 2-scenes for such a count.

EXAMPLE 4.3.1. We illustrate this conversion from the parallel 2-scene matrix for the 2-scene of Figure 4.6A to the standard rigidity matrix for the framework of Figure 4.6B.

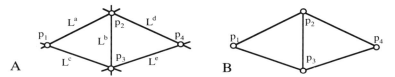

FIGURE. 4.6. *A plane incidence structure and 2-scene (A) based on a plane graph $G(\mathbf{p})$ (B).*

We begin with the parallel 2-scene matrix:

|        | $a$ | $b$ | $c$ | $d$ | $e$ | $1$ |     | $2$ |       | $3$ |     | $4$ |     |
|--------|-----|-----|-----|-----|-----|-----|-----|-----|-------|-----|-----|-----|-----|
| $(a,1)$ | $1$ | $0$ | $0$ | $0$ | $0$ | $A^a$ | $1$ | $0$ | $0$ | $0$ | $0$ | $0$ | $0$ |
| $(a,2)$ | $1$ | $0$ | $0$ | $0$ | $0$ | $0$ | $0$ | $A^a$ | $1$ | $0$ | $0$ | $0$ | $0$ |
| $(b,2)$ | $0$ | $1$ | $0$ | $0$ | $0$ | $0$ | $0$ | $A^b$ | $B^b$ | $0$ | $0$ | $0$ | $0$ |
| $(b,3)$ | $0$ | $1$ | $0$ | $0$ | $0$ | $0$ | $0$ | $0$ | $0$ | $A^b$ | $1$ | $0$ | $0$ |
| $(c,1)$ | $0$ | $0$ | $1$ | $0$ | $0$ | $A^c$ | $B^c$ | $0$ | $0$ | $0$ | $0$ | $0$ | $0$ |
| $(c,3)$ | $0$ | $0$ | $1$ | $0$ | $0$ | $0$ | $0$ | $0$ | $0$ | $A^c$ | $1$ | $0$ | $0$ |
| $(d,2)$ | $0$ | $0$ | $0$ | $1$ | $0$ | $0$ | $0$ | $A^d$ | $1$ | $0$ | $0$ | $0$ | $0$ |
| $(d,4)$ | $0$ | $0$ | $0$ | $1$ | $0$ | $0$ | $0$ | $0$ | $0$ | $0$ | $0$ | $A^d$ | $1$ |
| $(e,3)$ | $0$ | $0$ | $0$ | $0$ | $1$ | $0$ | $0$ | $0$ | $0$ | $A^e$ | $1$ | $0$ | $0$ |
| $(e,4)$ | $0$ | $0$ | $0$ | $0$ | $1$ | $0$ | $0$ | $0$ | $0$ | $0$ | $0$ | $A^e$ | $1$ |

If we row reduce on the columns for the faces, we have:

| $a$ | $b$ | $c$ | $d$ | $e$ | $1$ |     | $2$ |       | $3$ |     | $4$ |     |
|-----|-----|-----|-----|-----|-----|-----|-----|-------|-----|-----|-----|-----|
| $1$ | $0$ | $0$ | $0$ | $0$ | $0$ | $0$ | $A^a$ | $1$ | $0$ | $0$ | $0$ | $0$ |
| $0$ | $1$ | $0$ | $0$ | $0$ | $0$ | $0$ | $0$ | $0$ | $A^b$ | $1$ | $0$ | $0$ |
| $0$ | $0$ | $1$ | $0$ | $0$ | $0$ | $0$ | $0$ | $0$ | $A^c$ | $1$ | $0$ | $0$ |
| $0$ | $0$ | $0$ | $1$ | $0$ | $0$ | $0$ | $0$ | $0$ | $0$ | $0$ | $A^d$ | $1$ |
| $0$ | $0$ | $0$ | $0$ | $1$ | $0$ | $0$ | $0$ | $0$ | $0$ | $0$ | $A^e$ | $1$ |
| $-$ | $-$ | $-$ | $-$ | $-$ | $-$ | $-$ | $-$ | $-$ | $-$ | $-$ | $-$ | $-$ |
| $0$ | $0$ | $0$ | $0$ | $0$ | $A^a$ | $1$ | $-A^a$ | $-1$ | $0$ | $0$ | $0$ | $0$ |
| $0$ | $0$ | $0$ | $0$ | $0$ | $0$ | $0$ | $A^b$ | $1$ | $-A^b$ | $-1$ | $0$ | $0$ |
| $0$ | $0$ | $0$ | $0$ | $0$ | $A^c$ | $1^c$ | $0$ | $0$ | $-A^c$ | $-1$ | $0$ | $0$ |
| $0$ | $0$ | $0$ | $0$ | $0$ | $0$ | $0$ | $A^d$ | $1$ | $0$ | $0$ | $-A^d$ | $-1$ |
| $0$ | $0$ | $0$ | $0$ | $0$ | $0$ | $0$ | $0$ | $0$ | $A^e$ | $1$ | $-A^e$ | $-1$ |

Up to scalar multiplication, a row such as

$$[0 \quad 0 \quad 0 \quad 0 \quad 0 \quad | \quad 0 \quad 0 \quad 0 \quad 0 \quad A^e \quad 1 \quad -A^e \quad -1]$$

is the row

$$[0 \quad 0 \quad 0 \quad 0 \quad 0 \quad | \quad \mathbf{0} \quad \mathbf{0} \quad (\mathbf{p}_3 - \mathbf{p}_4)^\perp \quad (\mathbf{p}_4 - \mathbf{p}_3)^\perp]$$

– the row for the edge $\{3, 4\}$ in the parallel drawing matrix for the the graph, with additional zeros for the faces. More generally the bottom right box of this reduced matrix is equivalent to the parallel design matrix of the graph $G$ (or, by taking $\perp$, equivalent to the rigidity matrix of $G$).

## 5. The $C_1^0$-Cofactor Matroid

We present one more version of this matroid for plane graphs. Given a plane graph $G(\mathbf{p})$ with distinct vertices for each edge, an edge $\{i, j\}$ has an associated line $A^{i,j}x + B^{i,j}y + C^{i,j} = 0$ and the basic linear form $L^{i,j}(\mathbf{p}) = A^{i,j}x + B^{i,j}y + C^{i,j}$. As a simple convention, we can select the equation:

$$L^{i,j}(\mathbf{p}) = \det \begin{bmatrix} x_i & y_i & 1 \\ x_j & y_j & 1 \\ x & y & 1 \end{bmatrix} = -(\mathbf{p}_i - \mathbf{p}_j)^\perp \cdot (x, y) + (\mathbf{p}_i - \mathbf{p}_j)^\perp \cdot \mathbf{p}_j = 0.$$

Notice the antisymmetry: $L^{i,j}(\mathbf{p}) = -L^{j,i}(\mathbf{p})$.

A $C_1^0$-*cofactor* on a plane graph $G(\mathbf{p})$ is an assignment $\lambda$ to the edges such that, for each vertex $i$:

$$\sum_{j|\{i,j\}\in E} \lambda_{i,j} A^{i,j}x + B^{i,j}y + C^{i,j} \equiv 0.$$

These linear equations define the dependencies of a matroid. In fact, we show it is the same matroid we have studied under parallel designs.

PROPOSITION 5.1.1. *Given an plane graph $G(\mathbf{p})$, an assignment $\lambda$ is a $C_1^0$-cofactor if and only if $\lambda$ is a self-stress.*

PROOF. Assume that $\lambda$ is a $C_1^0$-cofactor on $G(\mathbf{p})$. For each vertex $i$, isolating then dropping the constant term gives:

$$\sum_{j|\{i,j\}\in E} \lambda_{i,j} A^{i,j}x + B^{i,j}y + C^{i,j} \equiv 0$$

$$\Rightarrow \quad - \sum_{j|\{i,j\}\in E} \lambda_{i,j}(\mathbf{p}_i - \mathbf{p}_j)^\perp \cdot (x, y) = \mathbf{0}$$

$$\Leftrightarrow \quad \sum_{j|\{i,j\}\in E} \lambda_{i,j}(\mathbf{p}_i - \mathbf{p}_j) = \mathbf{0}.$$

A $C_1^0$-cofactor is a self-stress on $G(\mathbf{p})$

For the converse, we need to confirm that:

$$\sum_{j|\{i,j\}\in E} \lambda_{i,j}(\mathbf{p}_i - \mathbf{p}_j) = \mathbf{0} \quad \Leftrightarrow \quad \sum_{j|\{i,j\}\in E} \lambda_{i,j}(A^{i,j}x + B^{i,j}y) = \mathbf{0}$$

$$? \Rightarrow \quad \sum_{j|\{i,j\}\in E} \lambda_{i,j} C^{i,j} = 0.$$

The key point is that, since the point $\mathbf{p}_i$ is on each of these lines, each $C^{i,j} = -(A^{i,j}x_i + B^{i,j}y_i) = -(A^{i,j}, B^{i,j}) \cdot (x_i, y_i)$. (Of course we get the same value of $C^{i,j}$ at the other vertex $(x_j, y_j)$.) Therefore,

$$\sum_{j | \{i,j\} \in E} \lambda_{i,j} C^{i,j} = \sum_{j | \{i,j\} \in E} \lambda_{i,j} (A^{i,j}, B^{i,j}) \cdot \mathbf{p}_i = \left[ \sum_{j | \{i,j\} \in E} \lambda_{i,j}(A^{i,j}, B^{i,j}) \right] \cdot \mathbf{p}_i = 0.$$

We have defined the original matroid of §2, §3 and §4 in a different guise. As mentioned in the introduction, there are two reasons for doing so:

1. this form leads to distinct generalizations in §10, §11 and §15;
2. this form has arisen naturally in applications to polyhedral pictures (see the next remark), and the connections between plane self-stresses and polyhedral pictures are an important part of the theory and history of this field.

REMARK 5.1.2. Consider a planar drawing of a planar graph $G(\mathbf{p})$. The 'regions' of the plane defined by the drawing, including the infinite exterior region, form the faces of a spherical polyhedron together with the edges and vertices of the graph. When does this polyhedron lift vertically to a spatial polyhedron, with plane faces meeting in pairs, continuously, over the edges of the plane graph $G(\mathbf{p})$?

MAXWELL'S THEOREM 5.1.3 [**Max,CrW2,3**]. *A plane framework $G(\mathbf{p})$ on a planar graph is the vertical projection of the edges and vertices of a plane faced spherical polyhedron with distinct planes for the faces at edge $\{i, j\}$ if and only if there is a self-stress on $G(\mathbf{p})$ with a non-zero coefficient $\omega_{i,j}$.*

If the configuration makes a planar drawing of the framework (no crossings of edges), this lifting can be viewed as a piecewise linear, globally continuous ($C^0$) function with the exterior region considered as an infinite face around the cap, not the 'underneath' of the finite cap. Such functions are called $C_1^0$ *bivariate splines* and the scalars we have defined are called 'smoothing cofactors' [**Bi,ChW,Wh10**].

We will not prove this correspondence here. However, we can briefly indicate the correspondence between these cofactors and the underlying polyhedron. Assume we have a polyhedron with planes: $\mathbf{P}^j = A^j x + B^j y + z + D^j$ and $\mathbf{P}^k = A^k x + B^k y + z + D^k$ for faces $j, k$. If these are to meet over the edge with vertices $\mathbf{p}_h, \mathbf{p}_i$, then for those points we have the same $z$ values:

$$z = -[A^j x_h + B^j y_h + D^j] = -[A^k x_h + B^k y_h + D^k]$$
$$= -[A^j x_i + B^j y_i + D^j] = -[A^k x_i + B^k y_i + D^k].$$

Equivalently

$$(A^j - A^k)x_h + (B^j - B^k)y_h + (D^j - D^k) = 0$$
$$(A^j - A^k)x_i + (B^j - B^k)y_i + (D^j - D^k) = 0.$$

We conclude that

$$(A^j - A^k)x + (B^j - B^k)y + (D^j - D^k) = \lambda_{h,i}(A^{h,i}x + B^{h,i}y + C^{h,i})$$

for some scalar $\lambda_{h,i}$. These scalars will be the $C_1^0$-cofactors (or self-stress) on the plane graph $G(\mathbf{p})$. The fact that equilibria are achieved around each vertex follows from the telescoping equation for the cycle of faces $k$ incident with $i$:

$$\sum_k (A^k - A^{k+1})x + (B^k - B^{k+1})y + (D^k - D^{k+1}) = \mathbf{0}.$$

## 6. Other 'Plane' Matroids

There are matroids related to plane rigidity and parallel drawing which arise out of other plane geometry problems – in particular problems of constraints in plane CAD [**Ow,SW,Wh12,13**]. We point out some similarities and some differences which occur for the underlying 'generic matroids' for these geometric problems. The first and third examples present important unsolved problems.

**6.1. Plane incidences.** Given a general incidence structure of points and lines (no direction constraints, length constraints etc.), what sets of incidences are independent for some (almost all) realizations as points and lines in the plane (not all lines collinear or all lines concurrent)?

Given an abstract structure $S = (V, F; I)$, the underlying algebraic constraints for 2-scenes are, for each $(i, j) \in I$:

$$A^j x_i + y_i + C^j = 0.$$

Working with these entries as variables, the Jacobian of this system corresponds to the equations of 'infinitesimal' deformations of a given 2-scene $S(\mathbf{p}, \mathbf{P})$:

$$A^j u_i + U^j x_i + w_i + W^j = 0.$$

This will be a system of $I$ equations in $2|V| + 2|F|$ variables – $u_i, w_i, U^j, W^j$. There are trivial first-order deformations, corresponding to small projective transformations of the configuration $\mathbf{p}, \mathbf{P}$ (which do not take any vertices to infinity or turn any lines vertical). For at least four points affinely spanning the plane, the space of trivial transformations will have dimension 8 [**Wh13**]. Therefore, a necessary condition for independence of sets of at least 4 points spanning the plane, will be:

$$|I'| \leq 2|F| + 2|V| - 8$$

Of course, this 'count' is *not* satisfied for small sets of incidences. For a single incidence we have: $|I| = 1 > 2 + 2 - 8 = 2|F| + 2|V| - 8$.

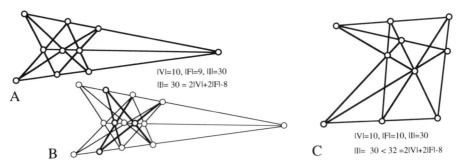

FIGURE. 6.1. *Projective Theorems such as Pappus' Theorem (A) and Desargue's Theorem (C) state that the final incidence is dependent on the previous incidences, leaving extra incidences preserving deformations (B).*

This counting condition is not enough to define a matroid, or to characterize our independence. All the theorems of projective geometry (Figure 6.1) are extra dependencies of the incidences, with the pattern:

If ... then the last three points will lie on a line;     or

If ... then the last three lines will be concurrent.

The incidences in standard 'projective constructions' are independent, but often they are too low a rank to be bases [**Wh13**]. We believe the corresponding 'generic' matroid has no efficient characterization.

CONJECTURE 6.1.1. *There is no polynomial time algorithm to determine the independence of incidence structures in the plane.*

Even without a characterization of independence of incidences, we can conjecture what happens when distance constraints are added to incidence constraints.

CONJECTURE 6.1.2. *Given an incidence structure $S = (V, F; I)$ which is independent for plane incidence, the set of distances $E$ and the incidences $I$ on the vertices are independent at some 2-scene $(\mathbf{p}, \mathbf{P})$ if and only if, for all non-empty sets $E'$ of distances and $I'$ of incidences on the vertices $V'$ and faces $F'$:*

$$|E'| + |I'| \leq 2|V'| + 2|F'| - 3.$$

**6.2. Plane directions and lengths.** In the spirit of constraints in plane CAD, there is another matroid which extends the plane first-order rigidity matroid. We combine the direction constraints of §4 with the length constraints of §3 in a *double graph* $FG = (V; D, E)$, where the same edge may lie in the direction set $D$ and the length set $E$ (Figure 6.2). At a plane configuration $\mathbf{p}$, these create a constraint matrix, $R_{FG}(\mathbf{p})$, with the two types of rows from the rigidity matrix for lengths and from the parallel design matrix for directions [**SW,Wh12**]. With the *generic configurations* for these matrices we define the *generic direction-length matroid* on the double graph.

 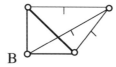 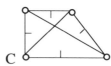

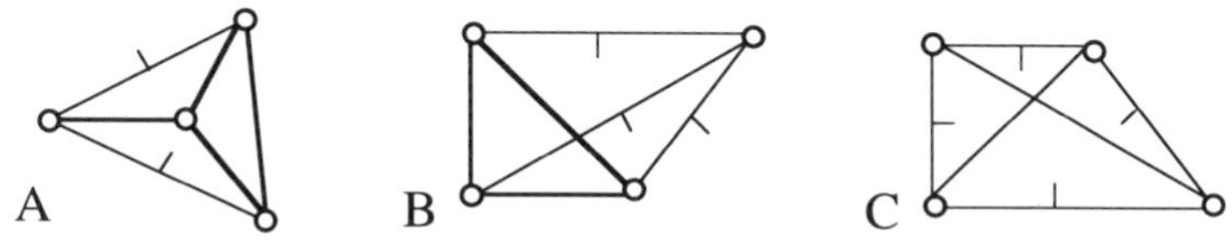

A     B     C

FIGURE. 6.2. *Examples of double graphs which are generic bases at plane configurations – heavy lines for distance constraints and light lines with spikes for direction constraints.*

THEOREM 6.2.1 [**SW**]. *For a generic plane configuration $\mathbf{p}$ on the vertices $V$, and a double graph $FG = (V; D, E)$ of length constraints $D$ and direction constraints $E$, the constraints are a basis for the if and only if:*
1. $|D| + |E| = 2|V(D \cup E)| - 2$;
2. $|D'| + |E'| \leq 2|V(D' \cup E')| - 2$ *for all subsets nonempty subsets $D', E'$;*
3. $|D'| \leq 2|V(D')| - 3$ *for all nonempty $D' \subseteq D$;*
4. $|E'| \leq 2|V(E')| - 3$ *for all nonempty $E' \subseteq E$.*

Within this matroid, we have analogs of all plane rigidity results: both combinatorics [**SW**] and geometry [**Wh12**]. We also have a 'swapping duality' – any result for a design $FG(\mathbf{p})$ also holds for the swapped design $GF(\mathbf{p})$ in which we swap direction constraints $D$ and length constraints $E$.

While these constraints, as written, are not important in plane CAD, they do imply partial results for angle and length constraints. On the basis of other preliminary results, we *conjecture* that the matroid for angle constraints in the plane is impossible to characterize with a polynomial time algorithm.

**6.3. Spherical angles and distances.** Closely related to these matroids on plane configurations are matroids for constraints and configurations on the sphere. In particular, the matroids for frameworks of points and bars (on great circles) are isomorphic to plane rigidity matroids under central projection.

THEOREM 6.3.1 [**Wh2**]. *Given a spherical framework $G(\mathbf{q})$ and a projection $\Pi(\mathbf{q}) = \mathbf{p}$ from the center of the sphere to a plane framework $G(\mathbf{p})$, then*

1. $G(\mathbf{q})$ *is first-order rigid on the sphere if and only if $G(\mathbf{p})$ is first-order rigid in the plane;*
2. $G(\mathbf{q})$ *is independent on the sphere if and only if $G(\mathbf{p})$ is independent in the plane.*

On the sphere we have an additional tool: polarity. Each point $\mathbf{q}_i$ is the normal to a plane $\mathbf{Q}^i$ through the origin and a great circle on the sphere. Such a polarity turns a distance constraint between spherical points $\mathbf{q}_i, \mathbf{q}_j$ into an angle constraint between spherical lines $\mathbf{Q}^i, \mathbf{Q}^j$. Such a combinatorial duality of the abstract structure also preserves the independence, rank etc. of the generic constraint matroid.

It would be desirable to work on the sphere with an incidence structure of great circles and points with added length and angle constraints. However, the incidences alone recreate the problems we described above in §6.1. We have a conjecture for structures with independent incidence constraints.

CONJECTURE 6.3.2. *Given independent incidences $I$, a set of distances $D$ and angles $A$ is a basis for some (almost all) realizations on the sphere if and only if:*

1. $|D| + |A| + |I| = 2|V| + 2|L| - 3$;
2. $|D'| + |A'| + |I'| \leq 2|V'| + 2|L'| - 3$ *for each non-empty subset.*

By appendix §A, the counts of Conjecture 6.3.2 define a matroid on the incidence structure. Our conjecture states that this count-matroid is the same as the generic constraint matroid for the incidence structure on the sphere. Unfortunately, the underlying difficulties of incidences and their possible dependencies block the inductive approaches which have been used for many of the analogous plane results. It is possible that some direct construction, such as Tay's new proof of Laman's Theorem [**Ta5**], can be extended, at least for interesting special cases.

## 7. Summary of Plane Results

To orient our move up to related matroids in 3-space and higher dimensions, we summarize some critical features of generic 2-rigidity for a graph $G = (V, E)$:

1. The matroid is 'controlled' by the count $2|V| - 3$ in the sense that:
   (a) $2|V| - 3$ is the rank of the complete graph $K_n$ ($n \geq 2$);
   (b) any set $E$ is independent if and only if $|E'| \leq 2|V'| - 3$ for every non-empty subset $E'$ on vertices $V'$.
2. The matroid is the matroid union of two copies of the graphic matroid on $G$, followed by a Dilworth truncation;
3. There is an inductive construction for all bases of the matroid. (It can be easily modified to construct all independent sets.)
4. All circuits of the generic matroid are spanning on their vertices (i.e. their closure is the complete graph on the vertices of the circuit).

5. Some of the combinatorial characterizations have associated $O(|V|^2)$ algorithms for verifying whether a graph is a basis of the generic 2-rigidity matroid.

6. The parallel design matroid for generic plane configurations of a graph is the same as the generic 2-rigidity matroid.

7. $C_1^0$-cofactors, defined by the algebraic criteria on the lines:

for each $i$, $\sum_{\{j|(i,j)\in E\}} \omega_{i,j}(A^{i,j}x + B^{i,j}y + C^{i,j}) = 0$;

generate the same matroid.

Generalized parallel 2-scenes on $S = (F, V, I)$ give a broader matroid with analogs of results for plane rigidity:

1. The matroid is 'controlled' by the count $|F| + 2|V| - 2$.

2. All circuits of the generic matroid are spanning on their vertices and faces.

3. There are polynomial $O(|I|^2)$ algorithms for detecting bases etc.

4. This general parallel drawing matroid contains all of the others as special cases: Laman's Theorem, Henneberg 2-constructions, etc. are all special cases of results for general plane parallel 2-scenes.

REMARK 7.1.1. There is an extension of plane bar frameworks which generates oriented matroids. In these *tensegrity frameworks*, the edges are partitioned into $E_+, E_0, E_-$ and the dependencies are restricted to self-stresses with the appropriate sign on each edge (with no restriction on $E_0$) [**CoW**,**RW**]. In structural engineering terms, the edges in $E_+$ are struts (taking only compression) and in $E_-$ are 'cables' (taking only tension). While there is an extensive theory for such frameworks, the signs of the dependencies at a generic configuration vary between regions of the plane [**WW1**] and there is no single 'generic' behaviour for the signed graph [**RW**]. We will not pursue this extension here.

Finally, we recall that all of the matroids were extracted from applications and the results have been used in these applications. These applications remain a continuing source for problems and a standard to evaluate our results against.

## Part II: Higher Dimensions.

We are ready for the other named strips of matroids in Figure 1.1. We begin with the parallel drawing matroids (§8), whose theory is a direct generalization of the results of Part I. However the core of Part II will be the rigidity matroid for 3-space (§9) and the analogous $C_2^1$-cofactor matroid for plane configurations (§10). As Figure 1.1 indicates, the generic 3-rigidity matroid and the bivariate $C_2^1$-cofactor matroids are conjectured to be isomorphic (? in Figure 1.1 – see §10.3)

The 'higher' cases: generic rigidity for $d \geq 4$ and the bivariate $C_s^{s-1}$-cofactor matroids provide important insights back toward these core matroids, through both counterexamples and examples for the analogs of our conjectures for rigidity in 3-space and $C_2^1$-cofactors. For higher levels, these families of matroids of graphs are known to be distinct (the black gap with $\neq$ in Figure 1.1 – see §11.5), though they are members of the more general class of abstract $d$-rigidity matroids [**GSS**].

For contrast with these difficulties, we will close Part II with a rigidity related matroid in $d$-space which has a complete theory as well as potential applications.

## 8. Parallel Scenes in Higher Dimensions

The definitions and results of §4 generalize directly to 3-space and higher dimensions. §8.1 presents the general definitions for scenes with preassigned normals, then §8.2 specializes to parallel drawings of graphs with preassigned directions for the edges. These results originated in the dual form: scene analysis of polyhedral pictures [**Su3,Wh8**] in which assigned normals for faces are dualized to assigned projections for vertices, i.e. the polyhedral pictures of §8.3.

**8.1. Parallel $d$-scenes.** For an abstract polyhedral incidence structure $S = (V, F; I)$, a *$d$-scene* is a pair of location maps: *points* for the vertices $\mathbf{p} : V \to \mathbb{R}^d$, $\mathbf{p}_i = (x_i, \dots, z_i, w_i)$ and *hyperplanes* for the faces $\mathbf{P} : F \to \mathbb{R}^{d+1}$, $\mathbf{P}^j = (A^j, \dots, C^j, 1, D^j)$; such that, for each incidence $(i, j) \in I$:

$$A^j x_i + \dots + C^j z_i + w_i + D^j = 0.$$

The *normal* to the hyperplane $\mathbf{P}^j$ is $\mathbf{n}^j = (A^j, \dots, C^j, 1)$. (We continue to assume that no hyperplane is 'vertical'.)

A $d$-scene $S(\mathbf{q}, \mathbf{Q})$ is *parallel* to $S(\mathbf{p}, \mathbf{P})$ if, for each face $j$, the normals are equal: that is, $(P_1^j, \dots, P_{d-1}^j, 1) = (Q_1^j, \dots, Q_{d-1}^j, 1)$. A *non-trivially parallel $d$-scene* for $S(\mathbf{p}, \mathbf{P})$ is a parallel 2-scene $S(\mathbf{q}, \mathbf{Q})$, such that the point configuration $\mathbf{q}$ is not a translation or dilation of the configuration $\mathbf{p}$ (Figure 8.1B). Otherwise it is *trivially parallel* (Figure 8.1A).

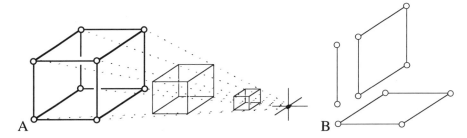

FIGURE. 8.1. *A 3-scene with trivially parallel scenes (A) and non-trivially parallel 3-scenes (B).*

We can also begin with an assignment $\mathbf{n}$ of *normals* for the faces: a $d$-vector $\mathbf{n}^j = (A^j, \dots C^j, 1)$ to each face $j \in F$. A $d$-scene $S(\mathbf{p}, \mathbf{P})$ *realizes the normals* $\mathbf{n}$, if for each face $j \in F$ with $\mathbf{P}^j = (A^j, \dots C^j, 1, D^j) = (\mathbf{n}^j, D^j)$ and vertex $i$:

$$\mathbf{n}^j \cdot (x_i, \dots, \dot{w}_i) + D^j = A^j x_i + \dots + C^j z_i + w_i + D^j = 0.$$

Given the normals $\mathbf{n}^j$, we have a linear system of $|I|$ equations in $|F| + d|V|$ variables recorded by the *parallel $d$-scene matrix* for $d$-space normals $\mathbf{n}$, where the variables are ordered: $[\dots, D^j, \dots ; \dots, x_i, \dots, w_i, \dots]$:

$$
\begin{array}{c}
 \\
(1,a) \\
\vdots \\
(i,j) \\
\vdots
\end{array}
\begin{array}{ccccccc|ccccc}
a & \dots & j & \dots & m & v_1 & \dots & v_i & \dots \\
\end{array}
\left(
\begin{array}{ccccc|cccc}
1 & \dots & 0 & \dots & 0 & \mathbf{n}^a & \dots & \mathbf{0} & \dots \\
\vdots & \ddots & \vdots & \ddots & \vdots & \vdots & \ddots & \vdots & \ddots \\
0 & \dots & 1 & \dots & 0 & \mathbf{0} & \dots & \mathbf{n}^j & \dots \\
\vdots & \ddots & \vdots & \ddots & \vdots & \vdots & \ddots & \vdots & \ddots
\end{array}
\right)
\begin{bmatrix}
D^a \\
\vdots \\
D^m \\
\hline
\mathbf{p}_1^t \\
\vdots \\
\mathbf{p}_i^t \\
\vdots
\end{bmatrix}
=
\begin{bmatrix}
0 \\
\vdots \\
0 \\
\vdots
\end{bmatrix}
$$

For matroid theory, our primary interest is the *generic $d$-parallel matroid* on the complete incidence structure $V \times F$, generated by independent rows of the parallel

$d$-scene matrix at generic normals for the faces. For bases of this matroid, the only realizations at generic normals will be *trivial* – having all points coincident and the parallel $d$-scenes will be the $d$-space of translations.

PARALLEL $d$-SCENES THEOREM 8.1.1 [**Wh5,8**]. *For an incidence structure* $S = (V, F; I)$, *the following are equivalent:*

1. *the incidences* $I$ *are independent in the generic $d$-parallel matroid on* $V \times F$;
2. *for all non-empty subsets* $I' \subseteq I$, $|I'| \leq d|V(I')| + |F(I')| - d$

*The following are also equivalent:*

3. $I$ *is a circuit of the generic $d$-parallel matroid on* $V \times F$:
4. $|I| = d|V(I)| + |F(I)| - d + 1$, *and for all proper subsets* $I'$:
   $|I'| \leq d|V(I')| + |F(I')| - d.$

For the translation to parallel drawings of graphs (§8.2), we need a corollary.

COROLLARY 8.1.2 [**Wh5,8**]. *For generic normals* **n** *in $d$-space for the faces of an incidence structure* $S = (V, F; I)$, *the following are equivalent:*

1. *the incidences* $I$ *are independent in a $d$-scene with distinct vertices;*
2. *for all subsets* $I'$ *with* $V(I') \geq 2$: $|I'| \leq d|V(I')| + |F(I')| - (d + 1)$.

EXAMPLE 8.1.3. Consider the twenty four incidences of the cubical structure of Figure 8.1(A). These incidences will be independent for generic normals, leaving a space of parallel 3-scenes of dimension $2|V| + |F| - |I| = 30 - 24 = 6$ (Figure 8.1B). Even the special normals of a symmetric cube will leave the same space of parallel 3-scenes: the incidences are independent for these non-generic normals.

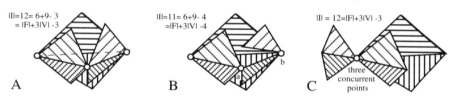

FIGURE. 8.2. *A dependent incidence structure when realized with distinct vertices but dependent normals (A), an independent subset with generic normals (B), and independent incidences with generic normals but with all vertices coincident (C).*

Consider the twelve incidences of Figure 8.2A. By the Parallel $d$-Scenes Theorem, this set is a basis of the generic $d$-parallel matroid and the only realizations for generic directions will have all vertices coincident (Figure 8.2C).

If we remove one incidence, there will be realizations of generic directions with all vertices distinct (Figure 8.2B), by Corollary 8.1.2. However, the additional incidence with distinct vertices restricts the normal of this last face to be orthogonal to the line $ab$, whose direction is already fixed.

Because this generic $d$-parallel matroid is combinatorially characterized by these 'submodular counts' (see the §A.1, §A.4), the basic plane results generalize:

1. there are efficient algorithms for independence, dependence, rank etc.;
2. the circuits contain bases for the complete incidence structure on their vertices and faces [**Im,Su3**];
3. inductive constructions for the bases of the generic matroid can be given;
4. we *conjecture* that $2d$-vertex connectivity of the incidence graph is sufficient for an incidence structure to be a basis for the complete incidence graph on its vertices and faces.

REMARK 8.1.4. For the incidence structure of the faces and vertices of a convex polyhedron or convex $d$-polytope, the parallel $d$-scenes are intimately connected to Minkowski sum and Minkowski decomposition of the polytope. A geometric theorem of Shephard [**Sh**] says:

> *A convex polytope is Minkowski decomposible (is the Minkowski sum of two polytopes with simpler incidence structures) if and only if there are non-trivially parallel d-scenes.*

For example, the cube of Figure 8.1A is the Minkowski sum of the bottom square and the line segment of Figure 8.1B.

**8.2. Parallel graphs in $d$-space.** Consider a geometric graph $G(\mathbf{p})$ in 3-space. The analogs of the parallel designs of §4.1 are:

configurations $\mathbf{q}$ such that, for each edge $\{h, i\} \in E$, $(\mathbf{p}_h - \mathbf{p}_i) \| (\mathbf{q}_h - \mathbf{q}_i)$.

For each edge, this condition gives two constraints on the configuration $\mathbf{q}$ (three equations with one added parameter) corresponding to selecting two planes intersecting in the line $\mathbf{p}_h \mathbf{p}_i$ and using those planes in the spirit of §8.1. For planes with normals $\mathbf{m}_e, \mathbf{n}_e$ through the edge $e = \{h, i\}$, we have the linear constraints:

$$\mathbf{m}_e \cdot \mathbf{q}_h - \mathbf{m}_e \cdot \mathbf{q}_i = 0 \quad \text{and} \quad \mathbf{n}_e \cdot \mathbf{q}_h - \mathbf{n}_e \cdot \mathbf{q}_i = 0$$

on the configurations $\mathbf{q}$. The graph $G$ and these normals $\mathbf{m}, \mathbf{n}$ from the configuration $\mathbf{p}$ yield a $2|E|$-by-$3|V|$ *3-parallel matrix* for $G(\mathbf{p})$ and define a matroid on the double copies $2E$ of the edges of the graph (or a hypermatroid on the edges $E$ of the graph §A.3). If there are two distinct points, the trivial null space has dimension 4 and the maximum possible rank will be $3|V| - 4$. An essential condition for independent rows is $2|D'| \leq 3|V(D')| - 4$, for all non-empty subsets $D' \subseteq 2E$.

As an convention, we take two copies of the edges of the graph and define a matroid on this set $2E$, based on a generic 3-configuration $\mathbf{p}$ and a generic selection of the two planes through each edge. The independence of the rows of this *generic 3-parallel matrix* defines the *generic 3-parallel matroid* on the set $2E$.

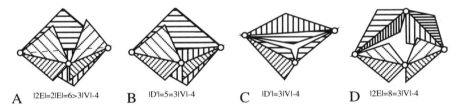

A    |2E|=2|E|=6>3|V|-4     B    |D'|=5=3|V|-4     C    |D'|=3|V|-4     D    |2E|=8=3|V|-4

FIGURE. 8.3. *Graphs in 3-space with up to two planes through each edge which are: (A) always dependent, (B) a generically independent subset of (A), and (C) a dependent choice of planes for (B) in special position, (D) generically independent.*

EXAMPLE 8.2.1. Consider the structure of Figure 8.3A. This is a graph shown with two planes for each edge. (All non-collinear triangles are generic here.) By the simple count $|2E| > 3|V| - 4$, $2E$ is always dependent, unless we have all points coincident and have generic directions for the normals. By the previous section, the subset $D'$ of Figure B is independent for generic normals, with $|D'| = 3|V| - 4$. However, if we select three planes with the same (vertical) normal for the three edges (Figure 8.3C), these three rows alone will be dependent: if the first two edges $\mathbf{q}_1 - \mathbf{q}_2$, $\mathbf{q}_2 - \mathbf{q}_3$ are horizontal, the third edge $\mathbf{q}_1 - \mathbf{q}_3$ is also horizontal. This indicates that dependence may come from the configuration of the points or from the selected planes for a given configuration.

The skew quadrilateral in Figure 8.3D gives an independent set $2E$ for any choice of pairs of distinct normals for the skew lines. With $|2E| = 3|V| - 4$, the only parallel graphs are dilations and translations of this quadrilateral. On the other hand, a coplanar quadrilateral will be dependent for any allowed choice of the normals, since there are non-trivially parallel graphs within this plane.

We could directly mimic much of §2–§4 to find combinatorial characterizations of the independent sets of edge copies (see §A.4 and [**Wh5**] for portions of this direct development). Instead, we follow the approach of §4.3 and extract the basic results from §8.1. For completeness, we give these results for all dimensions $d \geq 2$.

Given a graph $G$ and a generic configuration $\mathbf{p}$ in $d$-space, we select normals $\mathbf{n}_{i,j}^r$, $1 \leq r \leq d - 1$ for $d - 1$ independent, generically selected hyperplanes through each edge $\{i, j\}$. The system of equations: $\mathbf{n}_{i,j}^r \cdot \mathbf{q}_i - \mathbf{n}_{i,j}^r \cdot \mathbf{q}_j = 0$ creates the $(d - 1)|E|$-by-$d|V|$ *d-parallel matrix for the graph* $G$ and defines the *generic d-parallel matroid* on the set $(d - 1)E$ consisting of $(d - 1)$ copies of each edge in $E$. (The dependence or independence of a subset $D$ of $(d-1)E$ will *not* be changed by permuting the labels of the copies selected for each edge, because we have chosen generic vertices and generic hyperplanes for the $(d - 1)$ copies of each edge. Only the number of copies selected for each edge will matter.)

$d$-PARALLEL GRAPHS THEOREM 8.2.2 [**Wh5**]. *For the complete graph $K_V$ and a non-empty subset $D \subseteq (d - 1)E$, the following are equivalent:*

1. *$D$ is a basis of the generic $d$-parallel matroid on $K_V$;*
2. *$|D| = d|V| - (d + 1)$ and for all nonempty subsets $D'$,*
   *$|D'| \leq d|V(D')| - (d + 1)$;*
3. *$D$ can be partitioned into $d + 1$ edge-disjoint trees, exactly $d$ incident with each vertex, but no $d$ non-empty subtrees span the same subset of vertices.*

PROOF. 1. $\Rightarrow$ 2. The necessity of these counts for a basis follows directly from the observation that, for any set with at least two distinct vertices, there is a 4-space of trivially parallel configurations obtained by translation and dilation.

2. $\Rightarrow$ 1. Interpret the set $D$ as the faces of an incidence structure $S_D(V, F; I)$. Since each edge copy $e \in D$ converts to a face $e$ with two incident vertices, the count $|D'| \leq d|V(D')| - (d + 1)$ is equivalent to the count

$$|I'| = 2|D'| \leq |D'| + d|V(I')| - (d + 1) = |F(I')| + d|V(I')| - (d + 1).$$

To work with arbitrary subsets $I'$, any faces in $F(I')$ incident with only one vertex in $V(I')$ can be dropped or added without changing the inequality.

By Corollary 8.1.2, for generic normals $\mathbf{n}$ the incidences $I$ are independent in a $d$-scene $S(\mathbf{p}, \mathbf{P})$ with all vertices distinct. The row reduction of Example 4.3.2, generalized to this setting, directly converts the parallel $d$-scene matrix into a matrix with independent rows formed by a diagonal block $|F|$-by-$|F|$ identity with zeros below and a lower right $|D|$-by-$d|V|$ block for the rows of the $d$-parallel matrix for $D$. The rows of the $d$-parallel matrix for $D$ are therefore independent. Since the configuration $\mathbf{p}$ defines the lines $\mathbf{P}$ and the normals $\mathbf{n}$, we have one configuration $\mathbf{p}$ for which $D$ gives independent rows. By the usual algebraic arguments for 'generic configurations' (configurations not satisfying the finite set of relevant algebraic equations) this independence holds for all generic configurations.

Since $|D| = d|V| - (d + 1)$ is the maximal possible rank with at least two vertices, $D$ is a basis for the generic $d$-parallel matroid.

2. $\Leftrightarrow$ 3. [**Ha**] shows the equivalence of the counts and the $(d+1)\mathrm{Tree}(d)$-coverings.

The other results for generic 2-rigidity, such as gluing, efficient algorithms for independence, rank, etc., have appropriate generalizations to the $d$-parallel matroid on a graph $G$ [**Wh5**]. We note that, for all dimensions, gluing across a pair of vertices takes two 'tight' pieces into a 'tight' graph on the union of the vertices.

REMARK 8.2.3. The generic $d$-parallel matroid on $G$ is very different from the generic $d$-rigidity matroid on the same graph we will define in §9 and §11. A framework such as the skew quadrilateral of Figure 8.3D has only trivially parallel configurations but have non-trivial first-order motions. We do have a one-way connection, which we note now (also see §16.4).

THEOREM 8.2.4 [**Wh5**]. *If a geometric graph $G(\mathbf{p})$ in $d$-space, $d \geq 2$ has a non-trivially parallel drawing then the bar framework $G(\mathbf{p})$ has a non-trivial first-order motion in $d$-space.*

**8.3. Polarity to scene analysis.** The theorems on parallel $d$-scenes originated in a projectively polar form: for $d = 3$, our Parallel $d$-Scene Theorem was Sugihara's Conjecture for polyhedral pictures [**Su3,Wh8**]. An assigned normal to each face is replaced by an assigned projection into $(d - 1)$-space for each vertex (again $d - 1$ choices). These vertices are 'lifted' by the one additional value recording the height ($|V|$ variables), and the $d|F|$ coordinates for non-vertical faces are constrained by the $I$ incidence equations (Figure 8.4). (Also see [**Cr3,4,CRy,CR**] for a related analysis of liftings.)

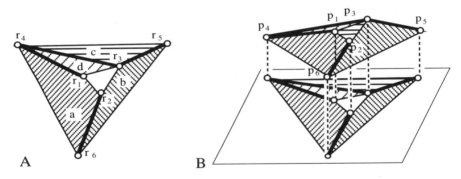

FIGURE. 8.4. *A 2-picture (A) on an incidence structure, with a lifting to a 3-scene (B).*

In computer science, the study of these 3-scenes lifting a fixed plane projection is called *scene analysis of the polyhedral picture* [**Su3**]. We briefly outline this dual vocabulary and the polarized theorems.

A $(d-1)$-*picture* of an incidence structure $S$ is a location map $\mathbf{r} : V \to \mathbb{R}^{d-1}$, $\mathbf{r}_i = (x_i, y_i, \dots, z_i)$. A *lifting* of a $(d-1)$-picture $S(\mathbf{r})$ is a $d$-scene $S(\mathbf{p}, \mathbf{P})$, with the vertical projection $\Pi(\mathbf{p}) = \mathbf{r}$. (I.e., if $\mathbf{p}_i = (x_i, \dots, z_i, w_i)$ then $\mathbf{r}_i = (x_i, \dots, z_i) = \Pi(\mathbf{p}_i)$.) A lifting $S(\mathbf{p}, \mathbf{P})$ is *trivial* if all the faces lie in the same plane, and is *sharp* if each pair of faces sharing a vertex have distinct planes. The *lifting matrix* for a picture $S(\mathbf{r})$ is the $|I|$-by-$(|V| + d|F|)$ coefficient matrix $M(S, \mathbf{r})$ of the system of

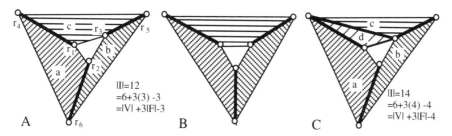

FIGURE. 8.5. *A generic 2-picture with only trivial liftings (A) but a sharp lifting for the special position (B). With the faces modified (C) the new structure has a sharp lifting for generic pictures.*

equations for liftings of a picture $S(\mathbf{r})$: for each $(i,j) \in I$: $A^j x_i + B^j y_i + \ldots + C^j z_i + w_i + D^j = 0$ where the variables are ordered: $[\ldots, w_i, \ldots; \ldots, A^j, B^j, \ldots, D^j, \ldots]$.

Independence of the rows of the lifting matrix defines the *lifting matroid* on $S(\mathbf{r})$. Generic points for the picture define the *generic d-lifting matroid*.

PICTURE THEOREM 8.3.1 [**Wh8**]. *The incidences $I$ are independent in the generic d-lifting matroid if and only if subsets $I' \neq \emptyset$, $|I'| \leq |V'| + d|F'| - d$.*

*A generic picture of an incidence structure $S = (V, F; I)$ has a sharp lifting if and only if, for all subsets $I'$ with $F(I') \geq 2$, $|I'| \leq |V'| + d|F'| - (d+1)$.*

REMARK 8.3.2. The translation between liftings of a plane picture and parallel $d$-scenes for a set of normals is a true geometric polarity in $d$-space. First we transform the incidence structure $S = (V, F; I)$ to the dual structure $S^* = (V^*, F^*; I^*)$, by setting $V^* = F$, $F^* = V$ and reversing the ordered pairs in $I$. Given a $d$-scene $S(\mathbf{p}, \mathbf{P})$ the *polar scene* is $S^*(\mathbf{p}^*, \mathbf{P}_*)$ where the point $\mathbf{p}_i = (x_i, \ldots, z_i, w_i)$ becomes the hyperplane $P_*^i = (x_i, \ldots, z_i, 1, w_i)$ and the hyperplane $P^j = (A^j, \ldots C^j, 1, D^j)$ becomes the point $p_j^* = (A^j, \ldots C^j, D^j)$. This transformation preserves incidences of points and hyperplanes, taking a $d$-scene on $S$ to a $d$-scene on $S^*$, the projections of points to normals of hyperplanes. Therefore it induces an isomorphism of the $d$-parallel matroid on $S(\mathbf{p}, \mathbf{P})$ and the $d$-lifting matroid on $S^*(\mathbf{p}^*, \mathbf{P}_*)$.

This transformation is the restriction to our 'affine coordinates' of the projective polarity about the paraboloid with Euclidean coordinates $x^2 + \ldots z^2 + 2w = 0$. This projective polarity also interchanges vertical planes with points at infinity – two sets which we excluded from our $d$-scenes.

REMARK 8.3.3. These generic properties of a structure are computationally robust, in the sense that all small changes in a generic picture with sharp liftings also have sharp liftings (Figure 8.5), and in the sense that small changes in the points of the picture require only small changes in the corresponding lifting. Even special positions of such structures will always have non-trivial liftings, although these may not be sharp. However, up to numerical round off, all pictures 'are generic'. Other structures, which do not have sharp liftings for generic pictures (Figure 8.5A), may have sharp liftings in special positions (Figure 8.5B), but a small change in the position of even one point can destroy this sharpness. (Numerical round off will typically produce such a small change in position.) In practice, the generic results are the essential ingredients for computer analysis of polyhedral pictures [**Su3**].

## 9. Rigidity of Frameworks in 3-space

We are ready for the generic 3-rigidity matroid for graphs. While the initial form in §9.1 is directly analogous to the generic 2-rigidity matroid in Part I, the problem of a combinatorial characterization of bases in this matroid is substantially harder and is still unsolved (§9.2). We will illustrate the difficulties with some critical examples, some partial results and some conjectures with a matroidal flavour in §9.3, §9.4.

**9.1. Statics and first-order kinematics.** A *3-space framework* is a standard graph $G = (V, E)$ and a *3-configuration* $\mathbf{p} : V \to \mathbf{IR}^3$. (The configuration $\mathbf{p}$ is a point in $\mathbf{IR}^{3|V|}$.) A *dependence* or *self-stress* on the framework $G(\mathbf{p})$ is an assignment $\omega : E \to \mathbf{IR}$, with $\omega\{i, j\} = \omega_{i,j} = \omega_{j,i}$, such that, for each vertex $i$:

$$\sum_{j | \{i,j\} \in E} \omega_{i,j}(\mathbf{p}_i - \mathbf{p}_j) = \mathbf{0}.$$

These self-stresses are the row dependencies of the *rigidity matrix* $R_G(\mathbf{p})$:

$$[\ldots \quad \omega_{i,j} \quad \ldots] \begin{bmatrix} \vdots & \ddots & \vdots & \cdots & \vdots & \ddots & \vdots \\ 0 & \cdots & (\mathbf{p}_i - \mathbf{p}_j) & \cdots & (\mathbf{p}_j - \mathbf{p}_i) & \cdots & 0 \\ \vdots & \ddots & \vdots & \cdots & \vdots & \ddots & \vdots \end{bmatrix} = [\mathbf{0} \quad \ldots \quad \mathbf{0}].$$

The independence of rows in the rigidity matrix $R_G(\mathbf{p})$ defines the *3-rigidity matroid* $\mathcal{R}_3(G; \mathbf{p})$ on the edges of the graph with a 3-configuration $\mathbf{p}$. The framework $G(\mathbf{p})$ is *3-independent* if its edge set is independent in $\mathcal{R}_3(G; \mathbf{p})$, and the *rank* of $G(\mathbf{p})$ is the rank of $\mathcal{R}_3(G; \mathbf{p})$. For the complete graph $K_n$, we write $\mathcal{R}_3(n; \mathbf{p})$.

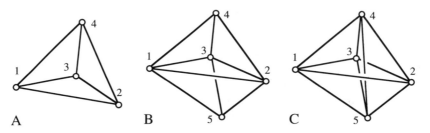

FIGURE. 9.1. *Independent frameworks in 3-space (A,B) and a circuit in the 3-rigidity matroid (C).*

EXAMPLE 9.1.1. Consider the 3-space framework $K_4(\mathbf{p})$ of Figure 9.1A.

| $R_G(\mathbf{p})$ | $\omega$ | $v_1$ | $v_2$ | $v_3$ | $v_4$ |
|---|---|---|---|---|---|
| $\{1, 2\}$ | 0 | $\mathbf{p}_1 - \mathbf{p}_2$ | $\mathbf{p}_2 - \mathbf{p}_1$ | $\mathbf{0}$ | $\mathbf{0}$ |
| $\{1, 3\}$ | 0 | $\mathbf{p}_1 - \mathbf{p}_3$ | $\mathbf{0}$ | $\mathbf{p}_3 - \mathbf{p}_1$ | $\mathbf{0}$ |
| $\{1, 4\}$ | 0 | $\mathbf{p}_1 - \mathbf{p}_4$ | $\mathbf{0}$ | $\mathbf{0}$ | $\mathbf{p}_4 - \mathbf{p}_1$ |
| $\{2, 3\}$ | 0 | $\mathbf{0}$ | $\mathbf{p}_2 - \mathbf{p}_3$ | $\mathbf{p}_3 - \mathbf{p}_2$ | $\mathbf{0}$ |
| $\{2, 4\}$ | 0 | $\mathbf{0}$ | $\mathbf{p}_2 - \mathbf{p}_4$ | $\mathbf{0}$ | $\mathbf{p}_4 - \mathbf{p}_2$ |
| $\{3, 4\}$ | 0 | $\mathbf{0}$ | $\mathbf{0}$ | $\mathbf{p}_3 - \mathbf{p}_4$ | $\mathbf{p}_4 - \mathbf{p}_3$ |

Provided the four points are not coplanar, the vectors such as $\mathbf{p}_1 - \mathbf{p}_2$, $\mathbf{p}_1 - \mathbf{p}_3$ and $\mathbf{p}_1 - \mathbf{p}_4$ at vertex 1 are independent, and the only dependence is the zero self-stress. The edges are independent in the 3-rigidity matroid.

If we add an additional 3-valent vertex (Figure 9.1B), the same argument applied at vertex 5 shows the rows are independent, if the points are in general position (no four coplanar). However, if we add one more edge to get $K_5$, this argument no longer applies (Figure 9.1C ). We will see that this is dependent for all 3-configurations and is a circuit for general position 3-configurations. (A configuration is in *general position in d-space* if any set of $\leq d + 1$ points is affinely independent.)

What is the rank of the matrix $R_{K_n}(\mathbf{p})$ and of the matroid for a general position 3-configuration? From the previous example and its subsets, we have:
rank $\mathcal{R}_3(5; \mathbf{p}) = 9$,  rank $\mathcal{R}_3(4; \mathbf{p}) = 6$,  rank $\mathcal{R}_3(3; \mathbf{p}) = 3$,  rank $\mathcal{R}_3(2; \mathbf{p}) = 1$.
In general, for $n > 2$ we observe that rank $\mathcal{R}_3(n; \mathbf{p}) = 3v - 6$.

We confirm this rank in two steps. We show this is an upper bound by giving a 6-dimensional solution space of the equations $R_G(\mathbf{p})\mathbf{u} = \mathbf{0}$. In general, the solutions $\mathbf{u} = (\ldots, \mathbf{u}_i, \ldots)$ are the *first-order flexes*, satisfying the equation for each edge $\{i, j\}$: $(\mathbf{p}_i - \mathbf{p}_j) \cdot (\mathbf{u}_i - \mathbf{u}_j) = 0$. The component $\mathbf{u}_i$ is the *velocity* of $\mathbf{p}_i$ in the first-order flex. The guaranteed *trivial first-order flexes* for any graph $G$ on a 3-configuration $\mathbf{p}$ are generated by the six vectors:

$$\begin{bmatrix} \mathbf{i}^t \\ \vdots \\ \mathbf{i}^t \end{bmatrix}, \quad \begin{bmatrix} \mathbf{j}^t \\ \vdots \\ \mathbf{j}^t \end{bmatrix}, \quad \begin{bmatrix} \mathbf{k}^t \\ \vdots \\ \mathbf{k}^t \end{bmatrix}, \quad \begin{bmatrix} (\mathbf{p}_1 \times \mathbf{i})^t \\ \vdots \\ (\mathbf{p}_v \times \mathbf{i})^t \end{bmatrix}, \quad \begin{bmatrix} (\mathbf{p}_1 \times \mathbf{j})^t \\ \vdots \\ (\mathbf{p}_v \times \mathbf{j})^t \end{bmatrix}, \quad \begin{bmatrix} (\mathbf{p}_1 \times \mathbf{k})^t \\ \vdots \\ (\mathbf{p}_v \times \mathbf{k})^t \end{bmatrix}.$$

For the standard basis $\mathbf{i}, \mathbf{j}, \mathbf{k}$ of 3-space, the first three solutions generate the *translations* and the final three generate the *rotations* about the origin. Checking a non-collinear triangle (say the first three rows and blocks for the first three vertices in Example 9.1), it is easy to verify that these six solutions are linearly independent. (Note that for two vertices, or a collinear configuration, the rotation about the line through these vertices will give $\mathbf{u}_i = \mathbf{0}$ for all vertices. This will appear as a dependence among the six generating first-order flexes and the space of trivial first-order flexes will have dimension 5.)

COUNTING LEMMA 9.1.2. *A set of at least two edges $E$ with $|E| > 3|V(E)| - 6$ is 3-dependent for every 3-space configuration $\mathbf{p}$.*

*Equivalently, a set $E$ is 3-independent at some 3-configuration only if, for all subsets $E'$ with at least two edges, $|E'| \leq 3|V(E')| - 6$.*

We demonstrate that some 3-independent graphs have this maximal rank $3|V| - 6$, at general position configurations $\mathbf{p}$ – i.e. they are bases of the matroid $\mathcal{R}_3(|V|; \mathbf{p})$. Given a graph $G = (V, E)$, a *vertex 3-addition of* 0 is the addition of one new vertex, 0, and three new edges $(0, i), (0, j), (0, k)$, creating the graph $G' = (V', E')$.

A graph $G = (V, E)$, with at least three vertices, is 3-*simple* if there is an ordering of the vertices $\sigma(1), \sigma(2), \ldots, \sigma(|V|)$ such that:
   (i) $G_3$ is the triangle $K_{\{\sigma(1), \sigma(2), \sigma(3)\}}$;
   (ii) for $i \geq 3$, $G_{i+1}$ is a vertex 3-addition of $\sigma(i + 1)$ to $G_i$;
   (iii) $G_{|V|}$ is $G$.

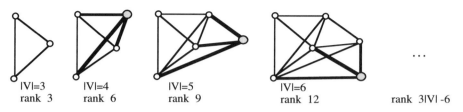

|V|=3   |V|=4   |V|=5   |V|=6            ...
rank 3  rank 6  rank 9  rank 12          rank 3|V| -6

FIGURE. 9.2. *Building a 3-simple graph as a basis for the complete 3-rigidity matroid $\mathcal{R}_3(n; \mathbf{p})$.*

VERTEX 3-ADDITION LEMMA 9.1.3. *Given a framework $G(\mathbf{p})$ and a vertex 3-addition of $0$ creating the framework $G'(\mathbf{p}_0, \mathbf{p})$, with $\mathbf{p}_0, \mathbf{p}_i, \mathbf{p}_j, \mathbf{p}_k$ not coplanar:*
  1. *$G'(\mathbf{p}_0, \mathbf{p})$ is 3-independent if and only if $G(\mathbf{p})$ is 3-independent;*
  2. *rank $\mathcal{R}_3(G'; (\mathbf{p}_0, \mathbf{p})) =$ rank $\mathcal{R}_3(G; \mathbf{p}) + 3$.*

PROOF. The proof for the Vertex 2-Addition Lemma 2.1.3 extends directly.

STATIC 3-RIGIDITY THEOREM 9.1.4. *For any $n \geq 3$ and any general position 3-configuration $\mathbf{p}$ on $n$ vertices, the edges $E$ of any 3-simple graph $G$ on $n$ vertices are a basis of $\mathcal{R}_3(n; \mathbf{p})$ of rank $3n - 6$.*

PROOF. If $n = 3$, $K_3$ is a triangle, which has rank $3 = 3 \times 3 - 6$. This graph is both 3-simple and a basis of the matroid.

If $n$ is greater than 3, we prove, by induction that there is a 3-simple graph $G$ of size $3n - 6$ and its edges are a basis for $K_n$. Assume $G_k$ is a 3-simple graph for $n = k$, which is a basis for $\mathcal{R}_3(k; \mathbf{p}|_k)$ of rank $3k - 6$. Let $G_{k+1}$ be a vertex 3-addition of $k + 1$ with edges $(1, k + 1), (2, k + 1), (3, k + 1)$. Since $\mathbf{p}$ is in general position, $\mathbf{p}_1, \mathbf{p}_2, \mathbf{p}_3, \mathbf{p}_{k+1}$ are not coplanar and $E_{k+1}$ is 3-independent of rank $(3k - 6) + 3 = 3(k + 1) - 6$. By Lemma 9.1.2, this is a maximal 3-independent set in $K_{k+1}$, so $E_{k+1}$ is a basis.

Any framework $G(\mathbf{p})$ on $|V| \geq 3$ for which $R_G(\mathbf{p})$ has rank $3|V| - 6$ (or for which $|V| \leq 2$, $G = K_{|V|}$ and $\mathbf{p}$ has distinct points) is *statically 3-rigid*. We also say that the edge set $E$ is *statically 3-rigid* on $V(E)$ at $\mathbf{p}$. Any framework $G(\mathbf{p})$ for which all first-order motions are trivial motions (are in the space generated by the translations and rotations) is *first-order 3-rigid*. Because of the rank of this trivial solution space and the standard result of linear algebra that the dimension of the entire solution space is $3|V| -$ rank $R_G(\mathbf{p})$, it is easy to check that static 3-rigidity is equivalent to first-order rigidity for a 3-configuration [**Co2,RW,Wh4**].

There are other edge sets which are not 3-simple but which satisfy the condition of Lemma 9.1.2 to be 3-independent for some configurations (Figure 9.3). These examples are also bases for the 3-rigidity matroid for some choices of $\mathbf{p}$ (see below).

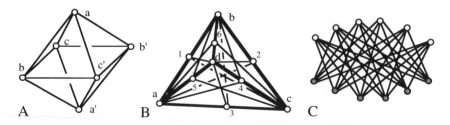

FIGURE. 9.3. *Graphs which are not 3-simple, but which are bases for the 3-rigidity matroid.*

At generic 3-configurations (defined either as configurations which achieve the maximum rank of rigidity matrices for graphs on these vertices or as points with algebraically independent coordinates), we create the *generic 3-rigidity matroid on the graph*: $\mathcal{R}_3(G)$. For the complete graph on $n$ vertices, this is written $\mathcal{R}_3(n)$.

**9.2. A basic problem.** We have shown that the generic 3-rigidity matroid on $K_V$ has rank $3|V| - 6$, for $|V| \geq 3$, and that any non-empty subset of edges $E'$ with $|E'| > 3|V(E')| - 6$ is dependent in this matroid. For plane graphs, these counts characterized the matroid, by characterizing the circuits (see also §A.1). The analogous definition here would be:

a non-empty set $E'$ of edges is a circuit if and only if
  (i) $|E'| = 3|V(E')| - 5$ and,
  (ii) for all subsets $E''$ on at least three vertices $V(E'')$:
     $|E''| \leq 3|V''| - 6$.

The first clue that this is not sufficient is that this definition does not apply to a single edge (which is 3-independent): $|E| = 1 = 3(2) - 5$. The next example explores this difficulty in more depth.

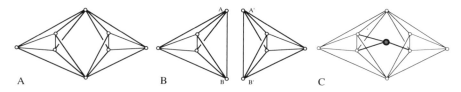

FIGURE. 9.4. *A non-rigid circuit (A) of the generic 3-rigidity matroid, obtained by circuit exchange of two smaller circuits (B). Insisting on 3-connectivity does not eliminate the dependence (C).*

EXAMPLE 9.2.1. Figure 9.4A illustrates the 'two bananas' example which has several critical properties:
  1. This 3-dependent set is obtained by a 'circuit exchange' on the common edge $a, b$ of two smaller circuits, $K_5$, which satisfy the criterion: $|E'| = 10 = 3|V(E')| - 5$.
  2. This is a 3-circuit (minimal 3-dependent) because deleting any one edge leaves a graph which is a 3-simple graph with one edge deleted.
  3. This circuit of the generic 3-rigidity matroid satisfies the Necessary Counts Lemma: all subsets $E''$ on at least 3-vertices satisfy $|E''| \leq 3|V(E'')| - 6$.
  4. This circuit is not 3-rigid: freezing one side permits a rotation about the 'hinge' $ab$ between the bananas.

This example lives in the matroidal properties of the count: $3|V| - 6$. It does not depend on particular properties of our rigidity matrix, but will reappear in any matroid with the basic rank $3n - 6$ on all complete graphs $K_n$, $n \geq 3$. In §10 we will see a second matroid with the same counts and this same difficulty.

Since the framework of Figure 9.4C is obtained by a vertex 3-addition to the two bananas, it is also 3-dependent. However, this is now 3-connected, confirming that an additional '3-connectivity assumption' will not eliminate our difficulty.

In §2, our second basic tool for characterizing bases in the generic rigidity matroid was the Henneberg 2-constructions. We have a partial result for 3-space. A graph $G'$ is an *edge 3-split* of the graph $G$ on $a, b; c, d$, if $\{a, b\}$ is an edge of $G$

and $G'$ is formed from $G$ by adding a new vertex $0$, removing the edge $\{a, b\}$, and adding four new edges $(0, a), (0, b), (0, c), (0, d)$ (Figure 9.5B).

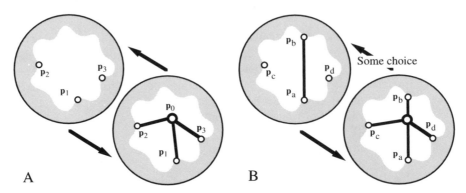

FIGURE. 9.5. *Two inductive steps which preserve 3-rigidity and give Henneberg 3-constructions for bases: (A) vertex 3-addition; (B) edge 3-split.*

EDGE 3-SPLIT THEOREM 9.2.2 [**TW2**]. *Assume $G'$ is an edge 3-split of $G = (V, E)$ on $a, b; c, d$, and $\mathbf{p}$ is a 3-configuration with $\mathbf{p}_a, \mathbf{p}_b, \mathbf{p}_c, \mathbf{p}_d$ not coplanar.*

*If $G(\mathbf{p})$ is 3-independent (statically 3-rigid), then $G'(\mathbf{p}_0, \mathbf{p})$ is 3-independent (statically 3-rigid) for almost all $\mathbf{p}_0$, including $\mathbf{p}_0$ a distinct point on $\mathbf{p}_a, \mathbf{p}_b$.*

*Conversely, if $G'(\mathbf{p}_0, \mathbf{p})$ is 3-independent (statically 3-rigid) for some choice of $\mathbf{p}_0$, with vertex $0$ connected to exactly vertices $a, b, c, d$ at four general position points then, for some edge $e$ of vertices in $a, b, c, d$, $E = E' \cup \{e\} - \{(0, a), (0, b), (0, c), (0, d)\}$ is independent (statically 3-rigid) at $\mathbf{p}$ and $G'$ is an edge 3-split of $G = (V' - 0, E)$.*

PROOF. One proof follows the same pattern as the proof given for the plane. The only change is that $K_4$ is now 3-independent and statically 3-rigid.

We outline a second approach in a more matroidal spirit. This is representative of certain 'replacement techniques' or 'small circuits techniques' which are helpful in analyzing the behaviour of particular frameworks [**Wh4**].

We first show that the edge 3-split preserves 3-independence and 3-rigidity. We add the vertex $0$ by a three valent addition to vertices $a, c, d$, choosing $0$ to lie on the line $a, b$, distinct from $a$ and $b$. This preserves 3-independence, 3-rigidity etc. Now consider the three collinear edges $\{a, b\}, \{a, 0\}, \{b, 0\}$. Realized on a line, this polygon (triangle) forms a circuit. Therefore, replacing any two of these with any other two gives an equivalent rank for the matrix (and matroid). We replace $\{a, b\}, \{a, 0\}$ with $\{a, 0\}, \{b, 0\}$ to complete the edge split.

Assume that $G'(\mathbf{p}_0, \mathbf{p})$ is 3-rigid, but that each of the possible subgraphs $G$ is 3-dependent. Therefore the complete graph on the four vertices $a, b, c, d$ is contained in the closure of $E_1 = E' - \{(0, a), (0, b), (0, c), (0, d)\}$. This complete graph $K_4$ is 3-independent if the points are not coplanar, so this $K_4$ extends to a 3-independent set $E_2$ with the same closure as $E_1$, $|E_2| = |E_1| = 3(|V|) - 10$. If we now add back the four edges $(0, a), (0, b), (0, c), (0, d)$, we have at least the 3-dependence on the $K_5$ $0, a, b, c, d$, so the rank of $E_2 \cup \{(0, a), (0, b), (0, c), (0, d)\}$ is now smaller than $|E_2| + 4$. However this has the same rank as $E' = E_1 \cup \{(0, a), (0, b), (0, c), (0, d)\}$ which was assumed to be $|E_1| + 4 = |E_2| + 4$. This contradiction completes the proof.

For a graph $G = (V, E)$ with at least three vertices, a *Henneberg 3-construction* is an ordering of the vertices $\sigma(1), \sigma(2), \ldots, \sigma(|V|)$ and a sequence $G_3, \ldots, G_{|V|}$ of graphs such that:

(i) $G_3$ is the triangle $K_{\{\sigma(1), \sigma(2), \sigma(3)\}}$;

(ii) for $i \geq 3$, $G_{i+1}$ is a 3-addition of vertex $\sigma(i+1)$ to $G_i$ or $G_{i+1}$ is an edge 3-split on $G_i$ which adds a vertex $\sigma(i+1)$;

(iii) $G_{|V|}$ is $G$.

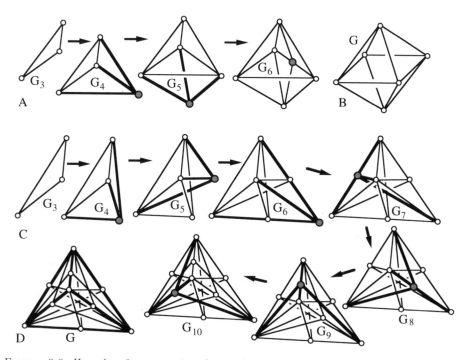

FIGURE. 9.6. *Henneberg 3-constructions for two bases for generic 3-rigidity matroids.*

HENNEBERG'S THEOREM 9.2.3 [**TW2**]. *If $G$ has a Henneberg 3-construction then $G$ is a basis for $\mathcal{R}_3(n)$.*

PROOF. The Henneberg 3-construction is a sequence of vertex 3-additions and edge 3-splits. These preserve the generic 3-independence and the generic 3-rigidity.

REMARK 9.2.4. Unlike the plane version, this theorem does not run both directions. Some graphs with $|E| = 3|V| - 6$ have all vertices of valence greater than or equal to 5. For example, the graph of an icosahedron or the graph of Figure 9.4C are bases of $\mathcal{R}_3(12)$. These graphs cannot be created by a Henneberg 3-construction. While Henneberg's original work contained a number of important results, it also contained critical errors which misrepresented this case [**He,TW2**]. In §9.4 we offer some conjectures for extended 3-constructions to create all bases.

**9.3. More partial results.** A number of additional plane results do generalize to generic 3-rigidity. Of course, these will remain incomplete as characterizations of the bases and independent sets.

FIRST-ORDER FLEX TEST 9.3.1. *For any 3-configuration $\mathbf{p}$ for the graph $K_n$, the following are equivalent:*

1. *the edge $\{h, k\}$ is not in the closure of the set $E$, $\langle E \rangle$, in $\mathcal{R}_3(n; \mathbf{p})$;*
2. *every self-stress $\omega$ on $E \cup \{h, k\}$ is zero on $\{h, k\}$;*
3. *there is a first-order flex $\mathbf{u}$ on $G = (V, E)$, such that $(\mathbf{p}_h - \mathbf{p}_k) \cdot (\mathbf{u}_h - \mathbf{u}_k) \neq 0$.*

The Plane Generic Gluing Lemma extends to the generic 3-rigidity matroid.

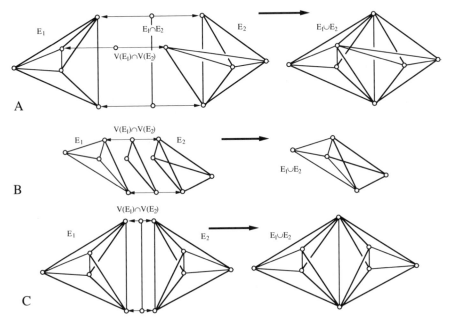

FIGURE. 9.7. *Gluing spatial frameworks: for 3-rigidity (A); for 3-independence (B); and for non-rigidity (C).*

GENERIC 3-GLUING LEMMA 9.3.2. *For two edge sets $E_1$, $E_2$,*

1. *if $E_1$ and $E_2$ are generically 3-rigid and $|V(E_1) \cap V(E_2)| \geq 3$, the set $E_1 \cup E_2$ is generically 3-rigid (Figure 9.7A);*
2. *if $E_1$ and $E_2$ are generically 3-independent and $E_1 \cap E_2$ is generically 3-rigid on $V(E_1 \cap E_2)$, the set $E_1 \cup E_2$ is generically 3-independent (Figure 9.7B);*
3. *if $|V(E_1) \cap V(E_2)| < 3$, then the closure $\langle E_1 \cup E_2 \rangle$ in $\mathcal{R}_3(V(E_1) \cup V(E_2))$ is contained in $K_{V(E_1)} \cup K_{V(E_2)}$ (Figure 9.7C).*

PROOF. The basic proofs follow the plane pattern of Lemma 3.1.4. For 3, the desired non-trivial first-order flex is a rotation about the hinge of the two shared vertices (or a general position hinge through the single shared vertex etc.).

REMARK 9.3.3. For any matroid on the edges of a complete graph, properties 1 and 3 are equivalent to the defining properties of an *abstract 3-rigidity matroid* [**GSS**]. Specifically, an *abstract m-rigidity matroid* is a matroid on the edges of complete graphs with the closure operator $\langle \cdot \rangle$ satisfying two additional properties:

C5. For any sets $E, F \subseteq K_n$, if $|V(E) \cap V(F)| < m$, then $\langle E \cup F \rangle \subset (K_{V(E)} \cup K_{V(F)})$;

C6. If $E, F \subset K_n$ satisfy $\langle E \rangle = K_{V(E)}$ and $\langle F \rangle = K_{V(E)}$ (they are *rigid*) and $|V(E) \cap V(F)| \geq m$, then $\langle E \cup F \rangle = K_{V(E \cup F)}$.

Our Generic Gluing Lemmas 3.1.4 and 9.3.2 show that $\mathcal{R}_2(n)$ is an abstract 2-rigidity matroid and that $\mathcal{R}_3(n)$ is an abstract 3-rigidity matroid.

A number of properties, including the necessary counts $2|V| - 3$ and $3|V| - 6$ follow from these properties [**GSS**]. Consider an abstract 3-rigidity matroid:

1. From C5 with $F = \emptyset$, we see that $\langle E \rangle \subseteq K_{V(E)}$;
2. Analyzing two sides of triangle as $E$, $F$ in C5, we see that the third edge is independent – so a triangle has rank 3;
3. Analyzing two triangles joined at an edge as $E$, $F$ in C5, we see that the final edge of a $K_4$ is independent – so $K_4$ has rank 6;
4. Using $E = K_N$ and $F = K_4$ (with an overlap of 3 vertices) in property C6, $\langle E \cup F \rangle = K_{V(E \cup F)} = K_{N+1}$ and the rank of $E \cup F$ is $\leq$ rank $E + 3$;
5. By induction from 2 and 4, we see that rank $\mathcal{R}_3(n) = 3n - 6$ for $n \geq 3$.

We will return to these abstract 3-rigidity matroids in §9.4 and §10.

There are two special classes of graphs for which we have substantial results: complete bipartite graphs and triangulated surfaces. We state the bipartite result without proof [**BR,Wh3**], but follow with a remark which gives the geometric origin of the generic result. Recall that a *complete bipartite graph* is a graph $K_{m,n} = (A \cup B, A \times B)$, where $A$ and $B$ are disjoint sets of cardinality $|A| = m$ and $|B| = n$.

BIPARTITE GRAPHS THEOREM 9.3.4. *A complete bipartite graph $K_{m,n}$, is generically rigid in 3-space if and only if $m + n \geq 10$ and $m, n > 3$.*

REMARK 9.3.5. The geometric basis of this generic result is the following corollary of the static analysis of Bolker and Roth [**BR**].

QUADRICS TO BIPARTITE MOTIONS 9.3.6 [**Wh3**]. *For a bipartite graph $K_{m,n}$ and a general position configuration $\mathbf{p}$ in d-space, the framework has only trivial first-order flexes in d-space if and only if the points of m and n each affinely span d-space and the complete set of vertices do not lie on a quadric surface in d-space.*

In 3-space, we need at least 4 vertices to affinely span the space and any 9 points lie on a quadric (satisfy a quadratic equation). The two 'minimal' 3-rigid complete bipartite graphs are $K_{4,6}$, which is also generically 3-independent with $|E| = 24 = 3|V| - 6$, and $K_{5,5}$, which is a generic 3-circuit with $|E| = 25 = 3|V| - 5$.

In the plane, this result gives $K_{3,3}$ as the minimal 2-rigid (and 3-independent) complete bipartite graph. In §11 we will apply this corollary to 4-space.

For graphs of triangulated surfaces (and other graphs), strong results can be proven by induction using a graph construction called a 'vertex split' (Figure 9.8).

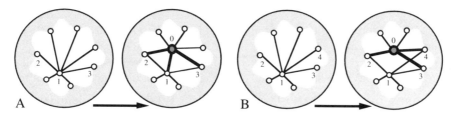

FIGURE. 9.8. *Vertex 3-splits on two edges (A) and three edges (B), which preserve generic 3-rigidity.*

For a graph $G$, with a vertex 1 incident to the edges $(1,2), (1,3), \ldots, (1,k), (1, k+1), \ldots, (1, m)$ the *vertex 3-split of 1 on two edges* $(1,2), (1,3)$ is the modified graph $G'$ with edges $(1,4), \ldots, (1,k)$ removed and an added vertex 0 incident with new edges $(0,1), (0,2), (0,3), \ldots, (0,k)$ (Figure 9.8A).

For a graph $G$, with a vertex 1 incident to the edges $(1,2), (1,3), (1,4), (1,5)$, $\ldots$, $(1,k)$, $(1,k+1), \ldots, (1,m)$ the *vertex 3-split of 1 on three edges* $(1,2), (1,3)$, $(1,4)$ is the modified graph $G'$ with edges $(1,5), \ldots, (1,k)$ removed and an added vertex 0 incident with new edges $(0,2), (0,3), (0,4), \ldots, (0,k)$ (Figure 9.8B).

For vertex 3-splits on two edges, the following result is proven in [**Wh9**], using a 'limiting special position' argument. For vertex 3-splits on three edges, the result was overlooked, but it has a simpler related argument.

VERTEX SPLITS THEOREM 9.3.7. *If the graph $G'$ is a vertex 3-split of a generically 3-rigid graph $G$ on three edges or a vertex 3-split of $G$ on two edges then $G'$ is generically 3-rigid.*

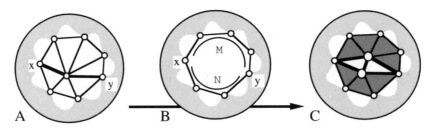

FIGURE. 9.9. *If a vertex 3-split on two edges of the graph of a triangulated surface (A) follows the cycle of edges at the vertex (B), then the new graph also comes from a triangulated surface (C).*

Applying 3-splits on two edges carefully (Figure 9.9), we take a triangulated surface to a triangulated surface. For example, all triangulated spheres can be created from the tetrahedron by a sequence of vertex 3-splits on 2-edges [**Wh9**].

TRIANGULATED 2-SURFACES THEOREM 9.3.8 [**Fo**]. *The graph of any triangulated 2-surface is generically 3-rigid* (Fogelsanger's Theorem).

*In particular, the graph of any triangulated sphere is generically 3-rigid and 3-independent* (Gluck's Theorem [**Gl**]).

REMARK 9.3.9. That the graphs of triangulated spheres are also 3-independent follows from Euler's formula. Since $|V| - |E| + |F| = 2$ and $2|E| = 3|F|$ for any triangulated surface:

$$3|E| = 3|V| + 3|F| - 6 \quad \Leftrightarrow \quad |E| = 3|V| - 6.$$

For other closed surfaces, such as a triangulated torus, the counts give $|E| > 3|V| - 6$ and the graphs cannot be independent in the generic 3-rigidity matroid.

While the general result is proven by an induction on the graphs of minimal 2-cycles in homology, the special result for spheres has an older geometric source:

THEOREM OF CAUCHY AND DEHN 9.3.10 [**Ca,Wh3**]. *The edges and vertices of any strictly convex triangulated sphere form an independent 3-rigid framework.*

This result and its relatives are the true mathematical source of rigidity results for the Geodesic Domes promoted by Buckminster Fuller's mystical pronouncements. For non-convex spheres, Connelly has found a special position counterexample which is not only first-order flexible, but actually flexible [**Co1**].

If we add a single additional edge (a 'shaft') to a triangulated sphere whose graph is 4-connected, we create a circuit of the generic 3-rigidity matroid [**Wh6**].

We have a final geometric (and induced combinatorial) result which establishes a critical pattern for 'lifting' first-order results from one dimension to the next.

The *cone graph* $G * u$ is created from $G = (V, E)$ by adding a new vertex $u$ and the $|V|$ edges $(u, i)$ for all vertices $i \in V$. For a 3-configuration $\mathbf{p}$ on $V$, the *cone projection from* $\mathbf{p}_0$ is a configuration $\mathbf{q} = \Pi_0(\mathbf{p})$ in the plane (placed as a plane $P$ in 3-space) on the vertices $V \backslash 0$, such that $\mathbf{p}_i$ is on the line $\mathbf{q}_i \mathbf{p}_0$ for all $i \neq 0$.

CONING THEOREM 9.3.11 [**Wh2**]. *For a 3-configuration* $\mathbf{p}$, *with no edge at* $\mathbf{p}_0$ *parallel to the plane* $P$, *a framework* $G(\Pi_0(\mathbf{p}))$ *is first-order rigid (independent) in the plane if and only if the cone* $(G * 0)(\mathbf{p})$ *is first-order rigid (independent) in 3-space.*

This gives an obvious generic corollary, which also extends to 2-circuits by a more subtle geometric argument which we omit.

GENERIC CONING COROLLARY 9.3.12. *A graph* $G$ *is generically 2-rigid (2-independent, a 2-circuit) if and only if the cone graph* $G * u$ *is 3-rigid (3-independent, a 3-circuit, respectively).*

The reader can verify that the same connections exist between bases (trees) and 2-circuits (polygons) and their cones in the plane (2-simple cones and wheels).

**9.4. Combinatorial conjectures for 3-space.** As we noted in §9.2, a basis for the generic 3-rigidity matroid may have all vertices of valence larger than 4. A quick check of the necessary count: $|E| = 3|V| - 6$ (or equivalently, $2|E| = 6|V| - 12$) guarantees that some vertices have valence 5 or less.

What inductive techniques create 5-valent vertices? An analysis of the rigidity matrix of a 3-rigid, independent graph $G$ at a 5-valent vertex confirms that it can be created from smaller 3-rigid, independent graphs by one of the two constructions: $X$-replacement; or double $V$-replacement of Figure 9.10 [**TW2**]. Simple examples confirm that we will require both of these operations, and that a single $V$-replacement may destroy first-order rigidity (by turning, say, a 3-valent vertex at the point of the $V$ into a 2-valent vertex).

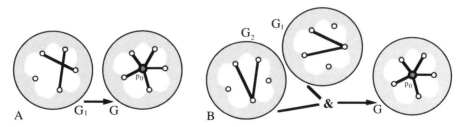

FIGURE. 9.10. *Two inductive techniques creating 5-valent vertices which are conjectured to preserve generic 3-rigidity: X-replacement (A) and double V-replacement (B).*

Certain special cases of these inductive steps, with additional patterns of edges assumed present, are known to preserve generic 3-rigidity [**GSS,TW2**]. For example, from the plane analog of $X$-replacement (Figure 2.8) and the Generic Coning Corollary, we get $X$-replacement within the non-cone edges of any cone. Also a form of single $V$-replacement within triangulated surfaces follows from vertex 3-splits on two edges. However, no general result has been demonstrated.

3-D REPLACEMENT CONJECTURE 9.4.1 [**TW2**]. *The $X$-replacement in Figure 9.10A takes a graph $G_1$ which is generically 3-rigid to a graph $G$ which is generically 3-rigid.*

*The double $V$-replacement in Figure 9.10B takes two graphs $G_1, G_2$ which are generically 3-rigid to a graph $G$ which is generically 3-rigid.*

REMARK 9.4.2. If these conjectured steps prove correct in 3-space, then we would have inductive techniques to generate the graphs of all generically 3-rigid and all generically 3-independent frameworks in 3-space. This would yield an exact $O(2^{|V|})$ algorithm for bases of the generic 3-rigidity matroid. Of course, a graph can be checked for generic 3-rigidity by a 'brute force' $O(2^{2^{|V|}})$ algorithm:

Assign the points independent variables as coordinates, form the rigidity matrix, then check the rank by symbolic computation.

On the other hand, if numerical coordinates are chosen for the points 'at random' then the rank of this numerical matrix (computed in $O(|E|^3)$ time) will be the generic value, with probability 1.

For the complexity of algorithms on graphs, generic 3-rigidity belongs to an interesting class. The decision problem for generic 3-rigidity has a random polynomial algorithm but no known polynomial time (or even exponential) algorithm. The matroid of §10 will provide a related example.

In a specific sense, it is conjectured that the generic 3-rigidity matroid is the 'freest' matroid of its type. A matroid $\mathcal{M}$ is *maximal in a class of matroids* on the same elements if every set $S$ which is independent in some matroid of this class is independent in $\mathcal{M}$. The whole process of Henneberg 2-constructions and Laman's Theorem implicitly verifies that the generic 2-rigidity matroid is maximal among all abstract 2-rigidity matroids.

THE MAXIMAL CONJECTURE 9.4.3 [**GSS**, Conjecture 2.5.1]. *There is a maximal abstract 3-rigidity matroid on the edges of the complete graph $K_n$.*

*The generic 3-rigidity matroid $\mathcal{R}_2(n)$ is this maximal abstract 3-rigidity matroid on $K_n$.*

The existence of a maximal matroid illustrates the essential problem of inducing matroids by submodular functions which are negative on singletons (see §A.1).

In the next section, we will see a second candidate for this maximal abstract 3-rigidity matroid. In §11, we will see a pair of counter-examples which demonstrates that generic 4-rigidity is *not* the maximal abstract 4-rigidity matroid.

Related to this Maximal Conjecture is a conjectured formula, due to Andreas Dress, for the rank (or equivalently, the degree of freedom) of a set of edges in the generic 3-rigidity matroid (or at least the maximal abstract 3-rigidity matroid). Effectively, the Dress Conjecture, described in the Unsolved Problems section of this book and [**GSS** §5.7], conjectures the rank function for such a maximal matroid.

Again there are certain easy connectivity results: every generically 3-rigid set on at least 4 vertices is vertex 3-connected as a graph. (This is implicit in the Generic 3-Gluing Theorem.) While a circuit may be only 2-connected in a vertex sense (recall the double bananas), it will be at least 5-connected in an edge sense. Finally, it is easy to adapt the counterexample of Figure 3.6 to give a graph which is 11-connected but not generically 3-rigid. We conjecture that 12-connectivity is sufficient (see §12.1 for some supporting evidence).

SUFFICIENT CONNECTIVITY CONJECTURE 9.4.4. *If a graph $G$ is vertex 12-connected then $G$ is generically 3-rigid.*

## 10. The $C_2^1$-Cofactor Matroid from Bivariate Splines

We will present a second abstract 3-rigidity matroid on graphs which has rank $3n - 6$ on complete graphs $K_n$ and shares numerous properties with generic 3-rigidity. While this matroid has its own role in the theory of bivariate splines, we present it here for additional insight into the underlying matroidal structure associated with the generic 3-rigidity matroid. Portions of this theory are explicit and implicit in the papers [**ASW,Wh10,11**] as well several unpublished manuscripts.

**10.1. The definition of the $C_2^1$-cofactor matroid.** Recall the form of a $C_1^0$-stress from §5. For a graph $G$ and a plane configuration $\mathbf{p}$, this is an assignment of scalars to the edges such that:

$$\sum_{j \mid \{i,j\} \in E} \lambda_{i,j} L^{i,j} = \sum_{j \mid \{i,j\} \in E} \lambda_{i,j} [A^{ij} x + B^{ij} y + C^{ij}] \equiv 0.$$

With a small adjustment in the algebra, the same plane configuration can be used to define the $C_2^1$-cofactor matroid. We write the quadratic form:

$$[L^{i,j}]^2 = [A^{i,j} x + B^{i,j} y + C^{i,j}]^2$$
$$= (A^{i,j})^2 x^2 + 2A^{i,j} B^{i,j} xy + (B^{i,j})^2 y^2 + 2A^{i,j} C^{i,j} x + 2B^{i,j} C^{i,j} y + (C^{i,j})^2,$$

for $i < j$ and $[L^{j,i}]^2 = -[L^{i,j}]^2$ for $j > i$, where $L^{i,j} = A^{i,j} x + B^{i,j} y + C^{i,j} = 0$ is the standard equation for the line, as defined in §5. Recall that the definition of $L^{i,j}$ gave $L^{i,j} = -L^{j,i}$. However since $(L^{i,j})^2 = (L^{j,i})^2$, we have to reinsert the antisymmetry into the vectors $[L^{j,i}]^2$.

A $C_2^1$-*cofactor on the plane graph* $G(\mathbf{p})$ is an assignment of scalars $\lambda_{i,j}$ to the edges $\{i, j\} \in E$ such that for each vertex $j$:

$$\sum_{j \mid \{i,j\} \in E} \lambda_{ij} [L^{i,j}]^2 \equiv 0.$$

These $C_2^1$-cofactor equations appear to impose $6|V|$ linear conditions in the $|E|$ variables $\lambda_{i,j}$. However this is misleading. If we focus on the *reduced $C_2^1$-vector*: $\mathbf{D}_{i,j}^2 = [(A^{ij})^2, 2A^{ij} B^{ij}, (B^{ij})^2]$ for $i < j$ and $\mathbf{D}_{j,i}^2 = -[(A^{ij})^2, 2A^{ij} B^{ij}, (B^{ij})^2]$ for $j > i$, then we can *uniquely* reconstruct $[L^{i,j}]^2$ using the point $\mathbf{p}_i$ (or $\mathbf{p}_j$).

$C_2^1$-COFACTOR REDUCTION LEMMA 10.1.1. *Given a plane graph $G(\mathbf{p})$, an assignment of scalars $\lambda_{i,j}$ is a $C_2^1$-cofactor if and only if the scalars satisfy the reduced $C_2^1$-vector equations:* $\sum_{j \mid \{i,j\} \in E} \lambda_{ij} \mathbf{D}_{i,j}^2 = \mathbf{0}$.

PROOF. Since the entries in $\mathbf{D}_{i,j}^2$ are just the first three of the six coefficients in $[L^{i,j}]^2$, it is clear that any $C_2^1$-cofactor satisfies the reduced $C_2^1$-vector equations.

Conversely, given $\mathbf{D}_{i,j}^2 = [\,(A^{i,j})^2,\ 2A^{i,j}B^{i,j},\ (B^{i,j})^2\,]$, $i < j$ and $\mathbf{p}_i = (x_i, y_i)$, we have $A^{i,j}x_i + B^{i,j}y_i + C^{i,j} = 0$ or $C^{i,j} = -(A^{i,j}x_i + B^{i,j}y_i)$, so

$$2A^{i,j}C^{i,j} = 2A^{i,j}(-A^{i,j}x_i - B^{i,j}y_i) = -2(A^{i,j})^2 x_i - 2A^{i,j}B^{i,j}y_i;$$
$$2B^{i,j}C^{i,j} = 2B^{i,j}(-A^{i,j}x_i - B^{i,j}y_i) = -2A^{i,j}B^{i,j}x_i - 2(B^{i,j})^2 y_i;$$
$$(C^{i,j})^2 = (-A^{i,j}x_i - B^{i,j}y_i)^2 = (A^{i,j})^2 x_i^2 + 2A^{i,j}B^{i,j}x_i y_i + (B^{i,j})^2 y_i^2;$$

which generate the other three coefficients.

These three 'reconstructions' are linear equations in the coefficients of $\mathbf{D}_{i,j}^2$. Therefore, assuming $\sum_{j\,\mid\,\{i,j\}\in E} \lambda_{ij}\mathbf{D}_{i,j}^2 = \mathbf{0}$, for the coefficients of $x$ in the extended $C_2^1$-cofactor equation we have:

$$\sum_{j\,\mid\,\{i,j\}\in E} \lambda_{ij}2A^{i,j}C^{i,j} = \sum_{j\,\mid\,\{i,j\}\in E} \lambda_{ij}\big[-2(A^{i,j})^2 x_i - 2A^{i,j}B^{i,j}y_i\big]$$
$$= -2x_1\Big[\sum_{j\,\mid\,\{i,j\}\in E} \lambda_{ij}(A^{i,j})^2\Big] - y_i\Big[\sum_{j\,\mid\,\{i,j\}\in E} \lambda_{ij}2A^{i,j}B^{i,j}\Big] = 0 + 0.$$

A similar check works for the remaining terms of the cofactor equation. We conclude that the reduced $C_2^1$-vector equations imply the complete $C_2^1$-cofactor equations.

With this lemma, we can write the $C_2^1$-cofactors as row dependencies of an $|E|$-by-$3|V|$ $C_2^1$-cofactor matrix:

$$M_2^1(G;\mathbf{p}) = \begin{bmatrix} \mathbf{D}_{1,2}^2 & -\mathbf{D}_{1,2}^2 & \cdots & 0\ 0\ 0 & \cdots & 0\ 0\ 0 & \cdots & 0\ 0\ 0 \\ \vdots & \vdots & \ddots & \vdots & \ddots & \vdots & \ddots & \vdots \\ 0\ 0\ 0 & 0\ 0\ 0 & \cdots & \mathbf{D}_{i,j}^2 & \cdots & -\mathbf{D}_{i,j}^2 & \cdots & 0\ 0\ 0 \\ \vdots & \vdots & \ddots & \vdots & \ddots & \vdots & \ddots & \vdots \end{bmatrix}$$

The analogy to the pattern of the 3-rigidity matrix is visible.

The row dependencies of this matrix define the $C_2^1$-cofactor matroid $\mathcal{M}_2^1(G;\mathbf{p})$, with $C_2^1$-independence and $C_2^1$-dependence. In particular, for any generic plane configuration $\mathbf{p}$ we have the generic $C_2^1$-cofactor matroid on $G$, $\mathcal{M}_2^1(G)$ and the generic $C_2^1$-cofactor matroid $\mathcal{M}_2^1(n)$ on $K_n$.

REMARK 10.1.2. A general sextuple represents a conic section in the plane. Since a scalar multiple does not change the conic represented by an equation, these are viewed as points in projective 5-space. The particular sextuples which represent 'double lines', $[L^{i,j}]^2$ in our cofactor equations, form a special 2-surface in this projective space studied in algebraic geometry – the Veronese surface [**SR**,VII.3].

Implicitly, we are working with some basic analogies between this Veronese surface for double lines and the Grassmannian for the lines in projective 3-space which are implicit in the study of 3-frameworks (see §16 and [**Wh15**]). We have not yet explored how much our presentation resembles material buried in the classical studies of these objects. It is likely that useful information for further work will be found in exploring these algebraic connections for all the matroids presented through the rest of the chapter.

EXAMPLE 10.1.3. Consider the plane graph of Figure 10.1. In this configuration, we have the matrix $M_2^1(G; \mathbf{p})$:

|  | $v_1$ |  |  | $v_2$ |  |  | $v_3$ |  |  | $v_4$ |  |  |
|---|---|---|---|---|---|---|---|---|---|---|---|---|
| $\{1,2\}$ | 0 | 0 | 1 | 0 | 0 | $-1$ | 0 | 0 | 0 | 0 | 0 | 0 |
| $\{1,3\}$ | 1 | 0 | 0 | 0 | 0 | 0 | $-1$ | 0 | 0 | 0 | 0 | 0 |
| $\{1,4\}$ | 1 | $-2$ | 1 | 0 | 0 | 0 | 0 | 0 | 0 | $-1$ | 2 | $-1$ |
| $\{2,3\}$ | 0 | 0 | 0 | 1 | 2 | 1 | $-1$ | $-2$ | $-1$ | 0 | 0 | 0 |
| $\{2,4\}$ | 0 | 0 | 0 | 1 | $-4$ | 4 | 0 | 0 | 0 | $-1$ | 4 | $-4$ |
| $\{3,4\}$ | 0 | 0 | 0 | 0 | 0 | 0 | 4 | $-4$ | 1 | $-4$ | 4 | $-1$ |

These rows are independent and the $C_2^1$-cofactor matroid on $K_4$ has rank 6.

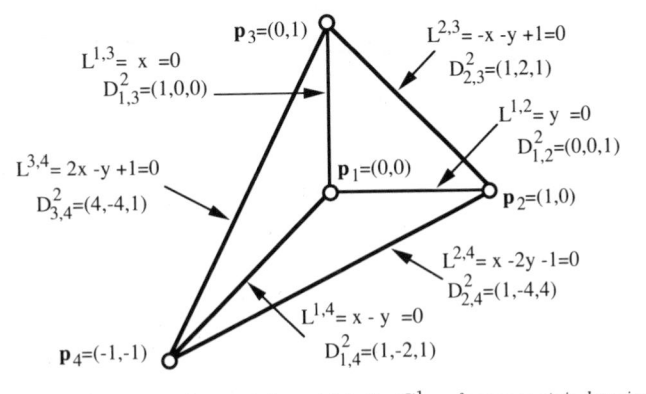

FIGURE. 10.1. *A sample geometric graph for which the $C_2^1$-cofactor matrix has independent rows.*

In particular, the three rows which attach vertex 1 to the independent triangle $2, 3, 4$ are clearly independent. The only way these three rows could be dependent is if the three lines used only two distinct slopes. (In approximation theory for $C_2^1$-splines, vertices with only two slopes are called 'singular' [**ASW,Wh10**].)

We will follow the basic steps used in §9.1 to show that the $C_2^1$-cofactor matroid has rank $3n - 6$ on $K_n$ at any general position plane configuration $\mathbf{p}$.

First, consider the $C_2^1$-*flexes* – solutions to the linear system $M_2^1(G; \mathbf{p})\mathbf{x} = \mathbf{0}$. For configurations on $n \geq 3$ non-collinear points, this contains a subspace of *trivial* $C_2^1$-flexes of dimension 6 generated by the following $C_2^1$-flexes:

1. the three space of $C_2^1$-*translations*: $(\mathbf{t}, \ldots, \mathbf{t})^t$, for $\mathbf{t} \in R^3$;
2. the flex $(2x_1, y_1, 0, \ldots, 2x_i, y_i, 0, \ldots, 2x_n, y_n, 0)^t$;
3. the flex $(0, x_1, 2y_1, \ldots, 0, x_i, 2y_i, \ldots, 0, x_n, 2y_n)^t$;
4. the flex $(x_1^2, 2x_1 y_1, y_1^2, \ldots, x_i^2, 2x_i y_i, y_i^2, \ldots, x_n^2, 2x_n y_n, y_n^2)^t$.

It is easy to see that the $C_2^1$-translations satisfy all equations of rows:

$$\mathbf{D}_{i,j}^2 \cdot \mathbf{t} + \mathbf{D}_{j,i}^2 \cdot \mathbf{t} = (\mathbf{D}_{i,j}^2 - \mathbf{D}_{i,j}^2) \cdot \mathbf{t} = 0.$$

For the flex in 2:

$$\mathbf{D}_{i,j}^2 \cdot (2x_i, y_i, 0) - \mathbf{D}_{i,j}^2 \cdot (2x_j, y_j, 0)$$
$$= 2(A^{i,j})^2 x_i + 2A^{i,j} B^{i,j} y_i - 2(A^{i,j})^2 x_j - 2A^{i,j} B^{i,j} y_j = -2A^{i,j} C^{i,j} + 2A^{i,j} C^{i,j} = 0.$$

An analogous argument works for 3 and 4. We conclude that these generate a space of $C_2^1$-flexes which work for the complete graph on the vertices, for all configurations.

What is the dimension of this space? Choosing the three points $(0,0)$, $(1,0)$ and $(0,1)$, we have the $C_2^1$-flexes:

$$\begin{bmatrix} 1 \\ 0 \\ 0 \\ 1 \\ 0 \\ 0 \\ 1 \\ 0 \\ 0 \end{bmatrix}, \begin{bmatrix} 0 \\ 1 \\ 0 \\ 0 \\ 1 \\ 0 \\ 0 \\ 1 \\ 0 \end{bmatrix}, \begin{bmatrix} 0 \\ 0 \\ 1 \\ 0 \\ 0 \\ 1 \\ 0 \\ 0 \\ 1 \end{bmatrix}, \begin{bmatrix} 0 \\ 0 \\ 0 \\ 2 \\ 0 \\ 0 \\ 0 \\ 1 \\ 0 \end{bmatrix}, \begin{bmatrix} 0 \\ 0 \\ 0 \\ 0 \\ 1 \\ 0 \\ 0 \\ 0 \\ 2 \end{bmatrix}, \begin{bmatrix} 0 \\ 0 \\ 0 \\ 1 \\ 0 \\ 0 \\ 0 \\ 0 \\ 1 \end{bmatrix}$$

which are visibly independent. Any other three non-collinear points are affinely equivalent, and the entire algebraic structure is affinely invariant (also projectively invariant – see §11 [**ASW,Wh10**]). We conclude that the kernel has dimension at least 6, and the maximum rank for the $C_2^1$-cofactor matroid on $K_n$ is $3n - 6$.

$C_2^1$-COFACTOR COUNTING LEMMA 10.1.4. *A set $E$ of at least two edges with $|E| > 3|V(E)| - 6$ is $C_2^1$-dependent for every plane configuration $\mathbf{p}$.*

*Equivalently, a set $E$ is $C_2^1$-independent at some plane configuration only if, for all subsets $E''$ with at least two edges, $|E''| \leq 3|V(E'')| - 6$.*

$\mathcal{M}_2^1$ VERTEX 3-ADDITION LEMMA 10.1.5. *Given a plane graph $G(\mathbf{p})$, and a vertex 3-addition of 0 creating the graph $G'$ and given that the points $\mathbf{p}_0, \mathbf{p}_i, \mathbf{p}_j, \mathbf{p}_k$ are in general position in the plane graph $G'(\mathbf{p}_0, \mathbf{p})$, then*

1. *$G'(\mathbf{p}_0, \mathbf{p})$ is $C_2^1$-independent if and only if $G(\mathbf{p})$ is $C_2^1$-independent;*
2. *rank $\mathcal{M}_2^1(G'; \mathbf{p}_0, \mathbf{p}) = $ rank $\mathcal{M}_2^1(G; \mathbf{p}) + 3$.*

PROOF. Observe in Example 10.1 that the three rows attaching the new vertex are independent in the three new columns for this vertex.

An induction on 3-simple graphs proves the analog of Theorem 9.1.4.

$\mathcal{M}_2^1$ RIGIDITY THEOREM 10.1.6. *For any $n \geq 3$ and any general position plane configuration $\mathbf{p}$ on $n$ vertices, the edges $E$ of any 3-simple graph $G$ on $n$ vertices are a basis of $\mathcal{M}_2^1(n; \mathbf{p})$ of rank $3n - 6$.*

Any plane graph $G(\mathbf{p})$ for which $M_2^1(G; \mathbf{p})$ has rank $3|V| - 6$ (or with $|V| \leq 2$ distinct points) is $C_2^1$-*rigid*. We also say that the edge set $E$ is $C_2^1$-*rigid* on $V(E)$ at $\mathbf{p}$. It is a simple exercise to show that this is equivalent to saying all $C_2^1$-flexes of $G(\mathbf{p})$ are trivial flexes in the space generated by the list above. An edge set $E$ is *generically $C_2^1$-rigid* if its closure in the generic $C_2^1$-cofactor matroid is $K_{V(E)}$. (This is equivalent to being $C_2^1$-rigid for some plane configuration $\mathbf{p}$.)

COROLLARY 10.1.7. *A plane graph $G(\mathbf{p})$ with vertices in general position is not $C_2^1$-rigid if and only if there is a $C_2^1$- flex $\mathbf{u}$ and a pair of vertices $h, k$ (not an edge) such that:*

$$(\mathbf{p}_h - \mathbf{p}_k) \cdot (\mathbf{u}_h - \mathbf{u}_k) \neq 0.$$

With the same counts and the same induction for 3-simple graphs as for $\mathcal{R}_3(n)$, the double bananas of Figure 9.4 are also a circuit in the $C_2^1$-cofactor matroid on any general position plane configuration and in the generic $C_2^1$-cofactor matroid.

REMARK 10.1.8. These $C_2^1$-cofactors originated in the theory of $C_2^1$-splines which are functions over decompositions of the plane into polygonal cells, piecewise polynomial of degree at most 2 and globally $C^1$ [**Bi,ChW,Wh10**]. For a planar drawing of a connected planar graph, up to addition of a global quadric to the function there is an isomorphism between these $C_2^1$-splines on the induced decomposition and the $C_2^1$-cofactors (called 'smoothing cofactors') on the planar graph. To obtain a matroid on all graphs, we have extended the algebra to non-planar graphs.

Recent work of Ripmeester has identified the $C_2^1$-flexes with 'dual splines' over the vertices and edges, using essentially the same $C_2^1$-cofactor matrix [**Ri**]. Like the work on smoothing cofactors, this work on dual splines extends to $C_s^r$-splines for all piecewise polynomials of degree at most $s$ and globally $C^r$ functions over plane polygonal decompositions. Effective use of this duality, from the two sides of the matrix, has already produced some new results for splines [**Ri**]. This duality holds the promise of more progress on the difficult problems of the dimensions of the spaces of multivariate splines for small $s$ and $r$, or equivalently, the rank of the $C_s^r$ on planar graphs $G(\mathbf{p})$ at special configurations in the plane.

**10.2. Partial results for the $C_2^1$-cofactor matroid.** The analogy between the generic $C_2^1$-cofactor matroid and the generic 3-rigidity matroid is strong. All of the known results for the generic 3-rigidity matroid extend to the generic $C_2^1$-cofactor matroid, although the underlying geometric results differ in detail and some of the geometric proofs (such as those for bipartite frameworks) must be changed. We conjecture that the two matroids are isomorphic although we have no algebraic or matrix technique to give this isomorphism (see §10.3).

We transfer more results of §9.2 and §9.3 to the generic $C_2^1$-cofactor matroid.

$\mathcal{M}_2^1$ EDGE 3-SPLIT THEOREM 10.2.1. *Assume $G'$ is an edge 3-split of $G = (V, E)$ on $a, b; c, d$, and $\mathbf{p}$ is a plane configuration with $\mathbf{p}_a, \mathbf{p}_b, \mathbf{p}_c, \mathbf{p}_d$ in general position.*

*If $G(\mathbf{p})$ is $C_2^1$-independent ($C_2^1$-rigid), then $G'(\mathbf{p}_0, \mathbf{p})$ is $C_2^1$-independent ($C_2^1$-rigid) for almost all choices of $\mathbf{p}_0$, including $\mathbf{p}_0$ a distinct point on the line $\mathbf{p}_a \mathbf{p}_b$, not on the line $\mathbf{cd}$.*

*Conversely, if $G'(\mathbf{p}_0, \mathbf{p})$ is $C_2^1$-independent ($C_2^1$-rigid) for some choice of $\mathbf{p}_0$, with vertex 0 connected to exactly vertices $a, b, c$ at three non-collinear points then, for some edge $e$ of vertices in $a, b, c, d$, $E' = E \cup \{e\} - \{(0, a), (0, b), (0, c), (0, c)\}$ is $C_2^1$-independent ($C_2^1$-rigid) at $\mathbf{p}$ and $G'$ is an edge 3-split of $G = (V' - 0, E)$.*

PROOF. The proof used for Theorem 9.2.2 extends to $C_2^1$-independence and $C_2^1$-rigidity. We add the vertex 0 by a three valent addition to vertices $a, c, d$, choosing 0 to lie on the line $a, b$, distinct from $a$ and $b$. This preserves independence, 3-rigidity etc. Now consider the three collinear edges $\{a, b\}, \{a, 0\}, \{b, 0\}$. Realized on a line, this triangle forms a $C_2^1$-circuit (all reduced $C_2^1$-vectors are multiples of the same vector). Therefore, replacing any two of these edges with any other two gives an equivalent rank for the matrix (and matroid). We replace $\{a, b\}, \{a, 0\}$ with $\{a, 0\}, \{b, 0\}$ to complete the edge 3-split.

$\mathcal{M}_2^1$ CONSTRUCTION THEOREM 10.2.2. *If $G$ has a Henneberg 3-construction then the edges of $G$ form a basis for $\mathcal{M}_2^1(|V|)$.*

PROOF. The Henneberg 3-construction is just a sequence of vertex 3-additions and edge 3-splits. These preserve the basic counts and the $C_2^1$-independence.

The proof of Theorem 3.1.3 extends directly to prove:

$C_2^1$-FLEX TEST 10.2.3. *For any plane configuration* $\mathbf{p}$ *for the graph* $K_n$, *the following are equivalent:*
1. *the edge* $\{h, k\}$ *is not in the closure of the set* $E$ *in* $\mathcal{M}_2^1(n; \mathbf{p})$;
2. *every* $C_2^1$-*cofactor* $\lambda$ *on* $E \cup \{h, k\}$ *is zero on* $\{h, k\}$;
3. *there is a* $C_2^1$-*flex* $\mathbf{u}$ *on* $G = (V, E)$, *such that* $(\mathbf{p}_h - \mathbf{p}_k) \cdot (\mathbf{u}_h - \mathbf{u}_k) \neq 0$.

GENERIC $\mathcal{M}_2^1$ GLUING LEMMA 10.2.4. *For two edge sets* $E_1$, $E_2$,
1. *if* $E_1$ *and* $E_2$ *are generically* $C_2^1$-*rigid and* $|V(E_1) \cap V(E_2)| \geq 3$, *the set* $E_1 \cup E_2$ *is generically* $C_2^1$-*rigid;*
2. *if* $|V(E_1) \cap V(E_2)| < 3$, *then the closure in the generic* $C_2^1$-*rigidity matroid,* $\langle E_1 \cup E_2 \rangle$, *is contained in* $K_{V(E_1)} \cup K_{V(E_2)}$;
3. *if* $E_1$ *and* $E_2$ *are generically 3-independent and* $E_1 \cap E_2$ *is generically* $C_2^1$-*rigid, the set* $E_1 \cup E_2$ *is generically* $C_2^1$-*independent.*

PROOF. 1. Since $E_1$ is $C_2^1$-rigid, it has the same closure as a 3-simple graph built onto a triangle in $|V(E_1) \cap V(E_2)|$. Similarly for $E_2$. Combining these two 3-simple graphs on the common triangle, we have a 3-simple graph which is $C_2^1$-rigid and is contained in the closure of $E_1 \cup E_2$. We conclude that the closure of $E_1 \cup E_2$ is also $K_{V(E_1) \cup V(E_2)}$, as required.

2. Consider a single edge through two distinct vertices. The $C_2^1$-matrix has rank 1 and a null space of dimension 5 spanned by the six trivial $C_2^1$-flexes. Therefore some non-trivial linear combination $F_{\mathbf{p}_1, \mathbf{p}_2}$ of these flexes is $\mathbf{0}$ restricted to these vertices. On the other hand, this set has dimension 6 on every non-collinear triangle, so $F_{\mathbf{p}_i, \mathbf{p}_j}$ gives a non-zero component for all vertices off this line. We have a $C_2^1$ analog of a 'rotation' about the line through these points, which is zero only for points on this line. Applying the zero $C_2^1$-flex to the vertices of $E_2$ and $F_{\mathbf{p}_i, \mathbf{p}_j}$ to the vertices of $E_2$, where $V(E_1) \cap V(E_2) \subseteq \{i, j\}$, will give the required $\mathbf{u}$ to demonstrate that $\{h, k\}$ is not in the closure for any $h \in V(E_1) - V(E_1) \cap V(E_2)$ and $k \in V(E_2) - V(E_1) \cap V(E_2)$, as required.

3. If we extend each of the independent sets $E_1$ and $E_2$ to generically $C_2^1$-rigid sets on the same vertices, we will add no edges to the $C_2^1$-rigid set $E_1 \cap E_2$. If $|V(E_1) \cap V(E_2)| \geq 3$, these extended sets $E_1'$ and $E_2'$ will now combine to a rigid set. In this case, a simple counting exercise shows that $E_1' \cup E_2'$ has $|E_1' \cup E_2'| = 3|V(E_1' \cup E_2')| - 6$. Since it is $C_2^1$-rigid, with $|V| \geq 3$, it must be independent and the original subset is also independent.

If $|V(E_1) \cap V(E_2)| \leq 2$, then we have a modified count $|E_1' \cup E_2'| < 3|V(E_1' \cup E_2')| - 6$, and a corresponding set of non-trivial $C_2^1$-flexes for the gap. Again this verifies the independence of the enlarged set and the original set.

COROLLARY 10.2.5. *The generic* $C_2^1$-*cofactor matroid on* $K_n$ *is an abstract 3-rigidity matroid.*

For the $C_2^1$-rigidity of bipartite graphs, we will have a combinatorial proof.

BIPARTITE $C_2^1$-RIGIDITY THEOREM 10.2.6. *A complete bipartite graph* $K_{m,n}$ *is generically* $C_2^1$-*rigid if and only if* $m + n \geq 10$ *and* $m, n > 3$.

PROOF. It is a simple task to show that $K_{4,6}$ has a Henneberg 3-construction, using edge 3-splits on all six edges of $K_4$. Therefore it is $C_2^1$-rigid. For $K_{5,5}$, there is a modified construction, following a Henneberg 3-construction with the simple addition of the last edge to existing vertices (Figure 10.2), so $K_{5,5}$ is also $C_2^1$-rigid.

Finally, any larger complete bipartite graph can be created from these two examples by a sequence of vertex 3-additions and adding edges between existing vertices. These will be $C_2^1$-rigid but not independent.

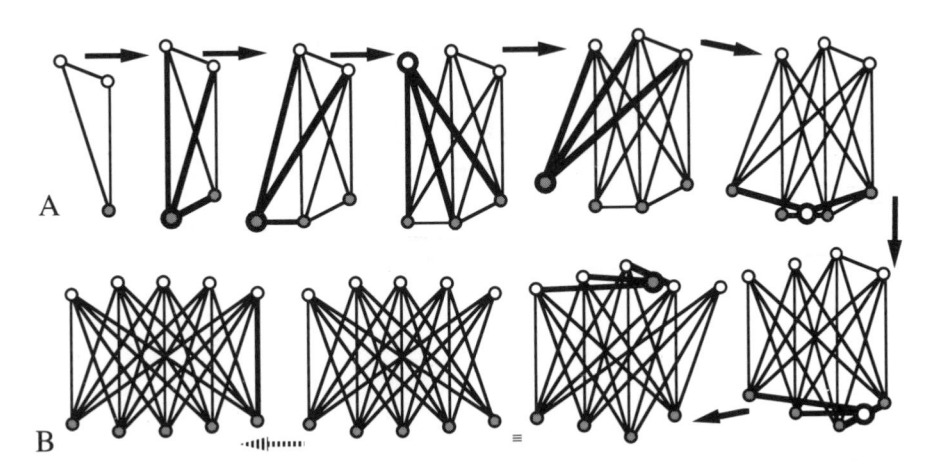

FIGURE. 10.2. *A Henneberg 3-construction for the bipartite graph $K_{5,5}$ minus one bar (A), and then $K_{5,5}$ by adding one edge (B).*

Vertex 3-splits on two edges were first developed for the $C_2^1$-cofactor matroid and they preserve $C_2^1$-rigidity [**ASW,Wh10**]. The vertex 3-split on three edges follows by a simpler argument of the same 'row reduction' style as given there.

$\mathcal{M}_2^1$ VERTEX 3-SPLITS THEOREM 10.2.7. *If the graph $G'$ is a vertex 3-split of a generically $C_2^1$-rigid graph $G$ on 3 edges or a vertex 3-split on 2 edges then $G'$ is generically $C_2^1$-rigid.*

$\mathcal{M}_2^1$ TRIANGULATED 2-SURFACES THEOREM 10.2.8. *The graph of any triangulated 2-surface is generically $C_2^1$-rigid.*

*In particular, the graph of any triangulated sphere is generically $C_2^1$-rigid and $C_2^1$-independent* (Billera's Theorem [**ASW,Bi,Wh10**]).

PROOF OUTLINE. The following three steps form the basis of Fogelsanger's proof for generic 3-rigidity [**Fo**]:

1. An inductive construction of homology 2-cycles using vertex 3-splits, gluing across triangles and basic tetrahedra;
2. The fact that generic tetrahedra are 3-rigid;
3. The fact that gluing across three vertices and vertex 3-splits preserve generic 3-rigidity.

Using the same base inductive construction of homology 2-cycles, we have all the analogs for generic $C_2^1$-rigidity to prove that these same objects are $C_2^1$-rigid.

In §11.4, we will prove a general result, of which the following is a special case.

$\mathcal{M}_2^1$ CONING COROLLARY 10.2.9. *A graph $G$ is $C_1^0$-rigid ($C_1^0$-independent) at the plane configuration* $\mathbf{p}$ *if and only if the cone graph $(G * u)$ is $C_2^1$-rigid ($C_2^1$-independent) at* $\mathbf{p}_u, \mathbf{p}$*, for all $\mathbf{p}_u$ in general position relative to* $\mathbf{p}$*.*

**10.3. Combinatorial $C_2^1$-cofactor conjectures.** With one exception, we will extend the conjectures of §9.4 to the generic $C_2^1$-cofactor matroid. The exception becomes a theorem.

$\mathcal{M}_2^1$ X-REPLACEMENT THEOREM 10.3.1. *The X-replacement in Figure 9.10A takes a generically $C_2^1$-rigid graph $G_1$ to a graph $G$ which is generically $C_2^1$-rigid.*

PROOF. Take a generic plane configuration $\mathbf{p}$ for $G_1$, with the edges $\{1,2\}$, $\{3,4\}$ to be replaced. We do a 3-addition attaching the vertex 0 to vertices 1, 3 and 5 and placing $\mathbf{p}_0$ at the point of intersection of $\mathbf{p}_1\mathbf{p}_2$ and $\mathbf{p}_3\mathbf{p}_4$. The resulting graph is $C_2^1$-rigid.

In this position, we use collinear substitution to replace $\{0,1\},\{1,2\}$ with $\{0,1\},\{0,2\}$ and to replace $\{0,3\},\{3,4\}$ with $\{0,3\},\{0,4\}$. This completes the proof.

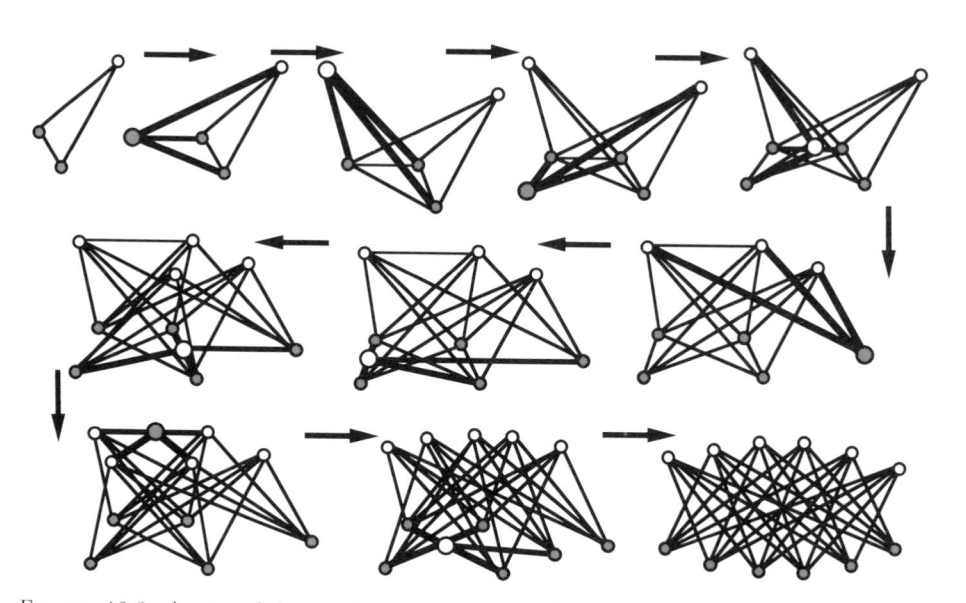

FIGURE. 10.3. *An extended 3-construction for the graph $K_{6,6}$ minus six edges.*

With this added inductive technique, we can verify other bases of the $C_2^1$-cofactor matroid. Figure 10.3 gives such an extended 3-construction, in which the last step is an X-replacement. [This extended 3-construction can be geometrically modified to work for generic 3-rigidity, by ensuring that the two 'crossing edges' for the X-replacement are created as intersecting lines, and kept intersecting as the other vertices are moved around. This is the special case of X-replacement in which the proof of Theorem 10.3.1 also adapts to 3-rigidity.]

The following table compares generic 3-rigidity and generic $C_2^1$-rigidity.

|  | Generic 3-Rigidity | Generic $C_2^1$-Rigidity |
|---|---|---|
| rank $K_n$, $n \geq 3$ | $3n - 6$ | $3n - 6$ |
| vertex 3-addition | Yes | Yes |
| edge 3-split | Yes | Yes |
| 3-constructions | Yes | Yes |
| abstract 3-rigidity | Yes | Yes |
| vertex 3-split | Yes | Yes |
| simplicial 2-surfaces | Rigid | Rigid |
| 3-coning | Yes | Yes |
| 3-$X$-replacement | Conjectured | Yes |
| double $V$-replacement | Conjectured | Conjectured |
| Dress Conjecture | Conjectured | Conjectured |
| $K_{4,6}$ | Basis | Basis |
| $K_{5,5}$ | Circuit | Circuit |
| maximal abstract 3-rigidity matroid | Conjectured | Conjectured |

All of our experience with this 'connection' indicates that the generic $C_2^1$-cofactor matroid is isomorphic to the generic 3-rigidity matroid.

$\mathcal{M}_2^1$ 3-Rigidity Isomorphism Conjecture 10.3.2. *For every $n$, the generic $C_2^1$-cofactor matroid on $K_n$ is the maximal abstract 3-rigidity matroid. In particular, the generic $C_2^1$-cofactor matroid on $K_n$ is isomorphic to the generic 3-rigidity matroid on $K_n$.*

## 11. Higher Dimensions

We have seen the nearly complete combinatorial theory of the generic 2-rigidity matroid and the isomorphic generic $C_1^0$-cofactor matroid break down into a mix of partial results and conjectures for the generic 3-rigidity matroid and the (possibly isomorphic) generic $C_2^1$-cofactor matroid. Up one step, the generic 4-rigidity matroid and the generic $C_3^2$-cofactor matroid cause even more difficulties. The analogs of most of the conjectures of §9.4 have counterexamples in the generic 4-rigidity matroid. Surprisingly, we have not found counterexamples in the generic $C_3^2$-cofactor matroid which is provably not isomorphic and remains a candidate for the maximal abstract 4-rigidity matroid.

As the chart of Figure 1.1 suggests, these matroids have analogs for higher dimensions (rigidity) and for higher algebraic powers (cofactors). We present the general pattern, then turn to the critical counterexamples in 4-space.

**11.1. Generic rigidity in $d$-space.** A *$d$-space framework* is a standard graph $G = (V, E)$ and a *$d$-configuration* $\mathbf{p} : V \to \mathbb{R}^d$. A *dependence* or *self-stress* on the framework $G(\mathbf{p})$ is an assignment $\omega : E \to \mathbb{R}$, with $\omega\{i,j\} = \omega_{i,j} = \omega_{j,i}$, such that, for each vertex $i$:

$$\sum_{j \mid \{i,j\} \in E} \omega_{i,j}(\mathbf{p}_i - \mathbf{p}_j) = \mathbf{0}.$$

As before, these self-stresses are the row dependencies of the *rigidity matrix* of the framework, $R_G(\mathbf{p})$.

The independence of rows in this matrix defines the *d-rigidity matroid on G* at a $d$-configuration $\mathbf{p}$, written $\mathcal{R}_d(G; \mathbf{p})$, on the edges of the graph. The framework $G(\mathbf{p})$ is *d-independent* if its edge set is independent in $\mathcal{R}_d(G; \mathbf{p})$, and the *rank* of $G(\mathbf{p})$ is the rank of $\mathcal{R}_d(G; \mathbf{p})$. Working at some (all) generic configurations in $d$-space (for example configurations with algebraically independent coordinates) we have the *generic d-rigidity matroid* $\mathcal{R}_d(G)$ and $\mathcal{R}_d(n)$ for the complete graph $K_n$.

We anticipate the rank $d|V| - \binom{d+1}{2}$ for $\mathcal{R}_d(n; \mathbf{p})$ at a general position $d$-configuration $\mathbf{p}$ on $n$ vertices, where $n \geq d$.

Given a graph $G = (V, E)$, a *vertex d-addition of* 0 is the addition of one new vertex, 0, and $d$ new edges $(0, i_1), \ldots, (0, i_d)$ creating the graph $G' = (V', E')$.

VERTEX $d$-ADDITION LEMMA 11.1.1. *Given a framework $G(\mathbf{p})$ and a vertex d-addition of* 0 *creating $G'$, the framework $G'(\mathbf{p}_0, \mathbf{p})$, with $\mathbf{p}_0, \mathbf{p}_{i_1}, \ldots, \mathbf{p}_{i_d}$ in general position in d-space, then*

1. *$G'(\mathbf{p}_0, \mathbf{p})$ is d-independent if and only if $G(\mathbf{p})$ is d-independent;*
2. *rank $\mathcal{R}_d(G'; \mathbf{p}_0, \mathbf{p}) = $ rank $\mathcal{R}_d(G; \mathbf{p}) + d$.*

PROOF. The core of the argument is that the vectors $\mathbf{p}_0 - \mathbf{p}_{i_1}, \ldots, \mathbf{p}_0 - \mathbf{p}_{i_d}$ are linearly independent in $d$-space when the points are in general position in $d$-space. Moreover, these vectors are the only non-zero entries in the columns under vertex 0, so their independence is sufficient for the independence of their rows.

The *first-order d-flexes* are the solutions $\mathbf{u} = (\ldots, \mathbf{u}_i, \ldots) \in \mathbb{R}^{d|V|}$ to the equations $R_G(\mathbf{p})\mathbf{u} = \mathbf{0}$. That is, for each edge $\{i, j\}$: $(\mathbf{p}_i - \mathbf{p}_j) \cdot (\mathbf{u}_i - \mathbf{u}_j) = 0$. The guaranteed *trivial first-order d-flexes* for any graph $G$ on a $d$-configuration $\mathbf{p}$ are generated by the $d$ translations and the $\binom{d}{2}$ rotations about 'axes' given by setting 2 of the coordinates zero. (The resulting velocities at a point $\mathbf{p}_i$ are found by the minors of a fixed set of $d - 2$ points spanning this axis along with the point $\mathbf{p}_i$ – a $d$-space generalization of 'cross product'.) It is a direct calculation to show that, for configurations in $d$-space on at least $d$ points affinely spanning a hyperplane, these generators are independent and the space of trivial first-order $d$-flexes has dimension $\binom{d+1}{2}$ (see below). Any framework $G(\mathbf{p})$ for which all first-order motions are trivial motions is *first-order d-rigid*.

$K_d$ LEMMA 11.1.2. *For the graph $K_d$ and a general position d-configuration $\mathbf{p}$ on d vertices:*

1. *the framework $K_d(\mathbf{p})$ is d-independent;*
2. *the space of trivial d-flexes has dimension $\binom{d+1}{2}$ on this configuration;*
3. *$K_k(\mathbf{p})$ is d-rigid for $k \leq d$.*

PROOF. These proofs are by induction through $K_k$, $1 \leq k \leq d$.

1.    For $K_1$, with no edges and one vertex, the matrix is vacuously $d$-independent. $K_{k+1}$ comes from $K_k$ by a vertex $k$-addition – essentially a vertex $d$-addition with some rows removed (clearly preserving $d$-independence).

2.    The $d$ translations $\mathbf{e}_i$, $1 \leq i \leq d$ applied to a vertex are independent first-order $d$-flexes. Assume $K_k(\mathbf{p})$ has a $\frac{k(2d-k+1)}{2}$ dimensional space of trivial $d$-flexes. As we add the vertex $k+1$, we will add the $d-k$ trivial rotations about $\{\mathbf{p}_i\}_{i \leq k}$, which were dependent on previous flexes on the $k$ vertices but give independent velocities

when extended to $\mathbf{p}_{k+1}$. For $K_d$, this gives the independence of the full set of $\binom{d+1}{2}$ trivial first-order $d$-flexes.

3. For general position configurations $\mathbf{p}$, the complete graph $K_k$ has rank $\binom{k}{2}$ from 1, so the space of first-order $d$-flexes has dimension $dk - \binom{k}{2}$. From 2 the space of trivial first-order $d$-flexes has dimension $\frac{k}{2}[2d - k + 1] = dk - \binom{k}{2}$, so all first-order $d$-flexes are trivial for $k \leq d$.

$d$-COUNTING LEMMA 11.1.3. *A set $E$ of edges on at least $d$ vertices with $|E| > d|V(E)| - \binom{d+1}{2}$ is $d$-dependent for every $d$-configuration $\mathbf{p}$.*

*Equivalently, a set $E$ on $n \geq d$ vertices is $d$-independent at some $d$-configuration $\mathbf{p}$ only if, for all subsets $E'$ with at least $d$ vertices, $|E'| \leq d|V(E')| - \binom{d+1}{2}$.*

A graph $G = (V, E)$, with at least $d$ vertices, is $d$-*simple* if there is an ordering of the vertices $\sigma(1), \sigma(2), \ldots, \sigma(|V|)$ such that:
  (i) $G_d$ is th complete graph on $\{\sigma(1), \ldots, \sigma(d)\}$;
  (ii) for $i \geq d$, $G_{i+1}$ is a vertex $d$-addition of $\sigma(i+1)$ to $G_i$;
  (iii) $G_{|V|}$ is $G$.

STATIC $d$-RIGIDITY THEOREM 11.1.4. *For any $n \geq d$ and any general position $d$-configuration $\mathbf{p}$ on $n$ vertices, the edges $E$ of any $d$-simple graph $G$ on $n$ vertices are a basis of $\mathcal{R}_d(n; \mathbf{p})$ of rank $dn - \binom{d+1}{2}$.*

PROOF. For $n = d$ this is the $K_d$ Lemma. If $n > d$, a simple induction on the number of vertices using vertex $d$-addition completes the proof.

Any $d$-framework $G(\mathbf{p})$ for which $R_G(\mathbf{p})$ has rank $d|V| - \binom{d+1}{2}$, (or for which $|V| \leq d$, $G = K_V$ and $\mathbf{p}$ is in general position) is *statically $d$-rigid*. We also say that the edge set $E$ is *statically $d$-rigid* on $V(E)$ at $\mathbf{p}$. It is easy to check that static $d$-rigidity is equivalent to first-order $d$-rigidity.

COROLLARY 11.1.5. *A framework $G(\mathbf{p})$ with vertices affinely spanning $d$-space is not first-order $d$-rigid (equivalently statically $d$-rigid) if and only if there is a first order flex $\mathbf{u}$ and a pair of vertices $h, k$ (not an edge) such that:*

$$(\mathbf{p}_h - \mathbf{p}_k) \cdot (\mathbf{u}_h - \mathbf{u}_k) \neq 0.$$

EXAMPLE 11.1.6. For $d \geq 4$, we have several variants of the 2-bananas example of Figure 9.4. By the count $|E| = \binom{d+2}{2} > d \times (d+2) - \binom{d+1}{2}$, $K_{d+2}$ is dependent at all configurations – and, in fact, is a circuit of the $d$-rigidity matroid. (Deleting one edge leaves a vertex $d$-addition of a $d$-simple $K_{d+1}$.) As with the 'two bananas' in 3-space, circuit exchange with two copies of $K_{d+1}$ across a single shared edge gives a dependent set (by matroid circuit exchange). Since all subsets with one edge removed are $d$-simple, this is a circuit.

If we glued up to $d - 1$ vertices together, we would have other dependent and flexible frameworks (see the Gluing Lemma below).

For $d$-constructions we need the analog of edge splits for $d$-space. A graph $G'$ is an *edge $d$-split* of the graph $G$ on $c_1, c_2; c_3, \ldots, c_{d+1}$, if $\{c_1, c_2\}$ is an edge of $G$ and $G'$ is formed from $G$ by adding a new vertex 0, removing the edge $\{c_1, c_2\}$, and adding $d + 1$ new edges $\{0, c_1\}, \ldots, \{0, c_{d+1}\}$.

EDGE $d$-SPLIT THEOREM 11.1.7. *Assume $G'$ is an edge $d$-split of $G$ on $c_1, c_2$; $c_3, \ldots, c_{d+1}$, and $\mathbf{p}$ is a $d$-configuration with $\mathbf{p}_{c_1}, \mathbf{p}_{c_2}, \ldots, \mathbf{p}_{c_{d+1}}$ in general position.*

*If $G(\mathbf{p})$ is $d$-independent (statically $d$-rigid), then $G'(\mathbf{p}_0, \mathbf{p})$ is $d$-independent (statically $d$-rigid) for almost all choices of $\mathbf{p}_0$.*

*Conversely, if $G'(\mathbf{p}_0, \mathbf{p})$ is $d$-independent (statically $d$-rigid) for some choice of $\mathbf{p}_0$, with vertex $0$ connected to exactly vertices $c_1, c_2, \ldots, c_{d+1}$ at $d+1$ general position points then, for some edge $e$ among the vertices $c_1, \ldots, c_{d+1}$, $E' = E \cup \{e\} - \{(0, c_1), \ldots, (0, c_{d+1})\}$ is $d$-independent (statically $d$-rigid) at $\mathbf{p}$ and $G'$ is an edge $d$-split of $G = (V' - 0, E)$.*

PROOF. We add the vertex $0$ by a $d$-valent addition to vertices $c_1, c_3, \ldots, c_{d+1}$, choosing $0$ to lie on the line $c_1, c_2$, distinct from $\mathbf{p}_{c_1}$ and $\mathbf{p}_{c_1}$. This preserves $d$-independence, $d$-rigidity etc. Now consider the three collinear edges $\{c_1, c_2\}$, $\{c_1, 0\}$, $\{c_2, 0\}$. Realized on a line, this triangle forms a circuit. Therefore, replacing any two of these with any other two gives an equivalent rank for the matrix (and matroid). We replace $\{c_1, c_2\}, \{c_1, 0\}$ with $\{c_1, 0\}, \{c_2, 0\}$ to complete the edge $d$-split.

The converse follows by an argument analogous to the Edge 3-Split Theorem, based on the observation that the $K_{d+1}$ among $c_1, \ldots, c_{d+1}$ is statically $d$-rigid, and the $K_{d+2}$ among $0, \ldots, c_{d+1}$ is a $d$-circuit in general position.

For a graph $G = (V, E)$ with at least $d$ vertices, a *$d$-construction* is an ordering of the vertices $\sigma(1), \sigma(2), \ldots, \sigma(|V|)$ and a sequence $G_d, \ldots, G_{|V|}$ of graphs such that:

(i)   $G_d$ is the complete graph on on $\{\sigma(1), \ldots, \sigma(d)\}$;
(ii)  for $i \geq d$, $G_{i+1}$ is a vertex $d$-addition of vertex $\sigma(i+1)$ to $G_i$
      or $G_{i+1}$ is an edge $d$-split on $G_i$ which adds a vertex $\sigma(i+1)$;
(iii) $G_{|V|}$ is $G$.

$d$-CONSTRUCTION THEOREM 11.1.8 [**TW2**]. *If a graph $G$ on $n$ vertices has a $d$-construction then $G$ a basis for $\mathcal{R}_d(n)$.*

As expected, the generic $d$-rigidity is an abstract $d$-rigidity matroid. We state the appropriate Gluing Lemma.

GENERIC $d$-GLUING LEMMA 11.1.9. *For two edge sets $E_1$, $E_2$,*

1.  *if $E_1$ and $E_2$ are generically $d$-rigid and $|V(E_1) \cap V(E_2)| \geq d$, the set $E_1 \cup E_2$ is generically $d$-rigid;*
2.  *if $|V(E_1) \cap V(E_2)| < d$, then the closure $\langle E_1 \cup E_2 \rangle$ in $\mathcal{R}_d(V(E_1) \cup V(E_2))$ is contained in $K_{V(E_1)} \cup K_{V(E_2)}$;*
3.  *if $E_1$ and $E_2$ are generically $d$-independent and $E_1 \cap E_2$ is generically $d$-rigid, the set $E_1 \cup E_2$ is generically $d$-independent.*

PROOF. The proofs follow the patterns we established for the generic 3-rigidity matroid and for the generic $C_2^1$-cofactor matroid.

COROLLARY 11.1.10. *Generic $d$-rigidity is an abstract $d$-rigidity matroid.*

However, we will see below that generic $d$-rigidity is not the 'most general' abstract $d$-rigidity matroid!

In closing this section, we note that vertex $d$-splits, on $d-1$ or $d$ edges, preserve generic $d$-rigidity [**Wh9**], that triangulated $(d-1)$-hypersurfaces are generically $d$-rigid [**Fo**], and that a graph $G$ is generically $(d-1)$-rigid ($(d-1)$-independent) if and only if the cone graph $G * u$ is generically $d$-rigid [**Wh2**].

REMARK 11.1.11. The generic $d$-ridigity of triangulated $(d-1)$-surfaces is a direct proof of a combinatorial result: the Lower Bound Theorem for edges of manifolds (without boundary) [**Ka1**]. Specifically, the counts for generic $d$-rigidity show that a triangulated manifold on $n$ vertices (including any simplicial $(d-1)$-sphere) satisfies s $|E| \geq dn - \binom{d+1}{2}$.

While this bound is exact for 2-spheres in 3-space, it is not, in general, exact for 3-spheres in 4-space or analogs in higher spaces. [**Ka1**] gives details of which spherical polytopes make this bound exact.

**11.2. Bipartite graphs and $X$-replacement for $\mathcal{R}_d(G; \mathbf{p})$.** Key to this subsection are some basic bipartite graphs.

$d$-SPACE BIPARTITE GRAPHS 11.2.1. *A complete bipartite graph $K_{m,n}$, with $m > 1$, is generically $d$-rigid if and only if $m + n \geq \binom{d+2}{2}$ and $m, n > d$.*

PROOF. It is easy to verify that if $1 < m \leq d$ then the bipartite framework is under counted and therefore not generically $d$-rigid.

The bound of $m + n \geq \binom{d+2}{2}$ follows from the fact that any $\binom{d+2}{2} - 1$ points lie on a quadric surface in $d$-space, so the resulting framework cannot be rigid by [**Wh3**]. With $m + n \geq \binom{d+2}{2}$, we can avoid such a quadric and obtain $d$-rigidity, by the geometric result in Remark 9.3.5.

EXAMPLE 11.2.2. Consider the complete bipartite graph $K_{6,7}$. It has the required number of edges for generic 4-rigidity: $|E| = 42 = 4 \times 13 - 10 = 4|V| - \binom{5}{2}$.

However with the $m + n = 13 < 15$ vertices, there must be a quadric surface through these points. [If we write a second degree polynomial in the four variables there are 15 coefficients which satisfy one homogeneous linear equation for each of the $m + n$ points. The solution space to these equations is a *family of quadric surfaces through the points* of dimension at least $15 - (m+n)$.] The 4-frameworks on this graph cannot be statically 4-rigid. We conclude that this graph is 4-dependent at all configurations in 4-space.

In fact, the subgraph $K_{6,6}$ is a generic 4-circuit. With 12 vertices, a generic configuration for the twelve points lies on a family of quadrics of dimension $15 - 12 = 3$. This means that generic configurations leave a 13-dimensional space of first-order flexes [**Wh3**], and the rank of the ridigity matrix is $4|V| - 13 = 35 = |E| - 1$. Therefore it is generically 4-dependent. Since any proper subset has a modified 4-construction (a 4-construction with edges omitted) which can be extracted from Figure 11.1, each proper subset is generically 4-independent.

The graph $K_{6,6}$ (or its relatives such as $K_{6,7}$ and $K_{7,7}$) provide a counterexample to the 4-dimensional versions of a number of the conjectures of §9.4.

Consider the the extended 4-construction of Figure 11.1. We begin with a generically 4-independent subgraph of $K_4$, namely $K_4$ with two incident edges omitted. Up to the last step, the construction steps of vertex 4-addition and edge 4-splits will preserve this generic 4-independence. Therefore the second last graph is generically 4-independent and only the last one, $K_{6,6}$, is 4-dependent. *The 4-dimensional version of $X$-replacement fails!*

The fact that $X$-replacement works in the generic 2-rigidity matroid and fails for generic 4-rigidity places the conjectured $X$-replacement for generic 3-rigidity in perspective as *the* borderline case. Recall that $X$-replacement was proven for the generic $C_2^1$-cofactor matroid in §10.4. In §11.4, we will prove that a related abstract

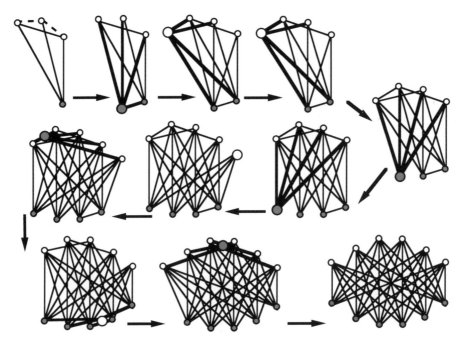

FIGURE. 11.1. *An extended 4-construction for $K_{6,6}$, in which the last step is an X-replacement.*

4-rigidity matroid does satisfy $X$-replacement. The problem is *not* a matroidal difficulty for general abstract 4-rigidity matroids, such as that created by the Gluing Lemmas and non-rigid circuits (see §11.5).

The difficulty is 'geometric' – embedded in the geometric roots of the generic 4-rigidity matroid. Essentially the problem is that distance, and distance preserving maps, rely on quadric equations. Quadric surfaces are both bad for bipartite frameworks and numerous in 4-space.

These examples and counterexamples generalize to generic $d$-rigidity for $d \geq 4$.

EXAMPLE 11.2.3. Repeated coning of $K_{6,6}$ generates a generically $d$-dependent set of edges in each dimension $d \geq 4$. Moreover, the extended 4-construction of $K_{6,6}$ in Figure 11.1 also extends: with $K_d$ replacing $K_4$; vertex $d$-addition replacing vertex 4-addition; edge $d$-splits replacing edge 4-splits; and $d$-$X$-replacement in place of 4-$X$-replacement. Since the end result is a generically $d$-dependent set, and vertex $d$-replacement and edge $d$-splits preserve generic $d$-independence, we conclude that the $d$-analog of $X$-replacement fails to preserve generic $d$-independence.

EXAMPLE 11.2.4. A second source of higher dimensional counterexamples will be $K_{d+2,d+2}$ in $d \geq 4$. Some simple counts of vertices, edges and quadric surfaces show that $K_{d+2,d+2}$ is a circuit for generic $d$-rigidity.

Specifically, $|E| = (d+2)^2$, $|V| = 2(d+2)$, and a quadric is defined by $\binom{d+2}{2}$ independent linear equations from $\binom{d+2}{2}$ points. Therefore for a generic $d$-configuration, the vertices lie on a space of $\binom{d+2}{2} - 2(d+2)$ quadrics, giving the same space of non-trivial first-order flexes. The maximal set of $d$-independent edges will have size

$$d[2(d+2)] - \binom{d+1}{2} - \left[\binom{d+2}{2} - 2(d+2)\right] = 2(d+1)(d+2) - (d+1)^2$$

$$= (d+1)^2 + 2(d+1) = (d+2)^2 - 1.$$

We conclude that, with $|E| = (d+2)^2$, the set contains a single generic $d$-circuit. That the circuit is the entire set follows from a modified count of a subset.

We anticipate that each of these graphs would have an extended $d$-construction, using one step of the $d$-analog of $X$-replacement. These, and their cones, would provide additional counterexamples to $X$-replacement in $d$-space.

**11.3. Higher $C_s^{s-1}$-cofactors.** The algebraic construction which defined the $C_1^0$-cofactor and $C_2^1$-cofactor matroids can be extended to the family of $C_s^{s-1}$-cofactor matroids, analogous to the $(s+1)$-rigidity matroids (recall Figure 1.1). For $i < j$, we write the $s$-form:

$$[L^{i,j}]^s = [A^{i,j}x + B^{i,j}y + C^{i,j}]^s \quad \text{and} \quad [L^{j,i}]^s = -[A^{i,j}x + B^{i,j}y + C^{i,j}]^s = -[L^{i,j}]^s,$$

where $L^{i,j} \equiv A^{i,j}x + B^{i,j}y + C^{i,j} = 0$ is the standard equation for the line, as defined in §5. Notice that, if $s$ is odd, $(-L^{i,j})^s = -[L^{i,j}]^s$ and the antisymmetry is built in from the ground. For convenience in tracking these signs, we define

$$Sign(i,j) = \begin{cases} 1 & \text{if } i < j \\ -1 & \text{if } i > j \\ 0 & \text{if } i = j \end{cases} \quad \text{and} \quad Sign_s(i,j) = \begin{cases} 1 & \text{if } s \text{ is odd and } i \neq j \\ 1 & \text{if } s \text{ is even and } i < j \\ -1 & \text{if } s \text{ is even and } i > j \\ 0 & \text{if } i = j \end{cases}$$

which gives $[L^{i,j}]^s = Sign_s(i,j)(L^{i,j})^s$ for all $i, j, s$.

A $C_s^{s-1}$-*cofactor on the plane graph* $G(\mathbf{p})$ is an assignment of scalars $\lambda_{i,j} = \lambda_{j,i}$ to the edges $\{i, j\} \in E$ such that for each vertex $j$:

$$\sum_{j \,|\, \{i,j\} \in E} \lambda_{ij}[L^{i,j}]^s \equiv 0.$$

These $C_s^{s-1}$-cofactor equations impose $\binom{s+2}{2}|V|$ linear conditions in the $|E|$ variables $\lambda_{i,j}$. However, we can again focus on the *reduced $C_s^{s-1}$-vector* formed by the $s+1$ terms of degree $s$ in $x, y$: $\mathbf{D}_{i,j}^s = [\,(A^{ij})^s, \; s(A^{ij})^{s-1}B^{ij}, \dots, \; (B^{ij})^s\,]$, for $i < j$ and $\mathbf{D}_{j,i}^s = -\mathbf{D}_{i,j}^s$ for $i > j$. We can uniquely reconstruct all entries of $[L^{i,j}]^s$ using the point $\mathbf{p}_i$ (or $\mathbf{p}_j$) and the reduced vector $\mathbf{D}_{i,j}^s$.

REDUCED $C_s^{s-1}$-COFACTOR LEMMA 11.3.1. *Given a plane graph* $G(\mathbf{p})$, *an assignment of scalars* $\lambda_{i,j}$ *is a* $C_s^{s-1}$-*cofactor if and only if the scalars satisfy the reduced* $C_s^{s-1}$-*cofactor equations:* $\sum_{j \,|\, \{i,j\} \in E} \lambda_{ij}\mathbf{D}_{i,j}^s = \mathbf{0}$.

PROOF. Since the entries in $\mathbf{D}_{i,j}^s$ are the first $s+1$ of the $\binom{s+2}{2}$ entries in $[L^{i,j}]^s$, it is clear that any $C_s^{s-1}$-cofactor satisfies the reduced cofactor equations.

Conversely, assume we are given the $(s+1)$-vector:

$$\mathbf{D}_{i,j}^s = [\,(A^{ij})^s, \; s(A^{ij})^{s-1}B^{ij}, \dots, \; (B^{ij})^s\,],$$

$i < j$ and $\mathbf{p}_i = (x_i, y_i)$. With $A^{i,j}x_i + B^{i,j}y_i + C^{i,j} = 0$ and $C^{i,j} = -(A^{i,j}x_i + B^{i,j}y_i)$, for $0 < k$ and $k + l \leq s$ we have

$$\binom{s}{k,l}(C^{i,j})^k(A^{i,j})^{s-k-l}(B^{i,j})^l = \binom{s}{k,l}(-1)^k\left[A^{i,j}x_i + B^{i,j}y_i\right]^k(A^{i,j})^{s-k-l}(B^{i,j})^l$$

$$= (-1)^k\binom{s}{k,l}\sum_{m=0}^{m=k}\binom{k}{m}(A^{i,j})^{s-m-l}(B^{i,j})^{m+l}x_i^{k-m}y_i^m$$

$$= \sum_{m=0}^{m=k}\binom{s}{m+l}(A^{i,j})^{s-l-m}(B^{i,j})^{m+l}(-1)^k\left[\frac{\binom{s}{k,l}\binom{k}{m}}{\binom{s}{m+l}}x_i^{k-m}y_i^m\right]$$

$$= \sum_{n=l}^{n=k+l}\binom{s}{n}(A^{i,j})^{s-n}(B^{i,j})^n(-1)^k\left[\frac{\binom{s}{k,l}\binom{k}{n-l}}{\binom{s}{n}}x_i^{k+l-n}y_i^{n-l}\right].$$

This is clearly a linear expression in the given entries $\mathbf{D}_{i,j}^s(n) = \binom{s}{n}(A^{i,j})^{s-n}(B^{i,j})^n$, $0 \leq n \leq s$ and in the coefficients which are computed from $\mathbf{p}_i$: $\frac{\binom{s}{k,l}\binom{k}{n-l}}{\binom{s}{n}}x_i^{k+l-n}y_i^{n-l}$ $= f_{k,l}(n, \mathbf{p}_i)$, $0 \leq n \leq s$. These equations give recipes for reconstructing all the entries of $[L^{i,j}]^s$ from $\mathbf{D}_{i,j}^s$ and $\mathbf{p}_i$.

Because each reconstruction is linear in the entries of $\mathbf{D}_{i,j}^s$ with fixed coefficients for each $i$, if $\sum_j \lambda_{i,j}\mathbf{D}_{i,j}^s = \mathbf{0}$, then $\sum_j \lambda_{i,j}[L^{i,j}]^s \equiv 0$ and the reduced cofactor equation is satisfied.

With this lemma, we can write the $C_s^{s-1}$-cofactors as row dependencies of the $C_s^{s-1}$-*cofactor matrix* which is $|E|$-by-$(s+1)|V|$:

$$M_s^{s-1}(G; \mathbf{p}) = \begin{bmatrix} \mathbf{D}_{1,2}^s & -\mathbf{D}_{1,2}^s & \cdots & \mathbf{0} & \cdots & \mathbf{0} & \cdots & \mathbf{0} \\ \vdots & \vdots & \ddots & \vdots & \ddots & \vdots & \ddots & \vdots \\ \mathbf{0} & \mathbf{0} & \cdots & \mathbf{D}_{i,j}^s & \cdots & -\mathbf{D}_{i,j}^s & \cdots & \mathbf{0} \\ \vdots & \vdots & \ddots & \vdots & \ddots & \vdots & \ddots & \vdots \end{bmatrix}$$

The analogy to the $(s+1)$-rigidity matrix is again apparent. The independence of rows in this matrix defines the $C_s^{s-1}$-*cofactor matroid*, $\mathcal{M}_s^{s-1}(G; \mathbf{p})$, on the plane geometric graph $G(\mathbf{p})$ and the matroid $\mathcal{M}_s^{s-1}(n; \mathbf{p})$ on the complete graph $K_n(\mathbf{p})$. Working at generic plane configurations $\mathbf{p}$, this also defines the *generic* $C_s^{s-1}$-*cofactor matroid* on the graph $G$, $\mathcal{M}_s^{s-1}(G)$ and defines $\mathcal{M}_s^{s-1}(n)$ on $K_n$.

The core theory of this matroid has not been presented elsewhere. To give the central structure of this family of matroids, without a long build-up or hand-waving, we will use a central technique for transferring results up from $C_s^{s-1}$ to $C_{s+1}^s$: coning. For the rigidity matroids, coning has been used both geometrically and generically for some time [Wh2]. While the analogous coning result was conjectured for the generic cofactor matroids several years ago, we offer the first proof.

For the clearest insight into this transfer, we will use a projective version of the cofactor matroid, including the invariance of the matroid under projective transformations on the configuration [Wh10]. In particular, we will want to place the vertex of the cone onto the line at infinity in order to 'pull' the matrix rows into a simpler pattern. Any reader willing to accept the Coning Theorem without proof can skip to Lemma 11.3.4.

Recall that for any point $\mathbf{p}_i = (x_i, y_i)$ the affine coordinates are $\overline{\mathbf{p}}_i = (x_i, y_i, 1)$. More generally, *homogeneous projective coordinates* for the point, as a column vector, are

$$\tilde{\mathbf{p}}_i = \lambda_i(x_i, y_i, 1)^t = (\lambda_i x_i, \lambda_i y_i, \lambda_i)^t = (u, v, w)^t,$$

giving a point with *weight* $\lambda_i \neq 0$. Coordinates of the form $(u_i, v_i, 0)^t$ will represent a *point at infinity* where the parallel lines with normal $(-v_i, u_i)$ meet. (The triple $(0, 0, 0)^t$ does not represent any point in the projective plane.) Working with these homogeneous coordinates, the linear form corresponding to an edge $i, j$ is also homogenized: $\widetilde{L}^{i,j} = A^{i,j}u + B^{i,j}v + C^{i,j}w$. Writing $\mathbf{U} = (u, v, w)^t$ for the column of variables, the form is $\widetilde{L}^{i,j}(\tilde{\mathbf{p}}) = |\tilde{\mathbf{p}}_i \tilde{\mathbf{p}}_j \mathbf{U}|$. With these homogeneous forms, each projective plane configuration $\tilde{\mathbf{p}}$ defines a corresponding space of $C_s^{s-1}$-cofactors.

In these homogeneous coordinates, a general plane projective transformation $T$ is represented by an invertible 3-by-3 matrix $[T]$: $T(\tilde{\mathbf{p}}) = [T]\tilde{\mathbf{p}}$. The following general result is implicit in [**Wh10**].

$\mathcal{M}_s^{s-1}$ PROJECTIVE INVARIANCE THEOREM 11.3.2. *Given a graph $G$, a projective plane configuration $\tilde{\mathbf{p}}$, and a projective transformation $T$, the plane graphs $G(\tilde{\mathbf{p}})$ and $G(T(\tilde{\mathbf{p}}))$ have isomorphic spaces of $C_s^{s-1}$-cofactors.*

PROOF. Consider any $C_s^{s-1}$-cofactor $\lambda$ for $G(\tilde{\mathbf{p}})$. For each $i$:

$$0 \equiv \sum_{j | \{i,j\} \in E} Sign_s(i,j)\lambda_{i,j}(\widetilde{L}^{i,j})^s = \sum_{j | \{i,j\} \in E} Sign_s(i,j)\lambda_{i,j}|\tilde{\mathbf{p}}_i \tilde{\mathbf{p}}_j \mathbf{U}|^s$$

If we apply the projective transformation $T$, we have:

$$0 \equiv \sum_{j | \{i,j\} \in E} Sign_s(i,j)\lambda_{i,j}\big|[T]^{-1}[T][\tilde{\mathbf{p}}_i \tilde{\mathbf{p}}_j \mathbf{U}]\big|^s$$

$$= \sum_{j | \{i,j\} \in E} Sign_s(i,j)\lambda_{i,j}|T|^{-s}\big|[T]\tilde{\mathbf{p}}_i [T]\tilde{\mathbf{p}}_j [T]\mathbf{U}\big|^s$$

Now replacing the variable vector $\mathbf{U}$ by the vector $[T]^{-1}\mathbf{U}$ (a classical 'linear substitution') has the effect of applying a single induced linear transformation $\widetilde{T}$ to the larger set of coefficients for these forms of degree $s$. This does not effect the equivalence to 0. Therefore, after dividing by the constant $|T|^{-s}$ we have:

$$0 \equiv \sum_{j | \{i,j\} \in E} Sign_s(i,j)\lambda_{i,j}\big|[T]\tilde{\mathbf{p}}_i [T]\tilde{\mathbf{p}}_j [T][T]^{-1}\mathbf{U}\big|^s$$

$$= \sum_{j | \{i,j\} \in E} Sign_s(i,j)\lambda_{i,j}\big|[T]\tilde{\mathbf{p}}_i [T]\tilde{\mathbf{p}}_j \mathbf{U}\big|^s.$$

This is the equation for a $C_s^{s-1}$-cofactor on $G(T(\tilde{\mathbf{p}}))$.

We have a linear injection from the space of $C_s^{s-1}$-cofactors for $G(\tilde{\mathbf{p}})$ to the space of $C_s^{s-1}$-cofactors for $G(T(\tilde{\mathbf{p}}))$. Since $T$ is invertible, this induced map is also invertible, giving the desired isomorphism of the spaces of cofactors.

If we restrict our attention to finite affine points $\overline{\mathbf{p}}_i$ and $\overline{\mathbf{q}}_i = \frac{1}{\lambda_i}T(\overline{\mathbf{p}}_i)$, then this isomorphism of $C_s^{s-1}$-cofactors can be scaled to a linear transformation of the non-homogeneous $C_s^{s-1}$-cofactors, taking $\lambda_{i,j}$ to $\lambda_{i,j}(\lambda_i \lambda_j)^s$.

We have defined the general transformation for the non-reduced equations. The Reduced Cofactor Lemma only works for the equations of finite points, as we implicitly used the points $(x_i, y_i, 1)$ in the computations. Accordingly, in the next proof, we will record the equations for finite points with the reduced vectors, but those for the single infinite point are recorded with the entire vector of coefficients of the $s$-forms.

$\mathcal{M}_s^{s-1}$ CONING THEOREM 11.3.3. *Given a graph $G$ with cone $G*0$ and a plane configuration $\mathbf{p}$ with a point $\mathbf{p}_0$ in general position relative to the points in $\mathbf{p}$, the space of $C_s^{s-1}$-cofactors for $G(\mathbf{p})$ is isomorphic to the space of $C_{s+1}^s$-cofactors for the cone $G*0(\mathbf{p}, \mathbf{p}_0)$.*

PROOF. For convenience, we switch to the corresponding projective forms and take a linear transformation placing the cone vertex at $\tilde{\mathbf{p}}_0 = (0, 1, 0)$ and leaving all other points finite. For all finite pairs of points $i < j$, the line is non-vertical with slope $m_{i,j}$ (by our general position assumption for $\mathbf{p}_0$). Therefore, for $0 < i < j$ we can write: $L^{i,j} = (a_{i,j})(m_{i,j}x + y + b_{i,j})$ with $a_{i,j} \neq 0$. The corresponding reduced cofactor is:

$$\mathbf{D}_{i,j}^s = (a_{i,j})^s [(m_{i,j})^s, \dots, \binom{s}{k}(m_{i,j})^k, \dots, 1].$$

For convenience, we absorb the non-zero scalar $(a_{i,j})^s$ into the coefficients of every cofactor, and write the general reduced $C_s^{s-1}$-vector for $i, j \neq 0$ as:

$$\mathbf{D}_{i,j}^s = Sign(i, j)[(m_{i,j})^s, \dots, \binom{s}{k}(m_{i,j})^k, \dots, 1].$$

The $C_{s+1}^s$-vector is (up to a non-zero scalar we absorb into the cofactor):

$$\mathbf{D}_{i,j}^{s+1} = Sign(i, j)[(m_{i,j})^{s+1}, (s+1)(m_{i,j})^s, \dots, \binom{s+1}{k}(m_{i,j})^k, \dots, 1].$$

For the edges $i, 0$ attached to $(0, 1, 0)$ the linear form for the line, in affine coordinates, is $L^{0,i} = x + c_{0,i}$ and the corresponding reduced $C_{s+1}^s$-vector is:

$$\mathbf{D}_{i,0}^s = -[1, 0, \dots, 0, \dots, 0].$$

Finally, for the equations at the single infinite vertex $\tilde{\mathbf{p}}_0$, we have the coefficients of the full form:

$$[L^{0,i}]^{s+1} = [1, 0, \dots, 0, c_{0,i}, 0, \dots, (c_{0,i})^{s+1}]$$

Consider any $C_{s+1}^s$-cofactor $\lambda^*$ on $G*0(\tilde{\mathbf{p}}, \tilde{\mathbf{p}}_0)$. For each finite point $\tilde{\mathbf{p}}_i$:

$$\mathbf{0} = \sum_{j | \{i,j\} \in E} \lambda_{i,j}^* \mathbf{D}_{i,j}^{s+1} \quad + \lambda_{i,0}^* \mathbf{D}_{i,0}^{s+1}$$

$$= \sum_{j | \{i,j\} \in E} Sign(i, j)\lambda_{i,j}^*[(m_{i,j})^{s+1}, (s+1)(m_{i,j})^s, \dots, \binom{s+1}{k}(m_{i,j})^k, \dots, 1]$$

$$- \lambda_{i,0}^*[1, 0, \dots, 0, \dots, 0]$$

Dropping the first coordinate (and the last vector which is now $\mathbf{0}$) we have:

$$\mathbf{0} = \sum_{j | \{i,j\} \in E} Sign(i, j)\lambda_{i,j}^*[(s+1)(m_{i,j})^s, \dots, \binom{s+1}{k}(m_{i,j})^k, \dots, 1].$$

After multiplying the entry for $(m_{i,j})^k$ by $\frac{\binom{s}{k}}{\binom{s+1}{k}}$, we have

$$\mathbf{0} = \sum_{j|\{i,j\}\in E} Sign(i,j)\lambda_{i,j}^*[(m_{i,j})^s,\dots,\binom{s}{k}(m_{i,j})^k,\dots,1] = \sum_{j|\{i,j\}}\lambda_{i,j}^*\mathbf{D}_{i,j}^s.$$

These scalars are a $C_s^{s-1}$-cofactor $\lambda$ on $G(\tilde{\mathbf{p}})$.

Conversely, assume that $\lambda$ is a $C_s^{s-1}$-cofactor on $G(\tilde{\mathbf{p}})$:

$$\mathbf{0} = \sum_{j|\{i,j\}\in E} Sign(i,j)\lambda_{i,j}[(m_{i,j})^s,\dots,\binom{s}{k}(m_{i,j})^k,\dots,1] = \sum_{j|\{i,j\}\in E}\lambda_{i,j}\mathbf{D}_{i,j}^s.$$

After multiplying the entry for $(m_{i,j})^k$ by $\frac{\binom{s+1}{i}}{\binom{s}{i}}$ we have:

$$\mathbf{0} = \sum_{j|\{i,j\}\in E} Sign(i,j)\lambda_{i,j}[(s+1)(m_{i,j})^s,\dots,\binom{s+1}{k}(m_{i,j})^k,\dots,1].$$

We now add the initial coordinate for $\mathbf{D}_{i,j}^{s+1}$ to each vector and define

$$\lambda_{i,0}^* = \sum_{j|\{i,j\}\in E} Sign(i,j)\lambda_{i,j}(m_{i,j})^{s+1},$$

giving:

$$\mathbf{0} = \sum_{j|\{i,j\}\in E} Sign(i,j)\lambda_{i,j}[(m_{i,j})^{s+1},(s+1)(m_{i,j})^s,\dots,\binom{s+1}{k}(m_{i,j})^k,\dots,1]$$
$$- \lambda_{i,0}^*[1,0,\dots,0,\dots,0]$$
$$= \sum_{j|\{i,j\}\in E\cup}\lambda_{i,j}\mathbf{D}_{i,j}^{s+1} + \lambda_{i,0}\mathbf{D}_{i,0}^{s+1}.$$

These scalars satisfy the $C_{s+1}^s$-cofactor equation at $i$ for all finite points $\tilde{\mathbf{p}}_i$.

What remains to prove is that these induced scalars $\lambda_{i,0}^*$ satisfy the $C_{s+1}^s$-cofactor equation at $\tilde{\mathbf{p}}_0$. The basic idea is simple and applies to arbitrary plane graphs. Any set of scalars which satisfy the $C_{s+1}^s$-cofactor equations at all by one vertex, also satisfy them at the last vertex. Consider a set of scalars $\lambda_{i,j}^*$ such that, for all vertices $i$ except the last one (0):

$$0 \equiv \sum_{j|\{i,j\}\in E}\lambda_{i,j}^*[\widetilde{L}^{i,j}]^{s+1}$$

For each edge $i,j$ (including the ones to 0) we have:

$$\lambda_{i,j}^*[\widetilde{L}^{i,j}]^{s+1} + \lambda_{i,j}^*[\widetilde{L}^{j,i}]^{s+1} \equiv 0.$$

Adding over all edges, and regrouping at each vertex $i$ we have:

$$0 \equiv \sum_{i\neq 0}\left(\sum_{k|\{i,k\}\in E}\lambda_{i,k}^*[\widetilde{L}^{i,k}]^{s+1}\right) + \sum_{k|\{0,k\}\in E}\lambda_{0,k}^*[\widetilde{L}^{0,k}]^{s+1}$$
$$\equiv \sum_{i\neq 0}0 + \sum_{k|\{0,k\}\in E}\lambda_{0,k}^*[\widetilde{L}^{0,k}]^{s+1} \equiv \sum_{k|\{0,k\}\in E}\lambda_{0,k}^*[\widetilde{L}^{0,k}]^{s+1}.$$

We conclude that the $C_{s+1}^s$-cofactor equation is satisfied at the final vertex, as required, and the extended $\lambda^*$ is a $C_{s+1}^s$-cofactor on $G * 0(\tilde{\mathbf{p}}, \tilde{\mathbf{p}}_0)$.

We have shown that each $C_{s+1}^s$-cofactor $\lambda^*$ on $G * 0(\tilde{\mathbf{p}}, \tilde{\mathbf{p}}_0)$ restricts to a $C_s^{s-1}$-cofactor on $G(\tilde{\mathbf{p}})$, and each $C_s^{s-1}$-cofactor on $G(\tilde{\mathbf{p}})$ extends uniquely to a $C_{s+1}^s$-cofactor $\lambda^*$ on $G * 0(\tilde{\mathbf{p}}, \tilde{\mathbf{p}}_0)$, as required. By a projective transformation, this applies to any cone $G * 0(\mathbf{p}, \mathbf{p}_0)$, with $\mathbf{p}_0$ distinct from every point in $\mathbf{p}$ and not-collinear with the pair of points in $\mathbf{p}$.

The generic $C_s^{s-1}$-cofactor matroid has rank $(s+1)n - \binom{s+2}{2}$ on $K_n$, like the analogous generic $(s+1)$-rigidity matroid. The verification follows from coning. For completeness, we also introduce the companion space of $C_s^{s-1}$-flexes.

The $C_s^{s-1}$-*flexes of a plane graph* $G(\mathbf{p})$ are the solutions of the system of equations $M_r^{s-1}(G, \mathbf{p})\mathbf{u} = \mathbf{0}$. The space of *trivial* $C_s^{s-1}$-*flexes* is spanned by the $s + 1$ 'translations': $\mathbf{F}_{0,l} = (\mathbf{e}_l, \dots, \mathbf{e}_l)$ for the standard basis vectors $\mathbf{e}_l$ for $\mathbb{R}^{s+1}$ and by the $\binom{s+1}{2}$ 'rotations'. This space is generated by the vectors $\mathbf{F}_{k,l}(\mathbf{p})$, $0 \leq l$, $0 < k$, $k + l \leq s - 1$, whose entries under each vertex are the coefficient vectors used in the proof of Lemma 11.3.1: $\mathbf{f}_{k,l}(\mathbf{p}_i) = (\dots, f_{k,l}(j-1, \mathbf{p}_i), \dots)$, $1 \leq j \leq s + 1$. Because $\mathbf{D}_{i,j}^s \cdot \mathbf{f}_{k,l}(\mathbf{p}_i) = \mathbf{D}_{i,j}^s \cdot \mathbf{f}_{k,l}(\mathbf{p}_j)$, for each $k, l$, we have $\mathbf{D}_{i,j}^s \cdot \mathbf{f}_{k,l}(\mathbf{p}_i) - \mathbf{D}_{i,j}^s \cdot \mathbf{f}_{k,l}(\mathbf{p}_j) = 0$. These will be $C_s^{s-1}$-flexes for any graph. (If we included the case $(C^{i,j})^0$ in the proof of Lemma 11.3.1, we get the entries of the 'translations', so our notation is consistent.) A plane graph $G(\mathbf{p})$, or a set of edges $E$, is $C_s^{s-1}$-*rigid* if all $C_s^{s-1}$-flexes are trivial.

$K_n$ LEMMA 11.3.4. *For a general position plane configuration* $\mathbf{p}$ *on* $n \geq s + 1$ *vertices:*

  1. *the plane graph* $K_{s+1}(\mathbf{p})$ *is* $C_s^{s-1}$-*independent;*
  2. *the space of trivial* $C_s^{s-1}$-*flexes has dimension* $\binom{s+2}{2}$ *on this configuration;*
  3. *for* $n \geq s$, $M_s^{s-1}(n; \mathbf{p})$ *has rank* $(s+1)n - \binom{s+2}{2}$.

PROOF. These proofs are by induction on $s$. By the results of §5 and §10.1, all of the above results hold for $s = 1$ and $s = 2$. Assume they hold for $s = r$.
1. Since $K_{r+1}$ is $C_r^{r-1}$-independent at $\mathbf{p}$, by the Coning Theorem 11.3.3, $(K_{r+1}) * u = K_{r+2}$ is $C_{r+1}^r$-independent at $(\mathbf{p}, \mathbf{p}_u)$ for all general position plane configurations $(\mathbf{p}, \mathbf{p}_u)$. We have the required induction step.
2. By 1, the rank of $M_{r+1}^r(r + 2; \mathbf{p})$ is $\binom{r+2}{2}$. Therefore the space of $C_{r+1}^r$-flexes on $K_{r+2}$ has dimension $(r + 1)(r + 2) - \binom{r+2}{2} = \binom{r+2}{2}$. It is an exercise to verify that the $\binom{r+2}{2}$ trivial $C_{r+1}^r$-flexes are independent and hence generate this space.
3. Assume that, for $m \geq r$, $M_r^{r-1}(m; \mathbf{p})$ has rank $sm - \binom{s+1}{2}$. This means that the space of $C_r^{r-1}$-cofactors on $K_m(\mathbf{p})$ has dimension $\binom{m}{2} - (sm - \binom{s+1}{2})$. By the Coning Theorem 11.3.3, the space of $C_{r+1}^r$-cofactors on $(K_m) * u(\mathbf{p}, \mathbf{p}_u) = K_{m+1}(\mathbf{p})$ has the same dimension and the rank of $M_{r+1}^r(m + 1; \mathbf{p})$ is:

$$\binom{m+1}{2} - \binom{m}{2} + \left(rm - \binom{r+1}{2}\right) = (r+1)(m+1) - \binom{r+2}{2}.$$

for all $m + 1 \geq r + 1$. This completes the induction step.

$\mathcal{M}_s^{s-1}$ COUNTING COROLLARY 11.3.5. *A set of at least* $s + 1$ *vertices, with* $|E| > (s+1)|V(E)| - \binom{s+2}{2}$ *is* $C_s^{s-1}$-*dependent for every plane configuration* $\mathbf{p}$.

*Equivalently, a set $E$ is independent in the generic $C_s^{s-1}$-cofactor matroid only if, for all subsets $E'$ on at least $s + 1$ vertices, $|E'| \leq (s+1)|V(E')| - \binom{s+2}{2}$.*

We transfer some additional results from the $d$-rigidity matroids.

$\mathcal{M}_s^{s-1}$ VERTEX ADDITION LEMMA 11.3.6. *Given a plane graph $G(\mathbf{p})$ and a vertex $(s+1)$-addition of $0$ attached to $c_1, \ldots c_{s+1}$ creating $G'$ and the plane graph $G'(\mathbf{p_0}, \mathbf{p})$, with $\mathbf{p_0}$ not collinear with any pair of points in $\mathbf{p}_{c_1}, \ldots, \mathbf{p}_{c_{s+1}}$, then*

1. *$G'(\mathbf{p_0}, \mathbf{p})$ is independent in the $C_s^{s-1}$-cofactor matroid if and only if $G(\mathbf{p})$ is independent in the $C_s^{s-1}$-cofactor matroid;*
2. *rank $\mathcal{M}_s^{s-1}(G'; \mathbf{p_0}, \mathbf{p}) = $ rank $\mathcal{M}_s^{s-1}(G; \mathbf{p}) + (s+1)$.*

PROOF. Without loss of generality, we can assume that none of the lines $\mathbf{p_0}, \mathbf{p}_{c_i}$ is vertical (after a Euclidean transformation). By the non-collinearity assumption, the $s + 1$ lines determined by pairs $(\mathbf{p_0}, \mathbf{p}_{c_i})$ have distinct slopes $m_i$. These lines give $L^{0,c_i} = a_k(m_i x + y + b_i)$ and reduced $C_s^{s-1}$-cofactors: $\mathbf{D}_{0,k}^s = (a_k)^{s+1}[m_i^s + \ldots \binom{s}{k}m_i^k + \ldots 1]$. Ignoring the (non-zero) row multipliers $(a_i)^{s+1}$, the added rows of the matrix for these edges, under the vertex $0$ are:

$$\begin{bmatrix} (m_1)^s & \cdots & \binom{s}{k}(m_1)^k & \cdots & 1 \\ \vdots & \ddots & \vdots & \ddots & \vdots \\ (m_i)^s & \cdots & \binom{s}{k}(m_i)^k & \cdots & 1 \\ \vdots & \ddots & \vdots & \ddots & \vdots \\ (m_{s+1})^s & \cdots & \binom{s}{k}(m_{s+1})^k & \cdots & 1 \end{bmatrix}$$

Up to column multipliers $\binom{s}{k}$, this is the Vandermonde matrix, which has independent rows if and only if the $m_i$ are all distinct. We conclude that for general position plane configurations, these rows are independent additions to any corresponding matrix $M_s^{s-1}(G; \mathbf{p})$, adding $s + 1$ to the rank.

An induction on $(s+1)$-simple graphs gives the following Corollary.

$(s+1)$-SIMPLE GRAPH THEOREM 11.3.7. *For any $n \geq s+1$ and any general position plane-configuration $\mathbf{p}$ on $n$ vertices, the edges $E$ of any $(s+1)$-simple graph $G$ on $n$ vertices are a basis of $\mathcal{M}_s^{s-1}(n; \mathbf{p})$ of rank $(s+1)n - \binom{s+2}{2}$.*

It is now easy to prove that any plane graph $G(\mathbf{p})$ is $C_s^{s-1}$-rigid if and only if:

1. $|V| \geq s + 1$ and $M_s^{s-1}(G; \mathbf{p})$ has rank $(s+1)|V| - \binom{s+2}{2}$; or
2. $|V| \leq s$ and $G = K_V$ with $\mathbf{p}$ in general position.

COROLLARY 11.3.8. *A plane graph $G(\mathbf{p})$ with vertices in general position is not $C_s^{s-1}$-rigid if and only if there is a $C_s^{s-1}$-flex $\mathbf{u}$ and a pair of vertices $h, k$ (not an edge) such that: $\mathbf{D}_{h,k}^s \cdot (\mathbf{u}_h - \mathbf{u}_k) \neq 0$.*

With the same counts and the same induction as for 3-simple graphs, the double bananas of Figure 9.4 also cone to a circuit for any general position plane configuration and a circuit for the generic $C_s^{s-1}$-cofactor matroid.

REMARK 11.3.9. These $C_s^{s-1}$-cofactors originated in the theory $C_s^{s-1}$-splines: functions over decompositions of the plane into polygonal cells which are piecewise polynomial of degree at most $s$, globally $C^{s-1}$ [**Bi,CW,Wh10**]. For a planar drawing of a connected planar graph, up to addition of a single global quadric to the function, there is an isomorphism between these $C_s^{s-1}$-splines on the induced decomposition and the $C_s^{s-1}$-cofactors on the planar graph. For our matroidal purposes, we have extended the algebra to non-planar graphs.

The analogy between generic $(s+1)$-rigidity and generic $C_s^{s-1}$-rigidity is already established. We will transfer additional results of §11.1 to the generic $C_s^{s-1}$-cofactor matroid, sometimes using alternate proofs.

$\mathcal{M}_s^{s-1}$ EDGE SPLIT THEOREM 11.3.10. *Assume $G'$ is an edge $(s+1)$-split of $G = (V, E)$ on $c_1, c_2; c_3, \ldots, c_{s+2}$, and $\mathbf{p}$ is a plane configuration with $\mathbf{p}_{c_1}, \ldots, \mathbf{p}_{c_{s+2}}$ in general position. If $G(\mathbf{p})$ is $C_s^{s-1}$-independent ($C_s^{s-1}$-rigid), then $G'(\mathbf{p}_0, \mathbf{p})$ is $C_s^{s-1}$-independent ($C_s^{s-1}$-rigid) for almost all choices of $\mathbf{p}_0$, including $\mathbf{p}_0$ a distinct point on $\mathbf{p}_{c_1}, \mathbf{p}_{c_2}$, not collinear with any other pair $\mathbf{p}_{c_i}, \mathbf{p}_{c_j}$, $3 \leq j \leq s+2$.*

*Conversely, if $G'(\mathbf{p}_0, \mathbf{p})$ is $C_s^{s-1}$-independent ($C_s^{s-1}$-rigid) for some choice of $\mathbf{p}_0$, with vertex $0$ connected to exactly vertices $\sigma(1), \ldots, \sigma(s+2)$ at $s+1$ points in general position then, for some edge $e$ with endpoints in $c_1, c_2; c_3, \ldots, c_{s+2}$, $E' = E \cup \{e\} - \{(0, c_i)\}$ is $C_s^{s-1}$-independent ($C_s^{s-1}$-rigid) at $\mathbf{p}$ and $G'$ is an edge $(s+1)$-split of $G = (V' - 0, E)$.*

PROOF. The proof used for Theorem 11.1.9 and Theorem 10.2.1 extends to $C_s^{s-1}$-independence and $C_s^{s-1}$-rigidity. $\blacksquare$

$\mathcal{M}_s^{s-1}$ CONSTRUCTION THEOREM 11.3.11. *If $G$ has an $(s+1)$-construction then the edges of $G$ form a basis for $\mathcal{M}_s^{s-1}(|V|)$.*

EXAMPLE 11.3.12. The complete bipartite graph $K_{d+1,\binom{d+1}{2}}$ has such a $d$-construction. We form the $(d+1)$-simplex by a single vertex $d$-addition, then do an edge $d$-split on each of these $\binom{d+1}{2}$ edges. We conclude that $K_{d+1,\binom{d+1}{2}}$ is both generically $d$-rigid and generically $C_{d-1}^{d-2}$-rigid.

$C_s^{s-1}$-FLEX TEST 11.3.13. *For any plane configuration $\mathbf{p}$ for the graph $K_n$, the following are equivalent:*
  1. *the edge $\{h, k\}$ is not in the $C_s^{s-1}$-closure $\langle E \rangle$ in $\mathcal{M}_s^{s-1}(n; \mathbf{p})$ of the set $E$;*
  2. *every $C_s^{s-1}$-cofactor $\lambda$ on $E \cup \{h, k\}$ is zero on $\{h, k\}$;*
  3. *there is a $C_s^{s-1}$-flex $\mathbf{u}$ on $G = (V, E)$, such that $\mathbf{D}_{h,k}^s \cdot (\mathbf{u}_h - \mathbf{u}_k) \neq 0$.*

GENERIC $\mathcal{M}_s^{s-1}$ GLUING LEMMA 11.3.14. *For two edge sets $E_1, E_2$,*
  1. *if $E_1$ and $E_2$ are generically $C_s^{s-1}$-rigid and $|V(E_1) \cap V(E_2)| \geq (s+1)$, the set $E_1 \cup E_2$ is generically $C_s^{s-1}$-rigid;*
  2. *if $|V(E_1) \cap V(E_2)| \leq s$, then the closure $\langle E_1 \cup E_2 \rangle$ in $\mathcal{M}_s^{s-1}(G)$ is contained in $K_{V(E_1)} \cup K_{V(E_2)}$;*
  3. *if $E_1$ and $E_2$ are generically $C_s^{s-1}$-independent and $E_1 \cap E_2$ is generically $C_s^{s-1}$-rigid, the set $E_1 \cup E_2$ is generically $C_s^{s-1}$-independent.*

PROOF. The proof of the Generic $C_2^1$-Gluing Theorem 10.24 extends directly. $\blacksquare$

COROLLARY 11.3.15. *The generic $C_s^{s-1}$-cofactor matroid is an abstract $(s+1)$-rigidity matroid.*

REMARK 11.3.16. Techniques such as vertex splits, and the resulting $C_s^{s-1}$-rigidity of simplicial $s$-surfaces (analogs of Fogelsanger's Theorem [**Fo**]), extend to these matroids.

The generic $C_s^{s-1}$-rigidity of simplicial $s$-surfaces is an alternate direct proof of the Lower Bound Theorem for edges of manifolds (without boundary) [**Ka1**]. It gives the same information for these specific structures. With this coning result, the extensions of [**Ka1**] to simplicial manifolds with boundary also transfer to these cofactor matroids.

**11.4. $X$-replacement and bipartite graphs in $\mathcal{M}_s^{s-1}(n)$.** The appropriate form of $X$-replacement preserves $C_s^{s-1}$-rigidity for all $s \geq 1$. Specifically, given a graph $G_1$ with edges $\{i_1, i_2\}, \{i_3, i_4\}$ and vertices $i_5, \ldots i_{d+2}$, $G$ is a $d$-$X$-replacement on $G_1$ if $G$ has one added vertex $i_0$ and replaces the edges $\{i_1, i_2\}, \{i_3, i_4\}$ with the $d + 2$ edges $\{i_0, i_j\}$, $1 \leq j \leq d + 2$.

$\mathcal{M}_s^{s-1}$ $X$-REPLACEMENT THEOREM 11.4.1. *An $(s + 1)$-$X$-replacement takes a generically $C_s^{s-1}$-rigid graph $G_1$ to a graph $G$ which is generically $C_s^{s-1}$-rigid.*

PROOF. Take a generic plane configuration **p** for $G_1$, with the edges $\{i_1, i_2\}$, $\{i_3, i_4\}$ to be replaced. We do a vertex $(s + 1)$-addition for the additional vertex $i_0$, attached to vertices $i_1$, $i_3$ and $i_5, \ldots, i_{s+3}$ and placed at the point of intersection of $\mathbf{p}_{i_1}\mathbf{p}_{i_2}$ and $\mathbf{p}_{i_3}\mathbf{p}_{i_4}$. This is $C_s^{s-1}$-rigid by the $\mathcal{M}_s^{s-1}$ Vertex $(s + 1)$-Addition Theorem.

In this position, we use collinear substitution to replace $\{i_0, i_1\}, \{i_1, i_2\}$ with $\{i_0, i_1\}, \{i_0, i_2\}$ and to replace $\{i_0, i_3\}, \{i_3, i_4\}$ with $\{i_0, i_3\}, \{i_0, i_4\}$. This is now the $C_s^{s-1}$-rigid graph of the $(s + 1)$-$X$-replacement, which completes the proof.

With this added inductive technique, we can verify directly that the bipartite counterexamples for the generic $(s + 1)$-rigidity matroid are not a problem for the generic $C_s^{s-1}$-cofactor matroid. Figure 11.2 gives an extended 4-construction of $K_{6,7}$, using $X$-replacement for the last two steps. We conclude that $K_{6,7}$ is a basis for the generic $C_3^2$-rigidity matroid.

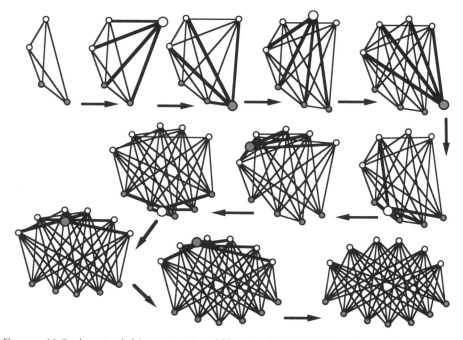

FIGURE. 11.2. *An extended 4-construction of $K_{6,7}$, in which the last two steps are $X$-replacement.*

$\mathcal{M}_3^2$ BIPARTITE THEOREM 11.4.2. *The complete bipartite graphs* $K_{5,10}$ *and* $K_{6,7}$ *are generically $C_3^2$-rigid and $C_3^2$-independent.*

*Every complete bipartite graph* $K_{m,n}$, $m \leq n$ *with* $m = 5, n \geq 10$ *or* $m \geq 6, n \geq 7$ *is generically $C_3^2$-rigid.*

PROOF. Example 11.3.1 gives a 4-construction for $K_{5,10}$ and Figure 11.2 gives an extended 4-construction for $K_{6,7}$. These verify the $C_3^2$-rigidity of these bipartite graphs. Larger complete bipartite graphs contain these, and can be created by a sequence of vertex 4-additions followed by adding the edges still missing.

Notice that the 'smaller' bipartite graphs, such as $K_{4,n}$, $K_{5,9}$ and $K_{6,6}$ are under counted, with $|E| < 4|V| - 10$. Example 11.3.1 also shows that $K_{s+2,\binom{s+2}{2}}$ is $C_s^{s-1}$-rigid. The extended 4-construction for $K_{6,7}$ generalizes, through coning, to an extended $(s+1)$-construction for $(s-3)$-fold cones of $K_{6,7}$. Therefore these are generically $C_s^{s-1}$-rigid and $C_s^{s-1}$-independent, but not $(s+1)$-independent. We expect that extended constructions (including $X$-replacement) will prove that $K_{7,10}$ is generically $C_4^3$-rigid, $K_{8,14}$ is generically $C_5^4$-rigid, etc. We also expect that extended $(s+1)$-constructions will verify that $K_{s+3,s+3}$ is generically $C_s^{s-1}$-independent for all $s \geq 3$, setting aside all the counterexamples of §11.2. This evidence supports the following conjecture for general $s$.

$\mathcal{M}_s^{s-1}$ BIPARTITE CONJECTURE 11.4.3. *A complete bipartite graph* $K_{m,n}$, $m, n \geq 2$, *is $C_s^{s-1}$-rigid if and only if* $m \times n \geq (s+1)(m+n) - \binom{s+2}{2}$.

Because these cofactor matroids, in this generality, do not have even the 'applications' of generic $d$-rigidity, they have not been studied in detail. It is possible that some surprises lie buried, as they did in the bipartite frameworks of $d$-rigidity.

**11.5. Comparisons of abstract $d$-rigidity matroids.** §11.1 and §11.3 demonstrated that we have two families of abstract $d$-rigidity matroids which share a number of properties. §11.2 and §11.4 demonstrated that they are not isomorphic for $d \geq 4$. The results of §11.4 confirm that the difficulties for 4-rigidity are not rooted in the structure of abstract $d$-rigidity matroids. Independently, [**Th**] verified this by constructing a specific abstract 4-rigidity matroid in which $K_{6,6}$ was independent. Therefore, generic $d$-rigidity is not a maximal abstract $d$-rigidity matroid for $d \geq 4$. We summarize the current situation for $d = 4$.

|  | Generic 4-Rigidity | Generic $C_3^2$-Rigidity |
|---|---|---|
| rank $K_n$, $n \geq 4$ | $4n - 10$ | $4n - 10$ |
| vertex 4-addition | Yes | Yes |
| edge 4-split | Yes | Yes |
| 4-constructions | Yes | Yes |
| abstract 4-rigidity | Yes | Yes |
| vertex 4-split | Yes | Yes |
| simplicial 4-polytopes | Rigid | Rigid |
| 4-coning | Yes | Yes |
| 4-$X$-replacement | No | Yes |
| $K_{5,10}$ | Basis | Basis |
| $K_{6,6}$ | Circuit | Independent |
| $K_{6,7}$ | Dependent | Basis |
| maximal abstract 4-rigidity matroid | No | Conjectured |

The Dress Conjecture in the chapter on Unsolved Problems has analogs for higher dimensions [**GSS**]. Because of examples such as $K_{6,6}$, the Dress conjecture and its relatives fail for generic $d$-rigidity for $d \geq 4$. However we *conjecture* that these extensions are correct for generic $C_s^{s-1}$-rigidity. This suggests there still is a 'maximal' abstract $d$-rigidity matroid. In the absence of counterexamples, we offer the following conjecture.

THE MAXIMAL MATROID CONJECTURE 11.5.1. *There is a maximal abstract $d$-rigidity matroid on the complete graph $K_n$ for $d \geq 2$.*

*For $d \geq 2$, the generic $C_{(d-1)}^{(d-2)}$-cofactor matroid $\mathcal{K}_{(d-1)}^{(d-2)}(n)$ is the maximal abstract $d$-rigidity matroid on $K_n$.*

It seems ironic that the abstract $d$-rigidity matroids, in their full generality, may be a better description of the cofactor matroids than the $d$-rigidity matroids! 

We close with a connectivity conjecture for which the results of the next section will give some support.

CONJECTURE 11.5.2. *If a graph $G$ is $2\binom{d+1}{2}$-connected in a vertex sense, then:*
1. *$G$ is generically $d$-rigid;*
2. *$G$ is generically $C_{d-1}^{d-2}$-rigid.*

The relationships among the matroids in Parts I and II were displayed in Figure 1.1. Looking back, we see both the close parallels and the subtle divergence between the generic rigidity matroids and generic cofactor matroids on graphs. The parallel drawing matroids are shown as an offshoot from the plane rigidity, in another direction. The additional boxes, with question marks for their 'names', are hypermatroids on graphs (with the indicated ranks on complete graphs of sufficient size) which will appear in Part III as lower homologies of the rigidity matroids on larger facets (see §16.4). Their direct geometric interpretation and specific combinatorial properties have never been investigated, though their place in this schematic diagram hints at the analogies to rigidity in higher dimensions which should be pursued. To condense the diagram, we completely omitted other hypermatroids on graphs which are offshoots of the higher cofactor matroids in several other directions, including the $C_d^s$-cofactors mentioned earlier and the lower homologies of the multivariate cofactor matroids of §15. While we believe these hypermatroids deserve an initial investigation, their enduring interest will depend on our interest in the matroids in Part III which bring them to light.

## 12. $d$-Space Structures Which Work!

We have seen the increasing difficulties of combinatorially characterizing the bases of the generic $d$-rigidity matroids for $d \geq 3$. In contrast, several related structures have simple, basically complete combinatorial theories and simpler matroids than $d$-rigidity. Since these give more solid underpinnings for work, even in 3-space, we briefly outline the associated matroids (and hypermatroids).

**12.1. Bar-and-body frameworks in $d$-space.** A bar-and-body framework [**Ta1,2,WW3,Wh7**] begins with a multigraph $\overline{G} = (V, \overline{E})$. A vertex $i \in V$ of the graph is interpreted as a large rigid *body*. Each edge $e$ has two identified vertices, $v_1(e)$, $v_2(e)$, which identify the two bodies which this 'bar' will join. Geometrically, a bar is described by giving an ordered pair of attaching points (universal joints) in $d$-space $(\mathbf{p}_e, \mathbf{q}_e)$, with $\mathbf{p}_e$ on $v_1(e)$ and $\mathbf{q}_e$ on $v_2(e)$. Each body is 'expandable' to contact all the points which are attach these bars to the body. Notice that there is no provision for specifying that two edges attached to some body share a common point of attachment.

Under first-order motions in $d$-space, each body will undergo a trivial first-order motion. This space has dimension $\binom{d+1}{2}$ and can be coordinatized by the *first-order screw centers* $S^i$ - vectors of size $\binom{d+1}{d-1} = \binom{d+1}{2}$. (In projective Grassmann-Cayley algebra, these are $(d-1)$-tensors in projective $d$-space [**DRS,Wht4,WW3**].) Each bar $\mathbf{p}_e, \mathbf{q}_e$ can be written as a vector of length $\binom{d+1}{2}$ the *Plücker coordinates* $\mathbf{b}_e$ of the segment $\mathbf{p}_e \wedge \mathbf{q}_e$. These are formed by taking all 2-by-2 minors of the 2-by-$(d+1)$ matrix $\begin{bmatrix} (\mathbf{p}_e)_1 & \cdots & (\mathbf{p}_e)_d & 1 \\ (\mathbf{p}_e)_1 & \cdots & (\mathbf{p}_e)_d & 1 \end{bmatrix}$. If we use appropriate bases for the space of screws, the constraint equation for a bar $\mathbf{b}_e$ is [**WW3**]:

$$\mathbf{b}_e \cdot S^{v_1(e)} = \mathbf{b}_e \cdot S^{v_2(e)} \quad \Leftrightarrow \quad \mathbf{b}_e \cdot \left(S^{v_1(e)} - S^{v_2(e)}\right) = 0.$$

As this writing indicates, this first-order constraint depends only on the line of the bar, not the specific points. (Changing the points along the line, but keeping them distinct, just multiplies the bar vector by a non-zero scalar reflecting the change in length (size) and direction (sign) from the change of points.) If we looked at long range flexes, as in mechanical engineering rather than first-order flexes of structural engineering, the choice of points along the line would matter a great deal!

In summary, a *bar-and-body framework in $d$-space* is a multigraph $\overline{G} = (V, \overline{E})$ and an assignment of *bar vectors* $\mathbf{b}_e$ (2-extensors $\mathbf{p}_e \wedge \mathbf{q}_e$ to the edges $e \in \overline{E}$. Together the bar vectors form a *line configuration* $\mathbf{b}$. A *first-order flex of* $\overline{G}(\mathbf{b})$ is an assignment of $\binom{d+1}{2}$-vectors $S^i$ to the vertices such that for each edge $e$, $\mathbf{b}_e \cdot (S^{v_1(e)} S^{v_2(e)}) = 0$. A first-order flex is *trivial* if each vertex has the same screw center: $S^1 = \ldots = S^{|V|}$. This space of trivial first-order flexes has dimension $\binom{d+1}{2}$. A bar-and-body framework $\overline{G}(\mathbf{b})$ is *first-order rigid* if all first-order flexes are trivial.

These linear equations define the *bar-and-body rigidity matrix* $R_{\overline{G}}(\mathbf{b})$:

$$
\begin{array}{ccccccccc}
 & 1 & \cdots & v_1(e) & \cdots & v_2(e) & \cdots & |V| \\
\end{array}
$$

$$
\begin{array}{c}
\vdots \\
e \\
\vdots
\end{array}
\left(
\begin{array}{ccccccc}
\vdots & \ddots & \vdots & \ddots & \vdots & \ddots & \vdots \\
\mathbf{0} & \cdots & \mathbf{b}_e & \cdots & -\mathbf{b}_e & \cdots & \mathbf{0} \\
\vdots & \ddots & \vdots & \ddots & \vdots & \ddots & \vdots
\end{array}
\right)
$$

The kernel of $R_{\overline{G}}(\mathbf{b})$ is the space of first-order flexes and the row dependencies of $R_{\overline{G}}(\mathbf{b})$ are the dependencies of the *bar-and-body matroid* on $\overline{G}(\mathbf{b})$.

EXAMPLE 12.1.1. Consider joining two bodies (say an object to the ground) in 3-space (Figure 12.1A). Since $6|V| - 6 = 6$, we will need 6 bars. For example, the 'top' and 'bottom' triangle of an octahedron (full rigid bodies) are attached by 6 bars (Figure 12.1B). In generic position (or any convex realization) this structure is first-order rigid both as a bar and joint framework and as a bar-and-body framework.

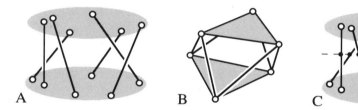

FIGURE. 12.1. *A generic bar-and-body framework (A), a special position of the same graph (B) which is first-order rigid, and a special position which is not first-order rigid in 3-space (B).*

If these six bars happen to all intersect a single line $\mathbf{c}$ (Figure 12.1C), then this line will be the axis of a non-trivial rotation of one body relative to the second body. The corresponding six rows of the bar-and-body rigidity matrix will be dependent.

In general, these rows will be dependent if and only if some 6-tuple $\mathbf{S}$ satisfies $\mathbf{b}_k \cdot \mathbf{S} = 0$, $1 \le k \le 6$. Such a sextuple represents a general screw $\mathbf{S}$ in space, and these lines are in the linear line complex of null lines of the screw [**Kl**,**WW1**].

If we take a generic line assignment $\mathbf{b}$ in $d$-space (i.e. use generic points for the two ends of each bar) the bar-and-body rigidity matrix $R_{\overline{G}}(\mathbf{b})$ defines the *generic body $d$-rigidity matroid* on $\overline{E}$. For a fixed set of vertices, we can recognize that any set of more than $\binom{d+1}{2}$ edges between two bodies will be dependent in this matroid. For simplicity, we can assume that no graph has more than $\binom{d+1}{2}$ edges between any pair of bodies, so the multigraph $\binom{d+1}{2}K_n$, with $\binom{d+1}{2}$ edges between each pair of vertices, is the context for this matroid. The following theorem characterizes these matroids, in analogy to the characterization of line rigidity in §2.1.

TAY'S THEOREM 12.1.2 [**Ta1,2**,**WW3**]. *For a multigraph $\overline{G} = (V\overline{E})$ the following are equivalent:*

1. *for some line assignment $\mathbf{b}$ in $d$-space, the bar-and-body framework $\overline{G}(\mathbf{n})$ is first-order rigid, with rank $\binom{d+1}{2}|V| - \binom{d+1}{2}$;*
2. *for almost all bar assignments $\mathbf{b}$ in $d$-space, the bar-and-body framework $\overline{G}(\mathbf{b})$ is first-order rigid;*
3. *the graph $\overline{G}$ is generically body $d$-rigid;*
4. *the multigraph $\overline{G}$ contains $\binom{d+1}{2}$ edge-disjoint spanning trees.*

*The following are also equivalent:*

1. *the set $E' \subseteq \overline{E}$ is independent in the generic body $d$-rigidity matroid;*
2. *for all subsets $E'' \subseteq E'$, $|E''| \leq \binom{d+1}{2}|V(E'')| - \binom{d+1}{2}$;*
3. *the set $E''$ can be covered by $\binom{d+1}{2}$ forests.*

One proof for this theorem connects our rigidity matrix to the matrix for the matroid union of $\binom{d+1}{2}$ copies of the graphic matroid on the normal graph $G$ which underlies the multigraph $\overline{G}$ (see [**Wh7**] and §A).

REMARK 12.1.3. A bar-and-body framework in which the attaching vertices of the bars affinely span $d$-space can be modeled as a bar-and-joint framework, with each body replaced by a basis for the $d$-rigidity matroid on these joints (say an appropriate $d$-simple framework). The first-order $d$-rigidity, flexibility or $d$-independence of the two structures will be the same. Thus our theorem does give explicit results for those special graphs which are models of such frameworks.

However, if we take a general graph as a bar framework, this will force certain attachments to share a single vertex on a 'body'. We get no new information for these general bar frameworks.

However, we do have enticing results on connectivity.

COROLLARY 12.1.4 [**Wh7**]. *A multigraph $\overline{G}$ is generically body $d$-rigid if the multigraph is $2\binom{d+1}{2}$ connected in an edge sense.*

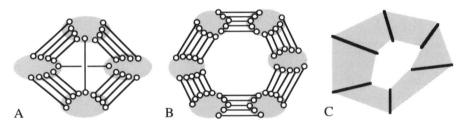

FIGURE. 12.2. *Two generically body 3-rigid multigraphs (A,B), and a corresponding body-and-hinge framework (C) whose graph is a hexagonal cycle.*

## 12.2. Body-and-hinge frameworks in 3-space.

A body-and-hinge framework can be described as an interesting special case of a bar-and-body framework with important applications [**CrW1,TW1,Wh7**]. For simplicity, we just outline the process for 3-space. However all these results generalize to arbitrary dimensions.

The basic idea is that a set of rigid bodies is connected, in pairs, along 'hinges' (lines 3-space). The bodies each move, preserving the contacts along the hinges. Central to our description is the observation that the rigid motions in space can be represented by 'screw centers' $S^i$ (weighted line segments in projective geometry – and their sums). If two bodies share two hinges on distinct lines, they will be locked into a single rigid unit, and might as well be called a single body. For this reason, we restrict ourselves to ordinary graphs, not multigraphs.

A *body-and-hinge framework* in 3-space is a graph $G = (V, E)$ and an assignment $\mathbf{h}$ of directed lines $\mathbf{h}_{ij}$ in 3-space, written as 2-extensors (6-vectors) in the Grassmann algebra for 3-space, to the directed edges, with $\mathbf{h}_{i,j} = -\mathbf{h}_{j,i}$.

A *first-order flex* for a body-and-hinge framework $G(\mathbf{h})$ is an assignment of screw centers of motion $\mathbf{S}^i$ (sum of 2-extensors in the Grassmann algebra) to each vertex such that, for every edge $\{i, j\}$: $\mathbf{S}^i - \mathbf{S}^j = \alpha_{i,j}\mathbf{h}_{i,j}$ for some scalar $\alpha_{i,j}$. A body-and-hinge framework $G(\mathbf{h})$ is *first-order rigid* if all first-order flexes are *trivial*, with all screw centers $\mathbf{S}_i = \mathbf{C}$ for a fixed center $\mathbf{C}$.

A *generic hinge assignment* in 3-space is achieved by assigning two generic points in 3-space, $\mathbf{p}_{i,j}, \mathbf{q}_{i,j}$, to each edge and then taking the Plücker coordinates of the line through these points as the hinge $\mathbf{h}_{i,j}$. A graph $G$ is *generically hinge 3-rigid* if the body-and-hinge framework $G(\mathbf{h})$ is first-order rigid for some generic hinge assignment.

Implicitly, each hinge $\mathbf{h}_{ij}$ can be replaced by a set of 5 independent bars, each intersecting the hinge line producing an *equivalent* bar-and-body framework on the multigraph $5G$ with 5 copies of each edge of $G$ (Figure 12.2 C,B). We can also see this count $5|E|$ since each hinge equation $\mathbf{S}^i - \mathbf{S}^j = \alpha_{i,j}\mathbf{h}_{i,j}$ is six linear equations in the unknowns $\mathbf{S}^i, \mathbf{S}^j, \alpha_{i,j}$. Row reducing to eliminate the auxiliary unknowns $\alpha_{i,j}$ leaves $5|E|$ equations for the unknown centers $\mathbf{S}^i, \mathbf{S}^j$.

Unfortunately, if we take a generic line assignment $\mathbf{b}$ for the $5|E|$ bars, the five lines for each hinge will not redefine an underling hinge. They will define a general 'screw' $\mathbf{S}_{i,j}$ which is the sum of the 6-tuples for two lines, but not a line. This screw will not satisfy the underlying quadratic Plücker equation [**Kl,Wh7**]. Fortunately, this can be worked around with some algebraic geometry [**Wh7**] and the bar-and-body results do translate to hinges.

3-HINGE THEOREM 12.2.1 [**TW1**]. *For a graph $G$ the following are equivalent:*
1. *For some hinge assignment $\mathbf{h}$, the body and hinge framework $G(\mathbf{h})$ is first-order rigid;*
2. *For almost all hinge assignments $\mathbf{h}$, the body and hinge framework $G(\mathbf{h})$ is first-order rigid;*
3. *The graph $G$ is generically hinge 3-rigid;*
4. *If each edge of the graph is replaced by five copies, the resulting multigraph $5G$ contains six edge-disjoint spanning trees.*

COROLLARY 12.2.2. *3-edge-connectivity of $G$ is sufficient for generic hinge 3-rigidity of a graph $G$.*

REMARK 12.2.3. There are two special geometries for hinge structures which occur in practice. A *panel-hinge framework* has all hinges of each body coplanar (as in the plane faces of a polyhedron with hinges for the edges). The geometrically polar structures, with all hinges of each body concurrent in a single point, are the *molecular frameworks*. The model here is a chemical molecule in which each atom and its attached bonds is a body and the bond lines are the hinges. See [**Fr1,2**] for a study of such frameworks in connection with models of glass.

We can define *generic molecular framework* by assigning generic points to the atoms, and then assigning the corresponding hinge the line joining the two vertices for the atoms it 'bonds'. These define the *generic molecular 3-rigidity matroid on* $G$. There are numerous examples (related to spherical polyhedra) which support the following conjecture [**TW1**].

MOLECULAR FRAMEWORK CONJECTURE 12.2.4. *The generic hinge 3-rigidity matroid on $G$ is the same as the generic molecular 3-rigidity matroid. In particular, a graph $G$ is generically hinge 3-rigid if and only if $G$ is generically molecular 3-rigid.*

## III. Matroids for Geometric Homologies.

## 13. Some Background

In the previous sections the matroids were defined for geometric graphs (1-skeleta of simplicial complexes). Many of the combinatorial results were also based on results for graphs (trees, unions of trees, inductions on graphs, etc.). The parallel drawing matroids for hyperplanes and points are an interesting exception. They were defined for points and hyperplanes, but they were presented in terms of the bipartite incidence graph (incidences were 'edges' joining vertices and faces). For over a decade, Henry Crapo has worked on an underlying homology (actually cohomology) for these structures - unraveling the subtle relationships for incidence sets which are not bases of the matroid [**Cr1,Cr3,4,CR2,CRy**]. These are 'geometric homologies', homologies based on both the abstract combinatorics of the incidence structure and on the geometry of the configuration of the points (or planes in the case of parallel drawings). While we will not present this developing theory here, this 'geometry of the circuits' of the underlying represented matroid is essential to a complete understanding of the underlying matroid [**Cr1,Cr4,CR2**].

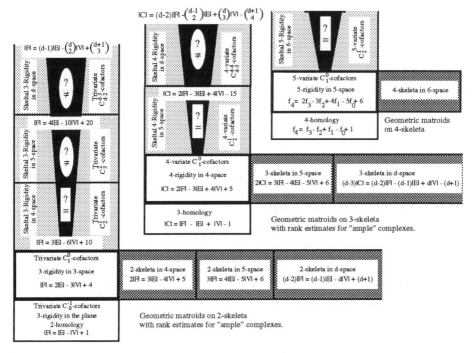

FIGURE. 13.1. *A schematic diagram for families of matroids associated with geometric homologies.*

In the last decade, several additional families of matroids based on geometric homologies have been defined for higher skeleta of simplicial complexes and other cell complexes realized in geometric spaces (real $d$-space or projective $d$-space). Figure 13.1 places these matroids into a pattern of 'family relationships', corresponding to the relationships we now see in the original Figure 1.1. Even this diagram includes

only a fraction of the rich variety of matroids and homologies which are implicit in
fields such as simplicial homology, multivariate splines and skeletal rigidity.

As we move to higher skeleta, the matroids of interest, which will be presented
as matrices over the reals, have ranks which implicitly depend on all of the lower
skeleta. This connection to the lower skeleta is explicitly unraveled through homology theory: a sequence of matrices (matroids) for each pair of adjacent skeleta.
The layers of Figure 13.1 and Figure 1.1 are stacked with 3-homology above 2-
homology above 1-homology, etc. The lower homologies of the other structures
may also appear in the layers below this structure (perhaps on a diagonal), and
other matroids could be described to fill each layer out into several 'quadrants' of
geometric matroids (see §16.4).

The second applied geometric homology to be explicitly described arose from
multivariate splines [**Bi**]. In conjectured ranks of the form:

$$\operatorname{rank}(F) \leq 2|E| - 3|V| + 4 \quad \text{or} \quad \operatorname{rank}(C) \leq 3|F| - 6|E| + 10|V| - 15,$$

we see an alternating sum of terms for the lower skeleta (faces, edges, vertices, and
a constant term). Billera anticipated that this sum was the Euler characteristic of
a chain complex in homology. With this insight, he developed a chain complex and
applied the tools of homology to develop some important results (see §15).

Homology was introduced into this applied context (approximation theory and
Computer Aided Geometric Design) because homology describes essential relationships. Any other approach is ad hoc, inadequate, or both. Initial work in the plane
can overlook this connection, as we did in previous sections. As the dimension
of the space increases, the structure given by a chain complex homology becomes
essential to keeping the relationships straight, at least implicitly [**ASW**].

Recent work on combinatorial and geometric proofs of the $g$-theorem has lead to
a theory of 'skeletal rigidity' for higher skeleta of simplicial polytopes (and general
simplicial complexes) [**Lee1,2,TWW1,2,3**]. Implicitly, and sometimes explicitly,
this is based on a second geometric homology. Again, an analysis of the lower
homologies is central to estimates of the rank of the matroid associated with the
highest cycles, which are the objects of primary interest (§16).

We will devote the next three sections to three related examples of homologies
and their matroids: ordinary simplicial homology and the $k$-cycle matroid (§14),
multivariate splines and the cofactor matroids (§15), and rigidity of higher skeleta
and their rigidity matroids (§16). There are a number of important unsolved problems in these areas and the general theory is undeveloped. The methods and the
insights of the previous sections, based on graphs and related matroid theory, give
valuable information for these structures - but they are not sufficient. Techniques
from homology (such as spectral sequences) have also been used [**TWW3**], but
good solutions will require new ideas.

## 14. Simplicial Homology Matroids

The applied problems of §15 and §16 will emphasize important gaps in our
understanding of the matroids for the standard simplicial homology of higher simplicial complexes. Clearly, this theory is sparse in comparison with the extensive
results and techniques for graph theory (homology of the 1-skeleton). In addition, this structure is essential to understanding the matroid of the later geometric
generalizations.

We begin with the basic simplicial matroid, or $k$-cycle matroid, based on standard simplicial homology [**CL,CR1**]. Previous presentations in matroid theory have focused on the top two homologies (see Remark 14.1.7). Our presentation will emphasize the important role of the lower homologies of the complex, because of my experiences with the extensions and applications of the the following sections. For graphs, with only two possibly non-trivial homologies to consider, these two approaches coincide. For larger simplices, attention to the lower homologies gives critical information.

**14.1. The simplicial $k$-cycle matroids.** The basic references for this section are [**CL,CR1**] along with a standard book on algebraic topology [**Mu**].

A *simplicial complex* $\Delta$ is a family of *simplices*: subsets of a finite set $V = \{v_1, v_2, \dots, v_n\}$ such that every subset of a simplex is also a simplex. For convenience, we use the linear ordering of the vertices and assume that each simplex is written in lexicographic order: $\{v_{i_0}, \dots, v_{i_j}\}$, $i_0 < i_1 < \dots < i_j$.

For each $-1 \le j \le n$, we have the subcomplex of $\Delta^j = \{\sigma \in \Delta \mid |\sigma| \le j + 1\}$ and the *$j$-simplices* $\Delta^{(j)} = \{\sigma \in \Delta \mid |\sigma| = j + 1\}$. The cardinality of this set is $f_j = |\Delta^{(j)}|$.

WARNING. We index simplices by the conventions of homology theory, not the indexing commonly used in matroid theory. In [**CL,CR1**], our $j$-simplex, a set of $j + 1$ elements, is called a $(j + 1)$-simplex and our $\Delta^{(j)}$ is becomes $\Delta^{(j+1)}$. For combinatorists, our choice is somewhat awkward, since combinatorists count entries not topological dimension. However, as we transfer results, techniques, and references from algebraic topology, it seems appropriate to work within their long established conventions.

The *$j$-chains* $C_j(\Delta)$ of the simplicial complex are the formal sums

$$\mathbf{c} = \sum_{\sigma \in \Delta^{(j)}} c_\sigma \cdot \sigma,$$

with coefficients $c_\sigma \in \mathbf{IR}$. Effectively, the $j$-chains are elements of a vector space $\mathbf{IR}^{f_j}$. [Everything we do will apply to an arbitrary field $F$, but we will not record this fact.] The critical maps of homology are the sequence of boundary maps on these chains: $\partial_j : C_j(\Delta) \to C_{j-1}(\Delta)$ defined on simplices by

$$\partial_j \{v_{i_0}, \dots, v_{i_j}\} = \sum_{l=0}^{j} (-1)^l \{v_{i_0}, \dots, \widehat{v_{i_l}}, \dots, v_{i_j}\}$$

where $\widehat{v_l}$ indicates the deletion of $v_l$. This map on simplices is extended linearly to all $j$-chains. It is a standard (and critical) result that $\partial_{j-1}\partial_j = 0$ for all $0 \le j < n$. This whole package of chains and operators is the *chain complex*:

$$\mathcal{C}_k(\Delta): \ \mathbf{0} \to C_k(\Delta) \xrightarrow{\partial_k} C_{(k-1)}(\Delta) \xrightarrow{\partial_{k-1}} \cdots \xrightarrow{\partial_1} C_0(\Delta) \xrightarrow{\partial_0} C_{-1}(\Delta) \xrightarrow{\partial_{-1}} \mathbf{0}.$$

Since $C_{-1}(\Delta) = \{c_\emptyset \cdot \emptyset\}$, $\mathcal{C}_k$ is an *augmented chain complex*, in the vocabulary of algebraic topology.

REMARK 14.1.1. It is often convenient to explicitly use the underlying *oriented simplices*. Taking all orders of the vertices of a simplex, these ordered simplices are placed into two orientation classes depending on whether their ordered sequence of indices represent an even or odd permutation. The equivalence class of an ordered simplex is denoted $[v_{i_0}, \dots, v_{i_k}]$ or $[\sigma]$ and the other equivalence class, differing by an odd permutation, is denoted $-[\sigma]$.

To simplify writing the boundary operator, we define $Sign(\rho, \sigma)$ for simplices $\rho \in \Delta^{(i-1)}$, $\sigma \in \Delta^{(i)}$, by:

$$Sign(\rho, \sigma) = \begin{cases} +1 & \text{if, for some } x \in V, \ [\rho, x] = [\sigma] \\ -1 & \text{if, for some } x \in V, \ [\rho, x] = -[\sigma] \\ 0 & \text{otherwise.} \end{cases}$$

With this notation, for each $\sigma \in \Delta^{(i)}$, $\partial_i[\sigma] = \sum_{\rho \ | \ \rho \in \Delta^{(i-1)}} Sign(\rho, \sigma) \cdot [\rho]$.

An $i$-chain $\mathbf{c} = \sum_{\sigma \in \Delta^{(i)}} c_\sigma \cdot [\sigma]$ is an $i$-cycle if $\partial \mathbf{c} = \mathbf{0}$. Explicitly, the space $Z_i(\Delta)$ of $i$-cycles is the solution space for the system of linear equations:

$$\partial\left( \sum_{\sigma \in \Delta^{(i)}} c_\sigma \cdot [\sigma] \right) = \sum_{\sigma \in \Delta^{(i)}} \left( \sum_{\rho \in \Delta^{(i-1)}} Sign(\rho, \sigma) c_\sigma \cdot [\rho] \right)$$

$$= \sum_{\rho \in \Delta^{(i-1)}} \left( \sum_{\sigma \in \Delta^{(i)}} Sign(\rho, \sigma) c_\sigma \right) \cdot [\rho] = \mathbf{0}.$$

In terms analogous to stresses in frameworks, these $k$-cycles are the row dependencies of the $f_k$-by-$f_{k-1}$ $k$-cycle matrix: $M_k(\Delta)$, with $M_k(\Delta)[\sigma, \rho] = [Sign(\rho, \sigma)]$ for each $\sigma \in \Delta^{(k)}$, $\rho \in \Delta^{(k-1)}$. These $k$-cycles are the dependencies of the *simplicial $k$-cycle matroid* $\mathcal{M}_k(\Delta)$, also called the simplicial matroid of $\Delta^k$ in [**CL**].

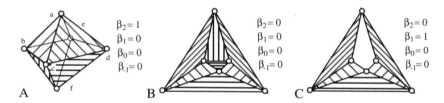

| | | |
|---|---|---|
| $\beta_2 = 1$ | $\beta_2 = 0$ | $\beta_2 = 0$ |
| $\beta_1 = 0$ | $\beta_1 = 0$ | $\beta_1 = 1$ |
| $\beta_0 = 0$ | $\beta_0 = 0$ | $\beta_0 = 0$ |
| $\beta_{-1} = 0$ | $\beta_{-1} = 0$ | $\beta_{-1} = 0$ |

FIGURE. 14.1. *Three 2-simplicial complexes with their Betti numbers for simplicial homology.*

EXAMPLE 14.1.2. Consider the simplicial complex $\Delta^2$ of Figure 14.1A: the triangles, edges and vertices of an 'octahedron'. $M_2(\Delta^2)$ is shown below, with blanks for the zero entries:

| $M_2(\Delta)$ | $\omega$ | $ab$ | $ac$ | $ad$ | $ae$ | $bc$ | $be$ | $bf$ | $cd$ | $cf$ | $de$ | $df$ | $ef$ |
|---|---|---|---|---|---|---|---|---|---|---|---|---|---|
| $abc$ | $1$ | $1$ | $-1$ | | $1$ | | | | | | | | |
| $abe$ | $-1$ | $1$ | | | $-1$ | | $1$ | | | | | | |
| $acd$ | $1$ | | $1$ | $-1$ | | | | | $1$ | | | | |
| $ade$ | $1$ | | | $1$ | $-1$ | | | | | | $1$ | | |
| $bcf$ | $-1$ | | | | | $1$ | | $-1$ | | $1$ | | | |
| $bef$ | $1$ | | | | | | $1$ | $-1$ | | | | | $1$ |
| $cdf$ | $-1$ | | | | | | | | $1$ | $-1$ | | $1$ | |
| $def$ | $-1$ | | | | | | | | | | $1$ | $-1$ | $1$ |

The second column lists the coefficients of a 2-cycle (row dependence) $\omega$, confirming that the rank of this matroid is at most 7. With any one face removed, say $\{d, e, f\}$

in Figure 14.1B, it is easy to check that the remaining rows are independent. The rank of the original matroid is 7, with the disk of Figure 14.1B as a basis. Up to scalar multiplication, this 2-cycle $\omega$ is the unique circuit of the 2-cycle matroid.

Finally, the 'ring' of Figure 14.1C is also independent, of rank 5. In all cases we have not required the complete graph of all edges on the six vertices. The presence, or absence, of edges which do not appear in the faces will simply change the number of 'all zero' columns in the submatrix for the faces we are considering but they will not change the $k$-cycles or the matroid.

The rank of the simplicial $k$-cycle matroid can be investigated through the row space and the $k$-cycles, by the analog of the 'statics of rigidity'. To complete the vocabulary for these analyses, we define two more spaces related to the boundary operators. The space of $i$-boundaries $B_i(\Delta)$ is the image of $\partial_{i+1}$. That is, $\mathbf{c} \in B_i(\Delta)$ if there is some chain $\mathbf{d} \in C_{i+1}(\Delta)$ with $\partial_{i+1}(\mathbf{d}) = \mathbf{c}$. Since $\partial_i \partial_{i+1} = 0$, $i$-boundaries are $i$-cycles and $B_i(\Delta) \subseteq Z_i(\Delta)$. The $i$-homology of $\Delta$ is the space: $\widetilde{H}_i(\Delta) = Z_i(\Delta)/B_i(\Delta)$, and the reduced Betti number is $\beta_i(\Delta) = \dim(\widetilde{H}_i(\Delta))$. We note that $B_k(\Delta^k) = \mathbf{0}$, so $\widetilde{H}_k(\Delta^k) = Z_k(\Delta^k)$. (Since we have an augmented complex, this is the reduced homology and we write $\widetilde{H}_i(\Delta)$ rather than $H_i(\Delta)$, although they are the same for $i > 0$.)

From our definition of the simplicial $k$-cycle matroid, we know that

$$\operatorname{rank} \mathcal{M}_k(\Delta) = f_k(\Delta) - \dim(Z_k(\Delta)) = f_k(\Delta) - \beta_k(\Delta^k).$$

The following basic identity for the homology of a general chain complex will lead to other computations for the rank.

THEOREM 14.1.3 [**Mu**]. *For any chain complex* $\mathcal{C}$:

$$\mathcal{C}: \ \mathbf{0} \to C_r \xrightarrow{\partial_r} C_{(r-1)} \xrightarrow{\partial_{r-1}} C_{(r-2)} \xrightarrow{\partial_{r-2}} \cdots \qquad \cdots \xrightarrow{\partial_1} C_0 \xrightarrow{\partial_0} C_{-1} \longrightarrow \mathbf{0}.$$

*the following identity defines the Euler characteristic of the chain complex:*

$$\chi(\mathcal{C}) = \sum_{i=-1}^{r} (-1)^i \dim(C_i) = \sum_{i=-1}^{r} (-1)^i \beta_i(\mathcal{C}).$$

COROLLARY 14.1.4. *The rank of the $k$-cycle matroid* $\mathcal{M}_k(\Delta)$ *is:*

$$\operatorname{rank} \mathcal{M}_k(\Delta) = f_k(\Delta) - \beta_k(\Delta^k) = \sum_{i=-1}^{k-1} (-1)^{k-1+i} f_i(\Delta) - \sum_{i=-1}^{k-1} (-1)^{k-1+i} \beta_i(\Delta).$$

PROOF. We observed above that $\operatorname{rank} \mathcal{M}_k(\Delta) = f_k(\Delta) - \beta_k(\Delta^k)$. From the Euler characteristic:

$$\sum_{i=-1}^{k-1} (-1)^{k-1+i} f_i(\Delta) - \sum_{i=-1}^{k} (-1)^{k-1+i} \beta_i(\Delta^k) = f_k(\Delta) - \beta_k(\Delta^k) = \operatorname{rank} \mathcal{M}_k(\Delta).$$

EXAMPLE 14.1.5. For any non-empty complex, $\partial_0 v_i = 1 \cdot [\emptyset]$, so $\beta_{-1}(\Delta) = 0$. For any connected complex ($\Delta^{(1)}$ is a connected graph) $\beta_0(\Delta^k) = 0, k \geq 1$.

More generally, $\beta_0(\Delta^k)$ is the number of components of $\Delta^1$, minus one. Therefore, for any non-empty connected graph $G = (V, E)$ and its simplicial complex,

$$\text{rank } \mathcal{M}_1(G) = |E| - \beta_1(G) = \left[ |V| - \beta_0(G) \right] - \left[ 1 - \beta_{-1}(G) \right] = |V| - 1.$$

The 1-cycle matroid of $G = \Delta^1$ is the standard cycle matroid of the graph, with polygons as 1-cycles.

Notice that, if $f_{k+1}(\Delta) \neq 0$ then $\emptyset \neq B_k(\Delta) \subseteq Z_k(\Delta^k)$. Therefore $\Delta^{(k)}$ will not be simplicially $k$-independent.

EXAMPLE 14.1.6. If we return to the complexes of Figure 14.1, we find that the Betti numbers and Euler characteristic are:
A. The characteristic is $\chi = 8 - 12 + 6 - 1 = 1$ and $\beta_2 = 1$, $\beta_0 = 0$, $\beta_{-1} = 0$. We conclude that $\beta_1 = 0$ as well.
B. The characteristic is $\chi = 7 - 12 + 6 - 1 = 0$ and $\beta_2 = 0$, $\beta_0 = 0$, $\beta_{-1} = 0$ so $\beta_1 = 0$ as well. (The 1-cycle around the boundary of the disc is the 1-boundary of the chain sum of all triangles.)
C. The characteristic is $\chi = 5 - 11 + 6 - 1 = -1$ and $\beta_2 = 0$, $\beta_0 = 0$, $\beta_{-1} = 0$. We conclude that $\beta_1 = 1$, representing the 1-cycle around the hole, which is not the boundary of a 2-chain.

REMARK 14.1.7. Assume $\Delta(n)$ is the complete simplicial complex on $n \geq k+1$ vertices (i.e. $\Delta(n) = 2^n$), then $\beta_i((\Delta(n))^k) = 0$ for all $i \leq k - 1$ [**Mu**]. This gives

$$\text{rank } \mathcal{M}_k(\Delta(n)) = \sum_{i=-1}^{k-1} (-1)^{k-1+i} f_i(\Delta(n)) = \binom{n-1}{k},$$

since $f_i(\Delta(n)) = \binom{n}{i+1}$ and $\sum_{i=-1}^{k-1} (-1)^{k-1+i} \binom{n}{i+1} = \binom{n-1}{k}$.

A direct analysis of the complete simplicial complex also gives the rank $\binom{n-1}{k}$ [**CL**]. The set of simplices $X_a = \{ \sigma \in (\Delta(n))^k \mid a \in \sigma \}$ for a fixed $a \in V$ forms a basis for $\mathcal{M}_k(\Delta(n))$, with cardinality $\binom{n-1}{k}$.

In [**CL,CR1**], all calculations for sets $X$ of $k$-simplices are done within this complete simplicial complex on $n$ points. Specifically, for a subset $X \subseteq \Delta^{(k)}$, all lower chains are indexed by the complete complex $\Delta^{k-1}(n)$, on the $n$ vertices, forming a subcomplex $X(n)$. With this definition, $\beta_i(X(n)) = 0$ for $i < k - 1$, since these calculations are unchanged from the complete simplicial complex. Since $\sum_{i=-1}^{k-1} (-1)^{k-1+i} f_i(X(\Delta(n))) = \binom{n-1}{k}$, we have

$$\text{rank } \mathcal{M}_k(X(n)) = |X| - \beta_k(X(n)) = \binom{n-1}{k} - \beta_{k-1}(X(n)).$$

In [**CR1**], these two equivalent calculations are the definition of the rank function of the $i$-cycle matroid.

Of course, the rank of the matroid $\mathcal{M}_k(\Delta)$ is unchanged by adding additional lower simplices (and their subsets), to $\Delta^{k-1}$. (The row rank of the cycle matrix is unchanged by adding additional zero columns.) This does change both the counts $f_i(\Delta)$ for lower faces and the lower Betti numbers $\beta_i(\Delta)$. Because we will use the details of the lower homologies and the $f_i$ to calculate (or estimate) the rank of $\mathcal{M}_k(\Delta)$, we examine the set $X \subseteq \Delta^{(k)}$ through the the subcomplex $\langle\langle X \rangle\rangle = \{Y \mid Y \subseteq X_i, X_i \in X\}$. For any set $X \subseteq \Delta^{(k)}$ we now have:

$$\text{rank}(X) = |X| - \beta_k \langle\langle X \rangle\rangle = \sum_{i=-1}^{k-1} (-1)^{k-1+i} f_i \langle\langle X \rangle\rangle - \sum_{i=-1}^{k-1+i} (-1)^{k+i} \beta_i \langle\langle X \rangle\rangle.$$

A set $X \subseteq \Delta^{(k)}$ is $k$-adequate if $\beta_i = 0, i < k-1$, in which case:

$$\text{rank}(X) = |X| - \beta_k \langle\langle X \rangle\rangle = \sum_{i=-1}^{k-1} (-1)^{k-1+i} f_i \langle\langle X \rangle\rangle - \beta_{k-1} \langle\langle X \rangle\rangle.$$

For these $k$-adequate sets, the rank calculations and other related constructions will be most direct.

EXAMPLE 14.1.8. Given a simplicial complex $\Delta$ and a new vertex $a$, the *complete cone with apex $a$* is the complex $a * \Delta = \{\psi \mid \psi \in \Delta \text{ or } \psi = \{a\} \cup \pi, \pi \in \Delta\}$. A standard result of topology gives $\beta_i(a * \Delta) = 0$ for all $i$ [**Mu**]. For $i < k$, $\beta_i((a*\Delta)^{k-1}) = \beta_i(a*\Delta) = 0$, so cones will be $k$-adequate, for all $k$. Any complete cone $a * \Delta^{k-1}$ is $k$-independent in $\mathcal{M}_k$. (Note that the explicit basis given above for $\Delta(n)$ was a cone $a * \Delta^{k-1}$.)

EXAMPLE 14.1.9. The complexes of Figure 14.1A,B have rank $\mathcal{M}_2(\Delta) = 7 = |E| - |V| + 1$. For any triangulated sphere $\Delta^2$, we also have $\beta_1 = 0$ (this is a consequence of 'simply connected' topology), so rank $\mathcal{M}_2(\Delta^2) = |E| - |V| + 1$. This estimate will apply to all connected simplicial complexes with $\beta_1(\Delta) = 0$.

For other complexes the estimate $|E| - |V| + 1$ for the rank may be either too high or too low.

1. For the complex of Figure 14.1C, we have

$$\text{rank } \mathcal{M}_2(\Delta^2) = 5 = 11 - 6 < |E| - |V| + 1.$$

This change from $|E| - |V| + 1$ occurs because $\beta_2(\Delta) = 0$, $\beta_0 = 0$, $\beta_{-1} = 0$ but $\beta_1(\Delta) = 1$. A generating 1-cycle which is not a 1-boundary is the polygon around the interior hole.

2. If we take two triangulated spheres sharing no vertices, we have: $\beta_1(\Delta) = 0$, $\beta_0(\Delta) = 1$ (two connected components), and $\beta_{-1}(\Delta) = 0$ so rank $\mathcal{M}_2(\Delta) = |E| - |V| + 1 + 1 > |E| - |V| + 1$.

3. For a triangulated torus $\Delta$, with $\beta_1(\Delta) = 2$, $\beta_0(\Delta) = 0$, we have:
rank $\mathcal{M}_2(\Delta) = |E| - |V| + 1 - 2 < |E| - |V| + 1$.

As these examples illustrate, it is not possible to test independence in the simplicial 2-cycle matroid by a simple inequality on our 'estimate' $|E| - |V| + 1$, as we tested the 1-cycle matroid with the estimate $|E| \le |V| - 1$.

REMARK 14.1.10. We have not found literature on the computational complexity of $\beta_k(\Delta)$ (and therefore the rank of the simplicial $k$-cycle matroid) of a simplicial complex. The simplicial $k$-cycle matrix certainly gives a deterministic algorithm, of order $O([f_k(\Delta)]^2)$. However this approach will jump to an exponential algorithm in the more general 'generic geometric' extensions in the next two section. One reason why characterizations in terms of graphs and their related 'counts' were so useful for plane rigidity is that these characterizations yield efficient polynomial time combinatorial algorithms for the geometric extension to plane frameworks.

**14.2. Cohomology, kinematics and gluing.** There is an alternate analysis of rank $\mathcal{M}_k(\Delta)$, using the column space and the solution space of the simplicial $k$-cycle matrix. This is the direct analog of the kinematics of rigidity, with their infinitesimal motions and trivial motions. As we shall see, these are the traditional cocycles and coboundaries of the cochain complex on $\Delta$ [**Mu**]. We present a simplified form, appropriate to work over a field. We implicitly draw on special cases of the work in [**TWW1,2,3**] which is described further in §16.

The $k$-cochains $C^k(\Delta)$ are also formal sums of simplices in $\Delta^{(k)}$. In principle, the $k$-cochains lie in the dual space $(\mathbb{R}^{f_k})^*$. In practice, these are isomorphic to the $k$-chains. For each $\rho \in \Delta^{(i)}$, the $i^{th}$ *coboundary operator* $\delta_i$ is defined by:

$$\delta_i[\rho] = \sum_{\sigma \in \Delta^{(i+1)}} Sign(\rho, \sigma) \cdot [\sigma].$$

extended linearly to all $i$-cochains. The *cochain complex* is then

$$\mathcal{C}^k(\Delta^k): \quad \mathbf{0} \xleftarrow{\delta_k} C^k(\Delta) \xleftarrow{\delta_{k-1}} C^{k-1}(\Delta) \xleftarrow{\delta_{k-2}} \cdots$$
$$\cdots \xleftarrow{\delta_1} C^1(\Delta) \xleftarrow{\delta_0} C^0(\Delta) \xleftarrow{\delta_{-1}} C^{-1}(\Delta) \leftarrow \mathbf{0}.$$

We verify that our explicit definition coincides with the usual implicit definition [**Mu**] and, implicitly, that $\delta_i \delta_{i-1} = 0$. Given an $i$-chain $\mathbf{c}$ and an $i$-cochain $\mathbf{d}$, we write the bilinear form as $\langle \mathbf{c}, \mathbf{d} \rangle = \sum_{\sigma \in \Delta^{(i)}} c_\sigma \cdot d_\sigma$.

LEMMA 14.2.1. *For all chains* $\mathbf{c} \in C_i$ *and cochains* $\mathbf{d} \in C^{i-1}$:

$$\langle \partial_i \mathbf{c}, \mathbf{d} \rangle = \langle \mathbf{c}, \delta_{i-1}\mathbf{d} \rangle.$$

PROOF. By the linearity of $\partial_i$ and $\delta_{i-1}$ and the bilinearity of $\langle \ , \ \rangle$, it suffices to check this for a general $\sigma \in \Delta^{(i)}$ and $\rho \in \Delta^{(i-1)}$

$$\langle \partial_i[\sigma], [\rho] \rangle = \Big\langle \sum_{\pi \in \Delta^{(i-1)}} Sign(\pi, \sigma) \cdot [\pi], \ [\rho] \Big\rangle = Sign(\rho, \sigma)$$
$$= \Big\langle [\sigma], \sum_{\psi \in \Delta^{(i)}} Sign(\rho, \psi) \cdot [\psi] \Big\rangle = \langle [\sigma], \delta_{i-1}[\rho] \rangle.$$

For a simplicial complex $\Delta$, the kernel of $\delta_i$ is the $i$-*cocycles*, $Z^i(\Delta)$, and the image of $\delta_{i-1}$ is the $i$-*coboundaries*, $B^i(\Delta)$. Since $\delta_i \delta_{i-1} = 0$, $B^i(\Delta) \subseteq Z^i(\Delta)$ and we have the *cohomology spaces* of the augmented cochain complex, $\widetilde{H}^i(\Delta^k) = Z^i(\Delta^k)/B^i(\Delta^k)$, and the corresponding *Betti numbers* $\beta^i(\Delta^k) = \dim \widetilde{H}^i(\Delta^k)$.

As explicit equations, the conditions for an $i$-cocycle have the form:

$$\delta\mathbf{d} = \sum_{\rho \in \Delta^{(i-1)}} d_\rho \cdot [\rho] = \sum_{\sigma \in \Delta^{(i)}} \Big( \sum_{\rho \in \Delta^{(i-1)}} Sign(\rho, \sigma)d_\rho \Big) \cdot [\sigma] = 0.$$

These $i$-cocycles are the solutions to the system of equations: $M_i(\Delta)\mathbf{x} = \mathbf{0}$, where $M_i(\Delta)$ is the $i$-cycle matrix of the previous section, with $i$-boundaries as rows, the $(i+1)$-cycles as row dependencies, the $(i+1)$-coboundaries as columns and the $(i+1)$-cocycles as column dependencies. The $i$-*cocycle matrix* with the $i$-cocycles as row dependencies is then $M^i = (M_{i+1})^t$.

EXAMPLE 14.2.2. Consider again the cell complex $\Delta^1$ of (Figure 14.1A,B), the edges and vertices of an 'octahedron' . The matrix with the 1-coboundaries as rows, the 0-boundaries as columns, the 0-cocycles as row dependencies and the 1-cycles as column dependencies is $M_1(\Delta)^t = M^0(\Delta)$:

|   | $\lambda$ | $ab$ | $ac$ | $ad$ | $ae$ | $bc$ | $be$ | $bf$ | $cd$ | $cf$ | $de$ | $df$ | $ef$ |
|---|---|---|---|---|---|---|---|---|---|---|---|---|---|
| $a$ | 1 | 1 | 1 | 1 | 1 | | | | | | | | |
| $b$ | 1 | -1 | | | | 1 | 1 | 1 | | | | | |
| $c$ | 1 | | -1 | | | -1 | | | 1 | 1 | | | |
| $d$ | 1 | | | -1 | | | | | -1 | | 1 | 1 | |
| $e$ | 1 | | | | -1 | | -1 | | | | -1 | | 1 |
| $f$ | 1 | | | | | | | -1 | | -1 | | -1 | -1 |

The column $\lambda$ is a sample 0-cocycle (which is unique up to choice of a scalar). In the language of 'kinematics of graphs on a line', this 0-cocycle is the unique (up to scalar multiplication) trivial motion – a translation. In this example, we can also see that the 1-coboundaries are all orthogonal to the rows of the 2-cycle matrix for $\Delta$ of Example 14.1.2 (the 1-boundaries of $\Delta$).

This orthogonality of $i$-boundaries and $i$-coboundaries is a special case of the more central orthogonality of the next lemma. This orthogonality gives explicit form to our analogy of cohomology and kinematics and can lead to a general matroidal orthogonality (§14.3).

LEMMA 14.2.3. *For any simplicial complex* $\Delta$,

$$Z_i(\Delta) = (B^i(\Delta))^\perp \text{ and } Z^i(\Delta) = (B_i(\Delta))^\perp,$$

*where* $\perp$ *denotes perpendicular subspace in the sense of* $\langle \, , \, \rangle$.

PROOF. For any $i$-chain $\mathbf{c}$, we have:

$$\mathbf{c} \in Z_i(\Delta) \iff \partial\mathbf{c} = 0 \iff \forall\rho \in \Delta^{i-1} \langle \, \partial_i\mathbf{c}, [\rho] \, \rangle = 0$$
$$\iff \forall\rho \in \Delta^{i-1} \langle \, \mathbf{c}, \delta_{i-1}[\rho] \, \rangle = 0 \iff \mathbf{c} \in (B^i(\Delta))^\perp.$$

An identical argument works for $Z^i(\Delta) = (B_i(\Delta))^\perp$.

COROLLARY 14.2.4 [**Mu**]. *For any finite simplicial complex* $\Delta$*, working over a field* $F$*, the homologies and cohomologies are isomorphic and* $\beta^i(\Delta^k) = \beta_i(\Delta^k)$.

We can use this orthogonality to complete the analogy with the kinematics of frameworks. The $(k-1)$-cocycles, $Z^{k-1}(\Delta)$, are the $k$-*motions* of a complex $\Delta$ (solutions to the equations $M_k(\Delta)\mathbf{x} = \mathbf{0}$). In the same spirit, the *trivial* $k$-*motions* will be the motions of a complete complex on the vertices, restricted to the $(k-1)$-simplices of $\Delta$ – that is the $(k-1)$-coboundaries of the complete complex $\Delta(n)$ on these vertices. For any $(k-2)$-simplex $\pi \in \Delta(n)^{(k-2)}$ and $(k-1)$-simplex $\sigma \in \langle\langle X \rangle\rangle^{(k-1)}$, we have $\langle \, [\rho], \delta_{k-2}[\pi] \, \rangle \neq 0$ if and only if $\pi \subseteq \rho$. Therefore, in $\langle\langle X \rangle\rangle$, $\delta_{k-2}[\rho] \neq \mathbf{0}$ if and only if $\rho \in \langle\langle X \rangle\rangle^{(k-2)}$. The trivial $k$-motions of $\langle\langle X \rangle\rangle$ are the $(k-1)$-coboundaries $B^{k-1}\langle\langle X \rangle\rangle$.

Completing this analogy to kinematics, a set $X$ of $k$-simplices will be *simplicially* $k$-*rigid* if and only if all $k$-motions are $k$-trivial motions. That is, the set $X$

is simplicially $k$-rigid if $Z^{k-1}\langle\langle X \rangle\rangle = B^{k-1}\langle\langle X \rangle\rangle$, or equivalently, if $\beta^{k-1}\langle\langle X \rangle\rangle = \beta_{k-1}\langle\langle X \rangle\rangle = 0$.

In the earlier sections, a simple but critical task was to determine (count) the exact dimension of the space of trivial motions. The importance of these estimates will be further clarified in the next sections and §A. Our previous calculations give one formula for this dimension.

PROPOSITION 14.2.5. *For any set $X$ of $k$-simplices, the space of trivial $k$-motions, $B^{k-1}\langle\langle X \rangle\rangle$, has dimension $T^k(X) = \sum_{i=-1}^{k-2}(-1)^{k-2+i}[f_i\langle\langle X \rangle\rangle - \beta^i\langle\langle X \rangle\rangle]$.*

PROOF. In the complex $\langle\langle X \rangle\rangle^{k-1}$, all $k-1$ faces are cocycles and $\beta^{k-1}\langle\langle X \rangle\rangle^{k-1} = f_{k-1}\langle\langle X \rangle\rangle - \dim B^{k-1}\langle\langle X \rangle\rangle$. Also, by the Euler characteristic of this cochain complex:

$$\sum_{i=-1}^{k-1}(-1)^{k-1+i}[f_i\langle\langle X \rangle\rangle^{k-1} - \beta^i\langle\langle X \rangle\rangle^{k-1}] = 0.$$

Therefore,

$$T^k(X) = f_{k-1}\langle\langle X \rangle\rangle - \beta^{k-1}\langle\langle X \rangle\rangle^{k-1} = \sum_{i=-1}^{k-2}(-1)^{k-2+i}[f_i\langle\langle X \rangle\rangle - \beta^i\langle\langle X \rangle\rangle].$$

REMARK 14.2.6. Our calculations for rank $\mathcal{M}_k\langle\langle X \rangle\rangle$ also yield a count:

$$|X| - \beta_k\langle\langle X \rangle\rangle = f_{k-1}\langle\langle X \rangle\rangle - \beta_{k-1}\langle\langle X \rangle\rangle - \left(\sum_{i=-1}^{k-2}(-1)^{k-2+i}[f_i\langle\langle X \rangle\rangle - \beta_i\langle\langle X \rangle\rangle]\right)$$

Therefore, the space of trivial motions has dimension:

$$T^k\langle\langle X \rangle\rangle = f_{k-1}\langle\langle X \rangle\rangle - \text{rank } \mathcal{M}_k\langle\langle X \rangle\rangle - \beta_{k-1}\langle\langle X \rangle\rangle$$

$$= \sum_{i=-1}^{k-2}(-1)^{k-2+i}[f_i\langle\langle X \rangle\rangle - \beta_i\langle\langle X \rangle\rangle].$$

Since $\beta_i\langle\langle X \rangle\rangle = \beta^i\langle\langle X \rangle\rangle$, these two calculations agree. Representative 'non-trivial motions' now correspond to $Z^{k-1}(\Delta)/B^{k-1}(\Delta) = \widetilde{H}^{k-1}(\Delta)$.

There is a corresponding 'static interpretation' of $\widetilde{H}_{k-1}\langle\langle X \rangle\rangle$. As for frameworks, the row space of $M_k\langle\langle X \rangle\rangle$ – the space $B_{k-1}\langle\langle X \rangle\rangle$ of $(k-1)$-boundaries – becomes the *resolvable $k$-loads*. The entire space of *equilibrium $k$-loads* is the orthogonal space to the trivial $k$-motions, that is, the space of $(k-1)$-cycles $Z_{k-1}\langle\langle X \rangle\rangle$. The space $\widetilde{H}_{k-1}(\Delta)$ is a space of *representative unresolved equilibrium loads* (the equilibrium loads modulo the resolved loads).

Completing the static analogy, a set $X$ is *statically rigid* if all equilibrium $k$-loads are resolvable, that is, if $Z_{k-1}\langle\langle X \rangle\rangle = B_{k-1}\langle\langle X \rangle\rangle$ or $\beta_{k-1}\langle\langle X \rangle\rangle = 0$. As happens with such definitions for finite objects, since $\beta_{k-1}\langle\langle X \rangle\rangle = \beta^{k-1}\langle\langle X \rangle\rangle$ we have the immediate corollary [**TWW1**]:

COROLLARY 14.2.7. *For a set of $k$-simplices $X$, the following are equivalent:*
1. *the set $X$ is simplicially $k$-rigid;*
2. *the set $X$ is statically $k$-rigid;*
3. $\beta^{k-1}\langle\langle X \rangle\rangle = 0$;
4. $\beta_{k-1}\langle\langle X \rangle\rangle = 0$.

What is the possible closure of a set $X \subseteq \Delta^{(k)}$ in $\mathcal{M}_k(\Delta)$? Looking at the matrix, it is clear that the only possible simplices have their boundary in the chains of $\Delta^{(k-1)}$. We denote the set of all such simplices (the analog of $K_{V(E)}$ in rigidity) as $[\Delta(k-1)]^{(k)}$.

CYCLE-COCYCLE TEST 14.2.8. *For any simplicial complex $\Delta$, the following are equivalent:*
1. *the simplex $\rho \in [\Delta(k-1)]^{(k)}$ is not in the closure of $X$ in $\mathcal{M}_k([\Delta(k-1)]^{(k)})$;*
2. *every $k$-cycle $\omega$ on $X \cup \{\rho\}$ is zero on $\rho$;*
3. *there is a $(k-1)$-cocycle $\mathbf{u}$ on $\langle\langle X \rangle\rangle$, such that $\langle \partial[\rho], \mathbf{u}\rangle \neq 0$.*

PROOF. Essentially the same proofs used for first-order flexes in rigidity and $C_r^{r-1}$-flexes applies. The equivalence of 1 and 2 is the definition of the matroid. (2. $\Rightarrow$ 3.) Assume $\rho$ is not dependent in the matroid. Therefore, adding this row to the $k$-cycle matrix for $X$ we increase the row dimension and reduce the nullity. If $\mathbf{u}$ is one of the solutions removed, we must have: $\langle\partial[\rho], \mathbf{u}\rangle \neq 0$. (3. $\Rightarrow$ 2.) We use the contrapositive. Noting that the rows of the $k$-homology matrix are the boundaries, any $k$-cycle with $\omega_\rho \neq 0$ gives:

$$\omega_\rho[\rho] = \sum_{\sigma \in \Delta^{(k)}} \omega_\sigma[\sigma] \quad \Rightarrow \quad \partial[\rho] = -\frac{1}{\omega_\rho} \sum_{\sigma \in \Delta^{(k)}} \omega_\sigma \partial[\sigma]$$

and therefore, any $(k-1)$-cocycle $\mathbf{u}$ gives

$$\langle\partial[\rho], \mathbf{u}\rangle = -\frac{1}{\omega_\rho} \sum_{\sigma \in \Delta^{(k)}} \omega_\sigma \langle\partial[\sigma], \mathbf{u}\rangle = -\frac{1}{\omega_\rho} \sum_{\sigma \in \Delta^{(k)}} \omega_\sigma 0 = 0.$$

EXAMPLE 14.2.9. If a complex has $\beta_i(\Delta) = 0$ for all $-1 \leq i$, it is called *acyclic*. If an acyclic complex $\Delta$ has dimension $d$ (that is, the maximal simplices are $d$-simplices) then $\Delta^d$ is simplicially $(d+1)$-independent, simplicially $(d+1)$-rigid and $(d+1)$-adequate. Since the reduced Euler characteristic is $\sum_{i=-1}^{d}(-1)^i f_i(\Delta) = \sum_{i=-1}^{d}(-1)^i \beta_i(\Delta) = 0$, the dimension of the space of trivial simplicial $d$-motions is

$$T^d(\Delta) = \sum_{i=-1}^{d-2}(-1)^{d+i} f_i(\Delta) = f_{d-1}(\Delta) - f_d(\Delta).$$

For the $(d-1)$-simplices of an acyclic $\Delta^d$, $\Delta^{d-1}$ is still $d$-adequate and $d$-rigid, but it is not $d$-independent. The reduced Euler characteristics of $\Delta^d$ and $\Delta^{d-1}$ give:

$$\beta_{d-1}(\Delta^{d-1}) = \sum_{i=-1}^{d-1}(-1)^{d-1+i} f_i(\Delta) = f_d(\Delta).$$

The $(d-1)$-cycle space is generated by the (independent) $(d-1)$-boundaries of the faces $f_d(\Delta)$.

For the $k$-simplices $k < d$ of an acyclic $d$-complex, $\Delta^k$ is simplicially $(k+1)$-adequate and $(k+1)$-rigid. The reduced Euler characteristics of $\Delta^d$ and $\Delta^k$ give

$$\beta_k(\Delta^k) = \sum_{i=-1}^{k}(-1)^{k+i} f_i(\Delta) = \sum_{i=k+1}^{d}(-1)^{k+i} f_i(\Delta).$$

For an acyclic $\Delta$, $\beta_k(\Delta^k)$ must be positive for $k < d$, since there are $k$-cycles (boundaries of $(k + 1)$-faces) but these boundaries are not used to compute the Betti number of $\Delta^k$.

EXAMPLE 14.2.10. If a set of $k$-simplices is not $k$-rigid, we may not find additional $k$-simplices to make it $k$-rigid unless we add new $k - 1$ simplices (Figure 14.2). For example, consider the annulus of Figure 14.2A, with $\beta_1 = 1$. This annulus is 2-independent ($\beta_2 = 0$) and 2-adequate ($\beta_0 = 0$, $\beta_{-1} = 0$ for any non-empty connected complex) but there is no 'additional simplex' on these edges.

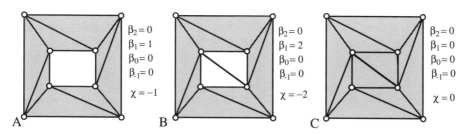

FIGURE. 14.2. *A non 2-rigid complex (A) with added edge (B) and faces(C) for simplicial 2-rigidity.*

This situation is very different from the rigidity of a plane framework, where we could always find 'missing edges' on the existing vertices which would produce rigidity. Effectively, all sets of vertices which span the plane are 'adequate' in that situation (see §15).

For the rigidity of frameworks, we computed the behaviour of $X \cup Y$ from the behaviour of $X$, $Y$ and the form of $X \cap Y$, using Gluing Lemmas. In homology, a related set of connections are based on the Mayer-Vietoris sequence of homology theory [**Mu**]. We illustrate with a few simple properties.

$k$-HOMOLOGY GLUING LEMMA 14.2.11. *Assume $X$, $Y$ are sets of $k$-simplices.*
1. *If $X$ and $Y$ are $k$-independent and $\langle\langle X \rangle\rangle \cap \langle\langle Y \rangle\rangle$ is simplicially $k$-rigid, then $X \cup Y$ is $k$-independent;*
2. $\mathrm{rank}(X) + \mathrm{rank}(Y) = \mathrm{rank}(X \cup Y) + \mathrm{rank}(X \cap Y)$ *if and only if $\beta_{k-1}(\langle\langle X \rangle\rangle \cap \langle\langle Y \rangle\rangle) = 0$;*
3. *If $\langle\langle X \rangle\rangle$, $\langle\langle Y \rangle\rangle$ and $\langle\langle X \rangle\rangle \cap \langle\langle Y \rangle\rangle$ are $k$-adequate then $\langle\langle X \cup Y \rangle\rangle$ is $k$-adequate;*
4. *If $X$ and $Y$ are simplicially $k$-rigid and $\langle\langle X \rangle\rangle \cap \langle\langle Y \rangle\rangle$ is $k$-adequate, then $X \cup Y$ is simplicially $k$-rigid;*
5. *If $X$ and $\langle\langle X \rangle\rangle \cap \langle\langle Y \rangle\rangle$ are acyclic, then $X \cup Y$ and $Y$ have equal Betti numbers and share any properties such as simplicial $k$-independence, simplicial $k$-rigidity, simplicial $k$-adequacy etc.*

PROOF. For general chain subcomplexes $\Delta$, $\Psi$, the Mayer-Vietoris sequence is an exact sequence of the form [**Mu**]:

$$\ldots \to \widetilde{H}_i(\Delta \cap \Psi) \to \widetilde{H}_i(\Delta) \oplus \widetilde{H}_i(\Psi) \to \widetilde{H}_i(\Delta \cup \Psi)$$
$$\to \widetilde{H}_{i-1}(\Delta \cap \Psi) \to \widetilde{H}_{i-1}(\Delta) \oplus \widetilde{H}_{i-1}(\Psi) \to \ldots$$

We set $\Delta = \langle\langle X \rangle\rangle$, $\Psi = \langle\langle Y \rangle\rangle$, and $\Delta \cup \Psi = \langle\langle X \rangle\rangle \cup \langle\langle Y \rangle\rangle = \langle\langle X \cup Y \rangle\rangle$. Although $(\langle\langle X \rangle\rangle \cap \langle\langle Y \rangle\rangle)^{(k)} = X \cap Y = \langle\langle X \cap Y \rangle\rangle^{(k)}$, for $i < k$ we may have $\langle\langle X \cap Y \rangle\rangle^{(i)} \subsetneq \langle\langle X \rangle\rangle^{(i)} \cap \langle\langle Y \rangle\rangle^{(i)} = \Delta \cap \Psi$. The exact sequence now takes the form:

$$0 \to \widetilde{H}_k(\langle\langle X \rangle\rangle \cap \langle\langle Y \rangle\rangle) \to \widetilde{H}_k\langle\langle X \rangle\rangle \oplus \widetilde{H}_k\langle\langle Y \rangle\rangle \to \widetilde{H}_k\langle\langle X \cup Y \rangle\rangle$$
$$\to \widetilde{H}_{k-1}(\langle\langle X \rangle\rangle \cap \langle\langle Y \rangle\rangle) \to \dots$$
$$\dots \to \widetilde{H}_i(\langle\langle X \rangle\rangle \cap \langle\langle Y \rangle\rangle) \to \widetilde{H}_i\langle\langle X \rangle\rangle \oplus \widetilde{H}_i\langle\langle Y \rangle\rangle \to \widetilde{H}_i\langle\langle X \cup Y \rangle\rangle$$
$$\to \widetilde{H}_{i-1}(\langle\langle X \rangle\rangle \cap \langle\langle Y \rangle\rangle) \to \widetilde{H}_{i-1}\langle\langle X \rangle\rangle \oplus \widetilde{H}_{i-1}\langle\langle Y \rangle\rangle \to \dots$$

Case 1. Assume $X$ and $Y$ are $k$-independent. Then the top homologies are zero $\widetilde{H}_k\langle\langle X \rangle\rangle = \widetilde{H}_k\langle\langle Y \rangle\rangle = \widetilde{H}_k(\langle\langle X \rangle\rangle \cap \langle\langle Y \rangle\rangle) = 0$. The top of this sequence includes the section:

$$\dots 0 \oplus 0 \to \widetilde{H}_k\langle\langle X \cup Y \rangle\rangle \to \widetilde{H}_{k-1}(\langle\langle X \rangle\rangle \cap \langle\langle Y \rangle\rangle) \to \dots$$

Clearly, if $\beta_{k-1}(\langle\langle X \rangle\rangle \cap \langle\langle Y \rangle\rangle) = 0$, then $\beta_k\langle\langle X \cup Y \rangle\rangle = 0$ and the $X \cup Y$ is simplicially $k$-independent.

Case 2. As above, the Mayer-Vietoris sequence gives:

$$\beta_k(X) + \beta_k(Y) = \beta_k(X \cup Y) + \beta_k(\langle\langle X \rangle\rangle \cap \langle\langle Y \rangle\rangle)$$

if and only if $\beta_{k-1}(\langle\langle X \rangle\rangle \cap \langle\langle Y \rangle\rangle) = 0$. The rest follows from $|X| + |Y| = |X \cap Y| + |X \cup Y|$.

Case 3. Assume $\langle\langle X \rangle\rangle$, $\langle\langle Y \rangle\rangle$ and $\langle\langle X \cap Y \rangle\rangle$ are $k$-adequate. For each $i < k - 1$:

$$\dots 0 \oplus 0 \to \widetilde{H}_i\langle\langle X \cup Y \rangle\rangle \to 0 \dots$$

This gives $\beta_i\langle\langle X \cup Y \rangle\rangle = 0, i < k - 1$ as required.

Case 4. Assume $\langle\langle X \rangle\rangle$ and $\langle\langle Y \rangle\rangle$ are simplicially $k$-rigid and $\langle\langle X \rangle\rangle \cap \langle\langle Y \rangle\rangle$ is $k$-adequate. The second band of the Mayer-Vietoris sequence gives:

$$\dots 0 \oplus 0 \to \widetilde{H}_{k-1}\langle\langle X \cup Y \rangle\rangle \to \widetilde{H}_{k-2}(\langle\langle X \rangle\rangle \cap \langle\langle Y \rangle\rangle) \to \dots .$$

Since $\beta_{k-2}(\langle\langle X \rangle\rangle \cap \langle\langle Y \rangle\rangle) = 0$ by the $k$-adequacy, we conclude that $X \cup Y$ is $k$-rigid.

Case 5. Assume $\langle\langle X \rangle\rangle$ and $\langle\langle X \rangle\rangle \cap \langle\langle Y \rangle\rangle$ are acyclic. The typical band of the Mayer-Vietoris sequence gives:

$$\dots 0 \to 0 \oplus \widetilde{H}_i\langle\langle Y \rangle\rangle \to \widetilde{H}_i\langle\langle X \cup Y \rangle\rangle \to 0 \dots .$$

This gives the desired isomorphism of homologies. Since all the listed properties are defined from the Betti numbers, they coincide for $\langle\langle Y \rangle\rangle$ and $\langle\langle X \rangle\rangle \cup \langle\langle Y \rangle\rangle$.

Figure 14.3 illustrates that, with acyclic complexes glued across inadequate intersections, we can create and track non-zero lower homologies with the Mayer-Vietoris sequence.

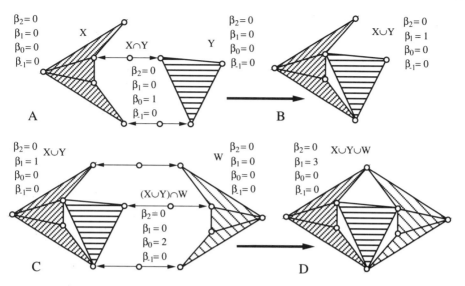

FIGURE. 14.3. *Gluing together three 2-acyclic complexes* $X$, $Y$ *and* $W$, *creating complexes which are not simplicially 2-rigid.*

EXAMPLE 14.2.12. In topology, suspensions 'transfer' Betti numbers up one dimension. Specifically, given a complex $\Delta$ the *suspension* is the union of two cones $(a * \Delta) \cup (b * \Delta)$ with $a \neq b$. Since the intersection is $(a * \Delta) \cap (b * \Delta) = \Delta$ and the two cones have $\beta_i(a*\Delta) = \beta_i(b*\Delta) = 0$ for all $i$, we find that $\beta_i((a*\Delta)\cap(b*\Delta)) = \beta_{i-1}(\Delta)$ for all $i$. In particular, the $k$-cycles of $\left(a * (\Delta^{k-1})\right) \cap \left(b * (\Delta^{k-1})\right)$ are isomorphic to the $(k-1)$-cycles of $\Delta^{k-1}$. The rank of the matroid will jump:

$$\text{rank } \mathcal{M}_k(a * (\Delta^{k-1}) \cap b * (\Delta^{k-1})) = \text{rank } \mathcal{M}_{k-1}(\Delta) + |\Delta^{(k-1)}|.$$

REMARK 14.2.13. We see that the preferred complexes for our calculations are the *simplicially $k$-ample* complexes, with $\beta_i = 0, -1 \leq i \leq k - 1$. (These are the complexes whose rank estimates were given in homology boxes of Figure 13.1.) There are standard complexes which are simplicially $k$-ample:

1. Any simplicial $d$-ball will have $\beta_i = 0$ for all $i$, in the reduced homology. This will be $k$-ample for all $k$.

2. More generally, any acyclic complex (Example 14.2.8) is $k$-ample for all $k$.

3. Any simplicial $d$-sphere is $k$-ample for all $k \leq d$. (A $d$-sphere has $\beta_i = 0$ for all $i < d$, and $\beta_d = 1$.) In the same manner as Example 14.2.8, we can also estimate the dimension of the $k$-cycle space of a $d$-sphere, using the fact that the reduced Euler characteristic is $(-1)^d$. This will give a $k$-cycle space of dimension:

$$\sum_{i=k+1}^{d} (-1)^{k+1+i} f_i(\Delta) \ + (-1)^{d-k}.$$

4. a Cohen-Macaulay complex $\Delta$ is homeomorphic to a wedge of $d$-spheres, with $\beta_i(\Delta) = 0, i \leq d - 1$. This will also be $k$-ample for all $k \leq d$.

These Cohen-Macaulay complexes (which includes spheres and balls) have their own important place in the literature of partially ordered sets and algebraic combinatorics, in part because of properties of their face lattice and the algebraic form of related constructions such as their face ring [**St2**]. The combinatorics of these complexes will recur for $k$-skeletal rigidity (§16.2).

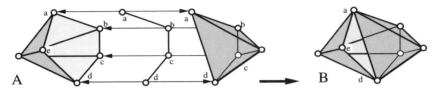

FIGURE. 14.4. *2-homology gluing across a 2-adequate set.*

REMARK 14.2.14. For the rigidity and cofactor matroids of Parts I and II, the Gluing Lemmas were directly connected to two defining properties of the abstract $d$-rigidity matroids. What would be the analogs here?

Recall that the 1-homology matroid was rigidity on the line. The reader can easily check that this is an abstract 1-rigidity matroid. Any connected graph is 1-rigid and any non-empty set of vertices is 1-adequate. Any non-empty connected graph is 1-ample. C5 asked that gluing two 1-rigid (and 1-ample) sets across any set with at least one vertex (i.e. a 1-adequate set) is 1-rigid (and 1-ample). Case 4 of Lemma 14.2.10 gives the $k$-rigidity analog of C5 and Cases 3 and 4 combine to give the $k$-ample analog for C5. (In §15 and §16, we will see that the assumed intersections of C5 really are the 'adequate' sets for these examples and that the rigid sets are also ample.)

For an analog of C6, we face real difficulties. Consider the 2-rigid complexes of Figure 14.4A. These are glued across the 2-ample strip $abcd$, to create a new 2-rigid complex of Figure 14.4B. Therefore the triangle $ade$ is in the closure of the union, but not in the closure of either piece. However, if we simply add an new, unattached vertex $f$ to both complexes their union is now 2-inadequate! The triangle $ade$ is now a counterexample to the analog of C6 for $k$-inadequate intersections. Unlike the matroids of Parts I and II, our 'inadequate sets' are not closed under subsets! We are still looking for a good analog of C6 for $k$-homology matroids or the rigidity and cofactor matroids of §15 and §16.

EXAMPLE 14.2.15. Figure 14.5 indicates three of the simplest 'Henneberg style extensions' which preserve the Betti numbers of 2-simplicial complexes by the Gluing Lemma. For extensions in homology, we could attach two complexes across any acyclic complex. In polyhedral combinatorics, the extensions of Figure 14.4A,B are two basic 'shelling' operations for 2-complexes (see below) – in which a new 2-simplex $\langle\langle X \rangle\rangle$ is attached to an existing complex $\langle\langle Y \rangle\rangle$ so that the common intersection $\langle\langle X \rangle\rangle \cap \langle\langle Y \rangle\rangle$ is a 1-disc in these examples. Since this makes $\langle\langle X \rangle\rangle$ and $\langle\langle X \rangle\rangle \cap \langle\langle Y \rangle\rangle$ acyclic, we conclude that $\beta_i(\langle\langle X \rangle\rangle \cup \langle\langle Y \rangle\rangle) = \beta_i \langle\langle Y \rangle\rangle$ for all $i$.

We also have a *triangle split* – in which we replace an existing triangle $abc$ by a new vertex 0 and three triangles $0ab$, $0bc$ and $0ca$ (D). This is verified by adding 0 and $0ab$ (step A), then edge $0c$ and triangle $0bc$ (step B). Finally, we appeal to the small 2-cycle of all faces of the tetrahedron $0abc$. From this circuit, we can 'exchange' the triangle $abc$ for the face $0ca$.

REMARK 14.2.16. In the literature of combinatorics and homology, an often used technique is *shelling* [**Bj**]: an inductive construction of pure $k$-complexes by a sequence of 'gluing on' single $n$-faces. Explicitly, a *shelling order* is an order

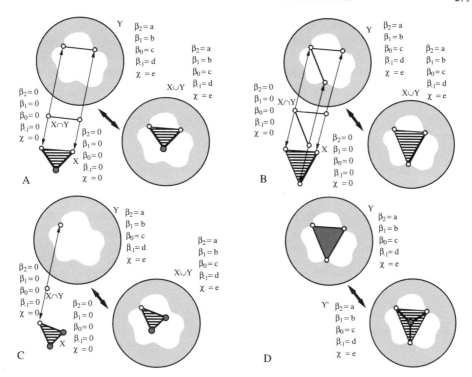

FIGURE. 14.5. *Standard extensions of a 2-complex by (A) vertex 1-addition: add one new vertex, two new edges and one triangle; (B) edge 1-addition: add a new edge and one new triangle; (C) face 1-addition: add two new vertices, three new edges and a new triangle; (D) face splits: replace a triangle by a subdivision into three triangles.*

for the $n$-simplices of $\Delta$ such that, for each $j$, the intersection of $\langle\langle\sigma\rangle\rangle_{j+1}$ with $\Delta_j = \cup_{i \leq j}\langle\langle\sigma\rangle\rangle_i$ is the union of $(n-1)$-simplices, or equivalently [**Bj**]:

  for each pair of facets $\sigma_i, \sigma_j$, $1 \leq i < j$ there is a facet $\sigma_k, k < j$ and a vertex $v \in \sigma_j$ such that $\sigma_i \cap \sigma_j \subset \sigma_k \cap \sigma_j = \sigma_j - v$.

Consider gluing 'up' the shelling order of a shellable $n$-complex $\Delta$, for the $k$-cycle matroids. Since the original simplices are $k$-acyclic and all the intersection complexes $\sigma_{j+1} \cap \Delta_j$ are $k$-adequate, the shellable complex $\Delta^k$ is $k$-ample – with all Betti numbers zero, except possibly the top $\beta_k(\Delta)$. If $k = n$, the top Betti number will be the number of times $\sigma_{j+1} \cap \Delta_j$ is all $(n-1)$-simplices of $\sigma_{j+1}$ (i.e. the intersection had $\beta_{n-1}(\sigma_{j+1} \cap \Delta_j) = 1$).

REMARK 14.2.17. In the traditional combinatorial approach to the $k$-simplicial matroid, in which $X(n)^{(k-1)}$ is the complete $(k-1)$-complex on the vertices, the Mayer-Vietoris sequence is singularly uninformative. While all lower homologies are 0 for $i < k-1$, the second layer of the exact sequence is:

$$\ldots \to \widetilde{H}_{k-1}(X(n) \cap Y(n)) \to \widetilde{H}_{k-1}X(n) \oplus \widetilde{H}_{k-1}Y(n) \to \widetilde{H}_{k-1}(X \cup Y)(n) \to \mathbf{0} \ldots$$

In general, with such a large set of $(k-1)$ faces and a small set of $k$ faces, it is unlikely that any of the $\beta_{k-1}$ are zero. The critical information contained in features such as $\beta_{k-1}(\langle\langle X\rangle\rangle \cap \langle\langle Y\rangle\rangle)$ is lost in this overlay of 'irrelevant' faces.

In closing this subsection, we note several basic steps which recur in §15, §16:
1. a top boundary operator takes $k$-chains to $(k-1)$-chains, creating a $k$-cycle matrix and a matroid with these dependencies;
2. this top operation and matrix extend to a full augmented chain complex with the lower homologies and the Euler characteristic as tools for analysis as an analog to the 'statics of frameworks';
3. the dual (orthogonal) cohomology gives an equivalent cochain complex, with equal Betti numbers and Euler characteristic, and a matroid analysis analogous to the 'kinematics of frameworks';
4. the Mayer-Vietoris sequence provides an inductive 'gluing' process, in which ample and rigid complexes play a distinctive role;
5. particular combinatorial (and geometric) constructions (here, coning and suspension) play a special role in connecting the matroids of related complexes;
6. special topological structures (spheres, balls etc.) guarantee nice properties for the matroid and its analysis (ample, adequate etc.).

**14.3. Orthogonality and cohomology.** Previous work on simplicial matroids has connected the orthogonal matroid of a $k$-cycle matroid and some cycle matroid of the dual complex [**Cr2,CL**]. When and how this connection occurs is clarified through the cohomology.

Given a matroid $\mathcal{M}$ on the finite set $A$, the *orthogonal matroid* $\mathcal{M}^*$ on $A$ is defined by [**NW**, Proposition 2.1.4]:

$B$ is a basis of $\mathcal{M}^*$ if and only if $A - B$ is a basis of $\mathcal{M}$.

For matroids represented as the rows of a matrix, this orthogonality takes on a more specific form [**Cr**, 5.4.1]:

If $M$ and $N$ are both matrices over the field $F$, with rows indexed by the set $A$, such that every column of $M$ is orthogonal to every column of $N$, and such that the columns of $M$ and $N$, taken together, have rank $|A|$, then the matroid of the rows of $M$ and the rows of $N$ are orthogonal.

Our observations for homology and cohomology contain this orthogonality. We will make this explicit in a more general setting. While other sections concentrate on the field $\mathbb{R}$, for orthogonality there has also been interest in the combinatorics for $F = Z/2$ [**We**]. This section is written for a general field.

We have constructed a matroid from the real (or rational) homology of a simplicial complex. In a number of geometric applications, we are interested in non-simplicial objects, such as the facets of general convex polytopes. These examples are special cases of the more general CW-complexes of algebraic topology [**Mu**]. They generate an homology theory over any field, with $i$-cycles, $i$-boundaries and $i$-Betti numbers, and induce the *$j$-cycle matroid* on the $j$-faces of these C-W complexes (see, for example, [**Cr2**, §5.7]).

For polyhedra, we could induce this same $j$-cycle matroid by taking a simplicial subdivision of the original (say a barycentric subdivision) and defining a set of cells to be $j$-independent if and only if this subdivision is $j$-independent in the simplicial $j$-cycle matroid. (The Betti numbers of a complex are unchanged by subdivision, as they are topological invariants.) However, for the geometric applications and extensions, this subdivision would change the independence. In those contexts it will be essential to work directly with the non-simplicial faces of the initial complex (see [**CrW4**]). We briefly outline how this works, giving a description for the orthogonal matroids for selected $j$-cycle matroids.

For any abstract complex $\Delta$, with $i$-faces $\Delta^{(i)}$ (possibly not simplices) and the largest faces in $\Delta^{(k)}$, we have the chain complex of linear maps over the field $F$:

$$\mathcal{C}(\Delta): \ \mathbf{0} \to \oplus_{\psi \in \Delta^{(k)}} F \xrightarrow{\partial_k} \cdots$$

$$\xrightarrow{\partial_{i+2}} \oplus_{\rho \in \Delta^{(i+1)}} F \xrightarrow{\partial_{i+1}} \oplus_{\sigma \in \Delta^{(i)}} F \xrightarrow{\partial_i} \oplus_{\pi \in \Delta^{(i-1)}} F \xrightarrow{\partial_{i-1}}$$

$$\cdots \xrightarrow{\partial_1} \oplus_{v \in \Delta^{(0)}} F \xrightarrow{\partial_0} F \xrightarrow{\partial_{-1}} \mathbf{0}$$

with boundary operators on $\sigma \in \Delta^{(i)}$, $\partial_i[\sigma] = \sum_{\pi \in \Delta^{(i-1)}} \epsilon_{\pi,\sigma} \cdot [\pi]$, where $\epsilon_{\pi,\sigma} \in \{-1, 0, 1\}$ represents the sign describing the orientation of $\pi$ as a subface of $\sigma$. As always, the boundary operators must satisfy $\partial_i \partial_{i+1} = 0$ for all $i$. For each $j$ we define the $j$-cycle matroid $\mathcal{M}_j(\Delta)$ on $\Delta^{(j)}$, defined by taking the minimal supports of $j$-cycles $Z_j(\Delta)$ as the circuits: $\mathbf{c} \in Z_j(\Delta)$ if and only if $\partial_j \mathbf{c} = 0$.

We also have the corresponding cochain complex on $\Delta$:

$$\mathcal{C}(\Delta): \ \mathbf{0} \xleftarrow{\delta_k} \oplus_{\psi \in \Delta^{(k)}} F \xleftarrow{\delta_{k-1}} \cdots$$

$$\xleftarrow{\delta_{i+1}} \oplus_{\rho \in \Delta^{(i+1)}} F \xleftarrow{\delta_i} \oplus_{\sigma \in \Delta^{(i)}} F \xleftarrow{\delta_{i-1}} \oplus_{\pi \in \Delta^{(i-1)}} F \xleftarrow{\delta_{i-2}}$$

$$\cdots \xleftarrow{\delta_1} \oplus_{v \in \Delta^{(0)}} F \xleftarrow{\delta_0} \oplus_{v \in \Delta^{(0)}} \xleftarrow{\delta_{-1}} F \leftarrow \mathbf{0}.$$

with $\delta_{i+1} \delta_i = 0$ for all $i$. This gives the $j$-cocycle matroid $\mathcal{M}^j(\Delta)$ on $\Delta^{(j)}$, taking the minimal supports of $j$-cocycles $Z^j(\Delta)$ as circuits of the matroid.

With the bilinear form on $j$-chains $C_j = \oplus_{\rho \in \Delta^{(j)}} F$ and $j$-cochains $C^j$:

$$\left\langle \sum_{\rho \in \Delta^{(i)}} c_\rho \cdot [\rho], \ \sum_{\rho \in \Delta^{(i)}} d_\rho \cdot [\rho] \right\rangle = \sum_{\rho \in \Delta^{(i)}} c_\rho d_\rho,$$

we also have the condition (sometimes the definition of $\delta_j$ [**Mu**]) that, for all $\mathbf{c} \in C_{j+1}(\Delta)$ and $\mathbf{d} \in C^j(\Delta)$

$$\langle \partial_{j+1} \mathbf{c}, \mathbf{d} \rangle = \langle \mathbf{c}, \delta_j \mathbf{d} \rangle.$$

By the argument used in §14.2, $Z_j(\Delta) = (B^j(\Delta))^\perp$, where $B^j(\Delta)$ is the space of $j$-coboundaries, $\delta_{j-1} C^{j-1}$. The $j$-cycle matroid is represented by the rows of the matrix $M_j(\Delta)$ with the coboundaries $\delta[\pi], \pi \in \Delta^{(j-1)}$ as columns. The $j$-cocycle matroid can be represented by the rows of the matrix $M^j(\Delta)$, in which the columns are the $j$-boundaries of simplices in $\rho \in \Delta^{(j+1)}$.

Recall that for $\rho \in \Delta^{(j+1)}$ and $\pi \in \Delta^{(j-1)}$,

$$\langle \partial_{j+1} \rho, \delta_{j-1} \pi \rangle = \langle \partial_j \partial_{j+1} \rho, \pi \rangle = \langle \mathbf{0}, \pi \rangle = 0$$

so the columns of $M_j(\Delta)$ and $M^j(\Delta)$ are mutually orthogonal, for *all* complexes. We have the initial condition for an orthogonality between these matroids.

When is rank $M_j(\Delta) +$ rank $M^j(\Delta) = |\Delta^{(j)}| = f_j$? Using the observations that $\dim Z_j(\Delta) = \dim B_j(\Delta) + \beta_j(\Delta)$ and that $\dim B_j(\Delta) + \dim Z^j(\Delta) = f_j$, by the orthogonality:

$$\text{rank } M_j(\Delta) + \text{rank } M^j(\Delta) = f_j - \dim Z_j(\Delta) + f_j - \dim Z^j(\Delta)$$

$$= 2f_j - [\dim B_j(\Delta) + \beta_j(\Delta) + \dim Z^j(\Delta)] = f_j - \beta_j(\Delta).$$

We conclude that:

COCYCLE ORTHOGONALITY 14.3.1. *For any simplicial complex* $\Delta$ *and any integer* $j$, *the* $j$-*cocycle matroid* $\mathcal{M}^j(\Delta)$ *is the orthogonal matroid of the* $j$-*cycle matroid* $\mathcal{M}_j(\Delta)$ *if and only if* $\beta_j(\Delta) = 0$ *(or equivalently,* $\beta^j(\Delta) = 0$).

This explains a wide range of orthogonal pairs of matroids coming from homology and cohomology.

EXAMPLE 14.3.2. *For any homology* $k$-*sphere* $\Delta$, $\beta_j(\Delta) = 0$ *for all* $j < k$. Therefore, for $j < k$ we have an orthogonal pair of matroids $\mathcal{M}_j(\Delta)$ and $\mathcal{M}^j(\Delta)$.

EXAMPLE 14.3.3. *For planar graphs* $G$, *the 'dual graph'* $G^*$ *is the graph of the dual complex* $\Delta^*$, *in which we write the 2-faces as 'vertices' and the edges as 'dual edges'.* This turns the 1-cocycle matroid of the spherical complex $\Delta$ into the 1-cycle matroid of $\Delta^*$ (see below). This orthogonality is also implicit in the Euler characteristic: $|F| - |E| + |V| - 1 = 1$   or   $|E| = (|V| - 1) + (|F| - 1)$.

REMARK 14.3.4. *When* $\beta_j(\Delta) = m > 0$, *the* $j$-*cohomology is still a partial representation of the orthogonal matroid.* We need only add $m$ additional columns, the generators for the $j$-homology, so that the extended column space generates the $j$-cycle space. The row space of this extended matrix now represents the orthogonal matroid $M_j(\Delta)^*$.

When is the orthogonal matroid to an $j$-cycle matroid on $\Delta$ the $j$-cycle matroid for a 'dual complex' $\Delta^*$ [**Cr2**, pages 91–94]? The basic Poincaré duality of homology theory gives one answer [**Mu**]. The 'dual block decomposition of $\Delta$' uses a barycentric subdivision of the original simplices (or cells), and then identifies 'dual blocks' (unions of these smaller simplices) for each of the original faces. This creates a polyhedral complex, which is probably not a simplicial complex. Without going into details, the proof of the Poincaré duality gives [**Mu**, page 379]:

COROLLARY 14.3.5. *If a cell complex* $\Delta$ *is a compact* $n$-*manifold, then the* $j$-*cocycle matroid of* $\Delta$ *is the* $(n - j)$-*cycle matroid of a dual block complex* $\Delta^*$.

The duality construction holds for the broader class of 'homology $k$-manifolds' – a class which includes all $k$-manifolds. Putting these two pieces together, we get the general result:

MANIFOLD ORTHOGONALITY 14.3.6. *If* $\Delta$ *is an abstract CW-complex whose space is a compact* $k$-*manifold with* $\beta_j(\Delta) = 0$, *then the* $j$-*cycle matroid of* $\Delta$, $M_j(\Delta)$, *and the* $(k - j)$-*cycle matroid of a dual block complex* $\Delta^*$, $M_{k-j}(\Delta^*)$, *are orthogonal matroids.*

EXAMPLE 14.3.7. *For the graph of a complex decomposing a 3-sphere* $\Delta$, *the orthogonal matroid is the 1-cocycle matroid of* $\Delta$ *or, equivalently, the 2-cycle matroid on the dual complex* $\Delta^*$ *for the 3-sphere.* In the same spirit, the 2-cycle matroid of the 3-sphere is the 1-cycle or graphic matroid of the dual $\Delta^*$.

For a polyhedral decomposition $\Delta$ of a 4-sphere, the orthogonal of the 2-cycle matroid is the 2-cycle matroid on the dual decomposition $\Delta^*$. This orthogonality is also reflected in the Euler characteristic for the 4-sphere:

$$f_4 - f_3 + f_2 - f_1 + f_0 - 1 = 1 \quad \text{or} \quad f_2 = (f_1 - f_0 + 1) + (f_3 - f_4 + 1).$$

This is a true analog for the graph and dual graph on the 2-sphere, an analogy which extends to the $j$-cycles in a $2j$-sphere.

REMARK 14.3.8. The complete simplicial complex $(K_n)^{(n-1)}$ is an $(n-2)$-sphere, with the dual complex $K_n^*$ isomorphic to $K_n$. In the duality, $(i-1)$-simplices ($i$-sets) go to $(n-i-1)$-simplices ($(n-i)$-sets). Therefore, the $(i-1)$-cycle matroid, usually written $S_i^n[F]$, has the $(i-1)$-cocycle matroid as its orthogonal matroid. Since this is the $(n-i-1)$-cycle matroid of the dual, we have the well known result that $S_{n-i}^n[F]$ is the orthogonal matroid to $S_i^n[F]$ [**Cr2**,**CL**].

REMARK 14.3.9. We could choose a subcomplex $\Delta'$ of $\Delta$ and work with the relative homology $H_i(\Delta, \Delta')$ [**Mu**] and a corresponding *relative k-cycle matroid*. Most of the theory of Section 14 extends immediately, including these orthogonality results, now for 'relative homology $n$-manifolds' with $\beta_i(\Delta, \Delta') = 0$.

The use of relative homology is central to a careful theory for existing work with multivariate splines [**Bi**,**ASW**]. Relative homology is also basic to the theory of 'pinned frameworks', in which some vertices are fixed (with velocity zero).

## 15. Multivariate Cofactor Matroids

This section has roots in approximation theory and has applications back to approximation theory (more than one might expect). Nevertheless, the chain complex here is not an object which workers in that field would normally describe. The first change, carried out by Billera [**Bi**], converted the original problem (defining polynomials over full $d$-cells in $d$-space, with required continuity across hyperplanes), into the homology of a chain complex on the interior faces of the original complex. This used a short exact sequence of chain complexes and the related long exact sequence of homologies. This change is closely related to the 'smoothing cofactors' in multi-variate splines [**Bi**,**ChW**,**Wh10**]. It has the specific advantage of reducing the computations by one dimension, which is very useful for small dimensions such as $d = 2$, $d = 3$, where most of the work is concentrated.

We make two additional changes, as we did in §10, §11. We work with the entire complex, rather than the 'interior' faces of some higher complex (a relative homology). This is not essential, but will simplify the comparisons with the other chain complexes. Finally, we work with a general $(d-1)$-simplicial complex realized in $d$-space (line segments in the plane, triangles in 3-space), rather than the interior $(d-1)$-faces of a $d$-ball, as is usual in approximation theory. Beyond the obvious generality this provides, techniques such as projection [**ASW**] illustrate the use of more general complexes as intermediate stages in the analysis of the splines.

**15.1. Trivariate $C_1^0$-cofactors.** Consider an abstract oriented 2-simplicial chain complex $\Delta$: oriented faces $F = \Delta^{(2)}$, oriented edges $E = \Delta^{(1)}$ and vertices $V = \Delta^{(0)}$, with the usual boundary operators. Add a 3-configuration $\mathbf{p}$ in $\mathbb{R}^3$, which assigns points to the vertices $\mathbf{p}(v_i) = \mathbf{p}_i = (p_{i,1}, p_{i,2}, p_{i,3})$, assigns lines to the edges and assigns planes to the faces, with the condition that the points $\mathbf{p}_i$ for any 2-simplex actually span a plane in $\mathbb{R}^3$. Thus each oriented face $\sigma = (v_1, v_2, v_3)$, induces an equation for its plane:

$$l_\sigma(\mathbf{p}) = A^\sigma x + B^\sigma y + C^\sigma z + D^\sigma = \det \begin{bmatrix} p_{1,1} & p_{1,2} & p_{1,3} & 1 \\ p_{2,1} & p_{2,2} & p_{2,3} & 1 \\ p_{3,1} & p_{3,2} & p_{3,3} & 1 \\ x & y & z & 1 \end{bmatrix} = 0.$$

A 3-*stress* on $\Delta(\mathbf{p})$ is an assignment of scalars $\omega_\sigma$ to the faces such that for each edge $\rho \in E$:

$$\sum_{\sigma \in F} Sign(\rho, \sigma)\omega_\sigma l_\sigma(\mathbf{p}) = \sum_{\sigma \in F} Sign(\rho, \sigma)\omega_\sigma (A^\sigma x + B^\sigma y + C^\sigma z + D^\sigma) \equiv 0.$$

This is a row dependence of an $|F|$-by-$4|E|$ matrix (with four columns for the entries $x, y, z, 1$ under each $\rho$). These 3-stresses define the dependencies of the $C_1^0$-*cofactor matroid on* $\Delta(\mathbf{p})$, $\mathcal{C}_1^0(\Delta; \mathbf{p})$.

The way we have written the 3-stress conditions is misleading. It suggests there are four equations (for $x, y, z, 1$), but these actually reduce to two equations for each edge. All of the planes share the common line of this edge and two of the four conditions are redundant. For example, if the line is $x = 0, y = 0$, then all planes through the line have a linear form:

$$l_\sigma(\mathbf{p}) = (A^\sigma x + B^\sigma y + C^\sigma z + D^\sigma) \equiv (A^\sigma x + B^\sigma y)$$

and we just need the first two entries under this edge. A similar 'reduction' occurs for each edge. Any plane through this line is a linear combination of two distinct planes through the line. If all edges are in general position relative to the coordinate axes, the coefficients of this linear combination can be (uniquely and linearly) computed using the first two coordinates of the new plane and the coordinates of the two points on the line. Any linear combination of the rows which is verified for these first two columns will also work for the remaining (last two) columns.

There is a more abstract, less arbitrary way to describe this. We treat every entry in the columns of $\rho$ as an element of the 2-dimensional subspace of planes through the line : the linear part $I_\rho^1(\mathbf{p})$ of the ideal $I_\rho(\mathbf{p}) = \{f \mid f(\mathbf{p}_i) = 0, i \in \rho\}$ [**Bi**]. This is a vector space of dimension 2 over $\mathbb{R}$. In this spirit (either pattern) we have the matrix equation for the 3-stresses:

$$\omega M_1^0(\Delta^2; \mathbf{p}) = [\ldots \quad \omega_\sigma \quad \ldots] \begin{bmatrix} & \vdots & \\ \ldots & Sign(\phi, \sigma)\sigma(\mathbf{p})|_{I(\rho)} & \ldots \\ & \vdots & \end{bmatrix} = \mathbf{0}$$

with the $|F|$-by-$2|E|$ matrix $M_1^0(\Delta^2; \mathbf{p})$.

This matrix defines a clear matroid $\mathcal{C}_1^0(\Delta^2; \mathbf{p})$ on the rows, with its rank, independence etc. From the work on rigidity, we have learned the value of working on the 'other side of such a matrix' and of exploring the lower homologies and cohomologies of the new chain complex. The complete chain complex is:

$$\mathcal{K}_1^0(\Delta^2; \mathbf{p}) : \mathbf{0} \to \oplus_{\sigma \in F} I_\sigma^1(\mathbf{p}) \xrightarrow{\partial_2} \oplus_{\rho \in E} I_\rho^1(\mathbf{p}) \xrightarrow{\partial_1} \oplus_{v \in V} I_v^1(\mathbf{p}) \xrightarrow{\partial_0} I^1(\emptyset) \xrightarrow{\partial_{-1}} \mathbf{0},$$

where for any $\psi \in \Delta^2$, $I_\psi^1(\mathbf{p}) = \{f \mid f(\mathbf{p}_i) = 0, i \in \rho, \ f \text{ of degree } \leq 1\}$ and for each $\psi \in \Delta^{(i)}$:

$$\partial_i(c_\psi \cdot [\psi]) = c_\psi \partial_i \cdot [\psi] = \sum_{\theta \in \Delta^{(i-1)}} Sign(\theta, \psi)c_\psi \cdot [\theta].$$

As usual, the boundary operator is extended linearly to all $i$-chains. This is well-defined since, if $Sign(\tau, \psi) \neq 0$, then $I_\psi^1(\mathbf{p}) \subset I_\tau^1(\mathbf{p})$ and $c_\psi$ is well defined in $I_\tau^1$.

What is the Euler characteristic of this chain complex? Since $I_\sigma^1(\mathbf{p}) = \{cl_\sigma(\mathbf{p}) \mid c \in \mathbb{R}\}$, $\dim C_2(\mathcal{K}_1^0(\Delta; \mathbf{p})) = |F|$. The dimension of $C_1(\mathcal{K}_1^0(\Delta; \mathbf{p})) = 2|E|$, the dimension of $C_0(\mathcal{K}_1^0(\Delta; \mathbf{p})) = 3|V|$, since the space of polynomials zero at a point (say the origin) has dimension 3, and the dimension of $C_{-1}(\mathcal{K}_1^0(\Delta; \mathbf{p})) = 4$, since all polynomials are zero on the empty set. The Euler characteristic is:

$$\chi(\mathcal{K}_1^0(\Delta^2)) = |F| - 2|E| + 3|V| - 4 = \beta_2(\mathcal{K}) - \beta_1(\mathcal{K}_1^0) + \beta_0(\mathcal{K}_1^0) - \beta_{-1}(\mathcal{K}_1^0).$$

Using this Euler characteristic, the rank of the matroid is

$$\begin{aligned}
\text{rank } \mathcal{C}_1^0(\Delta^2; \mathbf{p}) &= |F| - \beta_2(\mathcal{K}_1^0(\Delta^2; \mathbf{p})) \\
&= 2|E| - 3|V| + 4 - \beta_1(\mathcal{K}_1^0(\Delta; \mathbf{p})) + \beta_0(\mathcal{K}_1^0(\Delta; \mathbf{p})) - \beta_{-1}(\mathcal{K}_1^0(\Delta; \mathbf{p})).
\end{aligned}$$

There are simple geometric conditions for $\beta_{-1}(\mathcal{K}_1^0(\Delta; \mathbf{p})) = 0$ and $\beta_0(\mathcal{K}_1^0(\Delta; \mathbf{p})) = 0$.

PROPOSITION 15.1.1. *For a 2-complex $\Delta$, $\beta_{-1}(\mathcal{K}_1^0(\Delta; \mathbf{p})) = 0$ if and only if there are two distinct points $\mathbf{p}_i \neq \mathbf{p}_j$, $i, j \in V$.*

PROOF. For all $\Delta$ we have a fixed set of $(-1)$-cycles $C_{-1}(\mathcal{K}_1^0(\Delta; \mathbf{p})) = P_1$, the polynomials of degree at most 1. When is $B_{-1}(\mathcal{K}_1^0(\Delta; \mathbf{p})) = P_1$? Given one point $\mathbf{p}_i$, the boundaries of chains in $I_i^1(\mathbf{p})$ are the space of all linear forms, zero on $\mathbf{p}_i$. This generates 3 of the 4 dimensions needed. If we have a second distinct point $\mathbf{p}_j$, then the boundary of chains $I_j^1(\mathbf{p})$ will include a linear form zero on $\mathbf{p}_j$ but non-zero on $\mathbf{p}_i$, showing that $B_{-1}(\mathcal{K}_1^0(\Delta; \mathbf{p})) = P_1$, and $\beta_{-1}(\mathcal{K}_1^0(\Delta)) = 0$.

Conversely, if $\Delta(\mathbf{p})$ includes only one point, then $B_{-1}(\mathcal{K}_1^0(\Delta; \mathbf{p})) = I_i^1(\mathbf{p}) \neq P_1$, and $\beta_{-1}(\mathcal{K}_1^0(\Delta; \mathbf{p})) = 1$. (If $\Delta = \emptyset$, then $\beta_{-1}(\mathcal{K}_1^0(\Delta; \mathbf{p})) = 4$.)

PROPOSITION 15.1.2. *For the geometric complex $\Delta^2(\mathbf{p})$, $\beta_0(\mathcal{K}_1^0(\Delta^2; \mathbf{p})) = 0$ if and only if the geometric graph $\Delta^{(1)}(\mathbf{p})$ has only trivial parallel drawings in 3-space.*

PROOF. This is easiest to analyze using a matrix whose rows are the image of $\partial_1$ on the chains $c_{(i,j)} \cdot [i, j]$, with $c_{(i,j)} \in I_{[i,j]}^1(\mathbf{p})$. This space is spanned by two specific linear forms, say $l_{(i,j),1}(\mathbf{p}), l_{(i,j),2}(\mathbf{p})$, and the matrix has the form:

$$\begin{array}{c}
\begin{array}{ccccccc}
\cdots & \cdot & v_i & \cdots & v_j & \cdot & \cdots
\end{array} \\
\begin{array}{c}
\vdots \\
(i,j)_1 \\
(i,j)_2 \\
\vdots
\end{array}
\left(
\begin{array}{ccccccc}
\ddots & \vdots & \vdots & \cdots & \vdots & \vdots & \ddots \\
\cdots & \mathbf{0} & l_{(i,j),1}(\mathbf{p}) & \cdots & -l_{(i,j),1}(\mathbf{p}) & \mathbf{0} & \cdots \\
\cdots & \mathbf{0} & l_{(i,j),2}(\mathbf{p}) & \cdots & -l_{(i,j),2}(\mathbf{p}) & \mathbf{0} & \cdots \\
\ddots & \vdots & \vdots & \cdots & \vdots & \vdots & \ddots
\end{array}
\right).
\end{array}$$

These entries, now in $I_i^1(\mathbf{p})$ and $I_j^1(\mathbf{p})$, can be written with the first three coefficients of the linear forms (the normals of two planes through $\mathbf{p}_i, \mathbf{p}_j$). We now recognize this as the matrix for parallel drawings of the geometric graph $\Delta^{(1)}(\mathbf{p})$.

This matrix has only the trivial parallel drawings if and only if the row space is all 'equilibrium loads' (all 0-cycles). We conclude that $\beta_0(\mathcal{K}_1^0(\Delta; \mathbf{p})) = 0$ if and only if the geometric graph $\Delta^{(1)}(\mathbf{p})$ has only trivial parallel drawings in 3-space.

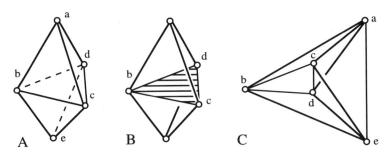

FIGURE. 15.1. *Some small 2-complexes for the matroid $C_1^0$ in 3-space.*

EXAMPLE 15.1.3. Consider the complexes of Figure 15.1. In Figure 15.1A, $|F| = 6, |E| = 9, |V| = 5$, we have $\chi(\mathcal{K}_1^0(\Delta^2; \mathbf{p})) = -1$. We also have $\beta_{-1} = 0$ and $\beta_0 = 0$, provided $\mathbf{p}$ spans at least a plane. If $\mathbf{p}$ affinely spans 3-space, then one of the edges, such as $ab$, has two distinct planes. A simple inspection shows that, in the 2-cycle equation, the two coefficients for these faces must be zero on both simplices. This zero coefficient will pass across all edges, giving all coefficients 0 and we conclude $\beta_2(\mathcal{K}_1^0(\Delta^2; \mathbf{p})) = 0$. Since $\beta_0(\mathcal{K}_1^0(\Delta^2; \mathbf{p})) = 0$ and $\beta_{-1}(\mathcal{K}_1^0(\Delta^2; \mathbf{p})) = 0$, the Euler characteristic gives $\beta_1(\mathcal{K}_1^0(\Delta; \mathbf{p})) = 1$. (If all points in $\mathbf{p}$ are coplanar, but not collinear, then $\beta_2(\mathcal{K}_1^0(\Delta; \mathbf{p})) = 1$, and $\beta_1(\mathcal{K}_1^0(\Delta; \mathbf{p})) = 2$.)

In Figure 15.1B, we add the additional face $bcd$. This gives the characteristic $\chi(\mathcal{K}_1^0(\Delta; \mathbf{p})) = 0$. If $\mathbf{p}$ is in general position (no four points coplanar) then $\beta_2(\mathcal{K}_1^0(\Delta; \mathbf{p})) = 0$ (the coefficients of a $C_1^0$ dependence at an edge with exactly two non-coplanar faces must be zero) so $\beta_1(\mathcal{K}_1^0(\Delta; \mathbf{p})) = 0$ as well. The geometric complex is $C_1^0$-*acyclic*.

Finally, in Figure 15.1C, we add the edge $ab$ and three planes $abc$, $abd$, $abe$, giving the complete 2-complex on 5 points. The Euler characteristic is now $\chi(\mathcal{K}_1^0(\Delta; \mathbf{p})) = 1$. We assume that the vertices are in general position, satisfying the unique affine dependence $\lambda_a \mathbf{a} + \lambda_b \mathbf{b} + \lambda_c \mathbf{c} + \lambda_d \mathbf{d} + \lambda_e \mathbf{e} = 0$. The 2-cycles are row dependencies of the matrix. The matrix below, with the $(\mathbf{p})$'s omitted for space, gives such an $\omega$ :

| | $\omega$ | $ab$ | $ac$ | $ad$ | $ae$ | $bc$ | $bd$ | $be$ | $cd$ | $ce$ | $de$ |
|---|---|---|---|---|---|---|---|---|---|---|---|
| $abc$ | $\lambda_a\lambda_b\lambda_c$ | $l_{abc}$ | $-l_{abc}$ | | | $l_{abc}$ | | | | | |
| $abd$ | $\lambda_a\lambda_b\lambda_d$ | $l_{abd}$ | | $-l_{abd}$ | | | $l_{abd}$ | | | | |
| $acd$ | $\lambda_a\lambda_c\lambda_d$ | | $l_{acd}$ | $-l_{acd}$ | | | | | $l_{acd}$ | | |
| $bce$ | $\lambda_b\lambda_c\lambda_e$ | | | | | $l_{bce}$ | | $-l_{bce}$ | | $l_{bce}$ | |
| $bde$ | $\lambda_b\lambda_d\lambda_e$ | | | | | | $l_{bde}$ | $-l_{bde}$ | | | $l_{bde}$ |
| $cde$ | $\lambda_c\lambda_d\lambda_e$ | | | | | | | | $l_{cde}$ | $-l_{cde}$ | $l_{cde}$ |
| $bcd$ | $\lambda_b\lambda_c\lambda_d$ | | | | | $l_{bcd}$ | $-l_{bcd}$ | $l_{bcd}$ | | | |
| $abe$ | $\lambda_a\lambda_b\lambda_e$ | $l_{abe}$ | | | $-l_{abe}$ | | | $l_{abe}$ | | | |
| $ace$ | $\lambda_a\lambda_c\lambda_e$ | | $l_{ace}$ | | $-l_{ace}$ | | | | | $l_{ace}$ | |
| $ade$ | $\lambda_a\lambda_d\lambda_e$ | | | $l_{ade}$ | $-l_{ade}$ | | | | | | $l_{ade}$ |

At each edge we have three distinct planes - and at most one set of scalars for a 2-cycle. Therefore $\beta_2(\mathcal{K}_1^0(\Delta; \mathbf{p})) \leq 1$. Since $\beta_1(\mathcal{K}_1^0(\Delta; \mathbf{p})) \geq 0$, and $\beta_2(\mathcal{K}_1^0(\Delta; \mathbf{p})) - \beta_1(\mathcal{K}_1^0(\Delta, \mathbf{p})) = 1$, we conclude that $\beta_2(\mathcal{K}_1^0(\Delta; \mathbf{p})) = 1$ and $\beta_1(\mathcal{K}_1^0(\Delta; \mathbf{p})) = 0$. The column under $\omega$ gives the actual coefficients of the 2-cycle, unique up to a single scalar multiple.

This 2-cycle in the matroid $\mathcal{C}_1^0(\Delta; \mathbf{p})$ is a typical projection of a 4-polytope. A general theorem of [**CW4**], which examines one source of this matroid in scene analysis, says that the projection of any 4-polytope (in fact of any oriented 3-manifold) which spans 4-space has $\beta_2(\mathcal{K}_1^0(\Delta^2; \mathbf{p})) \geq 1$.

In keeping with our analogies with rigidity and homology, we have the following terminology:

1. a set $X$ of 2-simplices is $\mathcal{K}_1^0$-*independent* if $\beta_2(\mathcal{K}_1^0\langle\langle X\rangle\rangle) = 0$;
2. a set $X$ of 2-simplices is $\mathcal{K}_1^0$-*rigid* if $\beta_1(\mathcal{K}_1^0\langle\langle X\rangle\rangle) = 0$;
3. a set $X$ of 2-simplices is $\mathcal{K}_1^0$-*adequate* if $\beta_0(\mathcal{K}_1^0\langle\langle X\rangle\rangle) = \beta_{-1}(\mathcal{K}_1^0\langle\langle X\rangle\rangle) = 0$;
4. a set $X$ of 2-simplices is $\mathcal{K}_1^0$-*acyclic* if $\beta_i(\mathcal{K}_1^0\langle\langle X\rangle\rangle) = 0$ for all $i$.

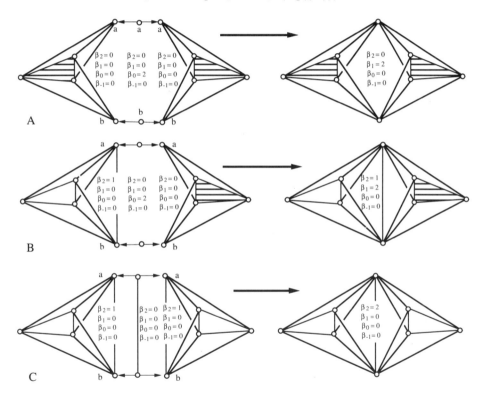

FIGURE. 15.2. *Gluing 2-complexes in the complex* $\mathcal{K}_1^0$ *in 3-space, with associated Betti numbers.*

EXAMPLE 15.1.4. We can use the Mayer-Vietoris sequence for this homology to analyze the three sums of Figure 15.2 A,B,C. The pieces 'glued' are those of Figure 15.1B,C. The basic sequence in homology is:

$$0 \to H_2(\Delta \cap \Psi) \to H_2(\Delta) \oplus H_2(\Psi) \to H_2(\Delta \cup \Psi) \to H_1(\Delta \cap \Psi) \to H_1(\Delta) \oplus H_1(\Psi)$$
$$\to H_1(\Delta \cup \Psi) \to H_0(\Delta \cap \Psi) \to H_0(\Delta) \oplus H_0(\Psi) \to H_0(\Delta) \cup H_0(\Psi) \ldots \quad .$$

The resulting $\beta_i$ are indicated in the figures.

EXAMPLE 15.1.5. The standard results of homology on cones do *not* extend directly. Observe that the complex $X$ of Figure 15.1C is a cone $(w * K_4)^2$, but has

$\beta_2 = 1 \neq 0$ and $\beta_1 = \beta_0 = \beta_{-1} = 0$. What we can observe in this example is that this cone $(w * K_4)^2$ has the same Betti numbers for $\mathcal{K}_1^0$ as the original tetrahedron $(K_4)^2$ has for simplicial homology (see Conjecture 15.3.2).

We offer one further application of the gluing principle to this complex.

ACYCLIC GLUING LEMMA 15.1.6. *If* $\langle\langle X \rangle\rangle \cap \langle\langle Y \rangle\rangle$ *is* $\mathcal{K}_1^0$-*acyclic, then* $\beta_i\langle\langle X \cup Y \rangle\rangle = \beta_i\langle\langle X \rangle\rangle + \beta_i\langle\langle Y \rangle\rangle$.

*If* $\langle\langle X \rangle\rangle$ *and* $\langle\langle X \rangle\rangle \cap \langle\langle Y \rangle\rangle$ *are both* $\mathcal{K}_1^0$-*acyclic, then* $\beta_i\langle\langle X \cup Y \rangle\rangle = \beta_i\langle\langle Y \rangle\rangle$.

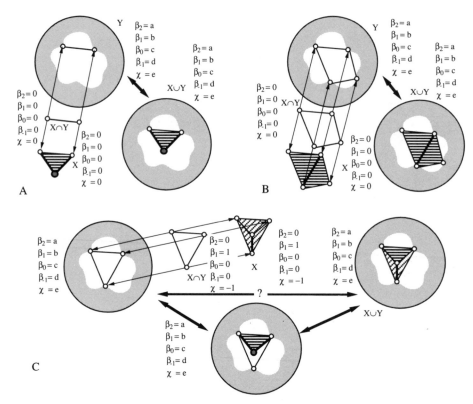

FIGURE. 15.3. *Standard extensions of a 2-complex in* $\mathcal{K}_1^0$ *by (A) vertex 1-addition: add one new vertex, two new edges and one triangle; (B) edge 2-addition: add a new edge with two new (non-coplanar) triangles; (C) add a new pyramid of one vertex, three edges and three triangles.*

EXAMPLE 15.1.7. Figure 15.3 illustrates three standard 'Henneberg-style extensions' for a 2-complex which preserve all Betti numbers in $\mathcal{K}_1^0$:

A. *vertex 1-addition*: adding a new triangle, sharing a single existing edge (adding a vertex and two new edges);

B. *edge 2-addition*: adding a new edge with two attached triangles. (Notice that the stated $\beta_0 = 0$ holds only if the four points (or two triangles) are not coplanar: a coplanar quadrilateral has non-trivial parallel drawings!)

C. The addition of a triangular pyramid can be seen either as step (A) followed by step (B) *or* as a gluing in which the added $\langle\langle X \rangle\rangle$ and shared $\langle\langle X \rangle\rangle \cap \langle\langle Y \rangle\rangle$ have the matching Betti numbers, non-zero in only one location.

Some of these extension principles must be proven by direct matrix arguments, not by general 'gluing'. In particular, if $C$ is analyzed in one step, the correspondence of Betti numbers for $\langle\langle X \rangle\rangle$ and $\langle\langle X \rangle\rangle \cap \langle\langle Y \rangle\rangle$ in item (C) is *not* sufficient to guarantee then the original and the final complexes have matching Betti numbers. Consider the analog for plane rigidity: attaching a 2-valent vertex $X = \{ab, ac\}$, with one degree of freedom ($\beta_0\langle\langle X \rangle\rangle = 1$ as we will see below), across two vertices $b, c$ to $Y$, will preserve the Betti numbers (independence, rigidity, etc.) of $Y$ if and only if the three points are not collinear – a condition which is not detected in the Betti numbers (independence or non-rigidity) of $X$!

**15.2. Cohomology for trivariate $C_1^0$-cofactors.** For this homology ('statics and stresses') there is a corresponding cohomology ('kinematics'). With the given coefficients for chains, we need 'dual' coefficients for the cochains in order to define the central bilinear form $\langle \mathbf{c}, \mathbf{d} \rangle \in \mathbb{R}$ on $i$-chains. Equivalently, we want the $(i-1)$-cocycles to be 'kinematic solutions' to the matrix equation: $M_1^0(\Delta; \mathbf{p})\mathbf{x} = \mathbf{0}$.

Treating the polynomial entries (linear forms) $Ax + By + Cz + D$ as vectors $(A, B, C, D)$, the coefficients of our chains must also be 4-vectors (with an appropriate equivalence relation). For this we need the extended affine coordinates (or homogeneous projective coordinates) for the points $\overline{\mathbf{p}}_i = (p_{i,1}, p_{i,2}, p_{i,3}, 1)$. We write $V_4/\overline{\sigma}$ for the space of 4-vectors with the equivalence relation $\overline{\mathbf{s}} \equiv \overline{\mathbf{t}} \bmod \overline{\sigma}$ if $\overline{\mathbf{s}} - \overline{\mathbf{t}} = \sum_{i \in \sigma} e_i \overline{\mathbf{p}}_i$ for some scalars $e_i$.

With this notation, the $C_1^0$-*cochain complex* on $\Delta(\mathbf{p})$ is:

$$\mathcal{K}_1^0(\Delta; \mathbf{p}) : \quad \mathbf{0} \leftarrow \oplus_{\rho \in F} V_4/\overline{\rho} \xleftarrow{\delta_1} \oplus_{\pi \in E} V_4/\overline{\pi} \xleftarrow{\delta_0} \oplus_{a_i \in V} V_4/\overline{\mathbf{a}}_i \xleftarrow{\delta_{-1}} V_4 \leftarrow \mathbf{0}.$$

For a general $i$-simplex $\rho$, with coefficient $c_\rho$,

$$\delta_i(c_\rho \cdot [\rho]) = \sum_{\sigma = \rho x} Sign(\rho, \sigma) c_\rho \cdot [\sigma].$$

This is extended linearly to $i$-cochains. The maps are well-defined on the equivalence classes, since, if $\pi \subset \sigma$, then $\overline{\mathbf{s}} \equiv \overline{\mathbf{t}} \bmod \overline{\pi}$ implies $\mathbf{s} \equiv \overline{\mathbf{t}} \bmod \overline{\sigma}$ (the space is larger). In an obvious fashion, the signs guarantee that $\delta_i \delta_{i-1} = 0$.

The elements of the kernel of $\delta_i$ are the $i$-cocycles $Z^i(\mathcal{K}_1^0(\Delta; \mathbf{p}))$, and the elements of the image of $\delta_{i-1}$ are the $i$-coboundaries, $B^i(\mathcal{K}_1^0(\Delta; \mathbf{p}))$. We have the usual (reduced) cohomology spaces of the cochain complex:

$$\widetilde{H}^i(\mathcal{K}_1^0(\Delta; \mathbf{p})) = Z^i(\mathcal{K}_1^0(\Delta; \mathbf{p}))/B^i(\mathcal{K}_1^0(\Delta; \mathbf{p})).$$

and the corresponding *Betti numbers* $\beta^i(\mathcal{K}_1^0(\Delta; \mathbf{p})) = \dim \widetilde{H}^i(\mathcal{K}_1^0(\Delta; \mathbf{p}))$.

Given an $i$-chain $\mathbf{c}$, with $c_\pi \in I_\pi^1(\mathbf{p})$ and an $i$-cochain $\mathbf{d}$, with $d_\pi \in V_4/\overline{\pi}$, we have a natural bilinear form $\langle \mathbf{c}, \mathbf{d} \rangle = \sum_{\pi \in \Delta^{(i)}} c_\pi \cdot d_\pi$. (The process of 'substituting' $d_\pi$ into the linear form $c_\pi$ is written $\cdot d_\pi$.) This is well-defined since, if $\overline{\mathbf{s}} = \overline{\mathbf{t}} \bmod \overline{\pi}$ and $c_\pi \in I_\pi^1(\mathbf{p})$, then

$$c_\pi \cdot \overline{\mathbf{s}} = c_\pi \cdot \overline{\mathbf{t}} + c_\pi \cdot [\sum_{i \in \pi} e_i \overline{\mathbf{p}}_i] = c_\pi \cdot \overline{\mathbf{t}} + \sum_{i \in \pi} e_i [c_\pi \cdot \overline{\mathbf{p}}_i] = c_\pi \cdot \overline{\mathbf{t}} \bmod \overline{\pi}$$

since all forms in $I_\pi^1$ are zero on points $\mathbf{p}_i$, $i \in \pi$, by definition.

With this bilinear form, the usual duality for an $(i+1)$-chain $\mathbf{c}$ and an $i$-cochain $\mathbf{d}$ holds: $\langle \partial_{i-1}\mathbf{c}, \mathbf{d} \rangle = \langle \mathbf{c}, \delta^i \mathbf{d} \rangle$ and the resulting isomorphisms of homology and cohomology spaces and equality of $i$-Betti numbers, Euler characteristic etc. follow. We also have the orthogonality of $i$-boundaries and $i$-cocycles: $(B_i(\Delta, \mathbf{p}))^\perp =$

$Z^i(\Delta, \mathbf{p})$ and the orthogonality of $i$-coboundaries and $i$-cycles: $(B^i(\Delta, \mathbf{p}))^\perp = Z_i(\Delta, \mathbf{p})$.

In the pattern established in Section 14.2, we define:
1. the *trivial $C_1^0$-flexes on* $\Delta(\mathbf{p})$ – the 1-coboundaries $B^1(\Delta, \mathbf{p})$;
2. the *$C_1^0$-flexes on* $\Delta(\mathbf{p})$ – the 1-cocycles $Z^1(\Delta, \mathbf{p})$; and
3. the *non-trivial $C_1^0$-flexes on* $\Delta(\mathbf{p})$ (the $C_1^0$-flexes modulo the trivial $C_1^0$-flexes) – the 1-cohomology $H^1(\Delta, \mathbf{p})$.

Notice that the space of 1-cocycles *is* the solution space of the matrix equation $M_1^0(\Delta; \mathbf{p})\mathbf{x} = \mathbf{0}$. This follows from the orthogonality of the rows of $M_1^0(\Delta; \mathbf{p})$ (the 1-boundaries ) and the 1-cocycles for the chain complex.

The estimate $3|V| - 4$ is the dimension of the 1-coboundaries (trivial flexes), provided that $\beta^0 = \beta_0 = 0$ and $\beta^{-1} = \beta_{-1} = 0$, that is, provided we have at least two distinct points and a geometric graph which has only trivial parallel drawings.

It is also possible to 'kinematically interpret' the estimate $3|V| - 4$. The coboundaries of the space $V_{d+1}/i(\mathbf{p}) \cdot [i]$ of cochains on a single vertex form a space of dimension 3. However, these $3|V|$ distinct coboundaries have 4 dependencies, corresponding to the four dimensions of 0-coboundaries of the $(-1)$-cochains, provided that $\beta^0 = 0, \beta^{-1} = 0$.

$C_1^0$-FLEX TEST 15.2.1. *For any simplicial 2-complex $\Delta$ with an allowed 3-configuration $\mathbf{p}$ for its vertices, and a 2-simplex $\psi \in [\Delta(1)]^{(2)}$ the following are equivalent:*
1. *$\psi$ is in the $C_1^0$-cofactor matroid closure of $\Delta^{(2)}$ in $[\Delta(1)]^{(2)}$;*
2. *there is a $C_1^0$-dependence $\omega$ on $[\Delta(1)]^{(2)}$ with $\omega_\psi \neq 0$;*
3. *all $C_1^0$-flexes $\mathbf{u}$ on $\Delta(\mathbf{p})$ satisfy $\partial_2[\psi] \cdot \mathbf{u} = 0$.*

PROOF. The equivalence of 1 and 2 the definition of the $C_1^0$-matroid and the closure operator.

(2. $\Rightarrow$ 3.) If $\psi$ is dependent on $\Delta^{(2)}(\mathbf{p})$, then the standard argument shows that any $C_1^0$-flex $\mathbf{u}$ which is orthogonal to $B_1(\Delta, \mathbf{p})$ is orthogonal to $\partial \psi$.

(2. $\Rightarrow$ 3.) If $\psi \in [\Delta(1)]^{(2)}$ is not dependent on $\Delta(\mathbf{p})$, then adding this row to the matrix $M_1^0(\Delta; \mathbf{p})$ will increase the rank by one and remove some $C_1^0$-flex $\mathbf{u}$, since they have the same set of 1-simplices. This contradiction completes the proof.

REMARK 15.2.2. From this corollary, we realize that a $C_1^0$-rigid complex $\Delta(\mathbf{p})$ has $[\Delta(1)]^{(2)}$ as its closure. However, from §14.2 we anticipate that the fact that the closure of $\Delta(\mathbf{p})$ is $[\Delta(1)]^{(2)}$ is *not* sufficient for $C_1^0$-rigidity. This will hold only if $[\Delta^{(1)}]^{(2)}$ is $C_1^0$-rigid.

REMARK 15.2.3. All of the definitions were given for a specific abstract complex $\Delta^k$ and a specific configuration $\mathbf{p}$. As usual, the ranks of the matrices can be checked by determinants in the entries – algebraic functions of the coordinates of the configuration. Therefore we have *generic* values for the rank, generic Betti numbers, and an open dense subset of generic configurations. These define the *generic $C_1^0$-cofactor matroid* $\mathcal{K}_1^0(\Delta^2)$.

There are geometric 'special configurations' for a complex $\Delta$ which also reduce the rank from this generic value. We have only seen very degenerate forms (for example, all points coplanar) because we have only examined very small complexes. Example 16.1.1 will illustrate this occurrence. (Recall that for plane rigidity, the first interesting special positions occurred for six vertices.)

As the corresponding box in the chart of Figure 13.1 indicates, we will return to this matroid in the §16.1, as skeletal 3-rigidity .

**15.3. Trivariate $C_s^{s-1}$-cofactor matroids.** As we did for plane graphs, we can replace the linear form $A^\sigma x + B^\sigma y + C^\sigma z + D^\sigma$ as coefficients on $[\sigma]$ by the $s$-form $[l_\sigma(\mathbf{p})]^s = [A^\sigma x + B^\sigma y + C^\sigma z + D^\sigma]^s$ to create a new matroid. We define a $C_s^{s-1}$-*dependence* on $\Delta^2(\mathbf{p})$ as scalars $\omega_\rho$ satisfying, for each $\rho \in \Delta^{(1)}$,

$$\sum_{\sigma \in \Delta^{(2)}} Sign(\rho, \sigma)\omega_\sigma [A^\sigma x + B^\sigma y + C^\sigma z + D^\sigma]^s = 0.$$

The independent sets of the $C_s^{s-1}$-*cofactor matroid* on $\Delta^2(\mathbf{p})$, $\mathcal{C}_s^{s-1}(\Delta; \mathbf{p})$ are those with only the trivial $C_s^{s-1}$-dependence. These are the row dependencies of a matrix:

$$\begin{array}{c} \\ \sigma \end{array} \begin{pmatrix} & \cdots & \begin{array}{c} \vdots \\ Sign(\rho, \sigma)[l_\sigma(\mathbf{p})]^s \\ \vdots \end{array} & \overset{\textstyle\rho}{\phantom{x}} & \cdots \\ \end{pmatrix}.$$

Of course, these equations define the 2-cycles of a larger chain complex. For each $\rho \in \Delta^2$, we define the ideal generated by all $s$'th powers of elements of $I_\rho^1(\mathbf{p})$, $I_\rho^s(\mathbf{p}) = \langle f^s(\mathbf{p}) \mid f(\mathbf{p}) \in I_\rho^1(\mathbf{p}) \rangle$. The corresponding chain complex is [**Bi**]:

$$\mathcal{K}_s^{s-1}(\Delta; \mathbf{p}) : 0 \to \oplus_{\sigma \in F} I_\sigma^s(\mathbf{p}) \xrightarrow{\partial_2} \oplus_{\rho \in E} I_\rho^s(\mathbf{p}) \xrightarrow{\partial_1} \oplus_{v \in V} I_v^s(\mathbf{p}) \xrightarrow{\partial_0} I_\emptyset^s \xrightarrow{\partial_{-1}} 0,$$

where, for each $\psi \in \Delta^{(i)}$:

$$\partial_i(c_\psi \cdot [\psi]) = c_\psi \cdot \partial_i[\psi] = \sum_{\theta \in \Delta^{(i-1)}} Sign(\theta, \psi)c_\psi \cdot [\theta].$$

and the boundary operator is extended linearly to all $i$-chains. This is well-defined since, if $Sign(\theta, \psi) \neq 0$ then $I_\psi^s \subset I_\theta^s(\mathbf{p})$. ($I_\emptyset^s$ is the set of all polynomials of degree at most $s$, also written $P_s$.)

If $\psi$ is an $i$-simplex, then $I_\psi^s(\mathbf{p})$ has dimension $\binom{s+2-i}{2-i}$ [**Bi**]. This gives the Euler characteristic for $\mathcal{K}_s^{s-1}(\Delta; \mathbf{p})$:

$$\chi(\mathcal{K}_s^{s-1}(\Delta; \mathbf{p})) = |F| - (s+1)|E| + \binom{s+2}{2}|V| - \binom{s+3}{3}.$$

If the complex $\Delta^2(\mathbf{p})$ is $C_s^{s-1}$-ample – i.e. $\beta_i(\mathcal{K}_s^{s-1}(\Delta; \mathbf{p})) = 0$ for $i \leq 1$ – then the rank for $\mathcal{C}_s^{s-1}(\Delta, \mathbf{p})$, recorded in Figure 13.1, is:

$$\text{rank } \mathcal{C}_s^{s-1}(\Delta, \mathbf{p}) = |F| - \beta_2(\mathcal{K}_s^{s-1}(\Delta; \mathbf{p})) = (s+1)|E| - \binom{s+2}{2}|V| + \binom{s+3}{3}.$$

In this generality, there has been very little work on the homologies of this chain complex. The definitions of cohomology and 'kinematics' do extend with $C_{s-1}^s$-flexes, $C_{s-1}^s$-rigidity and a $C_{s-1}^s$ Flex Test, in the spirit of §15.2 (using 'powers of affine points in the space of the simplex' for an equivalence relation on the appropriate vectors). The results for gluing across $C_s^{s-1}$-acyclic complexes also extend.

We offer a simple result and a conjecture to connect $\mathcal{K}_s^{s-1}(\Delta^2)$ and $\mathcal{K}_{s+1}^s(w*\Delta^2)$. This is directly analogous to the 'coning' of §11.3 and it is likely that the proof given there extends, but this has not yet been verified.

LEMMA 15.3.1. *Given any simplicial 2-complex $\Delta^2$, the truncated cone $(w*\Delta)^2$ satisfies $\chi(\mathcal{K}_s^{s-1}(\Delta^2; \mathbf{p})) = \chi(\mathcal{K}_{s+1}^s((w*\Delta)^2; \mathbf{p}_w, \mathbf{p}))$.*

PROOF. This is a pure counting problem. If $\Delta$ has the number of faces $|F|$, $|E|$, $|V|$ and 1, then $(w*\Delta)^2$ has the numbers $|F|+|E|$, $|E|+|V|$, $|V|+1$, and 1. In the Euler characteristic calculation we have:

$$\chi(\mathcal{K}_{s+1}^s((w*\Delta)^2))$$

$$= (|F|+|E|) - (s+2)(|E|+|V|) + \binom{s+3}{2}(|V|+1) - \binom{s+4}{3}$$

$$= |F| - (s+1)|E| + \left[\binom{s+3}{2} - (s+2)\right]|V| - \binom{s+4}{3} + \binom{s+3}{2}$$

$$= |F| - (s+1)|E| + \binom{s+2}{2}|V| - \binom{s+3}{3} \quad = \chi(\mathcal{K}_s^{s-1}(\Delta)).$$

CONJECTURE 15.3.2. *Given any simplicial 2-complex $\Delta$ with at least one 2-simplex, and a 3-configuration $\mathbf{p}$, the truncated cone $(w*\Delta)^2$ satisfies*

$$\beta_i(\mathcal{K}_s^{s-1}(\Delta; \mathbf{p})) = \beta_i(\mathcal{K}_{s+1}^s((w*\Delta)^2; \mathbf{p}_w, \mathbf{p}))$$

*for all $-1 \leq i \leq 2$ and all choices of $\mathbf{p}_w \in R^3$ in general position relative to $\mathbf{p}$.*

REMARK 15.3.3. The case $s = 0$ actually yields $I_\psi^0(\mathbf{p}) = \mathbf{IR}$ for each simplex. We have returned to the ordinary simplicial 2-cycle matroid of §14.

There is a second geometric situation in which we encounter the simplicial matroid. If all the points of $\mathbf{p}$ lie in a plane, then for all $\psi \in \Delta^{(k)}$, $I_\psi^s(\mathbf{p})$ is a multiple of a fixed single linear form $l^s$. With $Sign(\rho, \sigma)l^s$ placed in all non-zero entries in the matrix, we see that the 2-cycles are the same as the 2-cycles of regular homology. Thus these 'special positions' reduce all of these cofactor matroids to the simplicial 2-cycle matroid. While this isomorphism of 2-cycles is clear, notice that all lower counts (and lower homologies) will change. An analogous geometric reduction will also apply to §15.4.

**15.4. Multivariate $C_s^{s-1}$-cofactor matroids.** A related matroid exists for any $d$-simplicial complex $\Delta^d$ realized by a configuration $\mathbf{p}$ in $(d+1)$-space, for all $d \geq 1$. (As usual, we assume that the points $\mathbf{p}_i$ for any $d$-simplex span a hyperplane of $\mathbf{IR}^{d+1}$.) We have the spaces $I_\psi^s(\mathbf{p}) = \langle f^s(\mathbf{p}) \mid f(\mathbf{p}_j) = 0, \forall j \in \psi, f \text{ linear} \rangle$ and the corresponding chain complex is:

$$\mathcal{K}_s^{s-1}(\Delta; \mathbf{p}): \mathbf{0} \to \oplus_{\sigma \in \Delta^{(d)}} I_\sigma^s(\mathbf{p}) \xrightarrow{\partial_d} \oplus_{\rho \in \Delta^{(d-1)}} I_\rho^s(\mathbf{p}) \xrightarrow{\partial_{d-1}} \oplus_{\psi \in \Delta^{(d-2)}} I_\psi^s(\mathbf{p}) \xrightarrow{\partial_{d-2}}$$

$$\ldots \xrightarrow{\partial_1} \oplus_{v \in \Delta^{(0)}} I^s v(\mathbf{p}) \xrightarrow{\partial_0} I_\emptyset^s \xrightarrow{\partial_{-1}} \mathbf{0},$$

where, for each $\psi \in \Delta^{(i)}$:

$$\partial_i(c_\psi \cdot [\psi]) = c_\psi \partial_i \psi = \sum_{\theta \in \Delta^{(i-1)}} Sign(\theta, \psi) c_\psi \cdot [\theta].$$

and the boundary operator is extended linearly to all $i$-chains.

The $d$-cycles define the $C_s^{s-1}$-*cofactor matroid* $\mathcal{C}_s^{s-1}(\Delta^d, \mathbf{p})$, with

$$\text{rank } \mathcal{C}_s^{s-1}(\Delta^{(d)}(\mathbf{p})) = |\Delta^{(d)}| - \beta_d(K_s^{s-1}(\Delta^d, \mathbf{p})).$$

If $\psi$ is an $i$-simplex, then $I_\psi^s(\mathbf{p})$ has dimension $\binom{s+d-i}{s} = \binom{s+d-i}{d-i}$. (This is computed by considering the special case where the $i$-simplex is defined by setting $x_j = 0$, $j \leq d - i$, and looking at the homogeneous polynomials of degree $s$ in these $d - i$ variables [**Bi**].) This gives the Euler characteristic for $\mathcal{K}_s^{s-1}(\Delta^d; \mathbf{p})$

$$\chi(\mathcal{K}_s^{s-1}(\Delta^d; \mathbf{p})) = \sum_{i \leq d} (-1)^i \binom{s+d-i}{d-i} f_i(\Delta^d).$$

In particular, if $\Delta^d(\mathbf{p})$ is $C_s^{s-1}$-*ample* – i.e. $\beta_i(\mathcal{K}_s^{s-1}(\Delta; \mathbf{p})) = 0$ for $i \leq d - 1$ – then the rank for $C_s^{s-1}(\Delta, \mathbf{p})$, recorded in Figure 13.1, is:

$$\text{rank } C_s^{s-1}(\Delta, \mathbf{p}) = |F| - \beta_d(\mathcal{K}_s^{s-1}(\Delta; \mathbf{p})) = \sum_{i \leq d-1} (-1)^{i+d-1} \binom{s+d-1-i}{d-1-i} f_i(\Delta^d).$$

The few general results and conjectures we gave for trivariate cofactor matroids extend to these multivariate cofactor matroids. Based on a strong analogy with the chain complexes in the next section, we will make additional conjectures in §16.5.

REMARK 15.4.1. For bivariate $C_1^0$-cofactors, Propositions 5.1.1 and 5.1.2 gave connections between parallel drawings in 3-space and the lower Betti numbers of the cofactor chain complex. In precisely the same way, we have:

PROPOSITION 15.4.2. *For a $k$-complex $\Delta$ and a $(k+1)$-configuration $\mathbf{p}$:*
1. *$\beta_{-1}(\mathcal{K}_1^0(\Delta; \mathbf{p})) = 0$ if and only if there are two distinct points $\mathbf{p}_i \neq \mathbf{p}_j$, $i, j \in V$.*
2. *$\beta_0(\mathcal{K}_1^0(\Delta; \mathbf{p})) = 0$ if and only if the geometric graph $\Delta^{(1)}(\mathbf{p})$ has only trivial parallel drawings in $(k+1)$-space.*

REMARK 15.4.3. All these cofactor matroids can also be extended to general polyhedral complexes $\Phi$, provided the configuration $\mathbf{p}$ generates a unique flat of dimension $i$ for each $i$-face (that is, we have a piecewise linear realization). It is clear that the rest of the chain complex $\mathcal{K}_s^{s-1}(\Phi^d; \mathbf{p})$, which is based on the well-defined vector spaces $I_\psi^s(\mathbf{p})$, generalizes immediately. While the existence of these objects is understood in approximation theory, the only cases we have seen investigated correspond to the matroids $\mathcal{K}_1^0(\Phi^d; \mathbf{p})$ which are directly related to scene analysis and parallel drawings as in §8.3.

Finally, from multivariate splines (including bivariate splines) there are even more challenging chain complexes (and associated polymatroids) $\mathcal{K}_s^r(\Phi^d; \mathbf{p})$, for all integers $r < s$. The reader is referred to [**Bi**] for the definitions.

## 16. Skeletal Rigidity

As Figure 13.1 anticipates, there is a second family of matroids which share the rank estimates (and many other properties) of the multivariate $C_s^{s-1}$-cofactor matroids. These are direct generalizations of the first-order rigidity matroids for graphs. All of the results (and some of the conjectures) in this section come from a continuing joint project with Tiong-Seng Tay and Neil White [**TWW1,2,3**]. The origins of these matroids are the search for geometric and combinatorial proofs of fundamental results in polyhedral combinatorics, such as the $h$-theorem and the $g$-theorem for simplicial polytopes (see §16.4 and [**Ka1,Lee1,2**]). These matroids generalize the geometry of rigid frameworks and retain the potential for both nice geometric reproofs of known combinatorial results about the faces of simplicial convex polytopes and generalizations of these results to homology spheres and other combinatorial complexes.

The analogy with the matroids $\mathcal{K}_s^{s-1}(\Delta^r; \mathbf{p})$ is my own responsibility. Generalizing the conjectures of §10.3, §11.5, we conjecture a strong relationship between the generic behaviour of the cofactor matroids and the matroids of this section. At a minimum, this analogy is a fruitful source of conjectures and insights for both families of matroids (see §16.5).

There are at least five different matrices which capture the initial matroid we want to describe [**TWW1,2**]. However, efficient presentation of these matroids in the context of homology works best with an exterior algebra on the underlying affine (or projective) coordinates. We will use a modern form of this algebra: the Grassmann-Cayley algebra [**DRS,Wht4,TWW1**].

We offer a brief description of the notation for §16. This is essentially a projective idea [**TWW1,3**] but we simplify to an affine presentation. As we use the algebra here, it is notation for the lexicographically ordered minors of a non-square matrix. We use affine coordinates for the points in $d$-space $\overline{\mathbf{p}}_i = (p_{i,1}, p_{i,2}, \ldots, p_{i,d}, 1)$. Given two affine points $\overline{\mathbf{x}}, \overline{\mathbf{y}}$, the 2-*extensor* $\overline{\mathbf{x}} \vee \overline{\mathbf{y}}$ is the $\binom{d+1}{2}$-tuple of 2-by-2 minors of the matrix $[\overline{\mathbf{x}}\ \overline{\mathbf{y}}]$ (recall §12). Similarly, the 3-*extensor* $\overline{\mathbf{x}} \vee \overline{\mathbf{y}} \vee \overline{\mathbf{w}}$ is the $\binom{d+1}{3}$-tuple of 3-by-3 minors of $[\overline{\mathbf{x}}\ \overline{\mathbf{y}}\ \overline{\mathbf{w}}]$.

The field (the reals) or *0-extensors* can be written $V_{d+1}^{(0)}$; the points or *1-extensors* as the vector space $V_{d+1}^{(1)}$, and the space of *$j$-tensors* – sums of $j$-extensors – as $V_{d+1}^{(j)}$, where $\dim V_{d+1}^{(j)} = \binom{d+1}{j}$.

For a given oriented simplex $\sigma$ of dimension $i$, $\overline{\sigma}$ is the exterior product of its vertices, an $(i+1)$-extensor. This is well defined on the orientation class $[\sigma]$, since $\vee$ is alternating: $\mathbf{x} \vee \mathbf{y} = -\mathbf{y} \vee \mathbf{x}$. We will work with an equivalence relation *modulo the kernel of $\overline{\sigma}$* on the $j$-tensors defined by:

$$P \stackrel{\overline{\sigma}}{=} S \quad \text{if and only if} \quad P \vee \overline{\sigma} = S \vee \overline{\sigma}$$

where $\vee$ is extended linearly to tensors as sums of extensors. In particular, we denote this space of all $j$-tensors in a projective space of dimension $d$, mod a simplex $\sigma$ of dimension $\leq d - j$ as $V_{d+1}^{(j)}/\ker \overline{\sigma}$. We note that, if $P \stackrel{\overline{\sigma}}{=} P'$ and $Q \stackrel{\overline{\sigma}}{=} Q'$, then $P + Q \stackrel{\overline{\sigma}}{=} P' + Q'$ since

$$(P + Q) \vee \overline{\sigma} = P \vee \overline{\sigma} + Q \vee \overline{\sigma} = P' \vee \overline{\sigma} + Q' \vee \overline{\sigma} = (P' + Q') \vee \overline{\sigma}$$

and $P \vee Q \stackrel{\overline{\sigma}}{=} P' \vee Q'$, since

$$P \vee Q \vee \overline{\sigma} = P \vee Q' \vee \overline{\sigma} = (-1)^{j+k} Q' \vee P \vee \overline{\sigma} = (-1)^{j+k} Q' \vee P' \vee \overline{\sigma} = P' \vee Q' \vee \overline{\sigma}.$$

Therefore the equivalence relation is well-defined within the Cayley algebra. We also note that $V_{d+1}^{(0)}/\ker \overline{\sigma} = \mathbb{R}$, and that, if $\sigma \in \Delta^{(i)}$ and $P$ is a extensor of step $> d + 1 - i$, then $P \stackrel{\overline{\sigma}}{=} \mathbf{0}$, automatically. This space, $V_{d+1}^{(j)}/\ker \overline{\sigma}$, has dimension $\binom{d-i}{j}$, as a vector space over the reals.

We begin with an alternate presentation of the $C_1^0$-cofactor matroid for 2-complexes in 3-space. The principle value of this change is the distinct array of generalizations which flow from this 'rigidity' approach, as we observed in Part II.

**16.1. 3-rigidity in 3-space.** Consider a simplicial complex $\Delta^2$ with an affine 3-configuration $\overline{\mathbf{p}}$. A 3-*stress* on $\Delta(\overline{\mathbf{p}})$ is an assignment of scalars $\omega_\sigma$, $\sigma \in F$ such that, for each edge $\rho \in E$:

$$\sum_{\sigma|\rho v = \sigma} \omega_\sigma \overline{\mathbf{v}} \cdot [\rho] \overset{\overline{\rho}}{=} 0,$$

where $\overline{\mathbf{u}} \overset{\overline{\rho}}{=} \overline{\mathbf{v}}$, $\rho = \{a, b\}$ means that $\overline{\mathbf{u}} \vee \overline{\mathbf{a}} \vee \overline{\mathbf{b}} = \overline{\mathbf{v}} \vee \overline{\mathbf{a}} \vee \overline{\mathbf{b}}$ or, equivalently,

$$[\overline{\mathbf{u}}\,\overline{\mathbf{a}}\,\overline{\mathbf{c}}\,\overline{\mathbf{x}}] = \begin{bmatrix} u_1 & u_2 & u_3 & 1 \\ a_1 & a_2 & a_3 & 1 \\ c_1 & c_2 & c_3 & 1 \\ x & y & z & 1 \end{bmatrix} = \begin{bmatrix} v_1 & v_2 & v_3 & 1 \\ a_1 & a_2 & a_3 & 1 \\ c_1 & c_2 & c_3 & 1 \\ x & y & z & 1 \end{bmatrix} = [\overline{\mathbf{v}}\,\overline{\mathbf{a}}\,\overline{\mathbf{c}}\,\overline{\mathbf{x}}].$$

(In this form, we already see the underlying connection to the 3-stresses as defined for $C_1^0$-cofactors.) The geometric meaning of this calculation is:

*Does the weighted affine point* $\sum_{\sigma|\rho v = \sigma} \omega_\sigma \overline{\mathbf{v}} = \left( \sum_{\sigma|\rho v = \sigma} \omega_\sigma \right) \overline{\mathbf{w}}$ *lie on the affine line* $\overline{\mathbf{a}, \mathbf{b}}$ *(the line of $\rho$)?* [**Lee1,TWW1**]

The 3-stresses are the row dependencies of the *rigidity matrix* $R_{3,3}(\Delta; \overline{\mathbf{p}})$:

$$R_{3,3}(\Delta, \overline{\mathbf{p}}) = \begin{array}{c} \\ \rho v \end{array} \begin{array}{c} \cdots \quad \rho \quad \cdots \\ \vdots \qquad \vdots \\ \left( \quad \cdots \quad \overline{\mathbf{v}} \quad \cdots \quad \right) \\ \vdots \qquad \vdots \end{array} .$$

where the entries under $\rho$ are computed in the equivalence classes of $\overset{\overline{\rho}}{=}$ (vectors of the vector space $V_{d+1}^{(2)}/\ker \overline{\rho}$). These row dependencies define the *skeletal 3-rigidity matroid* $\mathcal{R}_{3,3}(\Delta; \mathbf{p})$. For a generic 3-configuration (or using the maximal ranks of the rigidity matrices over all 3-configurations) we have the *generic skeletal 3-rigidity matroid* $\mathcal{R}_{3,3}(\Delta)$.

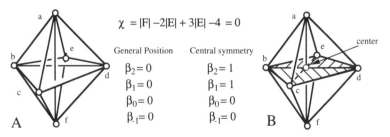

$$\chi = |F| - 2|E| + 3|E| - 4 = 0$$

| | General Position | Central symmetry | |
|---|---|---|---|
| | $\beta_2 = 0$ | $\beta_2 = 1$ | |
| | $\beta_1 = 0$ | $\beta_1 = 1$ | |
| | $\beta_0 = 0$ | $\beta_0 = 0$ | |
| | $\beta_{-1} = 0$ | $\beta_{-1} = 0$ | |

FIGURE. 16.1. *A 2-simplicial complex in 3-space which is 3-independent in general position (A) but has a 3-stress in special centrally symmetric position (B).*

EXAMPLE 16.1.1. Consider the extended complex of Figure 16.1A, where all four triangles to the central 'shaft' $a, f$ and the triangles $bcd, bde$ are added to the faces of the octahedron. The 3-rigidity matrix is:

|       | $\omega$ | $ab$ | $ac$ | $ad$ | $ae$ | $af$ | $bc$ | $bd$ | $be$ | $bf$ | $cd$ | $cf$ | $de$ | $df$ | $ef$ |
|-------|------|------|------|------|------|------|------|------|------|------|------|------|------|------|------|
| $abc$ | 1 | $\bar{c}$ | $\bar{b}$ |  |  |  | $\bar{a}$ |  |  |  |  |  |  |  |  |
| $abe$ | 1 | $\bar{e}$ |  |  | $\bar{b}$ |  |  |  | $\bar{a}$ |  |  |  |  |  |  |
| $acd$ | 1 |  | $\bar{d}$ | $\bar{c}$ |  |  |  |  |  |  | $\bar{a}$ |  |  |  |  |
| $ade$ | 1 |  |  | $\bar{e}$ | $\bar{d}$ |  |  |  |  |  |  |  | $\bar{a}$ |  |  |
| $bcf$ | 1 |  |  |  |  |  | $\bar{f}$ |  |  | $\bar{c}$ |  | $\bar{b}$ |  |  |  |
| $bef$ | 1 |  |  |  |  |  |  |  | $\bar{f}$ | $\bar{e}$ |  |  |  |  | $\bar{b}$ |
| $cdf$ | 1 |  |  |  |  |  |  |  |  |  | $\bar{f}$ | $\bar{d}$ |  | $\bar{c}$ |  |
| $def$ | 1 |  |  |  |  |  |  |  |  |  |  |  | $\bar{f}$ | $\bar{e}$ | $\bar{d}$ |
| $abf$ | $-1$ | $\bar{f}$ |  |  |  | $\bar{b}$ |  |  |  | $\bar{a}$ |  |  |  |  |  |
| $acf$ | $-1$ |  | $\bar{f}$ |  |  | $\bar{c}$ |  |  |  |  |  | $\bar{a}$ |  |  |  |
| $adf$ | $-1$ |  |  | $\bar{f}$ |  | $\bar{d}$ |  |  |  |  |  |  |  | $\bar{a}$ |  |
| $aef$ | $-1$ |  |  |  | $\bar{f}$ | $\bar{e}$ |  |  |  |  |  |  |  |  | $\bar{a}$ |
| $bcd$ | $-1$ |  |  |  |  |  | $\bar{d}$ | $\bar{c}$ |  |  | $\bar{b}$ |  |  |  |  |
| $bde$ | $-1$ |  |  |  |  |  |  | $\bar{e}$ | $\bar{d}$ |  |  |  | $\bar{b}$ |  |  |

If the points are in general position, there is no 3-stress:

(i) the points $b, c, d, e$ will be affinely independent, and no coefficients for $bcd$, $bde$ will add to 0 in the columns of $bd$ (mod$\{b, d\}$);

(ii) these guaranteed zero entries will pass, by similar arguments, to all rows.

We conclude that this set is independent for $\overline{\mathbf{p}}$ in general position. The remaining Betti numbers of the associated chain complex will be described below.

On the other hand, assume that we have a centrally symmetric configuration (Figure 16.1B) with $\overline{\mathbf{a}} + \overline{\mathbf{f}} = \overline{\mathbf{b}} + \overline{\mathbf{d}} = \overline{\mathbf{c}} + \overline{\mathbf{e}}$. The reader can check that the entries under $\omega$ are now a 3-stress, since we have such equations as:

column $ab$:  $\overline{\mathbf{c}} + \overline{\mathbf{e}} - \overline{\mathbf{f}} = \overline{\mathbf{a}} \in \overline{\mathbf{a}, \mathbf{b}}$;

column $ac$:  $\overline{\mathbf{b}} + \overline{\mathbf{d}} - \overline{\mathbf{f}} = \overline{\mathbf{a}} \in \overline{\mathbf{a}, \mathbf{b}}$;

column $af$:  $\overline{\mathbf{b}} + \overline{\mathbf{d}} + \overline{\mathbf{c}} + \overline{\mathbf{d}} = 2(\overline{\mathbf{a}} + \overline{\mathbf{f}}) \in \overline{\mathbf{a}, \mathbf{f}}$;

column $bc$:  $\overline{\mathbf{a}} + \overline{\mathbf{f}} - \overline{\mathbf{d}} = \overline{\mathbf{b}} \in \overline{\mathbf{b}, \mathbf{c}}$;

column $bd$:  $\overline{\mathbf{c}} + \overline{\mathbf{e}} = (\overline{\mathbf{b}} + \overline{\mathbf{d}}) \in \overline{\mathbf{b}, \mathbf{d}}$.

This is a special position which has a 3-stress. Clearly this self-stress is unique, up to a single scalar multiple and $\Delta^{(2)}(\overline{\mathbf{p}})$ is a circuit of the matroid. (We can still obtain a 3-stress with a configuration which is special, but less symmetric: if the lines $af, bd, c, e$ are concurrent then the same argument will apply, with appropriate scalars expressing the common point. We chose this symmetric configuration for the ease of verification.)

Once more, this basic matrix describes the 2-cycles (row dependencies) and 1-boundaries (rows) for a chain complex. For a simplicial complex $\Delta$ realized in affine 3-space, the 3-*skeletal chain complex* is

$$\mathcal{R}_{3,3}(\Delta; \overline{\mathbf{p}}): \mathbf{0} \to \oplus_{\sigma \in F} \mathbf{IR} \xrightarrow{\partial_2} \oplus_{\rho \in E} V_4^{(1)} / \ker \rho \xrightarrow{\partial_1} \oplus_{v \in V} V_4^{(2)} / \ker v \xrightarrow{\partial_0} V_4^{(3)} \to \mathbf{0}.$$

We define the boundary maps as follows. For a 2-simplex $\sigma = \{a_0, a_1, a_2\}$:

$$\partial_i(1 \cdot [a_0, a_1, a_2]) = \overline{\mathbf{a}}_0 \cdot [a_1, a_2] + \overline{\mathbf{a}}_1 \cdot [a_0, a_2] + \overline{\mathbf{a}}_2 \cdot [a_0, a_1],$$

extended linearly to all 2-chains. For a general $i$-simplex $\tau$, with coefficient $P_\tau$:

$$\partial_i(P_\tau \cdot [a_0, \dots, a_i]) = \sum_{\{j:\ a_j \in \tau\}} P_\psi \vee \overline{\mathbf{a}}_j \cdot [a_0, \dots, \hat{a}_j, \dots, a_i]$$

where $\hat{a}_j$ indicates that this vertex is omitted. This is extended linearly to all $i$-chains. That $\partial_{i-1}\partial_i = 0$ follows from the basic antisymmetry of the operation $x \vee y$. If $\psi x, y = \sigma$ then the coefficient of $[\psi]$ in the double boundary of $c_\sigma \cdot [\sigma]$ is

$$\partial_{i-1}\partial_i c_\sigma \cdot [\sigma] = \partial_{i-1}\left(\overline{\mathbf{x}} \cdot [\psi, y] + \overline{\mathbf{y}} \cdot [\psi, x]\right) = \left(\overline{\mathbf{x}} \vee \overline{\mathbf{y}} + \overline{\mathbf{y}} \vee \overline{\mathbf{x}}\right) \cdot [\psi] = \mathbf{0} \cdot [\psi].$$

We define skeletal 3-independence as $\beta_2(\mathcal{R}_{d,r}(\langle\langle X \rangle\rangle; \overline{\mathbf{p}}|_X)) = 0$; skeletal 3-rigidity as $\beta_1(\mathcal{R}_{d,r}(\langle\langle X \rangle\rangle; \overline{\mathbf{p}}|_X)) = 0$; and skeletal 3-adequate complexes $\langle\langle Y \rangle\rangle$ for gluing as $\beta_i(\mathcal{R}_{d,r}(\langle\langle Y \rangle\rangle; \overline{\mathbf{p}}|_Y)) = 0$ for $i \leq 0$.

To calculate the Euler characteristic, we need the dimensions of the $i$-chains. The 2-chains $\oplus_{\sigma \in F} \mathbf{IR}$ have dimension $|F|$. The 1-chains $\oplus_{\rho \in E} V_4^{(1)}/\ker \rho$ have dimension $2|E|$, the 0-chains $\oplus_{v \in V} V_4^{(2)}/\ker v$ have dimension $3|V|$ and the $(-1)$-chains $V_4^{(3)}$ have dimension 4. The chain complex on $\Delta^2(\overline{\mathbf{p}})$ has the Euler characteristic:

$$\chi(\mathcal{R}_{3,3}(\Delta; \overline{\mathbf{p}})) = |F| - 2|E| + 3|V| - 4.$$

The entire chain complex is isomorphic to the chain complex $\mathcal{K}_1^0(\Delta; \mathbf{p})$, provided $\mathbf{p}$ is the Euclidean coordinates of $\overline{\mathbf{p}}$. The same conditions worked out in §15.1 are required for the lower Betti numbers to be zero.

PROPOSITION 16.1.2. *For a simplicial complex* $\Delta^2$ *and configuration* $\overline{\mathbf{p}}$ *in affine 3-space,*
  1. $\beta_{-1}(\mathcal{R}_{3,3}(\Delta; \overline{\mathbf{p}})) = 0$ *if and only if* $\Delta^{(0)}(\overline{\mathbf{p}})$ *contains two distinct points;*
  2. $\beta_0(\mathcal{R}_{3,3}(\Delta; \overline{\mathbf{p}})) = 0$ *if and only if* $\Delta^1(\overline{\mathbf{p}})$ *has only trivial parallel drawings in 3-space.*

EXAMPLE 16.1.3. Recall the simplicial complex and general position configuration $\overline{\mathbf{p}}$ of Figure 16.1A. The Euler characteristic is $\chi = 14 - 2 \times 14 + 18 - 4 = 0$. Since $\beta_2 = 0$, $\beta_0 = 0$, and $\beta_{-1} = 0$, we compute that $\beta_1 = 0$ and $\Delta$ is acyclic for the 3-rigidity matroid.

The centrally symmetric position (B), with $\beta_2 = 1$, $\beta_0 = 0$, and $\beta_{-1} = 0$, must have $\beta_1 = 1$.

A *projective transformation* $T$ is expressed by a non-singular 4-by-4 matrix $[T]$ which is applied to the affine coordinates $[T]\overline{\mathbf{p}}_i = \lambda_i \overline{\mathbf{q}}_i$ ($\lambda_i \neq 0$). It is not difficult to show, even from our sketch of the chain complex, that such a transformation induces a non-singular linear transformation for all $i$-tensors, taking the $i$-cycles and $i$-boundaries of $\mathcal{R}_{3,3}(\Delta^2; \overline{\mathbf{p}})$ to the $i$-cycles and $i$-boundaries of $\mathcal{R}_{3,3}(\Delta^2; \overline{\mathbf{q}})$ for all $i$. We state, without proof, the basic projective invariance [**TWW3**].

PROPOSITION 16.1.4. *For a 2-complex* $\Delta^2$ *and a configuration* $\overline{\mathbf{p}}$, *any projective transformation* $T$ *to an affine configuration* $\overline{\mathbf{q}}$ *induces an isomorphism of $i$-cycles, $i$-boundaries and $i$-homology from* $\mathcal{R}_{3,3}(\Delta; \overline{\mathbf{p}})$ *to* $\mathcal{R}_{3,3}(\Delta; \overline{\mathbf{q}})$, *for all $i$.*

Notice that the basic condition used to analyze Figure 16.1B: the statement "$af$, $bd$, $ce$ are concurrent"; is projectively invariant. The theory of such special geometric positions is an extension of the 'pure conditions' of [**WW1**].

REMARK 16.1.5. This same projective invariance applies to all the skeletal rigidity chain complexes of this section and all the multivariate $C_s^{s-1}$-cofactor chain complexes of §15 [**ASW,TWW3,Wh10**].

All the results for $\mathcal{K}_1^0(\Delta; \mathbf{p})$ in §15 extend immediately to $\mathcal{R}_{3,3}(\Delta; \overline{\mathbf{p}})$. We will offer a brief overview of the corresponding skeletal cohomology in §16.3.

**16.2. Rigidity for $r$-skeleta in $d$-space.** The constructions for 2-skeleta in 3-space extend to 2-skeleta in $d$-space in a natural way. For brevity, we pass immediately to general construction for $k$-skeleta in dimensions $d \geq k$ – with $k$-skeletal rigidity in $k$-space being homology.

For a simplicial complex $\Delta$ realized in projective $d$-space, the *skeletal $r$-rigidity chain complex* is [**TWW3**]:

$$\mathcal{R}_{d,r}(\Delta; \overline{\mathbf{p}}) : \mathbf{0} \to \oplus_{\rho \in \Delta^{(r-1)}} V_{d+1}^{(0)} \xrightarrow{\partial_{r-1}} \oplus_{\sigma \in \Delta^{(r-2)}} V_{d+1}^{(1)} / \ker \sigma \xrightarrow{\partial_{r-2}}$$

$$\cdots \xrightarrow{\partial_1} \oplus_{v \in \Delta^{(0)}} V_{d+1}^{(r-1)} / \ker v \xrightarrow{\partial_0} V_{d+1}^{(r)} \to \mathbf{0}.$$

For a general $i$-simplex $\sigma$, with coefficient $c_\sigma$ (an $(r - i - 1)$-tensor modulo $\overline{\sigma}$), the boundary operator is:

$$\partial_i c_\sigma \cdot [\sigma] = \sum_{x \in \sigma} c_\sigma \vee \overline{\mathbf{x}} \cdot [\sigma/x].$$

where $[\sigma/x]$ is the lexicographic order for $\rho$ with $\pm[\rho x] = [\sigma]$. (This notation comes from indexing the simplices by square free monomials.) Again this is extended linearly to $i$-chains. Of course $\partial_{-1}(c \cdot \emptyset) = 0$.

The top $(r - 1)$-cycles define the *skeletal $r$-rigidity matroid* on the $(r - 1)$-simplices, $\mathcal{R}_{d,r}(\Delta; \overline{\mathbf{p}})$, for each configuration $\overline{\mathbf{p}}$, as well as the *generic $r$-rigidity matroid* $\mathcal{R}_{d,r}(\Delta)$, for algebraically independent coordinates (or alternately, using the maximal rank over all $\overline{\mathbf{p}}$). Some initial results for this are presented in [**TWW1,2**]. The rest of the homology plays the role of statics and kinematics to aid the analysis of this matroid [**TWW3**].

We define skeletal $r$-independence as $\beta_{r-1}(\mathcal{R}_{d,r}(\langle\langle X \rangle\rangle; \overline{\mathbf{p}}|_X)) = 0$; skeletal $r$-rigidity as $\beta_{r-2}(\mathcal{R}_{d,r}(\langle\langle X \rangle\rangle; \overline{\mathbf{p}}|_X)) = 0$; and skeletal $r$-acyclic complexes $\langle\langle Y \rangle\rangle$ for gluing as $\beta_i(\mathcal{R}_{d,r}(\langle\langle Y \rangle\rangle; \overline{\mathbf{p}}|_Y)) = 0$ for all $i$. Since the dimension of $V_{d+1}^{(r-i)} / \ker \rho$, $\rho \in \Delta^{(i)}$, is $\binom{d-i}{r-1-i}$, the Euler characteristic is:

$$\chi(\mathcal{R}_{d,r}(\Delta; \overline{\mathbf{p}})) = \sum_{i=-1}^{r-1} (-1)^i \binom{d-i}{r-i-1} f_i = \sum_{i=-1}^{r-1} (-1)^i \beta_i(\mathcal{R}_{d,r}(\Delta; \overline{\mathbf{p}})).$$

The Mayer-Vietoris sequence yields results such as: gluing two complexes across a skeletal $r$-acyclic complex creates a complex with the sum of the Betti numbers of the pieces; and gluing two skeletal $r$-ample complexes across a skeletal $r$-adequate complex produces a new $r$-ample complex. Direct matrix analyses also verifies some simple 'Henneberg style' extension principles.

REMARK 16.2.1. If we look carefully at skeletal 2-rigidity on a graph $G$ at a $d$-configuration $\overline{\mathbf{p}}$ in $d$-space, it is the first-order rigidity of $G(\mathbf{p})$ of Parts I and II of our survey. We have simply given an affine presentation of the 'vector' $\mathbf{p}_j - \mathbf{p}_i$ as the 'vector' $\overline{\mathbf{p}}_j \mod \overline{\mathbf{p}}_i$. This gives an isomorphism between the 1-cycle matrix for 2-rigidity and the rigidity matrix for first-order rigidity.

In the Part II, we concentrated on $\beta_1$ (self-stresses) and $\beta^0$ (first-order motions), with the implicit understanding that $\beta_{-1} = 0$ for sufficiently large complexes: $|V| \geq d-1$ in dimension $d$. All of the difficulties with the counts such as $3|V| - 6$ can be traced to the fact that a single bar has Euler characteristic $-1$ and $\beta_{-1} = 1$. *It is not skeletal 2-adequate for $d > 2$.* Therefore gluing across a single bar (Figure 9.4) produces a loss of 2-rigidity. (See Example 16.2.4 for the analogs in $r$-rigidity.)

REMARK 16.2.2. If we consider $r$-rigidity in $(r-1)$-space, then the $i$-coefficients have the form $c_\rho \in V_r^{(r-i)}/\ker\rho$, where $\rho \in \Delta^{(i)}$. Since this means $c_\rho \vee \bar{\rho}$ has step $r$ in an $r$-dimensional vector space – these coefficients are just scalars. This $r$-rigidity has reduced to the simplicial $r$-cycle matroid and the chain complex is the ordinary chain complex of simplicial homology.

For $r$-rigidity in $r$-space, the $i$-coefficients have the form $c_\rho \in V_{r+1}^{(r-i)}/\ker\rho$, where $\rho \in \Delta^{(i)}$. For the top boundary operator the coefficients are $r$-extensors $c_\sigma \bar{\mathbf{v}} \vee \bar{\rho}$ in a space of dimension $r+1$ – the coefficients of the hyperplane $l_\sigma(\mathbf{p})$. The $r$-rigidity in $r$-space is the $C_1^0$-cofactor matroid in $r$-space in all dimensions.

Other results from $\mathcal{R}_{d,2}$ in Parts I and II extend immediately to these matroids. One example is the Coning Theorem.

CONING THEOREM 16.2.3 [**TWW3**]. *If $\Pi_w \bar{\mathbf{p}}$ in affine $d$-space is the projection of $\bar{\mathbf{p}}$ in $(d+1)$-space from the affine point $\bar{\mathbf{p}}_w$, and $w * \Delta$ is the cone of $\Delta$ then $\beta_i(\mathcal{R}_{d+1,r}(w * \Delta; \bar{\mathbf{p}}_w, \bar{\mathbf{p}})) = \beta_i(\mathcal{R}_{d,r}(\Delta; \Pi_w \bar{\mathbf{p}}))$ for all $i$.*

EXAMPLE 16.2.4. Coning explains the properties of the complete complexes $K_n$ for skeletal $r$-rigidity in $d$-space [**TWW3**]. Since the complete complex $K_n$ is the cone of $K_{n-1}$, we can project down from $\mathcal{R}_{d,r}(K_n)$ to $\mathcal{R}_{d-i,r}(K_{n-i})$ until one of two terminal events occurs:

1. $i = n$ and we have the empty complex $K_0$ in dimension $d - n \geq r - 1$, which has the clear Betti numbers,

$$\beta_i(K_0) = \begin{cases} \binom{d-n-1}{r} & \text{for } i = -1 \\ 0 & \text{for } i \neq -1 \end{cases}$$

Therefore if $n \leq d + 1 - r$, then $\beta_{-1}(\mathcal{R}_{d,r}(K_n; \bar{\mathbf{p}})) = \binom{d-n+1}{r}$ in dimension $d$ and all other Betti numbers are zero, provided $\bar{\mathbf{p}}$ is in general position.

2. $d - i = r - 1$ and $n - i > 0$, we have the $r$-homology of §14, with the well-understood Betti numbers:

$$\beta_i(K_{n+r-d-1}) = \begin{cases} 0 & \text{for } i < r - 1 \\ \binom{n+r-d-2}{r} & \text{for } i = r - 1 \end{cases}$$

Therefore if $n > d - r + 1$, then $\beta_i(\mathcal{R}_{d-n,r}(K_n; \bar{\mathbf{p}})) = 0$, $i < r - 1$, for $\bar{\mathbf{p}}$ in general position and the complex is skeletal $r$-ample. (The value of $\beta_i(K_{n+r-d-1})$ is calculated from the Euler characteristic.) In particular, the complex is skeletal $r$-acyclic if and only if $d - r + 2 \leq n \leq d + 1$.

For $r = 2$, the standard first-order rigidity of frameworks, the complex $K_n$ is 2-acyclic in dimension $d$ if and only if $d \leq n \leq d + 1$. In the plane, the 2-acyclic complexes for gluing are $K_2, K_3$. In 3-space, the 2-acyclic complexes are $K_3, K_4$.

For skeletal 3-rigidity the skeletal 3-acyclic complexes are $K_n$, $d-1 \leq n \leq d+1$. In 3-space, these are $K_2, K_3, K_4$. In general, the smallest skeletal 3-acyclic complex in dimension $d$ is $K_{d-1}$, making explicit that $d-1$ is the minimum number of points in general position needed to make $\beta_{-1}(\mathcal{R}_{d,3}(\Delta; \overline{\mathbf{p}})) = 0$ in dimension $d$ (something we had not previously derived). This also means gluing two 3-ample complexes across a single 2-simplex in $d$-space, $d > 4$, will cause the resulting complex to have $\beta_0 > 0$. This is an analog of gluing two frameworks across a single edge in 3-space.

More generally, we find that $d + 2 - r$ is the minimum number of points in general position needed to make $\beta_{-1}(\mathcal{R}_{d,r}(\Delta; \overline{\mathbf{p}})) = 0$ in dimension $d$. Gluing two skeletal $r$-ample complexes across a single $(r - 1)$-simplex in $d$-space, $d > 2r - 2$, will create a complex with $\beta_0(\mathcal{R}_{d,r}(\Delta; \overline{\mathbf{p}})) > 0$.

REMARK 16.2.5. As we described in Remark 14.2.14, shelling is a basic inductive construction for classes of simplicial complexes. In particular, all convex simplicial $(d + 1)$-polytopes have a shelling. (This is given by the order in which the hyperplanes of the facets meet a line in general position relative to a convex realization in $(d + 1)$-space.) All simplicial decompositions of a convex $d$-ball in $d$-space by a Delaunay (or Voronoi) decomposition are also shellable.

For any shellable $n$-complex $\Delta$ realized in general position $\overline{\mathbf{p}}$ in $d \leq n$, this shelling can be retraced as a sequence of gluings for $r$-ample complexes:
(a) the initial simplex is $r$-ample;
(b) each $(n - 1)$-ball from the boundary of an $n$-simplex is $r$-adequate and the added $n$-simplex is $r$-ample, so the result of this gluing is $r$-ample;
(c) the $(n - 1)$-sphere is also $r$-ample, so the final complex $\Delta$ is $r$-ample.
Whether the result is skeletal $r$-acyclic ($r$-independent) will depend on the Euler characteristic (i.e. on the dimension $d$ and the face numbers of the polytope). This can also be traced by the explicit form of the intersections $\sigma_{j+1} \cap \Delta_j$, for all $j$. An a analogous result holds for the multivariate cofactor matroids and yields some traditional heuristics for multivariate splines [**Al**].

Two simple examples covered by this shelling proof are the 2- and 3-rigidity of triangulated spheres in the plane, or the 3-rigidity of 4-polytopial complexes in 3-space. We do not obtain the 2-rigidity of 2-spheres in 3-space (Theorem of Cauchy and Dehn §9.3.10) or its analogs – see below.

The 'flavour of homology' in our definitions would suggest that the $r$-ample result extends to classes defined by homology and is not restricted to the inductive construction of shelling. For example, we *conjecture* that all simplicial homology $n$-spheres (all simplicial complexes with the homology of an $n$-sphere, some of which are not shellable) and all simplicial $n$-balls are $r$-ample for $d \leq n$. Some extended results in this direction will appear in [**TWW3**].

In polyhedral combinatorics, there are critical sequences of numbers defined from the face numbers of any $n$ complex (in particular for any $n$-sphere):
1. the $h$-vector:

$$h_r(\Delta, n) = \sum_{j=0}^{r} (-1)^{j+r} \binom{n-j}{d-r} f_{j-1} = \sum_{j=-1}^{r-1} (-1)^{j+r+1} \binom{n-j-1}{n-r} f_j;$$

2. the $g$-vector:

$$g_r(\Delta, n) = h_r(\Delta, n) - h_{r-1}(\Delta, n) = \sum_{j=-1}^{r-1} (-1)^{j+r+1} \binom{n-j}{n-r+1} f_j.$$

These have a striking similarity to the Euler characteristics for skeletal rigidity defined above, in the special cases where $d = n - 1$ for $h_r$ and $d = n$ for $g_r$ [**TWW3**]. These give:

$$h_r(\Delta, n) = \sum_{j=-1}^{r-1} (-1)^{j+r+1} \binom{n-j-1}{n-r} f_j = (-1)^{r+1} \chi(\mathcal{R}_{n-1,r}(\Delta; \overline{\mathbf{p}}))$$

$$= \beta_{r-1}(\mathcal{R}_{n-1,r}(\Delta; \overline{\mathbf{p}})) + \sum_{i=-1}^{r-2} (-1)^{i+r+1} \beta_i(\mathcal{R}_{n-1,r}(\Delta; \overline{\mathbf{p}}))$$

$$g_r(\Delta, n) = \sum_{j=-1}^{r-1} (-1)^{j+r+1} \binom{n-j}{n-r+1} f_j = (-1)^{r+1} \chi(\mathcal{R}_{n,r}(\Delta; \overline{\mathbf{p}}))$$

$$= \beta_{r-1}(\mathcal{R}_{n,r}(\Delta; \overline{\mathbf{p}})) + \sum_{i=-1}^{r-2} (-1)^{i+r+1} \beta_i(\mathcal{R}_{n,r}(\Delta; \overline{\mathbf{p}})).$$

There are a number of fundamental results about these numbers, culminating in the $g$-theorem for the complexes of simplicial convex polytopes [**St1,2,Lee1,2**]. A critical aspect of this theorem is that the numbers given above are non-negative. If all the lower Betti numbers in these two expressions are zero, then, as the dimension of a vector space $Z_{r-1}$, $h_r(\Delta, n)$ and $g_r(\Delta, n)$ would be shown directly to be non-negative. The chain complex for skeletal rigidity was originally constructed for this purpose and significant partial results have been obtained [**TWW3**].

HOMOLOGY SPHERE THEOREM 16.2.6 [**TWW3**]. *Let $\Delta$ be a simplicial homology $n$-sphere realized in $d$-space, with the vertices of each face in general position in the configuration $\overline{\mathbf{p}}$.*
1. *If $d = n$, then for all $r$, $\beta_i(\mathcal{R}_{d,r}(\Delta; \overline{\mathbf{p}})) = 0, i < r - 1$;*
2. *If $d = n + 1$, then for all $r$, $\beta_i(\mathcal{R}_{d,r}(\Delta; \overline{\mathbf{p}})) = 0, i < r - 2$.*

Combinatorial theorems on convex $n$-polytopes $\Delta$ tell us that $h_i(\Delta) = h_{n-i}(\Delta)$, and $h_{i-1}(\Delta) < h_i(\Delta)$ for $i \leq \frac{n}{2}$ [**St2,Lee1,2**]. These results imply relationships on the spaces of dependencies in this sequence of skeletal $k$-cycle matroids on $\Delta(\overline{\mathbf{p}})$ in $n$-space. We conjecture that these relationships are geometric: there should be explicit isomorphisms and injections for the corresponding circuits in our matroids.

GEOMETRIC $g$-CONJECTURE 16.2.7. *The $r$-skeleton of a simplicial (convex) $(2r - 1)$-polytope is a basis for skeletal $r$-rigidity matroid in $(2r - 1)$-space and is $r$-ample, for all strictly convex realizations $\overline{\mathbf{p}}$.*
*The $r$-skeleton of a simplicial homology $(2r - 2)$-sphere is a basis for generic skeletal $r$-rigidity and is generically $r$-ample in $(2r - 1)$-space.*

We note that the Theorem of Cauchy and Dehn 9.2.10 gives precisely this result for $r = 2$: the 2-rigidity of triangulated convex spheres in 3-space. There is some indication that recent geometric results of McMullen [**Mc**] will prove the first part of this conjecture. If the generic conjecture for homology spheres were also proven, this would extend known results.

**16.3. $r$-skeletal cohomology.** We have a companion cohomology which describes the 'skeletal kinematics' dual to the 'skeletal statics' of the previous subsections. For a simplicial $(r-1)$-complex $\Delta^{r-1}$ realized in affine $d$-space, the *$r$-skeletal* *cochain complex* is

$$\mathcal{R}^{d,r}(\Delta;\overline{\mathbf{p}}): \mathbf{0} \leftarrow \oplus_{\rho \in \Delta^{(r-1)}} V_{d+1}^{(d+1-r)}/\ker \rho \xleftarrow{\delta_{r-1}} \oplus_{\pi \in \Delta^{(r-2)}} V_{d+1}^{(d+1-r)}/\ker \pi \xleftarrow{\delta_{r-2}}$$

$$\cdots \xleftarrow{\delta_1} \oplus_{v \in \Delta^{(0)}} V_{d+1}^{(d+1-r)}/\ker v \xleftarrow{\delta_0} V_{d+1}^{(d+1-r)} \leftarrow \mathbf{0}.$$

For a general $i$-simplex $\sigma$, with coefficient $c_\sigma$, a $(d+1-r)$-extensor modulo $\overline{\sigma}$:

$$\delta_i(c_\sigma \cdot [\sigma]) = \sum_{\rho=\sigma x} Sign(\sigma,\rho)c_\sigma \cdot [\rho]$$

Again this is extended linearly to $i$-cochains. The maps are well-defined on the equivalence classes $[\sigma]$ and we have $\delta_i \delta_{i-1} = 0$.

The elements of the kernel of $\delta_i$ are the *i-cocycles* $Z^i(\mathcal{R}^{d,r}(\Delta;\overline{\mathbf{p}}))$, and the elements of the image of $\delta_{i-1}$ are the *i-coboundaries*, $B^i(\mathcal{R}^{d,r}(\Delta;\overline{\mathbf{p}}))$. We have the usual cohomology spaces of the cochain complex:

$$\widetilde{H}^i(\mathcal{R}^{d,r}(\Delta;\overline{\mathbf{p}})) = Z^i(\mathcal{R}^{d,r}(\Delta;\overline{\mathbf{p}}))/B^i(\mathcal{R}^{d,r}(\Delta;\overline{\mathbf{p}})).$$

and the corresponding *Betti numbers* $\beta^i(\mathcal{R}^{d,r}(\Delta;\overline{\mathbf{p}})) = \dim H^i(\mathcal{R}^{d,r}(\Delta;\overline{\mathbf{p}}))$.

Given an $i$-chain $\mathbf{c}$, with $c_\pi \in V_{d+1}^{(r-i)}/\ker \pi$, and an $i$-cochain $\mathbf{d}$, with $d_\pi \in V_{d+1}^{(d+1-r)}/\ker \pi$, we have a bilinear form

$$\langle \, \mathbf{c},\mathbf{d} \, \rangle = \sum_{\pi \in \Delta^{(i)}} c_\pi \vee d_\pi \vee \overline{\pi}.$$

Notice that these products are $(r-i+d+1-r+i) = (d+1)$-tensors in $V_{d+1}$ – or real numbers. With this inner product, the usual duality for an $(i+1)$-chain $\mathbf{c}$ and an $i$-cochain $\mathbf{d}$ holds:

$$\langle \, \partial_{i+1}\mathbf{c}, \, \mathbf{d} \, \rangle = \langle \, \mathbf{c}, \, \delta^i\mathbf{d} \, \rangle$$

and the resulting orthogonality and isomorphisms of homology and cohomology spaces and equality of $i$-Betti numbers, Euler characteristic etc. follow.

We are just at the initial stages of exploring the balance of 'skeletal $r$-static theory' (homology) and 'skeletal $r$-kinematic theory' (cohomology). We note that the $(r-2)$-cochains (the $(r-2)$-motions) have a direct geometric interpretation [**Lee1,2**]. Informally, these 'motions' are infinitesimal displacements of the $(r-2)$-faces which instantaneously preserve the $(r-1)$-volume of the $(r-1)$-faces (but may not preserve the global incidences on the $(r-3)$-faces). Indeed, this is the generalization of skeletal 2-motions: infinitesimal displacements of the vertices which preserve the length of the edges. It also gives an intuitive kinematic interpretation of ordinary homology for $d = r - 1$.

REMARK 16.3.1. For a simplicial complex in affine $d$-space, this cohomology is directly related to the Stanley-Reisner ring of the simplicial complex, an algebraic object used in algebraic combinatorics [**St2,Lee1,2,TWW1,2,3**].

The Stanley-Reisner ring does not exist for non-simplicial complexes. However we can define skeletal $r$-rigidity for non-simplicial cell complexes. Given an abstract cell complex, we need a $d$-configuration which makes each face 'flat' and ensures the vertices of an $i$ face span an affine space of dimension $i$. With this assumption, we can complete extensions from §16 directly, using arbitrarily chosen $(i + 1)$-extensors for the subspaces spanned by oriented $i$-faces and taking more care with the boundary operators. These matroids have not yet been studied for skeletal

$r$-rigidity beyond 3-rigidity in 3-space [**CrW4**]. Their significance for polyhedral combinatorics, extended $h$ vectors etc. is unexplored.

REMARK. This cohomology, and the cohomologies of §15, do not 'represent' the orthogonal matroid, even for lower faces of a larger complex. In the terms of §14.3, our chain complexes have only zero $r$-chains, because of the definitions of the coefficients. With this observation, the only time $\beta_{r-1}(\mathcal{R}_{d,r}(\Delta; \overline{\mathbf{p}})) = 0$ is when the entire set is independent and the orthogonal matroid is trivial!

However, for homology $n$-spheres in $n$-space, there is a critical Euclidean geometric construction, called the *reciprocal diagram*, which originated with Clerk Maxwell [**Max**] for plane statics on 2-spheres. In this geometric reciprocity, the original complex $\Delta$ at $\mathbf{p}$ and the dual complex $\Delta^*$ and $\overline{\mathbf{p}}^*$ are realized with the face $\sigma(\mathbf{p})$ orthogonal in $n$-space to the dual face $\sigma^*(\mathbf{p}^*)$. This reciprocal relationship induces a reciprocal pair of a skeletal $i$-cycle in $\Delta(\overline{\mathbf{p}})$ and a skeletal $(n - i)$-cycle in $\Delta^*(\overline{\mathbf{p}}^*)$, for each $i$. There are also several correspondences either proven or conjectured between skeletal $i$-cycles on $\Delta(\overline{\mathbf{p}})$ and skeletal $(n - i)$-cocycles of $\Delta^*(\overline{\mathbf{p}}^*)$ [**CrW2,3,4**].

There are further known and conjectured correspondences between $i$-cocycles (kinematics) on an $n$-sphere in $(n+1)$-space, $\Delta(\overline{\mathbf{p}})$, and $(n-i)$-cocycles on the same geometric complex [**CrW1,TWW3**]. These correspondences are directly related to the known combinatorial symmetry of the $g$-sequence and $h$-sequence of a convex spherical polytope [**Lee1,2,St2**].

### 16.4. Lower homologies and hypermatroids.

In §15.1 we saw that $\widetilde{H}_0(\mathcal{K}_1^0(\Delta^2; \mathbf{p}))$ matched the non-trivial parallel drawings of the underlying geometric graph $\Delta^1(\mathbf{p})$. This geometry gives a hypermatroid with independent sets defined by $2|E| \leq 3|V| - 4$ (§5.3). This is one small piece of a larger picture.

PROPOSITION 16.4.1. *For the chain complex* $\mathcal{R}_{r,r}(\Delta; \overline{\mathbf{p}})$, $\beta_0$ *is the Betti number for the parallel drawing matroid (and chain complex) of the geometric graph* $\Delta^1(\overline{\mathbf{p}})$ *in $r$-space.*

*In particular,* $\beta_0(\mathcal{R}_{r,r}(\Delta; \overline{\mathbf{p}})) = 0$ *if and only if* $\Delta^1(\overline{\mathbf{p}})$ *has only trivial parallel drawings in $r$-space.*

COROLLARY 16.4.2. *For the chain complex* $\mathcal{R}_{r,r}(\Delta; \overline{\mathbf{p}})$, $\beta_0(\mathcal{R}_{r,r}(\Delta; \overline{\mathbf{p}})) = 0$ *if the geometric graph* $\Delta^1(\overline{\mathbf{p}})$ *is first-order rigid in $r$-space.*

PROOF. For a geometric graph $\Delta^1(\overline{\mathbf{p}})$ in $r$-space, a non-trivial parallel drawing generates one (or more) non-trivial first-order motions [**Wh5,Wh15**].

These results apply the the precise cases where skeletal rigidity is known to be isomorphic to the $C_1^0$-cofactor matroids. We do not know to what depth the generic lower homologies and the corresponding matroids of these two sequences will actually coincide.

Each lower homology of $\mathcal{R}_{d,k}(\Delta; \mathbf{p})$ defines a corresponding hypermatroid on these lower faces $\Delta^i$ of the complex. Most of these hypermatroids have not been studied or even explicitly described. The 'off shoots' of Figures 13.1 and 1.1 give the rank estimates for some of the lowest of these families: counts obtained from the Euler characteristic of the truncated chain complex. We cannot demonstrate that each of these hypermatroids will have an independent geometric significance – but we suspect that all of them will.

The following tables summarize some connections which are confirmed and conjectured for the lower homologies of rigidity. The vertical arrows ↑? represent an conjectured injection of spaces under vertical projection in dimension, assuming the configurations have no faces 'vertical'. While we have not worked out all the details, there is strong evidence for this injection, building on the results and techniques for coning in [**TWW3**]. The horizontal arrows $\overset{?}{\hookleftarrow}$ represent conjectured injections of the homologies which would generalize the connection between parallel drawings and first-order rigidity in the $\mathbb{R}^3$ line of the upper table. It is likely that these can be proven directly, using similar techniques in the geometric homology [**Wh15**]. Similarly, some of the conjectures in the $\mathbb{R}^4$ line of the lower table are probably implicit in the connection between parallel drawing and first-order rigidity.

| | 1-skeleton | 2-skeleton | 3-skeleton | 4-skeleton |
|---|---|---|---|---|
| $\mathbb{R}^6$ $\Pi(\bar{p})$ | $\tilde{H}_0(\mathcal{R}_{6,2}(\Delta^1;\bar{p}))$ $\overset{?}{\hookleftarrow}$ $\uparrow$ | $\tilde{H}_0(\mathcal{R}_{6,3}(\Delta^2;\bar{p}))$ $\overset{?}{\hookleftarrow}$ $\uparrow?$ | $\tilde{H}_0(\mathcal{R}_{6,4}(\Delta^3;\bar{p}))$ $\overset{?}{\hookleftarrow}$ $\uparrow?$ | $\tilde{H}_0(\mathcal{R}_{6,5}(\Delta^4;\bar{p}))$ $\uparrow?$ |
| $\mathbb{R}^5$ $\Pi(\bar{q})$ | $\tilde{H}_0(\mathcal{R}_{5,2}(\Delta^1;\bar{q}))$ $\overset{?}{\hookleftarrow}$ $\uparrow$ | $\tilde{H}_0(\mathcal{R}_{5,3}(\Delta^2;\bar{q}))$ $\overset{?}{\hookleftarrow}$ $\uparrow?$ | $\tilde{H}_0(\mathcal{R}_{5,4}(\Delta^3;\bar{q}))$ $\overset{?}{\hookleftarrow}$ $\uparrow?$ | $\tilde{H}_0(\mathcal{R}_{5,5}(\Delta^4;\bar{q}))$ $\uparrow?$ |
| $\mathbb{R}^4$ $\Pi(\bar{r})$ | $\tilde{H}_0(\mathcal{R}_{4,2}(\Delta^1;\bar{r}))$ $\overset{?}{\hookleftarrow}$ $\uparrow$ | $\tilde{H}_0(\mathcal{R}_{4,3}(\Delta^2;\bar{r}))$ $\overset{?}{\hookleftarrow}$ $\uparrow?$ | $\tilde{H}_0(\mathcal{R}_{4,4}(\Delta^3;\bar{r}))$ $\overset{?}{\hookleftarrow}$ $\uparrow?$ | $\tilde{H}_0(\Delta)$ |
| $\mathbb{R}^3$ $\Pi(\bar{s})$ | $\tilde{H}_0(\mathcal{R}_{3,2}(\Delta^1;\bar{s}))$ $\hookleftarrow$ $\uparrow$ | $\tilde{H}_0(\mathcal{R}_{3,3}(\Delta^2;\bar{s}))$ $\overset{?}{\hookleftarrow}$ $\uparrow?$ | $\tilde{H}_0(\Delta)$ | |
| $\mathbb{R}^2$ $\Pi(\bar{t})$ | $\tilde{H}_0(\mathcal{R}_{2,2}(\Delta^1;\bar{t}))$ $\overset{?}{\hookleftarrow}$ $\uparrow$ | $\tilde{H}_0(\Delta)$ | | |
| $\mathbb{R}^1$ | $\tilde{H}_0(\Delta)$ | | | |

| | 2-skeleton | 3-skeleton | 4-skeleton |
|---|---|---|---|
| $\mathbb{R}^6$ $\Pi(\bar{p})$ | $\tilde{H}_1(\mathcal{R}_{6,3}(\Delta^2;\bar{p}))$ $\overset{?}{\hookleftarrow}$ $\uparrow?$ | $\tilde{H}_1(\mathcal{R}_{6,4}(\Delta^3;\bar{p}))$ $\overset{?}{\hookleftarrow}$ $\uparrow?$ | $\tilde{H}_1(\mathcal{R}_{6,5}(\Delta^4;\bar{p}))$ $\overset{?}{\hookleftarrow}$ $\uparrow?$ |
| $\mathbb{R}^5$ $\Pi(\bar{q})$ | $\tilde{H}_1(\mathcal{R}_{5,3}(\Delta^2;\bar{q}))$ $\overset{?}{\hookleftarrow}$ $\uparrow?$ | $\tilde{H}_1(\mathcal{R}_{5,4}(\Delta^3;\bar{q}))$ $\overset{?}{\hookleftarrow}$ $\uparrow?$ | $\tilde{H}_1(\mathcal{R}_{5,5}(\Delta^4;\bar{q}))$ $\overset{?}{\hookleftarrow}$ $\uparrow?$ |
| $\mathbb{R}^4$ $\Pi(\bar{r})$ | $\tilde{H}_1(\mathcal{R}_{4,3}(\Delta^2;\bar{r}))$ $\overset{?}{\hookleftarrow}$ $\uparrow?$ | $\tilde{H}_1(\mathcal{R}_{4,4}(\Delta^3;\bar{r}))$ $\overset{?}{\hookleftarrow}$ $\uparrow?$ | $\tilde{H}_1(\Delta)$ |
| $\mathbb{R}^3$ $\Pi(\bar{s})$ | $\tilde{H}_1(\mathcal{R}_{3,3}(\Delta^2;\bar{s}))$ $\overset{?}{\hookleftarrow}$ $\uparrow?$ | $\tilde{H}_1(\Delta)$ | |
| $\mathbb{R}^2$ | $\tilde{H}_1(\Delta)$ | | |

These conjectures are summarized in the following form, with (1) and (2) representing the horizontal rows and (3) and (4) representing the vertical columns. For $\beta_0$ and for the horizontal arrows, the existing evidence is stronger than for the vertical arrows on higher Betti numbers.

CONJECTURE 16.4.3.
1. *For the chain complexes $\mathcal{R}_{d,r}(\Delta;\bar{p})$, and $\mathcal{R}_{d,r+1}(\Delta;\bar{p})$,*
    $\beta_i(\mathcal{R}_{d,r}(\Delta;\bar{p})) \geq \beta_i(\mathcal{R}_{d,r+1}(\Delta;\bar{p}))$ *for $i < r - 1$.*
2. *In particular, $\beta_i(\mathcal{R}_{d,r}(\Delta;\bar{p})) = 0$ if $\beta_i(\mathcal{R}_{d,r-k}(\Delta^i;\bar{p})) = 0$ for any $k \leq r - 1$ and $i < r - k - 1$.*
3. *For the chain complexes $\mathcal{R}_{d,r}(\Delta;\bar{p})$, and $\mathcal{R}_{d-1,r}(\Delta;\bar{q})$ with $\bar{q} = \Pi\bar{p}$,*
    $\beta_i(\mathcal{R}_{d,r}(\Delta;\bar{p})) \geq \beta_i(\mathcal{R}_{d-1,r}(\Delta;\bar{q}))$ *for $i < r - 1$.*
4. *In particular, $\beta_i(\mathcal{R}_{d,r}(\Delta;\Pi\bar{p})) = 0$ if $\beta_i(\mathcal{R}_{d+k,r}(\Delta^i;\bar{p})) = 0$ for any $i < r - 1$.*

The following table summarizes results for the top Betti numbers which follow from the coning theorems (if the cone point is then dropped).

| | 1-skeleton | 2-skeleton | 3-skeleton | 4-skeleton |
|---|---|---|---|---|
| $\mathbb{R}^5$ | $\tilde{H}_1(\mathcal{R}_{5,2}(\Delta^1;\overline{\mathbf{q}}))$ | $\tilde{H}_2(\mathcal{R}_{5,3}(\Delta^2;\overline{\mathbf{q}}))$ | $\tilde{H}_3(\mathcal{R}_{5,4}(\Delta^3;\overline{\mathbf{q}}))$ | $\tilde{H}_4(\mathcal{R}_{5,5}(\Delta^4;\overline{\mathbf{q}}))$ |
| $\Pi(\overline{\mathbf{q}})$ | $\downarrow$ | $\downarrow$ | $\downarrow$ | $\downarrow$ |
| $\mathbb{R}^4$ | $\tilde{H}_1(\mathcal{R}_{4,2}(\Delta^1;\overline{\mathbf{r}}))$ | $\tilde{H}_2(\mathcal{R}_{4,3}(\Delta^2;\overline{\mathbf{r}}))$ | $\tilde{H}_3(\mathcal{R}_{4,4}(\Delta^3;\overline{\mathbf{r}}))$ | $\tilde{H}_4(\Delta^4)$ |
| $\Pi(\overline{\mathbf{r}})$ | $\downarrow$ | $\downarrow$ | $\downarrow$ | |
| $\mathbb{R}^3$ | $\tilde{H}_1(\mathcal{R}_{3,2}(\Delta^1;\overline{\mathbf{s}}))$ | $\tilde{H}_2(\mathcal{R}_{3,3}(\Delta^2;\overline{\mathbf{s}}))$ | $\tilde{H}_3(\Delta^3)$ | |
| $\Pi(\overline{\mathbf{s}})$ | $\downarrow$ | $\downarrow$ | | |
| $\mathbb{R}^2$ | $\tilde{H}_1(\mathcal{R}_{2,2}(\Delta^1;\overline{\mathbf{t}}))$ | $\tilde{H}_2(\Delta^2)$ | | |
| $\Pi(\overline{\mathbf{t}})$ | $\downarrow$ | | | |
| $\mathbb{R}^1$ | $\tilde{H}_1(\Delta^1)$ | | | |

We have very little evidence about analogous relationships for $K_s^{s-1}(\Delta^m)$. We can only suggest that the possibility of similar connections should be investigated.

### 16.5. The analogy between skeletal matroids and cofactor matroids.

A recurrent theme for §15 and §16 has been the fundamental analogy between the generic matroids $\mathcal{K}_s^{s-1}(\Delta^m)$ and the generic matroids $\mathcal{R}_{d,r}(\Delta^{r-1})$, where $r = m + 1$ and $d = m + s$. Certain specific correspondences have been observed:

(a) the $i$-chains of the two complexes have identical dimensions and the resulting Euler characteristics are equal;

(b) $\mathcal{K}_1^0(\Delta^m;\mathbf{p})$ and $\mathcal{R}_{r,r}(\Delta^{r-1};\overline{\mathbf{p}})$ are isomorphic and the three chain complexes $\mathcal{K}_0^{-1}(\Delta^m)$, $\mathcal{R}_{r-1,r}(\Delta)$, and the simplicial $(r-1)$-homology of $\Delta^{r-1}$ are isomorphic.

Some additional correspondences have been conjectured:

(c) *Conjecture*: the matroids $\mathcal{K}_2^1(\Delta^1)$ and $\mathcal{R}_{3,2}(\Delta)$ are isomorphic (§10.3);

(d) *Conjecture*: all sets independent in $\mathcal{R}_{k,2}(\Delta)$ are independent $\mathcal{K}_k^{k-1}(\Delta^1)$ (§11.5);

(e) *Conjecture*: the geometric map from the cone $\mathcal{R}_{d+1,r}(w * \Delta, \overline{\mathbf{p}}_w; \overline{\mathbf{p}})$ to the projection $\mathcal{R}_{d,r}(\Delta; Pi(\overline{\mathbf{p}}))$ in skeletal $r$-rigidity transfers to a geometric correspondence from $\mathcal{K}_{s+1}^s((w * \Delta)^r; \mathbf{q}_w, \mathbf{q})$ to $\mathcal{K}_s^{s-1}(\Delta^r; \mathbf{q})$ (§15.2)

To these we add several new conjectures:

(f) *Conjecture*: all the results of Example 16.2.4 for $K_n$ extend to the corresponding $\mathcal{K}_s^{s-1}(K_n)$. For example, $K_n^m$ is $\mathcal{K}_s^{s-1}$-acyclic in dimension $m$ if and only if $s + 1 \leq n \leq m + s + 1$.

(g) *Conjecture*: for each $r$, there is a generic isomorphism between $\mathcal{K}_r^{r-1}(\Delta^{r-1})$ and $\mathcal{R}_{r+1,r}(\Delta^{r-1})$.

(h) *Conjecture*: For each $k, m$, all sets independent in $\mathcal{R}_{k+m,r}(\Delta^m)$ are independent in $\mathcal{K}_k^{k-1}(\Delta^m)$.

(i) The Homology Sphere Theorem 16.2.6 and Geometric $g$-Conjecture 16.2.7 transfer to the cofactor matroids.

REMARK 16.5.1. For applications back to multivariate splines it will be important to develop the appropriate theory of $\mathcal{K}_k^{k-1}(\Delta^r, \Delta'; \overline{\mathbf{p}})$ – the homology of the corresponding chain complexes relative to the 'boundary' of the simplicial complex. We conjecture that the same relationships conjectured for the original homologies also apply to these relative homologies, using 'pinned skeletal rigidity' for $\mathcal{R}_{r,d}(\Delta^r, \Delta'; \overline{\mathbf{p}})$. Only a few pieces of these theories are now evident –

one of which is a valuable geometric 'coning' result giving an isomorphism from $\mathcal{K}_k^{k-1}(w * \Delta^r, (\Delta^r \cup w * \Delta'); \overline{\mathbf{p}}_0, \overline{\mathbf{p}})$ to $\mathcal{K}_k^{k-1}(\Delta^r, \Delta'; \Pi(\overline{\mathbf{p}}))$ [**ASW**].

The interested reader can certainly make a longer list of conjectures and problems to be investigated for each of these structures. So little work has been completed that it remains unclear which directions will be most fruitful and which techniques implicitly require graphs and are not open to this generality.

## 17.   Summary of Themes

We have displayed a wide range of matroids arising from work in discrete geometry. In presenting each of these examples in Figures 1.1 and 13.1 these matroids have been displayed in families, organized:

1. in vertical strips: by dimension of the space of realization (for skeletal rigidity matroids); or algebraic powers (for cofactor matroids) for fixed topological dimension of the abstract complex;
2. by homological (lower homologies) and geometric relationships;
3. in layers by dimension of the underlying abstract objects: edges, 2-faces, ..., $r$-faces, ...;
4.  by 'off shoots' such as parallel drawings – and other unexplored generalizations which complete each strip to a full quadrant of interrelated matroids.

There are a number of common themes in the analysis of these matroids. Some of these have been explicit, but some of the patterns were left implicit in the flow of our presentation. Examples include:

5. homology and cohomology for augmented chain complexes over the reals, leading to a representing matrix for the matroid, a 'static theory' of cycles, a 'kinematic theory' of cocycles and an accounting of when lower homologies are zero;
6. inductive techniques, including 'gluing' of complexes (based implicitly or explicitly on the Mayer-Vietoris sequence of homology) and shellings for complexes;
7. combinatorial estimates of the rank of the matroid, based on the numbers of faces $f_i$ of each dimension $i$;
8. combinatorial / topological conditions which guarantee these rank estimates are generically correct (based on showing lower homologies are geometrically or generically zero);
9. geometric conditions for a change from this generic rank (implicitly or explicitly projective geometry) and some geometric conditions for the generic rank to be achieved geometrically.

There are numerous connections among the matroids in neighboring cells of this display. Some of these have been explicitly pointed out, but many more have been left to remarks or omitted entirely. Examples include connections:

10. by the analogy between skeletal rigidity matroids and cofactor matroids of the same rank on complete (ample) complexes – displayed as parallel strips which coincide for the first two (conjectured three) cells in each strip;
11. by coning up and projection down between cells of skeletal $k$-rigidity (conjectured to also hold for cofactor matroids);
12. by lower homologies, such as parallel drawings of edges for skeletal 3-rigidity in 3-space, and numerous similar connections we could not present;

13. by coning and sectioning between matroids on objects of adjacent dimensions;

The significance of these matroids comes from several sources. The original matroids for first-order rigidity, for scene analysis, and for cofactors, arose directly from applied problems. Of course we have generalized beyond the questions arising in these applications, in part to grasp the underlying structure, in part to find solutions to residual unsolved problems, and in part to enjoy the rich interplay of patterns.

The 'secondary' matroids, such as parallel drawings and skeletal rigidity, correspond precisely to existing geometrical problems (such as Minkowski decomposability and the $g$-theorem) but arose from our geometric play and from the continuing drive to generalize patterns which gave such insight to the geometry of polytopes.

The matroids make explicit the essential role of homology (and $k$-cycle matroids) and the need for substantial combinatorial and algorithmic theory for the homologies of larger complexes, both simplicial and non-simplicial, extending the base case of graph theory (1-cycle homology). We anticipate an expanding role for homology-based matroids and geometric homology [**Cr1,3,4,CR2,Wh 15**] and corresponding techniques within matroid theory and its applications.

A central example – generic rigidity in 3-space – highlights essential unsolved problems in matroid theory / graph theory / algorithms. We have no effective combinatorial characterization (other than take a matrix with variable entries and crush it); we have the 'maximal matroid' conjecture for $3|V| - 6$ highlighting the issue of submodular functions negative on singletons which still appear to describe a matroid; and we have an explicit example of a graph theoretic property which is random polynomial, but may not be polynomial in complexity.

As I mentioned in the introduction, I am a geometer. I view areas like graph theory, matroid theory, homology theory and related combinatorics as (abstract) layers in the rich hierarchy of geometries – an essential ground for further studies, but only one portion of a much larger study. The geometric patterns underlying these matroids was essential and delightful. The generic combinatorial patterns are sometimes accessible through combinatorial techniques, sometimes through geometric techniques. It seems very appropriate that geometric and topological techniques should appear in this study of 'combinatorial geometries'.

## Appendix: Matroids from Counts on Graphs and Hypergraphs.

**A.1. The basic counts.** A number of the 'rank counts' in this paper directly defined matroids on graphs (and hypergraphs). Some years ago, a joint project with Neil White [**WW2**] derived some basic results for these 'count matroids' which we will present (and extend) here. Independently, and earlier, the basic constructions of this section (and the connectivity results of the next section) were also described by Lorea [**Lor**]. An examination of these constructions will highlight the line which separates the well-understood matroids, such as generic 2-rigidity and parallel drawings, from the matroids with fundamental unsolved problems, such as generic 3-rigidity and homology.

Throughout this appendix we will work with general hypergraphs $H = (V, E)$, with multiple edges and loops (edges of cardinality 1) allowed.

COUNTS TO MATROIDS PROPOSITION A.1.1 [**Lor,WW2**]. *For integers $m \geq 0$ and $k$, the following definition gives the independent sets of a matroid $\mathcal{M}_{m,k}(E)$ on* *the edges of a hypergraph (in particular, of the complete hypergraph on a finite set of vertices $V$):*

*A set of edges $E$ is independent if and only if for all non-empty subsets $E'$ on vertices $V'$:  $|E'| \leq m|V'| + k$.*

PROOF. We verify the circuit exchange axiom. A *circuit* in this independence structure $\mathcal{M}_{m,k}$ is a minimal dependent set defined by:

*a non-empty set $E$ of edges in the hypergraph is a circuit if and only if*
(i) $|E| = m|V| + k + 1$ *and,*
(ii) *for all proper subsets $E'$ with vertices $V(E')$:  $|E'| \leq m|V(E')| + k$.*

Given circuits $|E_1| = m|V_1| + k + 1$, $|E_2| = m|V_2| + k + 1$, sharing an edge $e$, we show that $|E_1 \cup E_2| - \{e\}$ contains a circuit. First, we have:

$$|E_1 \cup E_2| = |E_1| + |E_2| - |E_1 \cap E_2|$$

$$|V(E_1)| + |V(E_2)| = |V(E_1 \cap E_2)| + |V(E_1) \cap V(E_2)|$$

$$\leq |V(E_1 \cap E_2)| + |V(E_1 \cap E_2)|$$

Since $|E_1 \cap E_2| \leq m|V(E_1) \cap V(E_2)| + k$, substitution gives:

$$|E_1 \cup E_2| \geq m|V(E_1)| + k + 1 + m|V(E_2)| + k + 1 - [m|V_1 \cap V_2| + k]$$

$$\geq m\big(|V(E_1)| + |V(E_2)| - |V(E_1 \cap E_2)|\big) + 2k - k + 2$$

$$\geq m\big(|V(E_1)| + |V(E_2)| - |V(E_1) \cap V(E_2)|\big) + k + 2$$

$$\geq m|V(E_1 \cup E_2)| + k + 2$$

In passing from $-m|V(E_1 \cap E_2)|$ to $-m|V(E_1) \cap V(E_2)|$ we used the assumption that $m \geq 0$. We now delete $e$ from the left hand side and 1 from the right:

$$|(E_1 \cup E_2) - \{e\}| \geq m|V(E_1 \cup E_2)| + k + 1 \geq m|V((E_1 \cup E_2) - \{e\})| + k + 1.$$

This set must contain a circuit. For example, a minimal non-empty subset $E_*$ of the set $E_1 \cup E_2 - \{e\}$ with $|E_*| = m|V(E_*)| + k + 1$ will give the required circuit.

Special cases of this matroid are abundant in matroid theory [**Lor**]:
(a) $\mathcal{M}_{1,-1}(E)$ is the cycle matroid of the graph $(V(E), E)$;
(b) $\mathcal{M}_{1,0}(E)$ is the bicycle matroid (circuits are two connected polygons);
(c) $\mathcal{M}_{1,0}(H)$ is the transversal matroid of a general hypergraph;
(d) for any positive integer $m$, $M_{m,0}(H)$ is the matroid union of $m$ copies of the transversal matroid of a general hypergraph;
(e) $\mathcal{M}_{1,-2}(H)$ is Crapo's geometry of triples, if $H$ is a hypergraph with all edges of cardinality 3.
(f) $\mathcal{M}_{2,-3}(E)$ is the generic 2-rigidity matroid on ordinary graphs.

REMARK A.1.2. If we try $k \leq -2m$, the matroid will have all ordinary graph edges (pairs) dependent. Each singleton $\{e\}$ will satisfy $|\{e\}| = 1 > 2m - 2m = m|V'| + k$, so it is dependent. Therefore, for ordinary graphs we should assume that $-k < 2m$.

In general, we need $k > -nm$ to make the matroid non-trivial on $n$-tuple edges. We also need $k > -m$ to make loops (single vertices) into independent elements. If $k \geq -mn + t$ then $t$ copies of $n$-tuple edges will be independent.

If we try non-integers $m > 0$, we do not get a matroid. For example, the count $|E'| \leq .5|V'|$ on non-empty subsets of $E$, defines an interesting structure: the matchings on a graph (Figure A.1). This is not a matroid: the circuits of Figure A.1.B 'exchange' on their shared edge to the independent set of Figure A.1.C.

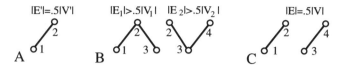

FIGURE. A.1. *A counterexample to* $|E| \leq .5|V|$ *defining independence in a matroid on graphs.*

If we try to adapt the proof above, and replace the condition for dependence $|E| > m|V| + k$ by $|E| = \lfloor m|V| + k \rfloor + 1$, the problem is that the floor function need not be submodular on non-integers.

For rational $m$, these counts do produce 'polymatroids' or 'hypermatroids' on appropriate multigraphs (see §A.3).

REMARK A.1.3. Most of the results in this appendix can be viewed as applications of a general result defining a matroid on a set $A$ from a submodular function which is non-negative on non-empty subsets of the set $A$ [**Ed,ER**]. Recall that an real valued function $f : 2^A \to \mathbb{R}$ is *submodular* if

for all subsets $B, C$, $f(B) + f(C) \geq f(B \cup C) + f(B \cap C)$.

SUBMODULAR THEOREM A.1.4 [**We**]. *Given a submodular function $\mu$ on $2^S$, non-negative on all non-empty subsets of $S$, the collection:*

$$\mathcal{I}(\mu) = \{A \mid |A \cap Y| \leq \mu(Y), Y \in 2^S - \emptyset\}$$

*are the independent sets of a matroid $\mathcal{M}(\mu)$ on $A$.*

*Moreover, the rank function $\rho_\mu$ is given for $A \subseteq S$ by*

$$\rho_\mu(A) = \min\left(|A|, \sum_{i=1}^k \mu(X_i) + |A \cap (S - \cup X_i)|\right).$$

LEMMA A.1.5. $f(E) = m|V(E)| + k$ *is a submodular function on $2^E$, provided $m \geq 0$ and $m|V(e)| + k \geq 0$ on singletons.*

PROOF. The core of our proof above amounted to:

$$f(E_1) + f(E_2) \geq f(E_1 \cup E_2) + f(E_1 \cap E_2).$$

To keep $f(E_1) \geq 0$ on non-empty subsets of large sets $E$, we need $m \geq 0$. Finally to make the matroid positive on singletons, we need $m|V(e)| + k \geq 1$.

One sign of trouble for the generic 3-rigidity count is that $f(\{e\}) = 3|V(e)| - 6 = 0$. The count of this matroid would define all edges of a graph as dependent.

**A.2. Some structure results from counts.** We let $\mathcal{M}_{m,k}(n)$ denote the $m, k$ counting matroid on the complete hypergraph on $n$ vertices (i.e. $E = 2^V$) and let $\mathcal{M}_{m,k}(d, n)$ denote the matroid on the $d$-complete hypergraph on $n$ vertices which contains $d$ copies of each edge.

Recall that the *matroid union* of two matroids $\mathcal{M}_1$, and $\mathcal{M}_2$ is the matroid $\mathcal{M}_1 \vee \mathcal{M}_2$ defined by:

*A set $I$ is independent in the union if and only if it can be partitioned into $I_1 \cup I_2$ with $I_1$ independent in $\mathcal{M}_1$ and $I_2$ independent in $\mathcal{M}_2$.*

The following general result connects matroid unions with sums of submodular functions.

PROPOSITION A.2.1 [**PP**]. *If $\mu_1, \mu_2$ are non-decreasing, integer valued, non-negative submodular functions on $2^S$ then $\mathcal{M}(\mu_1) \vee \mathcal{M}(\mu_2) = \mathcal{M}(\mu_1 + \mu_2)$.*

Applied to our matroids, this gives:

PROPOSITION A.2.2. *If $m = m_1 + m_2$ and $k = k_1 + k_2$, with $m_1, m_2 \geq 0$ and $m_1|V(e)| + k_1 \geq 0, m_2|V(e)| + k_2 \geq 0$ for all edges $e \in E$, then $\mathcal{M}_{m,k}(E)$ is the matroid union $\mathcal{M}_{m_1,k_1}(E) \vee \mathcal{M}_{m_2,k_2}(E)$.*

EXAMPLE A.2.3. The restriction in this proposition is essential. For example

$$\mathcal{M}_{2,-3}(E) \neq \mathcal{M}_{1,-1}(E) \vee \mathcal{M}_{1,-2}(E),$$

since $\mathcal{M}_{1,-2}$ is trivial on graphs (making all doubleton edges dependent). This matroid union is correct for a hypergraph with all edges of valence at least 3.

EXAMPLE A.2.4. Examples of this result include:
(i) $\mathcal{M}_{n,-n}(G) = \bigvee_{i=1}^{n} \mathcal{M}_{1,-1}(G)$. Equivalently, for $n|V| - n = n(|V| - 1)$ the matroid is the matroid union of $n$ copies of the cycle matroid for an ordinary graph (recall §12.1);
(ii) for $m \geq n \geq 0$, $\mathcal{M}_{m,-n}(G) = \bigvee_{i=1}^{n} \mathcal{M}_{1,-1}(G) \vee \bigvee_{j=1}^{m-n} \mathcal{M}_{1,0}$ or the matroid for $m|V| - n, m > n \geq 0$, is the matroid union of $n$ copies of the cycle matroid for a ordinary graph and $m - n$ copies of the bicycle matroid;
(iii) $\mathcal{M}_{2,0}(G) = \mathcal{M}_{1,1}(G) \vee \mathcal{M}_{1,-1}(G) = \mathcal{M}_{1,0}(G) \vee \mathcal{M}_{1,0}(G)$, so the decomposition is *not unique*.

Many of these matroids actually appear as the first-order rigidity matroids of generic frameworks on alternate surfaces [**Wh7**]:
(i) $\mathcal{M}_{2,-2}$ appears as the first-order rigidity matroid of generic frameworks on the flat torus or the cylinder (which have a 2-space of global congruences);
(ii) $\mathcal{M}_{2,-1}$ appears as the first-order rigidity matroid of generic frameworks on the surface of a cone (which has a 1-dimensional space of global congruences);
(iii) $\mathcal{M}_{2,0}$ appears as the first-order rigidity matroid of generic frameworks on the surface of a convex polyhedron (which has a 0-dimensional space of global congruences).

Similar connections can be found for matroids on graphs of the form $\mathcal{M}_{m,k}(G)$ for $m > 2, 0 \geq k \geq -\binom{m}{2}$ on surfaces of dimension $m$.

We next show that all count matroids $\mathcal{M}_{m,k}(n)$ (and therefore $\mathcal{M}_{m,k}(E)$ for all subsets $E$) are coordinatizable over $\mathbb{R}$ or over any infinite field.

COORDINATIZATION THEOREM A.2.5 [**WW2**]. *All count matroids $\mathcal{M}_{m,k}(n)$ are coordinatizable over each infinite field $F$.*

PROOF. We begin with a coordinatization of $\mathcal{M}_{m,k}(n)$ for $k \leq 0$.

LEMMA A.2.6. *For $k \leq 0$, $\mathcal{M}_{m,k}(n)$ can be constructed in rank $mn + k$ over any infinite field.*

PROOF. We choose $n$ flats of co-rank $m$ in general position in $F^{mn+k}$, labeled by the vertices $V$. For each edge $W \subseteq V$, we place a point corresponding to $W$ in general position on the intersection of the flats labeled by the elements of $V \setminus W$. We must verify that this intersection is non-empty, provided $W$ is not a loop (dependent edge) of $\mathcal{M}_{m,k}(n)$. If $j = |W|$, then the intersection of flats corresponding to $V \setminus W$ has co-rank $m(n - j)$ and this is nonempty if and only if $m(n - j) < mn + k$ or equivalently if and only if $mj + k > 0$. This is the condition that $W$ is not a loop.

If we have multiple copies of edges, and therefore several sets $W, W'$ corresponding to the same intersection, we pick distinct points (in general position to one another) in the appropriate intersection.

These points give the desired representation. For each set $V' \subseteq V$, the rank of the flat of its edges $2^{V'}$ is $m|V'| + k$ as required by the counts.

Our next step is to convert a representation of $\mathcal{M}_{m,0}(n)$ to a representation of $\mathcal{M}_{m,k}(n)$, $k > 0$.

LEMMA A.2.7 ([**WW2**]). $\mathcal{M}_{m,k+1}(n)$ *is the Higgs lift of* $\mathcal{M}_{m,k}(n)$.

PROOF. For $E'$ contained in $E$, $E'$ is independent in the Higgs lift of $\mathcal{M}_{m,k}(n)$ if and only if $E'$ has nullity at most one in $\mathcal{M}_{m,k}(n)$ [**Wht1**, p. 160], which is true if and only if

$|E'| \leq m|V'| + k + 1$ and
$|E''| \leq m|V''| + k + 1$ for every $E'' \subset E'$.

This is the definition of $\mathcal{M}_{m,k+1}(n)$ as a Higgs lift.

To complete the proof for $k > 0$, the Higgs lift of a coordinatized matroid is coordinatizable for all suitably large fields [**Wht1**, p. 161].

REMARK A.2.8. The representation of Lemma A.2.5 is *not* the representation one is likely to find in the applications. For example, the usual representation of the cycle matroid $\mathcal{M}_{1,-1}(n)$ lies in $F^n$ not in $F^{n-1}$.

An important problem in applying these matroids to represented matroids arising in applications is to 'recognize' such alternate representations which arise from the relevant systems of equations. For example, the proof that generic plane rigidity is the matroid $\mathcal{M}_{2,-3}(n)$ amounts to recognizing the representation of the matroid union of two copies of the cycle matroid (by its shape of zero and non-zero entries) and the changes due to the Dilworth truncation represented by the additional $-1$ [**Lov,LY,Wh7**].

There is much ingenuity that goes into the demonstration that alternate matrices, such as the rigidity matrix, indeed represent one of the matroids $\mathcal{M}_{m,k}(n)$. Such problems are the essence of several of the conjectures in this chapter.

Finally, we observe some connectivity results for circuits and bases which follow from the counts. Recall that a hypergraph $H = (V, E)$ is *$j$-vertex-connected* (or *$j$-connected*, for short) if there do not exist $j-1$ vertices whose removal disconnects $H$, that is, there does not exist a cover $V_1, V_2$ of the vertices, $|V_1 \cap V_2| \leq j - 1$ such that every edge lies in $V_1$ or in $V_2$. A hypergraph $H = (V, E)$ is *$j$-edge-connected* if for every partition $\emptyset \neq V_1, V_2 \subset V$, there exist at least $j$ edges intersecting both $V_1$ and $V_2$. When we talk about the vertex-connectivity (or edge-connectivity) of a set of edges $E$, we are really talking about the vertex-connectivity (or edge-connectivity) of the induced hypergraph $H = (V(E), E)$.

A matroid $\mathcal{M}_{m,k}(E)$ is called *full* if it has rank $m|V(E)| + k$, that is, if it contains at least some bases of the complete matroid $\mathcal{M}_{m,k}(|V(E)|)$. For example, all circuits in $\mathcal{M}_{m,k}(E)$ are full (corresponding to the observation that circuits in the plane rigidity matroid are rigid).

PROPOSITION A.2.9. *If $k \leq -(j-1)m$, then the circuits of $\mathcal{M}_{m,k}(E)$ are $j$-connected. If $\mathcal{M}_{m,k}(E)$ is full and $k < -(j-1)m$, then the bases are $j$-connected.*

PROOF. Suppose that $E'$ is a circuit of $\mathcal{M}_{m,k}(E)$ which is not $j$-connected. Then there exist $V_1, V_2$ containing all the edges with $|V_1 \cap V_2| \leq j - 1$. Let $E_1, E_2$ be the corresponding partition of the edges. Then

$$|E'| = |E_1| + |E_2| \leq m|V_1| + k + m|V_2| + k \leq m|V(E')| + m|V_1 \cap V_2| + 2k$$
$$\leq m|V(E')| + k + [m(j-1) + k] \leq m|V(E')| + k.$$

However, this violates the claim that $E'$ is a circuit of $\mathcal{M}_{m,k}(E)$.

The proof for a basis is similar, except that the last inequality is strict, giving $|E'| < m|V(E')| + k$, which contradicts the claim that $\mathcal{M}_{m,k}(E)$ is full.

PROPOSITION A.2.10. *If $k \leq 0$, then the circuits of $\mathcal{M}_{m,k}(E)$ are $(1-k)$-edge-connected. If $\mathcal{M}_{m,k}(E)$ is full, then the bases are $(-k)$-edge-connected.*

PROOF. Suppose that $E'$ is a circuit of $\mathcal{M}_{m,k}(E)$ which is not $(1-k)$-edge-connected, by virtue of the partition $V_1, V_2$ with at most $-k$ edges intersecting both. We partition the remaining edges of $E'$ into $E_1, E_2$. Then

$$|E'| \leq |E_1| + |E_2| + k \leq m|V_1| + k + m|V_2| + k - k \leq m|V(E')| + k.$$

Again we have contradicted the definition of a circuit. The obvious modifications complete the proof for bases.

PROPOSITION A.2.11. *If $k > 0$, then the circuits of $\mathcal{M}_{m,k}(E)$ have at most $k+1$ components.*

PROOF. Suppose that $E'$ is a circuit of $\mathcal{M}_{m,k}(E)$ with $j$ components, given by a partition of $V(E')$ into nonempty subsets $V_1, \ldots V_j$. Then $|E'| = m|V(E')| + k + 1$ and $|E_i| \leq m|V_i| + k$ for all $i$. If for some $h$, $|E_h| \leq m|V_h|$ then we can remove this set to give

$$|E' \setminus E_h| = m(|V(E')| - |V(E_h)|) + k + 1 > m|V(E' - E_h)| + k + 1.$$

This contradicts the minimality of the dependence of the circuit. Therefore, for each $i$, $|E_i| \geq m|V_i| + 1$. Now,

$$m|V(E')| + k + 1 = |E'| \geq \sum_{i=1}^{j}(m|V_i| + 1) = m|V(E')| + j.$$

Therefore $k + 1 \geq j$.

**A.3. Hypermatroids from counts.** In §8.2 and §12.2, we encountered counts to bound the rank of the matroid of the form $(d-1)|E| \leq d|V| - (d+1)$. Put in raw submodular terms, these correspond to rational valued submodular functions such as $f(E) = \frac{3}{2}|V| - 2$ and $f(|E|) = \frac{6}{5}(|B| - 1)$. A simple extension of the previous results describes how such submodular functions define hypermatroids.

Given a submodular function $f$, we define

$$r_f(A) = \min\{\ |A|, \ \sum_i f(H_i) + |A - \bigcup_i H_i|\ \}$$

minimum over all collections $\{H_i\}$ of non-empty, disjoint subsets of $A$.

PROPOSITION A.3.1. *For a real valued, increasing, submodular function, $f$ : $2^S \to \mathbb{R}$, nonnegative on all $A \neq \emptyset$, the following are equivalent:*

1. *the set $A$ is $f$-independent: $|A| \leq f(A)$ and for all nonempty subsets $B$, $|B| \leq f(B)$;*
2. *the set $A$ is $r_f$-independent: for all $B \subseteq A$, $|B| \leq r_f(B)$;*
3. *$r_f(A) = |A|$.*

PROOF. 1.$\Rightarrow$3. Since $f(H_i) \geq |H_i|$ for all $H_i$, for all partitions $\{H_i\}$,

$$\sum_i f(H_i) + |A - \bigcup_i H_i| \geq \sum_i |H_i| + |A - \bigcup_i H_i| = |A|.$$

The minimum for $r_f(A)$ is $|A|$.

3.$\Rightarrow$2. We proceed by contraction. Suppose $r_f(B) \leq |B|$ for some $B$, with the minimum based on the partition $\{H_i\}$. Then

$$r_f(A) \leq \sum_i f(H_i) + |A - \bigcup_i H_i| < |A|$$

2.$\Rightarrow$1. This is obvious since $r_f(B) \leq f(B)$ for each $B \neq \emptyset$.

If $f$ is rational valued, then for $d = \gcd(\ldots, f(A), \ldots)$ the function $g = df$ is integer valued, as is the corresponding rank function:

$$r_{df}(A) = \min\{\ d|A|, \ \sum_i df(H_i) + d|A - \bigcup_i H_i|\ \}.$$

Let $dB$ denote the multiset of $d$ copies of each edge in $B$. If $C \subseteq dE$, let $C_0$ be the ordinary set in which each edge in $C$ is taken with multiplicity 1. We further define $f^d(C) = df(C_0)$ for subsets $C \subseteq dA$. In particular, $f^d(C_0) = f^d(dC_0) = df(C_0)$.

THEOREM A.3.2. *For any rational-valued, nonnegative, non-decreasing submodular function $f$ on $E$, and $d$ the gcd for $\{f(B) \mid B \subseteq E\}$, the following equalities hold for each $A \subseteq E$,*

$$r_{df}(A) = d(r_f(A)) = r_{f^d}(dA).$$

In general $r_f$ gives a hypermatroid. Since $f^d$ is integer valued on $dE$, $r_{f^d}$ is a matroid rank function on $dE$. [**Lor**] calls $r_{df} = d(r_f(A))$ a hypermatroid rank function.

EXAMPLE A.3.3. For body-and-hinge frameworks in three space (§12.2), the rational function is $f(H) = \frac{6}{5}|B(H)| - \frac{6}{5}$ and $df(H) = 5f(H) = 6|B(H)| - 6$.

We interpreted $5|E| \leq 6|B(H)| - 6$ via a matrix which gave 5 equations for each hinge and 6 variables for each body. The count $5|E| \leq 6|B(H)| - 6 = 6(|B(H)| - 1)$, directly implies the fact that a basis in the matroid on $5E$ is formed by 6 edge-disjoint trees in the multigraph with five distinct copies for each edge §11.2.

**A.4. Counts for partitioned vertex sets.** The counting which character-ized independent sets for the generic parallel drawings of hyperplanes in $d$-space indicates a mild generalization of the basic Counts to Matroid Proposition A.1.1. In this setting, we partition the vertices of the hypergraph into different 'types', $H = (V^1, \ldots V^p; E)$, and these classes are assigned different coefficients. (If we worked with subsets $V^i$ of $V$ which was not a partition, this could be easily changed to a partition using $\{V^1 \cap \ldots \cap V^p, \ldots, \overline{V^1} \cap \ldots \cap \overline{V^p}\}$, where $\overline{V^p}$ represents the complement of $V^p$.)

We present one case of a more general *reduction* result of [**Su2**]. This result applies to the counts in the Parallel $d$-Scene Theorem of §8.

PROPOSITION A.4.1. *For a hypergraph $H = (V; E)$ with partitioned vertices $\{V^1, \ldots V^p\}$ and non-negative integers $m_1, \ldots, m_p$, and integer $k$, the following definition gives the independent sets of a matroid $\mathcal{M}_{m_1, \ldots, m_p; k}(H)$ on the edges $E$ of the hypergraph (in particular a complete graph on a finite set of vertices $V$):*

*A set of edges $E'$ is independent if and only if for all non-empty subsets $E_* \subseteq E'$ on the vertices $V_*^1, \ldots, V_*^p$, $|E_*| \leq m_1|V_*^1| + \ldots + m_p|V_*^p| + k$.*

PROOF. To clarify the underlying structure, we verify that

$$f(E) = \sum_{1 \leq i \leq p} m_i |V^i(E)| + k$$

is submodular and then apply the Submodular Theorem A.1.4.

$$f(E_1) + f(E_2) = \sum_{1 \leq i \leq p} m_i |V^i(E_1)| + k + \sum_{1 \leq i \leq p} m_i |V^i(E_2)| + k$$

$$= \sum_{1 \leq i \leq p} m_i |V^i(E_1) \cup V^i(E_2)| + k + \sum_{1 \leq i \leq p} m_i |V^i(E_1) \cap V^i(E_2)| + k$$

$$\geq \sum_{1 \leq i \leq p} m_i |V^i(E_1 \cup E_2)| + k + \sum_{1 \leq i \leq p} m_i |V^i(E_1 \cap E_2)| + k$$

$$= f(E_1 \cup E_2) + f(E_1 \cap E_2).$$

Notice that the last step used $V^i(E_1 \cap E_2) \subseteq V^i(E_1) \cap V^i(E_2)$ and $m_i \geq 0$. Since $f$ is an appropriate submodular function, we have the desired matroid.

We note that in this matroid, the independent sets $A$ are defined, as usual, by the condition $|B| \leq \sum_{1 \leq i \leq p} m_i |V^i(B)| + k$ for all non-empty subsets $B \subseteq A$.

REMARK A.4.2. All of the results of §A.2 regarding matroid unions, coor-dinatizability, and connectivity extend to these matroids. Specifically, for all $k$, the proof of the Coordinatizability Theorem A.2.4 carries over immediately. The connectivity results also carry over – using the minimum $m_i$ for the guaranteed connectivity.

**A.5. Variable counts on edge sets.** The 'counting' properties listed in §6 for mixed directions and distances and for spherical incidences, lengths and angles, point to another generalization of the basic counting matroids. We have a set of integers $k(A)$, indexed by selected subsets of an overall set $E$. These negative integers represent 'minus the degree of freedom' of different sets.

Sugihara [**Su2**] analyzes some related patterns of 'counts' arising from the variables and 'degrees of freedom' in systems of equations. He offers certain conditions which guarantee that these counts generate matroids or hypermatroids. Significant work remains to be carried out in this area.

We present a different pattern which also generates a matroid and applies to our examples. We follow with some specific application to counts on graphs, multigraphs and hypergraphs.

PROPOSITION A.5.1. *Given a set of edges $E$ on vertices $V$, let $\Phi$ be a lattice of subsets of $V$ (including the full set $V$) with intersection as meet and union as join, and a submodular, integer valued function $k : \Phi \to \mathbb{Z}$. Define $k(B) = \min\{k(W) \mid V(B) \subseteq W \in \Phi\}$. Then the function: $f(B) = m|V(B)| + k(B)$ is submodular.*

PROOF. Let $W_B$ be the subset generating the minimum for $k(B)$.

$$
\begin{aligned}
f(B)+f(C) &= m|V(B)| + k(B) + m|V(C)| + k(C) \\
&= m(|V(B)| + |V(C)|) + k(W_B) + k(W_C) \\
&\geq m(|V(B) \cup V(C)| + |V(B) \cap V(C)|) + k(W_B \cup W_C) + k(W_B \cap W_C) \\
&\geq m|V(B \cup C)| + k(B \cup C) + m|V(B \cap C)| + k(B \cap C) \\
&= f(B \cup C) + f(B \cap C).
\end{aligned}
$$

REMARK A.5.2. It is natural to consider that case where the constant $m$ also varies with the lattice $\Phi$, in a submodular way. To keep the submodular function non-decreasing over reasonable sets, we would need $m(W)$ to be non-decreasing. In addition, to guarantee that the overall function is submodular, the proof also requires $m(W_B \cup W_C) \leq m(W_B), m(W_C)$. The net conclusion is that this proof requires $m(W)$ to be a constant. Sugihara [**Su2**] considers alternate submodular functions not directly defined by counts which do vary over a lattice.

EXAMPLE A.5.3. For the matroid on directions and lengths in §6.2 and [**SW**], we employ the simple lattice on the full set of multiple edges: $D \cup E$, the two designated sets of all edges of the graph $D$ and $E$, and the empty set. With $k(D \cup E) = -2$ and $k(D) = -3, k(E) = -3$, and $k(\emptyset) = -4$, we have: $k(D)+k(E) = 6 = k(D \cup E) + k(D \cap E)$.

For frameworks in 3-space, the true degree of freedom is $k(\{v\}) = -3$ for singletons, $k(\{v_1, v_2\}) = -5$ on all pairs and $k(B) = -6$ on all subsets with $|B| \geq 3$. Unfortunately, with two larger sets $B, C$ intersecting on a pair:

$$
k(B) + k(C) = -6 - 6 < -6 - 5 = k(B \cup C) + k(B \cap C).
$$

The appropriate degrees of freedom do not generate a matroid.

EXAMPLE A.5.4. One of the basic difficulties in characterizing matroids such as the simplicial homology matroid by 'counts' is our inability to give a simple formula for $k(B)$ for arbitrary simplicial complexes. While we have estimates such as $k(B) = -|E| + |V| - 1$ for sets of triangles, this is not correct for complexes for which the edges are not 'full enough' on the vertices (e.g. are not a connected graph). In fact, this estimate may be either too high or too low! Working out the rank carefully requires an understanding of each of the lower homologies of the complex.

This same problem arises, often in more complicated form, for all of the matroids and counts of Part III. To understand these estimates and the bases of these matroids one must understand the sequence of matroids corresponding to all the lower homologies.

With a correct calculation of the degrees of freedom, it is unlikely that the true degrees of freedom $(-k(B))$ will be submodular on arbitrary subsets. The combinatorics of these matroids lies beyond simple counting.

REMARK A.5.5. Consider a general set of counting conditions as described in this Appendix and set of 'edges' $E$ to be tested for independence. The test appears to be exponential: "for all nonempty subsets $A \subseteq E$". Sugihara and Imai [**Su2,Im**] have developed general polynomial algorithms, typically $O(|E|^2)$, for all of these counting conditions as well as other more general (non-matroidal and non-hypermatroidal) counts. For the special case of graphs, with the counts $m|V| + k$, $-2m < k \leq -m$, there are also specific matroidal algorithms for detecting the appropriate tree coverings [**Cr5,Ha**]. These algorithms also appear to be $O(|E|^2)$.

## References

[Al]      P. Alfeld, *A case study of multivariate piecewise polynomials*, Geometric Modeling: Algorithms and New Trends, SIAM Publications, 1987, pp. 149–160.

[ASW]     P. Alfeld, L. Schumaker and W. Whiteley, *The generic dimension of the space of $C^1$ splines of degree $d \geq 8$ on tetrahedral decompositions*, SIAM J. Numer. Anal. **30** (1993), 889–920.

[AR]      L. Asimow and B. Roth, *Rigidity of graphs II*, J. Math. Anal. Appl. **68** (1979), 171–190.

[Bi]      L. Billera, *Homology of smooth splines: generic triangulations and a conjecture of Strang*, Trans. Amer. Math. Soc. **310** (1988), 325–340.

[Bj]      A. Bjorner, *Homology and shellibility of matroids and geometric lattices*, Matroid Applications, Encyclopedia of Mathematics and its Applications, vol. 40, Cambridge University Press, Cambridge England, 1993, pp. 229–283.

[BR]      E. Bolker and B. Roth, *When is a bipartite graph rigid?*, Pacific J. Math. **90** (1980), 22–37.

[Br]      T. Brylawski, *Coordinatizing the Dilworth truncation*, Matroid Theory (Szeged 1982), North Holland, New York, 1985, pp. 61–95.

[Ca]      A. Cauchy, *Sur les polygons et les polèdres*, Oeuvres Complètes d'Augustin Cauchy, 2è Série Tom, vol. 1, 1905, pp. 26–38.

[ChW]     C. K. Chui and R. H. Wang, *On smooth multivariate spline functions*, Math. Comp. **41** (1983), 131–142.

[Co1]     R. Connelly, *A flexible sphere.*, Math. Intelligencer **I** (1982), 130–131.

[Co2]     ———, *Basic Concepts of Rigidity*, The Geometry of Rigid Frameworks, H. Crapo and W. Whiteley (ed.) (to appear).

[CoW]     R. Connelly and W. Whiteley, *Second-order rigidity and pre-stress stability for tensegrity frameworks*, SIAM J. Discrete Mathematics (to appear).

[CL]      R. Cordovil and B. Linstrom, *Simplicial Matroids*, Combinatorial Geometries, Cambridge University Press, Cambridge, England, 1987, pp. 98–113.

[Cr1]     H. Crapo, *The combinatorial theory of structures*, Matroid Theory (Szeged 1982), North-Holland, New York, 1985, pp. 107–213.

[Cr2]     ———, *Orthogonality*, Theory of Matroids, Encyclopedia of Mathematics Vol. 26, Cambridge University Press, Cambridge, England, 1986, pp. 76–96.

[Cr3] ———, *Applications of geometric homology*, Geometry and Robotics: proceedings of the workshop, Toulouse , May 26-28, 1988,, Lecture Notes in Computer Science #391, Springer-Verlag, 1990, pp. 213–224.

[Cr4] ———, *Invariant theoretic methods in scene analysis and structural mechanics*, J. Symbolic Computation **11** (1991), 523–548.

[Cr5] ———, *On the generic rigidity of structures in the plane*, Advances in Applied Math (to appear).

[CR1] H. Crapo and G-C. Rota, *Combinatorial Geometry*, MIT Press, Cambridge, Mass., 1970.

[CR2] ———, *The resolving bracket*, Invariant Methods in Discrete and Computational Geometry, Neil White (ed.), Kluwer Academic Publisher, 1995, pp. 197–222.

[CRy] H. Crapo and J. Ryan, *Spatial relizations of linear scenes*, Structural Topology **13** (1986), 33–68.

[CrW1] H. Crapo and W. Whiteley, *Statics of frameworks and motions of panel structures: a projective geometric introduction*, Structural Topology **6** (1982), 42–82.

[CrW2] ———, *Plane stresses and projected polyhedra*, Structural Topology **20** (1993), 55–78.

[CrW3] ———, *Spaces of stresses, projections and parallel drawings for spherical polyhedra*, Contributions to Algebra and Geometry **35** (1994), 259–281.

[CrW4] ———, *3-stresses in 3-space and projections of 4-polytopes: reciprocals, liftings and parallel configurations*, Preprint, Department of Mathematics and Statistics, York University, North York, Ontario (1994).

[CrW5] H. Crapo and W. Whiteley (eds.), *The Geometry of Rigid Structures*, (Draft chapters, Department of Mathematics and Statistics, York University, North York Ont.) (to appear).

[DRS] P. Doubilet, G-C. Rota and J. Stein, *On the foundations of combinatorial theory IX: combinatorial methods in invariant theory*, Stud. Appl. Math. **57** (1974), 185–216.

[Ed] J. Edmonds, *Submodular functions, matroids, and certain polyhedra*, Proceedings of Calgary International Conference on Combinatorial Structures and Their Applications, Gordon Breach, New York, 1970, pp. 69–87.

[ER] J. Edmonds and G-C. Rota, *Submodular set functions*, Abstract of the Waterloo Combinatorics Conference, University of Waterloo, Waterloo Ont., 1966.

[Fo] A. Fogelsanger, *The generic rigidity of minimal cycles*, Ph.D. Thesis, Department of Mathematics, Cornell University (1988).

[Fr1] D. Franzblau, *Combinatorial algorithm for a lower bound on frame rigidity*, SIAM J. Disc. Math. **8** (1995), 338–400.

[Fr2] D. Franzblau, *Computing degrees of freedom of a 'molecular' frame: when is greediness sufficient?*, preprint, DIMACS, Rutgers University, (1995).

[Gl] H. Glück, *Almost all simply connected surfaces are rigid*, Geometric Topology, Lecture Notes in Math No. 438, Springer-Verlag, New York, 1975, pp. 225–239.

[GSS] J. Graver, B. Servatius and H. Servatius, *Combinatorial Rigidity*, Graduate Studies in Mathematics, AMS, Providence RI, 1993.

[Ha] R. Haas, *Characterizing the arboricity of trees*, Preprint, Smith College, Northampton, Mass. (1995).

[Hen] L. Hennebeg, *Die Graphische Statik der starren Systeme*, (Johnson Reprint), 1911.

[Im] H. Imai, *On combinatorial structures of line drawings of polyhedra*, Disc. Applied Math. **10** (1985), 79–92.

[Ka1] G. Kalai, *Rigidity and the lower bound theorem*, Invent. Math. **88** (1987), 125–151.

[Ka2] ———, *Symmetric matroids*, J. Comb. Theory B **50** (1990), 54–64.

[Kl] F. Klein, *Elementary Mathematics from an Advanced Standpoint: Geometry*, Dover reprint, 1948.

[Ku] J. Kung, *The geometric approach to matroid theory*, Gian Carlo Rota on Combinatorics: Introductory Papers and Commentaries, Birkhaüser, Boston, 1995, pp. 604–622.

[La] G. Laman, *On graphs and rigidity of plane skeletal structures*, J. Engrg. Math. **4** (1970), 331–340.

[Lee1] C. Lee, *P.L.-spheres, convex polytopes and stress*, preprint, Department of Mathematics, University of Kentucky (1993).

[Lee2] ———, *Generalized stress and motions*, Polytopes: Abstract, Convex and Computational, Kluwer Academic Publishers, Dordrecht, 1994, pp. 249–271.

[Lor]    M. Lorea, *On matroidal families*, Discrete Math. **28** (1979), 103–106.

[Lov]    L. Lovasz, *Flats in matroids and geometric graphs*, Proceedings of Sixth British Combinatorial Conference, Academic Press, London, 1977, pp. 45–86.

[LY]     L. Lovasz and Y. Yemini, *On generic rigidity in the plane*, SIAM J. Alg. Disc. Methods **3** (1991), 91–98.

[Max]    J.C. Maxwell, *On reciprocal figures and diagrams of forces*, Phil. Mag. Ser. 4 **27** (1864), 250–261.

[Mc]     P. McMullen, *On simple polytopes*, Invent. Math. **113** (1993), 419–444.

[Mu]     J. E. Munkres, *Elements of Algebraic Topology*, Addison-Wesley, Reading, Mass., 1984.

[NW]     G. Nicoletti and N. White, *Axiom Systems*, Theory of Matroids, Encyclopedia of Mathematics Vol. 26, Cambridge University Press, Cambridge, England, 1986, pp. 29–44.

[Ow]     J. Owen, *Algebraic solutions for geometry from dimensional constraints*, Symposium on Solid Modeling, Foundations and CAD/CAM Applications, ACM Press, 1991.

[PP]     J.S. Pym and H. Perfect, *Submodular fundtions and independence structures*, J. Math. Analysis Appl. **30** (1970), 1–31.

[Re1]    A. Recski, *A network approach to the rigidity of skeletal structures. Part 1. Modeling and interconnections*, Discrete Appl. Math. **7** (1984), 313–324.

[Re2]    ———, *A network approach to the rigidity of skeletal structures. Part 2. Laman's Theorem and topological formulae*, Discrete Appl. Math. **8** (1988), 63–68.

[Re3]    ———, *A network approach to the rigidity of skeletal structures. Part 3. Electric model of planar frameworks*, Discrete Appl. Math. **9** (1988), 59–71.

[Re4]    ———, *Matroid Theory and its Applications*, Springer-Verlag, Berlin, 1989.

[Ri]     D-J. Ripmeester, *Dimension of Spline Spaces*, Ph.D. Thesis, Universiteit van Amsterdam, (1995).

[RW]     B. Roth and W. Whiteley, *Tensegrity frameworks*, Trans. Amer. Math. Soc. **265** (1981), 419–446.

[SR]     J.G. Semple and L. Roth, *Introduction to Algebraic Geometry*, Oxford University Press, Oxford, 1985.

[SW]     B. Servatius and W. Whiteley, *Constraining Plane Configurations in CAD: combinatorics of directions and lengths*, Preprint, York University, North York, Ontario (1995).

[Sh]     G. Shephard, *Decomposibility of polytopes and polyhedra*, Mathematika **10** (1963), 89–95.

[St1]    R. Stanley, *The number of faces of a simplicial convex polytope*, Advances in Math **35** (1980), 236–238.

[St2]    ———, *Combinatorics and Commutative Algebra*, Progress in Mathematics Vol. 41, Birkhäuser, Boston, 1983.

[Su1]    K. Sugihara, *A unifying approach to descriptive geometry and mechanism*, Discrete Applied Mathematics **5** (1983), 313–328.

[Su2]    ———, *Detection of structural inconsistency in systems of equations with degrees of freedom and its applications*, Discrete Applied Mathematics **10** (1985), 297–312.

[Su3]    ———, *Machine Interpretation of Line Drawings*, MIT Press, Cambridge Mass, 1986.

[Ta1]    T-S. Tay, *Rigidity problems in bar and joint frameworks*, Ph.D. Thesis, Department of Pure Mathematics, University of Waterloo (1980).

[Ta2]    ———, *Rigidity of multigraphs I: linking rigid bodies in n-space*, J. Comb. Theory Ser. B **26** (1984), 95–112.

[Ta3]    ———, *Rigidity of multigraphs II*, Graph Theory Singapore, Springer Lecture Notes in Math, vol. 1073, 1984.

[Ta4]    ———, *On generically dependent bar and joint frameworks in space*, Structural Topology **20** (1995), 27–48.

[Ta5]    ———, *A new proof of Laman's Theorem*, Graphs and Combinatorics **9** (1993), 365–370.

[TWW1]   T-S. Tay, N. White and W. Whiteley, *Skeletal rigidity of simplicial complexes, I*, Eur. J. Combin. **16** (1995), 381–403.

[TWW2]   ———, *Skeletal rigidity of simplicial complexes, II*, Eur. J. Combin. **16** (1995), 503–523.

[TWW3]   ———, *Homology of skeletal rigidity*, preprint (1995).

[TW1]    T-S. Tay and W. Whiteley, *Recent advances in generic rigidity of structures*, Structural Topology **9** (1985), 31–38.

[TW2]     _____, *Generating isostatic frameworks*, Structural Topology **11** (1985), 21–69.

[Th]      N. J. Thurston, *On rigidity of graphs*, B.A. Thesis, Reed College (1991).

[We]      D. Welsh, *Matroid Theory*, London Math. Society Monographs, vol. 8, Academic Press, London, England, 1976.

[Wht1]    N. White, *Theory of Matroids*, Encyclopedia of Mathematics Vol. 26, Cambridge University Press, Cambridge, England, 1986.

[Wht2]    _____, *Combinatorial Geometries*, Encyclopedia of Mathematics Vol. 29, Cambridge University Press, Cambridge, England, 1987.

[Wht3]    _____, *Matroid Appplications*, Encyclopedia of Mathematics Vol. 40, Cambridge University Press, Cambridge, England, 1992.

[Wht4]    _____, *Tutorial on Grassmann-Cayley Algebra*, Invariant Methods in Discrete and Computational Geometry, Kluwer, 1995.

[WW1]     N. White and W. Whiteley, *The algebraic geometry of stresses in frameworks*, SIAM J. Algebraic Discrete Methods **4** (1983), 481–511.

[WW2]     _____, *A class of matroids defined on graphs and hypergraphs by counting properties*, Unpublished preprint, 1983.

[WW3]     _____, *The algebraic geometry of bar and body frameworks.*, SIAM J. Algebraic Discrete Methods **8** (1987), 1–32.

[Wh1]     W. Whiteley, *Motions and stresses of projected polyhedra*, Structural Topology **7** (1982), 13–38.

[Wh2]     _____, *Cones, infinity and one-story buildings*, Structural Topology **8** (1983), 53–70.

[Wh3]     _____, *Infinitesimal rigidity of a bipartite framework*, Pacific J. Math. **110** (1984), 233–255.

[Wh4]     _____, *Infinitesimally rigid polyhedra I: statics of frameworks frameworks*, Trans. Amer. Math. Soc. **285** (1984), 431–461.

[Wh5]     _____, *Parallel redrawing of configurations in 3-space*, preprint, Department of Mathematics and Statistics, York University, North York, Ontario (1987).

[Wh6]     _____, *Infinitesimally rigid polyhedra II: modified spherical frameworks*, Trans. Amer. Math. Soc. **306** (1988), 115–139.

[Wh7]     _____, *Matroid unions and rigidity*, SIAM J. Discrete Math. **1** (1988), 237–255.

[Wh8]     _____, *A matroid on hypergraphs with applications to scene analysis and geometry*, Discrete Comput. Geometry **4** (1989), 75–95.

[Wh9]     _____, *Vertex splitting in isostatic frameworks*, Structural Topology **16** (1990), 23–30.

[Wh10]    _____, *Combinatorics of bivariate splines*, Applied Geometry and Discrete Mathematics – the Victor Klee Festschrift, DIMACS, vol. 4, AMS, 1991, pp. 587–608.

[Wh11]    _____, *Matroids and rigidity*, Matroid Applications, Encyclopedia of Mathematics and its Applications, vol. 40, Cambridge University Press, Cambridge England, 1993, pp. 1–53.

[Wh12]    _____, *Constraining plane configurations in CAD: geometry of directions and lengths*, Preprint, York University, North York, Ontario (1995).

[Wh13]    _____, *Representing plane configurations*, Learning and Geometry, D. Kueker and C. Smith (eds), Progess in Computer Science and Logic Vol 14, Birkaüser, Boston, 1996.

[Wh14]    _____, *Rigidity and scene analysis*, Handbook of Discrete and Computational Geometry, J. Goodman and J. O'Rourke (eds) Chapter 51, CRC Press, to appear.

[Wh15]    _____, *An analogy in geometric homology: rigidity and cofactors on geometric graphs*, Preprint, York University, North York, Ontario (1996).

DEPARTMENT OF MATHEMATICS AND STATISTICS, YORK UNIVERSITY, 4700 KEELE STREET, NORTH YORK, ONTARIO M3J1P3

*E-mail address:* `whiteley@mathstat.yorku.ca`

Contemporary Mathematics
Volume **197**, 1996

# Oriented Matroid Pairs, Theory and an Electric Application

Seth Chaiken

ABSTRACT. The property that a pair of oriented matroids $\mathcal{M}_L^\perp, \mathcal{M}_R$ on $E$ have free union and no common (non-zero) covector generalizes oriented matroid duality. This property characterizes when certain systems of equations whose only nonlinearities occur as real monotone bijections have a unique solution for all values of additive parameters. Instances include sign non-singularity of square matrices and generalizations of positive definiteness given by Fiedler and Pták. Other instances of this property include various kinds of characterizations of when an electric network problem is well-posed. Such characterizations have been given in terms of matrix pairs by Sandberg and Willson and in terms of electrical network graphs by Duffin, Minty, Hasler and Neirnyck, and by Nishi and Chua.

Cases of the general common covector problem are classified. Natural matroid rank conditions are sufficient for a common covector to exist. An algorithm to construct a common covector by composing certain fundamental cocircuits is given. If $\mathcal{M}_L$ and $\mathcal{M}_R$ have two common bases with opposite relative orientation (chirotope value) then $\mathcal{M}_L^\perp, \mathcal{M}_R$ have a common covector. This abstracts the realizable case of a determinant expansion having terms of opposite sign. An open problem is whether $\mathcal{M}_L^\perp, \mathcal{M}_R$ having a common covector implies that $\mathcal{M}_L$ and $\mathcal{M}_R$ have two common bases with opposite relative orientation, when the latter have one common basis and are not realizable. A weaker conjecture is $\mathcal{M}_L^\perp, \mathcal{M}_R$ have a common covector if and only if $\mathcal{M}_L^\perp, \mathcal{M}_R$ have a common vector, when $\mathcal{M}_L$ and $\mathcal{M}_R$ have a common basis.

The computational complexity of the problem "Do $\mathcal{M}_L^\perp, \mathcal{M}_R$ have a common covector?" when $\mathcal{M}_L$ and $\mathcal{M}_R$ have a common basis is at least as high as telling if a square matrix is not sign solvable or if a digraph has an even directed circuit. When $\text{rank}(\mathcal{M}_L^\perp) + \text{rank}(\mathcal{M}_R) < |E|$ the problem is strongly NP-complete and it generalizes non L-matrix sign pattern detection.

## Introduction

The theory begins with the definition of an elementary property of a pair of real linear subspaces, say the row spaces of two real matrices. The signature function $\sigma : \mathbf{R}^E \to \{0, +, -\}^E$ maps each real tuple into the pattern of its signs.

1991 *Mathematics Subject Classification.* Primary 52B40, 05B35; Secondary 94C05, 15A06.
*Key words and phrases.* oriented matroids, electrical circuits, nonlinear networks.
This research was mostly performed during a Sabbatical from the State University of New York at Albany.

DEFINITION 0.1. Two linear subspaces $L_1$ and $L_2$ of $\mathbf{R}^E$ for finite set $E$ have a common covector if there exist $x \in L_1$ and $y \in L_2$ for which $\sigma(x) = \sigma(y) \neq 0$.

This definition of common covectors for realized oriented matroid pairs naturally generalizes. The covector set of an oriented matroid is denoted by $\mathcal{L}$. The dual of an oriented matroid $\mathcal{M}$ is denoted by $\mathcal{M}^\perp$. See [1] for an exposition of oriented matroids that emphasizes how the matroid dual abstracts the orthogonal complement of a real linear space.

DEFINITION 0.2. A pair of oriented matroids $\mathcal{M}_L^\perp, \mathcal{M}_R$ on the same ground set $E$ have a common covector $X$ if $X \in \mathcal{L}(\mathcal{M}_L^\perp) \cap \mathcal{L}(\mathcal{M}_R)$ and $X \neq 0$.

Orthogonal pairs of subspaces, and, more generally, dual pairs of oriented matroids, never have common covectors.

**The Electric Network Model.** This section distills material from [11, 12, 18, 21, 26, 29, 30, 34]. A finite, lumped analog DC electric network model is a set of devices and a network graph which represents their interconnection. The graph nodes model maximally connected electrically conducting regions typically comprised of physically connected metal wires. Some graph edges correspond to idealized two terminal electrical devices such as voltage sources (batteries), resistors, diodes, etc. Each terminal is identified with a node. Every two terminal device will be identified with its edge. Other devices such as transistors, ideal operational amplifiers, and other kinds of controlled sources have three or more terminals. For each device, the model has some edges between some pairs of that device's terminals. See [12, Ch. 13].

The usual schematic diagram of such a network uses solid lines for the wires, dots for wire junctions and standard symbols for the devices. See parts (a-c) of Figure 1 and Figure 4 for examples. The edges for devices with three or more terminals are usually omitted. One node is often distinguished as the "ground." The ground node is understood to be connected by wires between multiple ground symbols in addition to the explicit wire lines.

Let $E$ be the set of network graph edges. The matroids that motivate our subject all have ground sets that are either subsets of $E$ or subsets of disjoint unions of copies of $E$. Many are graphic or cographic.

The electric network model determines a set of real equations on $2|E|$ variables: Variable $v_e$ for $e \in E$ represents the potential difference or *voltage* between the endpoints of $e$, and $i_e$ represents the rate of charge flow or *current* through edge $e$. Flow is conserved at nodes. The equations fall into two classes: the structural laws (Kirchhoff's laws) and the constitutive laws (the device characteristics). Kirchhoff's voltage law (KVL) says $v_E = (v_e, e \in E)$ is in the cocycle space of the network graph. Kirchhoff's current law (KCL) says $(i_e, e \in E)$ belongs to the cycle space. See [21, 29, 30]. The fact that these spaces are orthogonal is known in the electric circuit theory literature as Tellegen's theorem.

The constitutive law for a voltage source edge $e$ (i.e., an ideal battery) is $v_e$ equals a constant. For current source edge $e$, $i_e$ equals a constant. These constants are considered independent "input signals" to the system. They will generally be parameters. Notice that when, say, $e$ is a voltage source, the current $i_e$ is an unknown variable.

The constitutive law for a positive, linear resistor edge $e$ is called Ohm's law: $v_e = r_e i_e$, where constant $r_e > 0$ is called the resistance (of $e$). The reciprocal

$g_e = r_e^{-1}$ is called the conductance. For a diode the law is $i_e = D(v_e) - D(0)$ where $D : \mathbf{R} \to \mathbf{R}^+$ is exponential. For a more realistic model with reverse breakdown, this current function would be onto $\mathbf{R}$ but still monotonic. An ideal operational amplifier device has 4 terminals and two disjoint edges, say $e$ and $f$. The output edge $f$ is incident to the ground. The constitutive law is $v_e = 0$ and $i_e = 0$. This law is the limit, as $A$ goes to infinity and $v_f$ is bounded, of the more realistic (DC) law $i_e = 0$ and $v_f = Av_e$. The constant $A$ here is called the open loop gain, which is typically at least $10^5$ and is over $10^7$ in some modern commercial units [23]. Either model is a good approximation when the non-ideal operational amplifier has sufficiently large gain, the system is stable (as a dynamic system stabilized by feedback), and the voltages and currents of the amplifier are within the ranges for "active operation." See [12, Ch. 9 and 11].

DEFINITION 0.3. The network model is called *well-posed* when for all real values for the input signal parameters, the equations (in the voltage and current variables) have a unique solution. Otherwise it is *ill-posed*.

The linear or non-linear constitutive laws for many devices other than the (constant) sources are generally known only approximately. The central motivating question for this paper is what combinatorial properties of the network graph can distinguish three possibilities: (1) the network model is well-posed for every choice of continuous, monotone increasing constitutive law functions; (2) the model is well-posed for some and ill-posed for other choices of such constitutive laws; (3) the model is ill-posed for all such choices. In this paper, we will relate the answer to this question given by [18, 19, 20, 12, Ch. 31] and work cited below to results about the common covector problem for oriented matroid pairs. For example, the uniqueness proofs given when the constitutive laws for two terminal devices are monotone cite Tellegen's theorem. However, they only use the its consequence that the network graph's cycle and cocycle spaces over $\mathbf{R}^E$ have no common covector.

We analyze the voltage divider in part (a) of Figure 1 for an example. Let us eliminate the current and voltage variables for the voltage source $V_0$. Kirchhoff's laws constrain the rest of the voltages $v = (v_e, v_f)$ and currents $i = (i_e, i_f)$ to affine lines in $\mathbf{R}^2$. The equations below show representative homogeneous coordinates in $\mathbf{R}^3$ of the points on these lines as $s$ and $t$ range over $\mathbf{R}$. The corresponding $\mathbf{R}^2$ coordinates $v$ and $i$ are also shown. The cocycle and cycles spaces of the 2 edge circuit graph are denoted by $\mathcal{C}^\perp$ and $\mathcal{C}$ respectively. This graph is the contraction by edge $V_0$ of the original network graph.

$$[s, 1] \begin{array}{c} \phantom{[s,1]} \\ \hline \end{array} \begin{array}{cc} e & f \\ \hline 0 & -1 & 1 \\ 1 & V_0 & 0 \\ \hline \end{array} = [1, V_0 - s, s] \qquad [t, 1] \begin{array}{cc} e & f \\ \hline 0 & 1 & 1 \\ 1 & 0 & 0 \\ \hline \end{array} = [1, t, t]$$

$$\{v = (V_0 - s, s) \ : \ s \in \mathbf{R}\} \qquad \{i = (t, t) \ : \ t \in \mathbf{R}\} = \text{currents}$$
$$= \text{voltages } v \text{ feasible under KVL.} \qquad \text{(flows) } i \text{ feasible under KCL.}$$
$$v \in v^0 + \mathcal{C}^\perp \qquad\qquad i \in i^0 + \mathcal{C}$$

Ohm's law for this problem is

$$v = iR = i \begin{pmatrix} r_e & 0 \\ 0 & r_f \end{pmatrix}.$$

To prove that a solution is unique, let $\delta v = v - v'$ and $\delta i = i - i'$ for two solutions $(v; i)$, $(v'; i')$. Then $\delta v \in \mathcal{C}$, $\delta i \in \mathcal{C}^\perp$ and $\delta v = i'R - iR$. If $\delta v$ and $\delta i$ are not

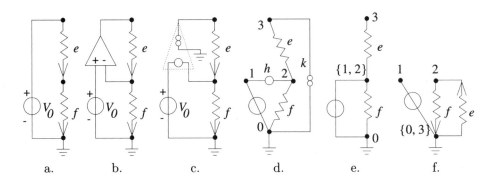

FIGURE 1. Examples of electrical network models with unique solutions because the oriented matroids coding feasible current and voltage sign patterns have no common covector. Edges $V_0$ are voltage sources with value $V_0$. Part (a) is a classical voltage divider. Part (b) is the schematic of a feedback system with an ideal operational amplifier. Part (c) shows that device with its edges. The nullator edge $h = (1, 2)$ and the norator edge $k = (0, 3)$ are ideal two-terminal devices that signify the constitutive law for the amplifier. Part (d) is the network graph drawn as in graph theory books. Suppose the amplifier's constitutive laws are used to eliminate $v_n$ and $i_n$ for both $n = (1, 2)$ and $n = (0, 3)$. The remaining voltages are constrained by KVL to the cocycle space $\mathcal{C}_V^{\perp}$ of the "voltage graph" shown in part (e). The remaining currents are constrained to the cycle space $\mathcal{C}_I$ of the "current graph" of part (f). [11, 26]

both zero, then $\sigma(\delta v) \neq \sigma(\delta i)$ since $\mathcal{C}$ and $\mathcal{C}^{\perp}$ have no common covector. However $\sigma(\delta v) = \sigma(\delta i)$ since the resistance values (entries in diagonal matrix $R$) are positive. The same argument would apply for nonlinear resistance functions $v_e = r_e(i_e)$ that are strictly monotone increasing. The oriented matroids with no common covector are realized by matrices $M_L^{\perp} = [-1\ 1]$ (whose row space is $\mathcal{C}^{\perp}$) and $M_R = [1\ 1]$ (whose row space is $\mathcal{C}$.)

A network model as in part (b) of Figure 1 with an ideal operational amplifier can be expressed by a network model as in parts (c-d) of Figure 1 with two kinds of special device edges in addition to resistor, voltage sources and current sources: *nullators* and *norators*. Kirchhoff's laws constrain the voltage drops and currents to the cocycle and cycle spaces of this graph as before. However, a nullator edge $h$ represents the further constraint that its current $i_h$ is 0 and its voltage $v_e$ is 0. Edge $k$ is called a norator to indicate that it conducts current but is not subject to any constitutive law constraint directly.

Let us analyze the network given by part (b) and equivalently by part (c) of Figure 1 as we did for part (a). This time, we eliminate the variables $v_h, i_h, v_k$ and $i_k$ for the nullator and norator in addition to the voltage source.

Here are the equations:

$$[s,1]\begin{array}{c}\phantom{x}\;e\;\;\;f\\\begin{array}{|ccc|}\hline 0 & 1 & 0\\ 1 & 0 & V_0\\\hline\end{array}\end{array}=[1,s,V_0] \qquad [t,1]\begin{array}{c}\phantom{x}\;e\;\;\;f\\\begin{array}{|ccc|}\hline 0 & 1 & 1\\ 1 & 0 & 0\\\hline\end{array}\end{array}=[1,t,t]$$

$\{v=(s,V_0)\ :\ s\in\mathbf{R}\}=$ voltages $\qquad$ $\{i=(t,t)\ :\ t\in\mathbf{R}\}=$ currents
$v$ feasible under KVL. $\qquad\qquad\qquad$ (flows) $i$ feasible under KCL.

$$v\in v^0+\mathcal{C}_V^\perp \qquad\qquad\qquad i\in i^0+\mathcal{C}_I$$

Kirchhoff's voltage law now constrains the remaining voltages $v=(v_e,v_f)$ to (Constant)$v^0+\mathcal{C}_V^\perp$, where $\mathcal{C}_V^\perp$ is the cocycle space of the *voltage graph* (part (e) of Figure 1). The KCL constraint on $i=(i_e,i_f)$ uses the cycle space $\mathcal{C}_I$ of a *different* graph (part (f) of Figure 1) called the *current graph*.

A solution for the model in parts (b-c) of Figure 1 is unique because the *non-orthogonal* row spaces $\mathcal{C}_V^\perp$ and $\mathcal{C}_I$ of $M_L^\perp=[1\ 0]$ and $M_R=[1\ 1]$ respectively do not have a common covector.

Let $\mathcal{G}$ be a network graph with nullators $P$ and norators $Q$. After eliminating both variables for each edge in $P\cup U$, the voltages feasible under KVL are the cocycles $\mathcal{C}_V^\perp$ of the voltage graph $\mathcal{G}/P\backslash Q$. The feasible currents are the cycles $\mathcal{C}_I$ of the current graph $\mathcal{G}/Q\backslash P$. Such distinct graphs to represent KVL and KCL constraints for nullator and norator models as well as models with controlled sources are described in [10, 26, 11, 18, 19, 34]; see also [6]. Realistic (DC) models for multiterminal devices such as transistors can be expressed either by generally nonlinear relations among voltages and currents of the device's edges (called *ports*) or by a network of 2-terminal devices whose edges either have (generally nonlinear) resistance or conductance functions, or are nullators or norators. Thus a multiterminal device would be replaced by a subnetwork composed only of 2-terminal devices (which are called 1-ports). Nullators and norators generalize to matroid pairs $\mathcal{M}_L,\mathcal{M}_R$:

- When $e$ is a nullator the reduction by $e$ is $(\mathcal{M}_L/e),(\mathcal{M}_R\backslash e)$.
- When $e$ is a norator the reduction by $e$ is $(\mathcal{M}_L\backslash e),(\mathcal{M}_R/e)$.

**Related Work and Summary.** The no common covector condition for uniqueness also can be used to establish the *existence* of solutions when rank conditions are satisfied and the nonlinear real functions are onto as well as monotone. This theme appears in the work of Sandberg and Willson [36] (see also the survey [42]). We will relate this theory, expressed in terms of $\mathcal{W}_0$ pairs of square matrices [40, 41], to oriented matroids in section 4. However, similar results developed with graph theory appear in [32] and in [18, 19, 20]. Many of the arguments given in [18, 19] extend immediately to oriented matroids because they are based on Minty's painting theorem and simple properties of digraphs which together can axiomatize oriented matroids. Earlier work of Duffin [13] and Minty [28] treated only orthogonal subspaces as sources for sign relationships that imply existence and uniqueness. Also see [35].

The role of common bases in telling if an electric network model is well-posed with generic coefficients in linear constitutive laws is apparent in [18, 19] and is treated explicitly in [29, 30, 34]. Common bases used to address solution properties appears in [8]. Common bases and algorithms for cases of the graph theory analysis [32] are used in [27]. See also the literature on symbolic simulation [43, 12,

Ch. 52], and the matrix tree theorem [**6, 8, 7**]. Ported matroid Tutte polynomi-als [**9**] will be extended to oriented matroids and applied to electric problems in a future publication.

Section 1 begins with theorems that show that natural conditions on the ranks of two oriented matroids and their union are sufficient for them to have a common covector. G. Ziegler mentioned [**44**] that such results could be proved using the methods of [**5**]. However, our proofs construct the covector by elementary algo-rithms.

The rank conditions do not apply to those cases of the linear subspace (i.e., realizable oriented matroid) common covector problem that are formulated to dis-tinguish possibilities (1) from (2) among the three possibilities given after defini-tion (0.3). Instead, in these cases, a common covector exists if and only if there are terms of opposite sign in the Laplace expansions of certain determinants. In section 1.1 we prove that the natural generalization of this term sign condition to general oriented matroid chirotopes implies that common covectors exist. We leave as an open problem the converse. A combinatorial proof of the converse might lead to algorithms that search for "substructures" (i.e., minors) in electrical networks and other nonlinear systems that are necessary and sufficient for non-uniqueness in some instances of systems with a given "structure." In the graph of a network that includes transistors, each transistor appears as a triangle with one distinguished edge[1]. For networks with the (quite accurate) Ebers-Moll model used for transis-tors, Nielsen and Willson applied the theory of $\mathcal{W}_0$ pairs of matrices to prove [**31**] that all instances of networks with the same structure (i.e., network graph) have a unique solution if and only if the graph does not have a "feedback structure" graph minor, which is a triangle of parallel edge pairs from exactly two transistors with the two distinguished edges in two distinct sides. (See [**38, 12**, Ch. 31].)

Section 2 classifies instances of the common covector problem and summarizes the results. Properties known only for the realizable case are given in section 3. In particular, the existence of a common covector is equivalent to the existence of a common vector when the rank conditions do not imply either. These properties are applied in section 4 to give an oriented matroid interpretation of the class of $\mathcal{W}_0$ matrix pairs [**41**]: A pair $(A, B)$ of square real matrices is in $\mathcal{W}_0$ if and only if the row spaces of $[A\ B]$ and $[I\ -I]$ have full rank and no common covector. We use this to derive a problem dual to the original problem given by Willson (see Theorem 4.3) where matrix pairs of type $\mathcal{W}_0$ were applied.

Section 5 has some rather pessimistic facts about the computational complexity of the common covector problem. First, when $\text{rank}(\mathcal{M}_L^\perp) + \text{rank}(\mathcal{M}_R) < |E|$, the common covector problem (even in the realizable case) is strongly NP-complete. Second, the case relevant to the given applications (complementary rank and free union) includes the (complement of the) sign non-singularity (SNS) question for square matrices of signs [**3**]. This problem is known to be polynomial time equiv-alent to the even cycle problem for digraphs [**22**]. These problems have been rec-ognized as deep, unsolved combinatorial problems for which it is unknown whether they lie in complexity classes P, NP-complete or in between [**22, 39**].

**Rigidity and Elasticity.** It would be interesting to know electrical analogs of rigidity [**17**] properties, or if some rigidity properties are equivalent to no common covectors. We mention the basic analogies. Stress (a signed scalar for each bar) in

[1]The distinguished edge represents the emitter and collector terminal pair.

a multidimensional bar framework is an analog of edge conductance in an electrical network: the force vector in a bar is analogous to current; joint position is analogous to absolute node potential. The fact that a non-zero stress must be positive in some edges and negative in others is a manifestation of the fact that the (dual pair of) graphic and cographic oriented matroids of the same graph have no common covector. We therefore note that the electric network analysis problem "given the conductances find the voltages" and the problem applicable to rigidity analysis "determine what stresses a given framework can sustain" are opposite problems.

The electrical analog of an elastic "spring" network with some vertices pinned is a network with fixed positive conductances whose only sources are voltage sources all joined at a common node. The elastic analog of parts (b-c) of Figure 1 is easy to visualize: A robot standing on the ground watches node 2 and pulls up on node 3 just enough to align node 2 with the top of a rod that stands $V_0$ meters high.

**Standard Theory and Terminology.** Our use of standard matroid and oriented matroid terminology and results generally follows [**2**]. Matroid union is denoted by $\vee$. The row space of matrix $M$ is denoted by $L(M)$. The sign tuples of members of this space comprise the covectors $\mathcal{L}(M)$ of the oriented matroid $\mathcal{M}(M)$ realized by $M$. The collection of *vectors* of oriented matroid $\mathcal{M}$ is denoted by $\mathcal{V}(\mathcal{M})$. The vectors of realizable $\mathcal{M}(M)$ are the sign tuples of members of the orthogonal complement of $L(M)$.

Section 1 uses the tableau matrix notation to express fundamental cocircuits and conditions for basis exchanges that is developed in Chapter 10 of [**2**]. Our notation differs slightly as we include the current basis elements in the column set of the tableau. A matrix decomposed horizontally into disjoint blocks $A$, $B$, etc. is denoted by $[A \ B \ \cdots]$.

## 1. Common Covector Existence Theorems

The first theorem is used for the others. Its proof contains an algorithm to construct a common covector efficiently by composing covectors with cocircuits.

THEOREM 1.1. *Let $\mathcal{M}_1$ and $\mathcal{M}_2$ be oriented matroids on the ground set $A \ \cup \ Z \ \cup \ S \ \cup \ R$. Assume the covectors $C_0 \in \mathcal{L}(\mathcal{M}_1)$ and $D_0 \in \mathcal{L}(\mathcal{M}_2)$ satisfy the properties:*

1. *$A \neq \emptyset$ and $C_0(a) = D_0(a) \neq 0$ for all $a \in A$,*
2. *$S \cup Z$ is independent in $\mathcal{M}_1$ and $C_0(S \cup Z) = 0$, and*
3. *$R \cup Z$ is independent in $\mathcal{M}_2$ and $D_0(R \cup Z) = 0$.*

*Then $\mathcal{M}_1, \mathcal{M}_2$ have a common (non-zero) covector $C \in \mathcal{L}(\mathcal{M}_1) \cap \mathcal{L}(\mathcal{M}_2)$ that is compatible with both $C_0$ and $D_0$. In other words, $C_0 \preceq C$ and $D_0 \preceq C$.*

PROOF. There exist sets of fundamental cocircuits $\{c_e : e \in S\}$ and $\{d_e : e \in R\}$ and one covector $C_0$ and $D_0$ in each of $\mathcal{M}_1$ and $\mathcal{M}_2$ as described by the two tableaux in Figure 2. Observe $c_e(S \backslash e) = 0$, $d_e(R \backslash e) = 0$, and $c_e(Z) = d_e(Z) = 0$. The assertions marked "//" in the algorithm can be verified by induction.
**Input:** Covector $C_0$ of $\mathcal{M}_1$, a covector $D_0$ of $\mathcal{M}_2$, a cocircuit $c_e$ of $\mathcal{M}_1$ for each $e \in S$, and a cocircuit $d_e$ of $\mathcal{M}_2$ for each $e \in R$ as described.
**Output:** Common covector $C = D$ of $\mathcal{M}_1$ and $\mathcal{M}_2$.

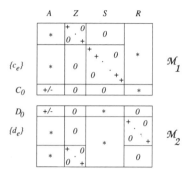

FIGURE 2. The tableau for $\mathcal{M}_1$ shows the cocircuits $c_e$ for $e \in S$, other cocircuits for $e \in Z$, and the covector $C_0$. These cocircuits are fundamental with respect to some basis that extends $Z \cup S$. The algorithm constructs a covector $C$ by starting with $C \leftarrow C_0$ and composing $C \leftarrow C \circ (\pm c_e)$ to make $C(e) = D(e)$ when necessary, while similar operations are applied to $D$ using cocircuits from $\mathcal{M}_2$.

(1)    $C \leftarrow C_0;\ D \leftarrow D_0;$
    Repeat
(2)        For each $e \in S$ such that $D(e) \neq 0$ and $C(e) = 0$
(3)            do $C \leftarrow C \circ (D(e)c_e);$
              $//C(f)$ for $f \in (S \backslash e) \cup A \cup Z$ is unchanged.
              $//C \in \mathcal{L}(\mathcal{M}_1).$
(4)        For each $e \in R$ such that $C(e) \neq 0$ and $D(e) = 0$
(5)            do $D \leftarrow D \circ (C(e)d_e);$
              $//D(f)$ for $f \in (R \backslash e) \cup A \cup Z$ is unchanged.
              $//D \in \mathcal{L}(\mathcal{M}_2).$
(6)    Until $C(S) = D(S)$ & $D(R) = C(R);$

Throughout the execution, whenever $C(e) \neq D(e)$, such $e$ must satisfy either (i) $e \in S$, $D(e) \neq 0$, and $C(e) = 0$, or (ii) $e \in R$, $C(e) \neq 0$, and $D(e) = 0$. Each execution of step (3) or (5) makes $C(e) = D(e) \neq 0$ for one such $e$. The step might cause, for some $f$, one of $C(f)$ or $D(f)$ to change so that $C(f) = D(f)$ is no longer true. However, $C(f) \neq D(f)$ where both $C(f) \neq 0$ and $D(f) \neq 0$ is impossible. A later step will make $C(f) = D(f)$ true again. The common value will then be non-zero so neither $C(f)$ nor $D(f)$ will change again. Therefore the execution must terminate after $|R| + |S|$ or fewer composition steps.  $\square$

The next lemma is a special case of the theorem that follows it.

LEMMA 1.2. *If* $|E| < rank(\mathcal{M}_L^{\perp}) + rank(\mathcal{M}_R)$ *and* $\mathcal{M}_L^{\perp} \vee \mathcal{M}_R$ *is a free matroid, that is,* $E = B_L \cup B_R$ *for some* $B_L \in \mathcal{B}(\mathcal{M}_L^{\perp})$ *and* $B_R \in \mathcal{B}(\mathcal{M}_R)$*, then* $\mathcal{M}_L^{\perp}, \mathcal{M}_R$ *have a common covector. Moreover, every sign tuple* $X$ *over* $B_L \cap B_R$ *with some non-zero entry is the restriction of a common covector.*

PROOF. Since $\text{rank}(\mathcal{M}_L^{\perp}) + \text{rank}(\mathcal{M}_R) > |E|$, every $B_L$ and $B_R$ as above satisfy $B_L \cap B_R \neq \emptyset$. The pair of tableaux for these bases is shown in part (a) of Figure 3. For each $e \in B_L \cap B_R$, $\{c_e\}$ and $\{d_e\}$ are the fundamental cocircuits in $\mathcal{M}_L^{\perp}$, $\mathcal{M}_R$, respectively, of $e$. Given a sign tuple $X \neq 0$, let $C_0$ be an arbitrary composition of

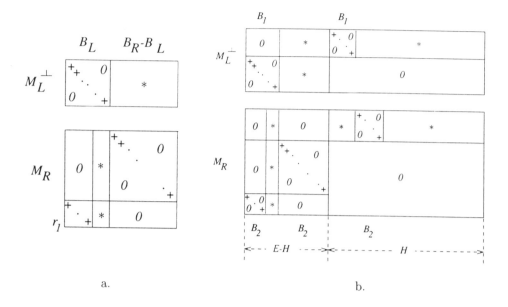

FIGURE 3. Tableau pairs used respectively in the proofs of Lemma 1.2 and Theorem 1.3.

$X(e)c_e$ and let $D_0$ be an arbitrary composition of $X(e)d_e$. Now $C_0$ and $D_0$ satisfy the hypotheses of Theorem 1.1 with $A \cup Z = B_L \cap B_R$, $A \neq \emptyset$, $S = B_L \backslash B_R$ and $R = B_R \backslash B_L$. □

THEOREM 1.3. *If* $\operatorname{rank}(\mathcal{M}_L^\perp \vee \mathcal{M}_R) < \operatorname{rank}(\mathcal{M}_L^\perp) + \operatorname{rank}(\mathcal{M}_R)$, *then* $\mathcal{M}_L^\perp, \mathcal{M}_R$ *have a common covector.*

PROOF. Let $B_1 \in \mathcal{B}(\mathcal{M}_1)$, $B_2 \in \mathcal{B}(\mathcal{M}_2)$ and $H \subseteq E$ realize the extrema in the formula for the rank $r$ of the union matroid $\mathcal{M}_1 \vee \mathcal{M}_2$ below.

$$r = \max_{\substack{B_1' \in \mathcal{B}(\mathcal{M}_1) \\ B_2' \in \mathcal{B}(\mathcal{M}_2)}} |B_1' \cup B_2'| = \min_{H' \subseteq E} (\operatorname{rank}_1(H') + \operatorname{rank}_2(H') + |E \backslash H'|)$$

For these values, the general inequalities

$$|B_1 \cup B_2| = |(B_1 \cup B_2) \cap H| + |(B_1 \cup B_2) \backslash H|$$
$$\leq |B_1 \cap H| + |B_2 \cap H| + |E \backslash H|$$
$$\leq \operatorname{rank}_1(H) + \operatorname{rank}_2(H) + |E \backslash H|$$

become equations and so

$$|B_1 \cap H| = \operatorname{rank}_1(H), \qquad\qquad |B_2 \cap H| = \operatorname{rank}_2(H),$$
$$B_1 \cap B_2 \cap H = \emptyset, \qquad \text{and } |(B_1 \cup B_2) \backslash H| = |E \backslash H|.$$

Hence there are cocircuits described by the tableau pair shown in part (b) of Figure 3. Lemma 1.2 can now be applied to the cocircuits whose support is contained in $E \backslash H$. □

**1.1. An Orientation Condition.** Theorem 1.3 does not apply to the case covered by the next theorem. For realizable oriented matroids, the proof and the proof of its converse (Theorem 3.1) are much easier. Whether the converse of Theorem 1.6 is true for non-realizable oriented matroid pairs is an open problem.

DEFINITION 1.4. The oriented matroids $\mathcal{M}_L$ and $\mathcal{M}_R$ with chirotope functions $\chi_L$ and $\chi_R$ have a pair $B_1$ and $B_2$ of common bases with opposite relative orientations if the ordered sets $B_1$ and $B_2$ satisfy

$$(1.1) \qquad \chi_L(B_1)\chi_R(B_1)\chi_L(B_2)\chi_R(B_2) = -.$$

REMARK 1.5. Matroids $\mathcal{M}_L$ and $\mathcal{M}_R$ have a common basis if and only if $\operatorname{rank}(\mathcal{M}_L) = \operatorname{rank}(M_R)$ and $\mathcal{M}_L^{\perp} \cup \mathcal{M}_R$ is a free matroid on $E$.

THEOREM 1.6. *If $\mathcal{M}_L$ and $\mathcal{M}_R$ have a pair $B_1$ and $B_2$ of common bases with opposite relative orientation, then $\mathcal{M}_L^{\perp}, \mathcal{M}_R$ have a common covector.*

PROOF. Let $B_1$ and $B_2$ satisfy (1.1) with minimum separation $|B_1 \backslash B_2| = |B_2 \backslash B_1|$. Consider the tableau of the fundamental cocircuits in $\mathcal{M}_L^{\perp}$ relative to basis $B_1^c$ of $\mathcal{M}_L^{\perp}$ and the tableau of the fundamental cocircuits of $\mathcal{M}_R$ relative to basis $B_1$.

To conveniently denote submatrices of these tableaux, we assume $E$ is ordered with the subset $B_1^c \cap B_2^c$ coming first, followed by $B_2 \backslash B_1$, $B_1 \backslash B_2$ and finally $B_1 \cap B_2$. Let $P$ be the submatrix of the tableau for $\mathcal{M}_L^{\perp}$ whose rows are indexed by $B_2 \backslash B_1$ and whose columns are indexed by $B_1 \backslash B_2$. When this tableau is restricted to rows $B_2 \backslash B_1$, matrix $P$ appears as a block in $[0\ \ I\ \ P\ \cdots]$ where $I$ is the identity matrix whose rows and columns are indexed by $B_2 \backslash B_1$.

Similarly, let $Q$ denote the block with columns $B_2 \backslash B_1$ in $[\cdots\ Q\ \ I\ \ 0]$; the latter is the submatrix with rows $B_1 \backslash B_2$ in the tableau of $\mathcal{M}_R$.

The minimality assumption implies that $B_1$ and $B_2$ are the only common bases of the restrictions of $\mathcal{M}_L$ and $\mathcal{M}_R$ to $B_1 \cup B_2$. For if $B' \subset B_1 \cup B_2$ were a common basis strictly between $B_1$ and $B_2$ the minimality subject to (1.1) would be violated for exactly one of the pairs $B_1$ and $B'$ or $B_2$ and $B'$ since $\chi_R(B')\chi_L(B') = \pm 1$.

Consider the tableau for any matroid $\mathcal{M}$ relative to the basis $B \in \mathcal{B}(\mathcal{M})$ and let $T(X, Y)$ be the square submatrix with rows corresponding to $X \subseteq B$ and columns $Y \subseteq E \backslash B$. The non-zero entries of $T(X, Y)$ define the bipartite graph $G$ with vertices $X \cup Y$.

THEOREM 1.7. *(Krogdahl, see* [24] *or* [37, Ch. 3].*)*
1. *If $B \backslash X \cup Y \in \mathcal{B}(\mathcal{M})$, then $G$ contains a perfect matching.*
2. *If $G$ contains a unique perfect matching, then $B \backslash X \cup Y \in \mathcal{B}(\mathcal{M})$.*

Part 1. of Theorem 1.7 shows that the graphs of $P$ and of $Q$ each contain perfect matchings. Consider these bipartite graphs to be binary relations: their composition is a binary relation $R$ on $B_2 \backslash B_1$ that therefore contains a permutation. Now part 2. of Theorem 1.7 together with the fact that $B_1$ and $B_2$ are the only common bases of $M_L$ and $M_R$ in $B_1 \cup B_2$ show that the graphs of $P$ and $Q$ are just perfect matchings and $R$ is a single cycle permutation. For if this were not true, $R$ would contain a minimum length cycle of length less than $|B_1 \backslash B_2|$. This cycle would be the composition of the binary relations of proper square submatrices of $P$ and $Q$, where these relations are each perfect matchings.

We return to oriented matroid analysis. The product $PQ$ of signed permutation matrices $P$ and $Q$ is now known to represent a single cycle permutation. Let $\mathcal{M}_l$

$= \mathcal{M}_L \backslash (B_1^c \cap B_2^c)/(B_1 \cap B_2)$ and $\mathcal{M}_r = \mathcal{M}_R \backslash (B_1^c \cap B_2^c)/(B_1 \cap B_2)$. Hence $\mathcal{M}_l^\perp = \mathcal{M}_L/(B_1^c \cap B_2^c)\backslash (B_1 \cap B_2)$. The (particularly simple) oriented matroids $\mathcal{M}_l^\perp$ and $\mathcal{M}_r$ are realized by $[I\ P]$ and $[Q\ I]$, respectively, interpreted as real matrices with entries in $\{0, +1, -1\}$. This is because each column of $[I\ P]$ and $[Q\ I]$ has a single non-zero entry, so the circuits, cocircuits, etc., are completely determined by the sign patterns of these matrices.

CLAIM 1.1. $|P|\,|Q| = -(-1)^{|B_1 \backslash B_2|}$.

PROOF. The ground set of $\mathcal{M}_l$ and $\mathcal{M}_r$ is $A = (B_1 \backslash B_2) \cup (B_2 \backslash B_1)$. Each of $\mathcal{M}_R$ and $\mathcal{M}_L$ are spanned by $(B_1^c \cap B_2^c)^c = B_1 \cup B_2$. Therefore (see [**2**, pages 133-135]) chirotope functions for $\mathcal{M}_l$ and $\mathcal{M}_r$ are given by

$$\chi_l(X) = s_{l0}\chi_L(X; F) \ \text{ and } \ \chi_r(X) = s_r\chi_R(X; F),$$

where $F = B_1 \cap B_2$. Here, ";" denotes concatenation of ordered sets or sequences. The $s_i$ denote constant signs. A chirotope function for $\mathcal{M}_l^\perp$ is given by

$$\chi_l^\perp(X) = s_l\chi_l(\overline{X})\epsilon(X, A).$$

Here, $\overline{X} = A\backslash X$ and $\epsilon(X, A)$ is the parity of the number of inversions when $X$ would be shuffled in $A$ so $A$ is ordered by $X; \overline{X}$. Let the signs $s_l$ and $s_r$ used be those for which $\chi_l^\perp(B_2 \backslash B_1) = +1$ and $\chi_r(B_1 \backslash B_2) = +1$. Therefore $\chi_l^\perp$ and $\chi_r$ are realized by matrices $[I\ P]$ and $[Q\ I]$ respectively. Hence we have

$|P|\ |Q|\ |I|\ |I|$

$= \chi_l^\perp(B_1 \backslash B_2)\chi_r(B_2 \backslash B_1)\chi_l^\perp(B_2 \backslash B_1)\chi_r(B_1 \backslash B_2)$

$= s_l^2\chi_l(B_2 \backslash B_1)\epsilon(B_1 \backslash B_2, A)\chi_l(B_1 \backslash B_2)\epsilon(B_2 \backslash B_1, A)\chi_r(B_2 \backslash B_1)\chi_r(B_1 \backslash B_2)$

$= (-1)^{|B_1 \backslash B_2|}s_{l0}^2\chi_L(B_2 \backslash B_1; F)\chi_L(B_1 \backslash B_2; F)s_r^2\chi_R(B_2 \backslash B_1; F)\chi_R(B_1 \backslash B_2; F)$

$= \chi_L(B_2)\chi_L(B_1)\chi_R(B_2)\chi_R(B_1)(-1)^{|B_1 \backslash B_2|}$

$= -(-1)^{|B_1 \backslash B_2|}.$

The calculation uses the fact that $\epsilon(X, A)\epsilon(\overline{X}, A) = (-1)^{|X||\overline{X}|}$ and when $|X| = |\overline{X}|$ this is $(-1)^{|X|}$. ◁

CLAIM 1.2. The number of $-1$ entries in $P$ and $Q$ together is even.

PROOF. The non-zero entries of $PQ$ represent a permutation of $|B_1 \backslash B_2|$ elements with exactly one cycle. Therefore,

$$|PQ| = -(-1)^{|B_1 \backslash B_2|}(-1)^{\text{number of } -1 \text{ entries in } P \text{ and } Q}.$$

But by claim 1.1, $|PQ| = -(-1)^{|B_1 \backslash B_2|}$. ◁

CLAIM 1.3. There exist covectors $C_0 \in \mathcal{L}(\mathcal{M}_L^\perp)$ and $D_0 \in \mathcal{L}(\mathcal{M}_R)$ such that
- $C_0(a) = D_0(a) \neq 0$ for all $a \in A = (B_1 \backslash B_2) \cup (B_2 \backslash B_1)$,
- $C_0(B_1^c \cap B_2^c) = 0$ (note $B_1^c \cap B_2^c$ is independent in $\mathcal{M}_L^\perp$), and
- $D_0(B_1 \cap B_2) = 0$ (note $B_1 \cap B_2$ is independent in $\mathcal{M}_R$).

PROOF. For $e \in B_2 \backslash B_1$ let $c_e \in \mathcal{L}(\mathcal{M}_L^\perp)$ be the unique cocircuit for which $c_e(e) = +$ and $c_e(f) = 0$ for all $f \in B_1^c \backslash e$. Thus $\{c_e : e \in B_2 \backslash B_1\}$ is a subset of the fundamental cocircuits in $\mathcal{M}_L^\perp$ with respect to $B_1^c \in \mathcal{B}(\mathcal{M}_L^\perp)$. It corresponds to the rows indexed by $B_2 \backslash B_1$ in the full tableau of which the tableau we showed for $\mathcal{M}_l^\perp$ is a submatrix.

For $e \in B_1 \backslash B_2$ let $d_e \in \mathcal{L}(\mathcal{M}_R)$ be the unique cocircuit for which $d_e(e) = +$ and $d_e(f) = 0$ for all $f \in B_1 \backslash e$. These are some of the fundamental cocircuits in $\mathcal{M}_R$ with respect to $B_1$.

Consider the bipartite graphs of $P$ and of $Q$ to which we applied Theorem 1.7. Form $\mathcal{N}$ as the union of $P$ and the reverse of $Q$. We have shown that $\mathcal{N}$ is the cycle $(v_0, v_1, ..., v_{N-1})$ where $N = 2|B_1 \backslash B_2|$. Call an arc in $\mathcal{N}$ negative if the entry in $P$ or $Q$ it corresponds to is $-1$. Define $s : \{0, \ldots, N-1\} \to \{+1, -1\}$ by

$$s(i) = (-1)^{\text{number of negative arcs in the path from } v_0 \text{ to } v_i \text{ in } \mathcal{N}}.$$

Observe that since claim 1.2 shows that number of negative arcs in $\mathcal{N}$ is even,

$$s(i)s(i+1) = \begin{cases} -1 & \text{if arc } (v_i, v_{i+1}) \text{ is negative,} \\ +1 & \text{otherwise} \end{cases}$$

is true for all subscripts $0 \leq i \leq N-1$ with $i+1$ taken mod $N$. Let $v_0 \in B_2 \backslash B_1$ be arbitrary. The compositions satisfy the claim:

$$C_0 = (s(0)c_{v_0}) \circ (s(2)c_{v_2}) \circ \cdots \circ (s(N-2)c_{v_{N-2}})$$
$$D_0 = (s(1)d_{v_1}) \circ (s(3)d_{v_3}) \circ \cdots \circ (s(N-1)d_{v_{N-1}}) \quad \triangleleft$$

Claim 1.3 says $C_0$ and $D_0$ satisfy the hypotheses of Theorem 1.1 with $\mathcal{M}_1 = \mathcal{M}_L^\perp$, $\mathcal{M}_2 = \mathcal{M}_R$, $A = (B_1 \backslash B_2) \cup (B_2 \backslash B_1)$, $S = B_1^c \cap B_2^c$, $R = B_1 \cap B_2$ and $Z = \emptyset$. Hence $C = D$ from Theorem 1.1 is the common covector. $\square$

## 2. Common Covector Problem Classification

Since $\text{rank}(\mathcal{M}_L^\perp \vee \mathcal{M}_R) \leq \text{rank}(\mathcal{M}_L^\perp) + \text{rank}(\mathcal{M}_R)$ let us distinguish oriented matroid pairs with $\text{rank}(\mathcal{M}_L^\perp \vee \mathcal{M}_R) < \text{rank}(\mathcal{M}_L^\perp) + \text{rank}(\mathcal{M}_R)$ from pairs with equality here. The latter we will say have "full union rank." Theorem 1.3 says that pairs that do not have full union rank always have a common covector. See [25, 33] for polynomial time algorithms to compute $\text{rank}(\mathcal{M}_L^\perp \vee \mathcal{M}_R)$.

We will classify common covector problems into three categories. For the first category, full union rank is impossible. For the other two categories we summarize the properties of pairs with full union rank. Whether or not such pairs have a common covector is the interesting question. The ground set cardinality $|E|$ is denoted by $m$.

**Excess Rank Sum:** $\text{rank}(\mathcal{M}_R) > \text{rank}(\mathcal{M}_L)$, in other words, $\text{rank}(\mathcal{M}_L^\perp) + \text{rank}(\mathcal{M}_R) > m$. Since $m \geq \text{rank}(\mathcal{M}_L^\perp \vee \mathcal{M}_R)$ Theorem 1.3 always applies.

**Balanced Rank Sum:** $\text{rank}(\mathcal{M}_R) = \text{rank}(\mathcal{M}_L)$, in other words, $\text{rank}(\mathcal{M}_L^\perp) + \text{rank}(\mathcal{M}_R) = m$. Assume full union rank. This case includes the given applications to electrical networks and to $\mathcal{W}_0$ matrix pairs. Theorem 5.2 below shows the common covector problem is as hard as deciding if a square matrix is not sign non-singular [3] (SNS) and thus it is as hard as the digraph even cycle problem [22], even for rather simple classes of oriented matroids. Theorem 1.6, its converse for realizable oriented matroids, and its conjecture for all oriented matroids apply to this case.

**Deficient Rank Sum:** $\text{rank}(\mathcal{M}_R) < \text{rank}(\mathcal{M}_L)$, in other words, $\text{rank}(\mathcal{M}_L^\perp) + \text{rank}(\mathcal{M}_R) < m$. Assume full union rank. Corollary 5.5 shows the common covector problem is NP-complete.

## 3. Realizable Oriented Matroid Pairs

THEOREM 3.1. *If realizable $\mathcal{M}_L^\perp$ and $\mathcal{M}_R$ have a common non-zero covector and $\mathcal{M}_L$ and $\mathcal{M}_R$ have a common basis then $\mathcal{M}_L$ and $\mathcal{M}_R$ have a pair of oppositely directed bases.*

PROOF. The determinant ("bracket") of the square submatrix of $M_i$ with columns $B$ is denoted by $M_i[B]$. A chirotope representation $\chi_i$ for $\mathcal{M}(M_i)$ has values $\chi_i(B) = \sigma(M_i[B])$. The product of real variables $g_e$ for $e \in B$ is denoted $g_B$. Let $G = \mathrm{diag}(g_e)$. Laplace's theorem and Lemma 1.1 in [**4**] show that

(3.1)

$$\Delta = \left| \left[ \begin{array}{c} M_R G \\ M_L^\perp \end{array} \right] \right| = \sum_{B \subset E} \epsilon(B, E) M_R[B] M_L^\perp[E \backslash B] g_B = C \sum_{B \subset E} M_R[B] M_L[B] g_B$$

where $C = \pm M_L^\perp[E \backslash B_0]/M_L[B_0]$ for an arbitrary $B_0$ for which $M_L[B_0] \neq 0$. Thus $\Delta$ is not identically 0 since $\mathcal{M}_L$ and $\mathcal{M}_R$ have a common basis. Since $\Delta = 0$ for some positive values for the $g_e$, two terms in (3.1) have opposite sign.   □

THEOREM 3.2. *Suppose realizable $\mathcal{M}_L$ and $\mathcal{M}_R$ have a common basis. The following conditions are equivalent.*

- *$\mathcal{M}_L^\perp, \mathcal{M}_R$ have a common covector.*
- *$\mathcal{M}_L, \mathcal{M}_R^\perp$ have a common covector.*
- *$\mathcal{M}_L^\perp, \mathcal{M}_R$ have a common vector.*
- *$\mathcal{M}_L, \mathcal{M}_R^\perp$ have a common vector.*

PROOF. By Theorems 3.1 and 1.6, the first two conditions are each equivalent to $\mathcal{M}_L$ and $\mathcal{M}_R$ having a pair of oppositely directed common bases. The other two conditions follow because $\mathcal{L}(\mathcal{M}^\perp) = \mathcal{V}(\mathcal{M})$ and $\mathcal{L}(\mathcal{M}) = \mathcal{V}(\mathcal{M}^\perp)$.   □

## 4. Sandberg-Willson Theory and its Dual

Consider the problem to solve the equation $AF(x) + Bx = c$ for $x \in \mathbf{R}^n$, where $A$ and $B$ are $n \times n$ matrices, $F : \mathbf{R}^n \to \mathbf{R}^n$ has the form $F(x)_k = f_k(x_k)$ with each $f_k$ being a strictly monotone increasing function from $\mathbf{R}$ *onto* $\mathbf{R}$, and $AF(x)$ denotes the real column vector whose $k$th entry is $\sum A_{ki} f_i(x_i)$. Suppose the equation has two distinct solutions $x$ and $x'$. Then $A(F(x') - F(x)) + B(x' - x) = 0$. The strict monotonicity assumption for $F$ means $\sigma(F(x') - F(x)) = \sigma(x' - x) = X \neq 0$. Therefore $\mathcal{M}[A\ B]$ and $\mathcal{M}[I\ -I]$ have a common non-zero vector $[X\ X]$. Conversely, suppose $\mathcal{M}[A\ B]$ and $\mathcal{M}[I\ -I]$ have a common non-zero vector. This means some $x, y \in \mathbf{R}^n$ satisfy $Ay + Bx = 0$ and $\sigma(x) = \sigma(y) \neq 0$. Define $F = (f_e)$ so $f_e(t) = (y_e/x_e)t$ if $x_e \neq 0$ and $f_e(t) = t$ otherwise. With this $F$, $AF(x) + Bx = 0$ has multiple solutions.

These ideas were observed by Sandberg and Willson who proved that, for given $(A, B)$, the solution $x$ exists and is unique for each choice of functions $f_k$ and $c \in \mathbf{R}^n$ is equivalent to the properties of $(A, B)$ below.

THEOREM 4.1. *(Willson, [**41**]. ) These properties of a pair of $n \times n$ matrices $(A, B)$ are equivalent.*

1. *$|AD + B| \neq 0$ for every diagonal matrix $D > 0$.*

2. *There exists a matrix[2] $M \in C(A, B)$ such that $|M| \neq 0$ and for all $N \in C(A, B)$, $|M| \cdot |N| \geq 0$.*

3. *For each $x \in \mathbf{R}^n$ with $x \neq 0$, there is an index $k$ such that $(xA)_k \neq 0$ or $(xB)_k \neq 0$, and such that $(xA)_k (xB)_k \geq 0$.*

4. *For each $x \in \mathbf{R}^n$ with $x \neq 0$, there is a diagonal matrix $D_x \geq 0$ such that either $xAD_x A^t x^t > 0$ or $xBD_x B^t x^t > 0$ and such that $xAD_x B^t x^t \geq 0$.*

5. *For each complementary pair $(M, N)$ taken from $C(A, B)$, (that is, $M = (A, B)(S' \cup (E \backslash S)'')$ and $N = (A, B)((E \backslash S)' \cup S'')$) we have that each real root $\lambda$ of $|M - \lambda N|$ is non-negative.*

6. *There exists a complementary pair $(M, N)$ taken from $C(A, B)$ such that $M^{-1}N \in \mathcal{P}_0$, in the sense of Fiedler and Pták [14].*

7. *There exists a non-singular $M \in C(A, B)$ and for any complementary pair $(M, N)$ taken from $C(A, B)$ with $M$ non-singular, $M^{-1}N \in \mathcal{P}_0$.*

*A pair of matrices $(A, B)$ that satisfies these properties is called a $\mathcal{W}_0$ pair, denoted $(A, B) \in \mathcal{W}_0$.*

This section shows two conditions on the oriented matroid $\mathcal{M} = \mathcal{M}[A \ B]$ realized by the row space of $[A \ B]$ are each equivalent to $(A, B) \in \mathcal{W}_0$. Each condition is a combinatorial property of $\mathcal{M}$ together with the involution $i \leftrightarrow (n+i)$ given on the ground set $E$ where $|E| = 2n$. The two conditions are known to be equivalent for realizable oriented matroids from Theorem 3.2. One condition reflects the argument given above for uniqueness of solutions to $AF(x) + Bx = c$. The other pertains to a problem dual to $AF(x) + Bx = c$ in the sense that the row space of $[A \ B]$ plus a constant is an affine feasible set that is then further constrained by strict monotone diagonal nonlinearities.

REMARK 4.2. A common covector of $\mathcal{M}[A \ B], \mathcal{M}[I \ -I]$ is $[Z \ -Z]$ where for some $t \in \mathbf{R}^n$, $\sigma(tA) = -\sigma(tB) = Z$. A common *vector* of $\mathcal{M}[A \ B], \mathcal{M}[I \ -I]$ is $[W \ W]$ where there exist $x, y \in \mathbf{R}^n$ such that $Ax + By = 0$ and $W = \sigma(x) = \sigma(y)$.

THEOREM 4.3. *For a pair of $n \times n$ matrices $(A, B)$, the following conditions are equivalent.*

1. *$(A, B) \in \mathcal{W}_0$ in the sense of Theorem 4.1, e.g., $|AD + B| \neq 0$ for all positive diagonal $D$, etc.*

2. *rank $\mathcal{M}[A \ B] = n$ and $\mathcal{L}[A \ B] \cap \mathcal{L}[I \ -I] = \{0\}$.*

3. *rank $\mathcal{M}[A \ B] = n$ and $\mathcal{V}[A \ B] \cap \mathcal{V}[I \ -I] = \{0\}$.*

4. *(Fundamental theorem of Sandberg and Willson [36, 40]) For all functions $F : \mathbf{R}^n \to \mathbf{R}^n$ of the form $F(x)_k = f_k(x_k)$ where each $f_k$ is a strictly monotone increasing function from $\mathbf{R}$ onto $\mathbf{R}$ and for all $c \in \mathbf{R}^n$, the equation*

$$AF(x) + Bx = c$$

*has a unique solution $x$.*

5. *For all functions $G : \mathbf{R}^n \to \mathbf{R}^n$ of the form $G(w)_k = g_k(w_k)$ where each $g_k$ is a strictly monotone increasing function from $\mathbf{R}$ onto $\mathbf{R}$ and for all $d', d'' \in \mathbf{R}^n$, the equations*

(4.1) $$u^t = z^t A + d', \quad w^t = z^t B + d'', \quad u = -G(w)$$

*have a unique solution $(u, w, z)$.*

---

[2]The following notation is used in [41]: $C(A, B)$ is the collection of all $2^n$ matrices of order $n \times n$ that are constructed by juxtaposing for each $i$ in the order $1, 2, \ldots, n$, either column $A_i$ or $B_i$.

PROOF. The equivalence of 1. and 4. was proved in [**40, 41**]. We will use it to prove 5. below.

The equivalence of 1. and 2. is proved using property 3. of Theorem 4.1. The first part of property 3., $x[A\ B] = [xA\ xB] \neq 0$ for all $x \neq 0$ is equivalent to $\operatorname{rank}\mathcal{M}[A\ B] = \operatorname{rank}[A\ B] = n$.

Suppose $\operatorname{rank}\mathcal{M}[A\ B] = n$ and $\mathcal{L}[A\ B] \cap \mathcal{L}[I\ -I] = \{0\}$. Then for all $x \neq 0$, $\sigma(xA) \neq -\sigma(xB)$; so for at least one $k$, $\sigma(xA)(k) \neq -\sigma(xB)(k)$. At least one of $(xA)_k$ and $(xB)_k$ is non-zero and $(xA)_k(xB)_k \geq 0$.

For the converse, note that when $\operatorname{rank}[A\ B] = n$, $\mathcal{L}[A\ B] \cap \mathcal{L}[I\ -I] = \{0\}$ is equivalent to $\sigma(xA) \neq -\sigma(xB)$ for all $x \neq 0$. Therefore $\mathcal{L}[A\ B] \cap \mathcal{L}[I\ -I] = \{0\}$ because $\sigma(xA)(k) \neq -\sigma(xB)(k)$ for the index $k$ that satisfies property 4.1(3). Therefore, 1. and 2. are equivalent.

To use Theorem 3.2 (known for realizable oriented matroids only) to prove that 2. implies 3. one must show $\operatorname{rank}(\mathcal{M}[A\ B] \vee \mathcal{M}[I\ -I]) = 2n$, i.e., this union matroid is free. However, if it were not, Theorem 1.3 would contradict $\mathcal{L}[A\ B] \cap \mathcal{L}[I\ -I] = \{0\}$ since $\operatorname{rank}(\mathcal{M}[A\ B]) = n$ is assumed and $\operatorname{rank}(\mathcal{M}[I\ -I]) = n$.

Let the rows of matrix $[P\ Q]$ be a basis for the orthogonal complement of the row space $L[A\ B]$. When $\operatorname{rank}[A\ B] = n$, $[P\ Q]$ is a rank $n$ matrix with $n$ rows and $2n$ columns. By oriented matroid duality principles, that $\mathcal{M}[P\ Q]$ and $\mathcal{M}[I\ I] = \mathcal{M}[I\ -I]^{\perp}$ have no common covector is equivalent to $\mathcal{V}[A\ B] \cap \mathcal{V}[I\ -I] = \{0\}$. Given condition 3., Theorem 1.3 implies as before that $\mathcal{M}[P\ Q] \vee \mathcal{M}[I\ I]$ is free. Hence Theorem 3.2 tells us $\mathcal{M}[P\ Q], \mathcal{M}[I\ I]$ have no common vector, since we are working with realizable oriented matroids. But no common vector for this pair means that their duals $\mathcal{M}[A\ B], \mathcal{M}[I\ -I]$ have no common covector. Therefore, condition 3. implies condition 2.

Equations (4.1) are equivalent to

$$Pu - Q(-w) = Pd''^t + Qd'''^t \qquad u = -G(w) = G_1(-w)$$

for some vector function $G_1$ satisfying the same conditions as $G$.

Suppose $(A, B)$ satisfies 1. and therefore 2. Hence $\operatorname{rank}\mathcal{M}[A\ B] = n$ and so $\operatorname{rank}(\mathcal{M}[P\ -Q]) = n$. By duality, $\mathcal{L}[A\ B] \cap \mathcal{L}[I\ -I] = \{0\}$ is equivalent to $\mathcal{V}[P\ Q] \cap \mathcal{V}[I\ I] = \{0\}$. In general, the existence of common non-zero (co)vectors of oriented matroids $\mathcal{M}_1$ and $\mathcal{M}_2$ on ground set $E$ is invariant under reorientation of $\mathcal{M}_1$ and $\mathcal{M}_2$ on the same subset of $E$. Specifically, $\mathcal{V}[P\ Q] \cap \mathcal{V}[I\ I] = \{0\}$ if and only if $\mathcal{V}[P\ -Q] \cap \mathcal{V}[I\ -I] = \{0\}$. Condition 3., applied to $(P, -Q)$, is now known to imply condition 4. with $(P, -Q)$ taking the place of $(A, B)$. Therefore, the solution components $(u^t, -w^t)$ exist and are unique. The $z^t$ component is unique since $\operatorname{rank}[A\ B] = n$. Hence condition 5. is proven for $(A, B)$.

Conversely, suppose condition 5. is true so (4.1) has a unique solution $(u, w, z)$ for all $G$ as specified and for all $d'$ and $d''$. Then $\operatorname{rank}[A\ B] = n$ since $z$ is unique. Therefore $\operatorname{rank}[P\ -Q] = n$ because $\operatorname{rank}[P\ Q] = n$. The latter also shows that for all $c$ there exist $d'$ and $d''$ so $c = Pd' + Qd''$. So, for all $c$, $Pu^t - Q(-w^t) = c$ and $u = G_1(-w)$ have a unique solution $(u^t, -w^t)$. This satisfies condition 4. applied to the matrix pair $(P, -Q)$. Thus 3. applies to $(P, -Q)$. By reorientation, $\mathcal{V}[P\ Q] \cap \mathcal{V}[I\ I] = \{0\}$. By duality, $\mathcal{L}[A\ B] \cap \mathcal{L}[I\ -I] = \{0\}$. However, this and $\operatorname{rank}(\mathcal{M}[A\ B]) = n$ is condition 2. for $(A, B)$.  □

COROLLARY 4.4. *Let there be given four real $n$ column matrices in pairs $(A, B)$ and $(P, Q)$, where each pair has full row rank and the row spaces are orthogonal complements, i.e., $L[A\ B] = L[P\ Q]^{\perp}$. The following conditions are equivalent.*

1. $(A, B) \in \mathcal{W}_0$.
2. $(P, -Q) \in \mathcal{W}_0$.
3. $\operatorname{rank}(\mathcal{M}[A\ B]) = n$ *and* $\mathcal{M}[A\ B], \mathcal{M}[I\ -I]$ *have no common covector.*
4. $\operatorname{rank}(\mathcal{M}[A\ B]) = n$ *and* $\mathcal{M}[A\ B], \mathcal{M}[I\ -I]$ *have no common vector.*
5. $\operatorname{rank}(\mathcal{M}[P\ Q]) = n$ *and* $\mathcal{M}[P\ Q], \mathcal{M}[I\ I]$ *have no common covector.*
6. $\operatorname{rank}(\mathcal{M}[P\ Q]) = n$ *and* $\mathcal{M}[P\ Q], \mathcal{M}[I\ I]$ *have no common vector.*
7. *For all $x, y \in \mathbf{R}^n$, $Ax + By = 0$ and $\sigma(x) = \sigma(y)$ implies $x = y = 0$; i.e., if $x \neq 0$ or $y \neq 0$, then for some index $k$, $x_k \neq 0$ or $y_k \neq 0$, and $x_k y_k \leq 0$.*
8. *For all $u \in \mathbf{R}^n$, $\sigma(u^t A) = -\sigma(u^t B)$ implies $u = 0$ (q.v. Theorem 4.1( 3).)*

REMARK 4.5. Case 3. of Corollary (4.4) is a specialization of $\mathcal{L}(\mathcal{M}_L^{\perp}) \cap \mathcal{L}(\mathcal{M}_R) = \{0\}$ and the matroids $\mathcal{M}_L$ and $\mathcal{M}_R$ have a common basis. However, the latter condition is equivalent to $\mathcal{M}_L^{\perp} \oplus \mathcal{M}'_R$ and $\mathcal{M}[I_2\ -I_2]$ having no common covector and $\mathcal{M}_L \oplus \mathcal{M}'^{\perp}_R$ and $\mathcal{M}[I_2\ -I_2]$ having a common basis. Here $\mathcal{M}'_R$ is isomorphic to $\mathcal{M}_R$ on a disjoint copy of the ground set of $\mathcal{M}_L$ of size $m$, and $I_2$ is the order $2m$ identity matrix.

## 5. Sign Solvability and Computational Complexity

A sign matrix $A$ is by definition an *L-matrix* if every real matrix with sign pattern $A$ has all linearly independent rows. A square L-matrix is said to be sign non-singular (SNS, see [**3**] for a discussion of these topics.) We show that $A$ is not an L-matrix is equivalent to a pair of rather simple linear subspaces (i.e., realized oriented matroids) having a common covector.

LEMMA 5.1. *Given $m \times n$ sign matrix $A$ with no rows of zeros, let $E$ be the set of positions $ij$ where $A_{ij} \neq 0$ and define an $m \times |E|$ matrix $M_L$ and an $n \times |E|$ matrix $M_R$ by*

$$M_L(i, e) = \begin{cases} A_{ij} & \text{if } e = ij \\ 0 & \text{otherwise} \end{cases} \quad \text{and} \quad M_R(j, e) = \begin{cases} 1 & \text{if } e = ij \\ 0 & \text{otherwise.} \end{cases}$$

*Then $A$ is an L-matrix if and only if $\mathcal{M}(M_L)$ and $\mathcal{M}(M_R)^{\perp}$ have no common covector.*

PROOF. Let $G$ be the diagonal matrix of $g_{ij}$ for $ij \in E$. Every real $A'$ with $\sigma(A') = A$ can be written as $A' = M_L G M_R^t$ for some real $g_e > 0$.

Suppose some linear combination of the rows of $A'$ were 0. Some non-zero member of the row space $x \in L(M_L)$ would be in $L(M_R G)^{\perp}$. The signatures from the latter subspace are the covectors of $\mathcal{M}(M_R)^{\perp}$. Hence $\sigma(x)$ is a common covector.

Conversely, suppose $x \in L(M_L)$ and $y \in L(M_R)^{\perp}$ satisfy $\sigma(x) = \sigma(y) \neq 0$. Define $g_e = y(e)/x(e)$ when $x(e) \neq 0$ and $g_e = 1$ otherwise. Hence $G$ is positive diagonal, $xG \in L(M_R)^{\perp}$ and so $x \in L(M_R G)^{\perp}$. $\square$

THEOREM 5.2. *The problem of telling if a square sign matrix matrix $A$ is not SNS is polynomial time reducible to the common covector problem for $\mathcal{M}_L = \mathcal{M}(M_L)$ and $\mathcal{M}_R^{\perp} = \mathcal{M}(M_R)^{\perp}$ where $M_L$ and $M_R$ realize oriented matroids with a common basis and whose underlying matroids are partition matroids.*

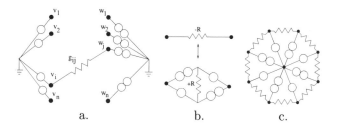

a.                    b.                    c.

FIGURE 4.  a. Network for matrix $A'$ of Theorem 5.2, with positive resistors $E$, nullator edges $P$ and norator edges $Q$. Let $\mathcal{M}$ be the graphic oriented matroid. Let $\mathcal{M}_L = \mathcal{M}/P\backslash Q$ and $\mathcal{M}_R = \mathcal{M}\backslash P/Q$. This electric network model is well-posed for all positive resistance values if and only if $\mathcal{M}_L, \mathcal{M}_R^{\perp}$ have no common covector. The SNS problem for $0,+1$ matrices is reducible to cases of this electrical problem. For $0,\pm1$ matrices, negative resistors can be simulated by (b.). When $E$ is a cycle with $4k$ edges, the network determinant $\Delta$ has exactly two terms and they have opposite sign. The Wheatstone bridge (a $K_4$ with the nullator and norator as a disjoint pair of edges) is the case of $k = 1$. The case of $k = 2$ is (c.), $\Delta = g_1 g_3 g_5 g_7 - g_2 g_4 g_6 g_8$.

PROOF. To reduce, first test if $\det A'$ is identically $0$ by a polynomial time bipartite matching algorithm [**25, 33**]. If so, $A$ is not SNS. Otherwise, the reduction given in Lemma 5.1 satisfies the theorem.    □

REMARK 5.3. Matrix $A'$ above is the system matrix for the nullator, norator, and resistor network shown in Figure 4. Therefore the common covector problem cases from electrical applications, to determine if a network model is sometimes but not always ill-posed [**18, 19, 20**], are no easier than the (non) SNS problem.

REMARK 5.4. Generalizing part (c) of Figure 4 gives a family of graph pairs $\{(\mathcal{G}_L^k, \mathcal{G}_R^k)\}$. For each member, $\mathcal{M}(\mathcal{G}_L^k), \mathcal{M}(\mathcal{G}_R^k)^{\perp}$ have a common covector. But no proper minor pair $(\mathcal{G}_L^k/X\backslash Y, \mathcal{G}_R^k/X\backslash Y)$ satisfies this property. See [**32, 15**].

THEOREM 5.5. *The common covector problem for row spaces of integer matrices is strongly NP-complete.*

PROOF. The NP algorithm is to guess the common covector and verify it by solving two instances of the integer linear programming feasibility problem. Theorem 13.4 on page 320 of [**33**] gives an upper bound on the magnitudes of some solution to a feasible integer linear program in terms of the magnitudes of the coefficients. The upper bound implies that the verification can be done in time polynomial in the number of bits needed to code the matrices.

To prove the NP-hardness, use Lemma 5.1 to reduce the problem of telling if rectangular $A$ is not an L-matrix to the common covector problem. The former problem was shown to be NP-complete by Klee, Ladner and Manber in [**22**]. Since the instances from the reduction are coded with $0,\pm1$s, the NP-completeness is strong [**16**].    □

REMARK 5.6. The proof presented at the conference used reduction from the "feedback arc set" problem for directed graphs [16].

# References

[1] A. Bachem and W. Kern, *Linear Programming Duality, an Introduction to Oriented Matroids*, Springer-Verlag, Berlin-New York, (1992).

[2] A. Björner, M. Las Vergnas, B. Sturmfels, N. White and G. M. Ziegler, *Oriented matroids, Encyclopedia of Mathematics and its Applications*, 46. Cambridge University Press, Cambridge, (1993).

[3] R. A. Brualdi and B. L. Shader, *Matrices of Sign-Solvable Linear Systems,* Cambridge University Press, New York, (1995).

[4] T. Brylawski, A determinental identity for resistive networks, *SIAM J. Appl. Math.,* **32,** 1-22, (1977).

[5] T. H. Brylawski and G. M. Ziegler, Topological representation of dual pairs of oriented matroids, *Discrete Comput. Geom.,* **10,** 237-240, (1993).

[6] S. Chaiken and P. Narendran, "The all-minors VCCS matrix tree theorem, half-resistors and applications in symbolic simulation," in *IEEE International Symposium on Circuits and Systems,* (ISCAS-95) Seattle, Washington, vol. 2, 1239-1242, (1995).

[7] S. Chaiken, A combinatorial proof of the all minors matrix tree theorem, *SIAM J. Alg. Disc. Meth.,* **3,** 319-329, (1982).

[8] S. Chaiken, A matroid abstraction of the Bott-Duffin constrained inverse, *SIAM J. Alg. and Disc. Meth.,* **4,** 467-475, (1983).

[9] S. Chaiken The Tutte polynomial of a P-ported matroid, *J. Combin. Theory Ser. B,* **46,** 96-117, (1989).

[10] W. K. Chen, Unified theory on topological analysis of linear systems, *Proc. IEEE,* **114,** 1630-1636, (1967).

[11] W. K. Chen. *Applied Graph Theory, Graphs and Electrical Networks.* 2nd ed., North-Holland, New York. 1976.

[12] W. K. Chen, ed., *Circuits and Filters Handbook,* CRC Press (and IEEE), Boca Raton, Florida, (1995).

[13] R. J. Duffin, Nonlinear networks IIa, *Bull. Amer. Math. Soc.,* **53,** 963-971, (1947).

[14] M. Fiedler and V. Pták, Some generalizations of positive definiteness and monotonicity, *Numer. Math.,* **9,** 163-172, (1966).

[15] M. Fosséprez and M. Hasler, Resistive circuit topologies that admit several solutions, *Internat. J. Circuit Theory Appl.,* **18,** 625-638, (1990).

[16] M. R. Garey and D. S. Johnson, *Computers and Intractability,* W. H. Freeman, San Francisco, CA, (1979).

[17] J. Graver, B. Servatius, and H. Servatius, *Combinatorial Rigitity,* Graduate Studies in Mathematics, 2, American Mathematical Society, Providence, RI, (1993).

[18] M. Hasler and J. Neirynck, *Nonlinear Circuits,* Artech House, Norwood, MA, (1986).

[19] Non-linear nonreciprocal resistive circuits with a unique solution, *Internat. J. Circuit Theory Appl.,* **14,** 237-262, (1986).

[20] M. Hasler, C. Marthy, A. Oberlin and D. de Werra, A discrete model for studying existence and uniqueness of solutions in nonlinear resistive circuits, *Discrete Appl. Math.,* **50,** 169-184, (1994).

[21] Iri, M, "Applications of matroid theory," in *Mathematical Programming: The State of the Art,* Proceedings of the 11th International Symp. on Math. Prog., Bonn, 1982, A. Bachem, M. Grötschel and B. Korte, ed., Springer-Verlag, Berlin-New York, (1983).

[22] V. Klee, R. Ladner and R. Manber, Sign Solvability revisited, *Linear Algebra Appl.,* **59,** 131-157, (1984).

[23] E. J. Kennedy and J. V. Wait, "Operational Amplifiers," in *The Electrical Engineering Handbook,* R. C. Dorf, ed., CRC Press, Boca Raton, Florida, 616-631, (1993).

[24] S. Krogdahl, The dependence graph for bases in matroids, *Discrete Math.,* **19,** 47-59, (1977).

[25] E. L. Lawler, *Combinatorial Optimization: Networks and Matroids,* Holt, Rinehart and Winston, New York-Montreal, Que.-London, (1976).

[26] W. Mayeda, *Graph Theory,* Wiley-Interscience, New York, (1972).

[27] C. Maas, Algorithmic remarks on the Nishi-Chua uniqueness criterion for electrical networks containing controlled sources, *IEEE Trans. Circuits Systems I Fund. Theory Appl.*, **CAS-36**, 1510-1520, (1989).

[28] G. J. Minty, Monotone networks, *Proc. Roy. Soc. London Ser. A*, **257**, 194-212, (1960).

[29] K. Murota, *System Analysis by Graphs and Matroids, Structural Solvability and Controllability*, Springer-Verlag, Berlin-New York, (1987).

[30] K. Murota, Some recent results in combinatorial approaches to dynamical systems, *Linear Algebra Appl.*, **122/123/124**, 725-759, (1989).

[31] R. O. Nielsen and A. N. Willson, Jr., A fundmental result concerning the topology of transistor circuits with multiple operating equilibria, *Proc. IEEE*, **68**, 196-208, (1980).

[32] T. Nishi and L. O. Chua, Topological criteria for nonlinear resistive circuits containing controlled sources to have a unique solution, *IEEE Trans. Circuits Systems I Fund. Theory Appl.*, **CAS-31**, 722-741, (1984).

[33] C. H. Papadimitriou and K. Steiglitz, *Combinatorial Optimization: Algorithms and Complexity*, Prentice-Hall, Englewood Cliffs, NJ., (1982).

[34] A. Recski, *Matroid Theory and its Applications in Electric Network Theory and in Statics*, Springer-Verlag, Berlin-New York, (1989).

[35] R. T. Rockafellar, Convex programming and systems of monotonic relations, *J. Math. Anal. Appl.*, **19**, 543-564, (1967).

[36] I. W. Sandberg and A. N. Willson, Jr., Some theorems on properties of dc equations of non-linear networks, *Bell Syst. Tech. J.*, **48**, 1-34, (1969).

[37] A. Schrijver, *Matroids and Linking Systems*, Math. Center Tracts **88**, Mathematisch Centrum, Amsterdam, (1978).

[38] L. Trajković and A. N. Willson, Jr., Theory of DC operating points of transistor networks, *Archiv für Elektronik und Übertragungstechnik, Int. J. of Electronics and Communication*, **46**, 228-241, (1992).

[39] V. V. Vazirani and M. Yannakakis, Pfaffian orientations, 0-1 permanents, and even cycles in directed graphs, *Discrete Appl. Math.*, **25**, 179-190, (1989).

[40] A. N. Willson, Jr., New theorems on the equations of nonlinear dc transistor networks, *Bell Syst. Tech. J.*, **49**, 1713-1738, (1970).

[41] A. N. Willson, Jr., A useful generalization of the $P_0$ matrix concept, *Numer. Math.*, **17**, 62-71, (1971).

[42] A. N. Willson, Jr., Some aspects of the theory of nonlinear networks, *Proc. IEEE*, **61**, 1092-1113, (1973).

[43] Q. Yu and C. Sechen, "Efficient Approximation of Symbolic Network Functions Using Matroid Intersection Algorithms," in *IEEE International Symposium on Circuits and Systems*, (ISCAS-95) Seattle, WA, vol. 3, 2088-2091, (1995).

[44] G. Ziegler, personal conversation during the conference.

DEPARTMENT OF COMPUTER SCIENCE, STATE UNIVERSITY OF NEW YORK AT ALBANY, ALBANY NY 12222

*E-mail address*: sdc@cs.albany.edu

Contemporary Mathematics
Volume **197**, 1996

# A min-max theorem using matroid separations

Jack S. Dharmatilake

ABSTRACT. The tangle number of a matroid $M$ is denoted by $\theta(M)$ and is defined to be the maximum of the orders of its tangles. The branch-width of $M$ is denoted by $\beta(M)$ and is defined to be the minimum of the widths of its branch-decompositions. Both $\theta(M)$ and $\beta(M)$ are defined in terms of separations of $M$, with ternary trees being used to obtain the separations for the latter. The min-max theorem states that $\beta(M) = \theta(M)$ if and only if $M$ has no coloop and $\beta(M) \neq 1$. Robertson and Seymour[3] proved the graph version of this min-max theorem.

## 1. Separations of matroids

We shall assume familiarity with matroid theory—for an introduction, see Oxley [2]. Throughout this paper $M$ denotes a matroid which has a finite ground set $S(M)$ and a rank function $\rho$. The rank function of $M^*$ (the dual of $M$) is denoted by $\rho^*$. If $x \in S(M)$ we may write $x$ instead of $\{x\}$, when no confusion may be caused. The vertex-set and edge-set of a graph $G$ are denoted by $V(G)$ and $E(G)$, respectively. The polygon matroid $M(G)$ of $G$ has the edge-set of $G$ as its ground set, and the circuits of $G$ as its circuits.

A *separation* of $M$ is a pair $(A, B)$ of complementary subsets of $S(M)$, and the *order* $\xi(M, A, B)$ of this separation is defined as follows.

$$\xi(M, A, B) = \rho(A) + \rho(B) - \rho(M) + 1 \,, \quad \text{if } A \neq \emptyset \neq B$$
$$= 0 \,, \qquad\qquad\qquad\qquad \text{otherwise.}$$

From the submodular inequality for $\rho$ it follows that if $A \neq \emptyset \neq B$, then $\xi(M, A, B)$ is at most 1. If $|A| \geq k \leq |B|$ and $\xi(M, A, B) = k$, then $(A, B)$ is called a $k$-*separation* of $M$. If $M$ has no $k'$-separation for any $k'$ such that $1 \leq k' < k$, then $M$ is said to be $k$-*connected*.

If $(A, B)$ is any separation of $M$, then $\xi(M, A, B) = \xi(M, B, A)$. When $M$ is understood, we shall write $\xi(A, B)$ instead of $\xi(M, A, B)$.

Using separations we will define 2 matroid invariants known as "tangle number" and "branch-width". The tangle number of $M$ is the maximum "order" of a

---

While Jack Dharmatilake was preparing this paper, which is based on a portion of his 1994 Ph.D. dissertation, he was afflicted with a sudden illness from which he did not recover. This, the final version of the paper, was completed by his dissertation advisor, Neil Robertson, and presented by him at the conference.

"tangle" of $M$. Roughly speaking, a tangle of $M$ of order $t$ is obtained from the set of separations of $M$ of order less than $t$, where for each such separation $(A, B)$ either $(A, B)$ or $(B, A)$ is selected in a consistent way. If $\mathcal{T}$ is a tangle of order $t > 0$ and $(A, B) \in \mathcal{T}$, then $A$ and $B$ are referred to as the *small side* and the *big side*, respectively, of $(A, B)$ (with respect to $\mathcal{T}$). Tangle axioms stipulate that the union of no 3 small sides be equal to $S(M)$, and that no small side be of full rank. The branch-width of $M$ is defined in terms of the "branch-decompositions" of $M$. A branch-decomposition of $M$ consists of a tree $T$ whose non-pendant vertices are of valence 3, and a "labeling" of the set of pendant vertices of $T$ by elements of $M$. A labeling is a bijection between the set of pendant vertices of $T$ and $S(M)$. Now, the sets of labels of the two respective end-trees of any edge of $T$ form a separation of $M$. The "width" of the branch-decomposition is the maximum order of all such separations, and the branch-width of $M$ is the minimum width of all branch-decompositions of $M$.

The main results of this paper are as follows:

1. If $M$ has sufficiently high connectivity, then its tangles may be constructed solely by restricting the sizes of the small sides of separations.
2. The branch-width of $M$ is at most 2 if and only if $M$ is the polygon matroid of a series parallel graph.
3. The min-max theorem: The branch-width of $M$ is equal to the tangle number of $M$ if and only if $M$ has no coloop and the branch-width of $M$ is unequal to 1.
4. If $M$ has sufficiently high connectivity, then the branch-width of $M$ is determined by the number of tangles of $M$, and vice-versa.

We conclude this section with some lemmas about matroid separations.

LEMMA 1.1. *If $(A, B)$ is a separation of $M$, then it is also a separation of $M^*$ and $\xi(M^*, A, B) = \xi(M, A, B)$.*

LEMMA 1.2. *Let $|S(M)| \geq 2$, and $(x, Y)$ and $(A, B)$ be separations of $M$, where $x \in S(M)$ and $A \subseteq S(M)$. Then*

1. *If $x$ is a loop or a coloop, then $\xi(x, Y) = 1$, otherwise $\xi(x, Y) = 2$.*
2. *$\xi(A, B) = 1$ if and only if $A$ is the union of (connected) components of $M$ and $\emptyset \neq A \neq S(M)$.*

LEMMA 1.3. *If $(A, B)$ is a separation of $M$, then*

$$\xi(M, A, B) \leq 1 + \min\{\rho(A), \rho(B), \rho^*(A), \rho^*(B)\} \leq 1 + \min\{|A|, |B|\}.$$

LEMMA 1.4. *Let $M'$ be a minor of $M$ and $(A, B)$ be a separation of $M$. If $A' = A \cap S(M')$ and $B' = B \cap S(M')$, then $(A', B')$ is a separation of $M'$, and $\xi(M', A', B') \leq \xi(M, A, B)$.*

The previous result can be found, for example, on page 292 of [2].

LEMMA 1.5. *$M$ has a non-loop circuit if and only if there is a separation $(A, B)$ of $M$ such that $\xi(A, B) > 1$.*

PROOF. The result follows from (1.2). $\square$

LEMMA 1.6. *Let $(A, B)$ be a separation of $M$ such that $|A| \geq 1$ and $|B| \geq 2$. Also let $b \in B$. Then*

$$|\xi(A, B) - \xi(A \cup b, B \backslash b)| \leq 1.$$

PROOF. The result follows since $0 \leq \rho(X \cup y) - \rho(X) \leq 1$ for every $X \subseteq S(M), y \in S(M)$. □

LEMMA 1.7. *Let $M$ be $k$-connected, where $k \geq 2$, and $m = \min\{\lfloor S(M)/2 \rfloor, k - 1\}$. Then*

1. $M^*$ *is also $k$-connected;*
2. *$M$ has no circuit or cocircuit that has at most $m$ elements;*
3. *If $A \subseteq S(M)$ such that $|A| \leq m$, then $A$ is independent in $M$ as well as in $M^*$, and $A^c$ spans $M$ as well as $M^*$;*
4. *Neither $M$ nor $M^*$ has a separation of order 1;*
5. *Suppose $(A, B)$ is a separation of $M$ such that $|A| \leq |B|$, and $t$ is an integer such that $2 \leq t \leq m$. Then $\xi(M, A, B) = t$ if and only if $|A| = t - 1$.*

PROOF.      1. This follows from (1.1).
2. By (1) it suffices to prove the result for circuits. Assume $M$ has a circuit $A$ with $|A| = t \leq m$. Then $|A^c| \geq t$. This now yields the contradiction $\rho(A^c) > \rho(M)$.
3. Without loss of generality suppose $A \neq \emptyset$. That $A$ is independent in $M$ as well as $M^*$ follows from (2). Since $|A| \leq m$ it follows that $|A^c| \geq |A|$. Therefore $\rho(A^c) = \rho(M)$.
4. This follows from (1.2).
5. First suppose $\xi(M, A, B) = t$. Then $|A| \leq t - 1$. By (1.3) it follows that $|A| \geq t - 1$. Therefore $|A| = t - 1$. Conversely, if $|A| = t - 1$, then by (3) it follows that $\rho(A) = t - 1$ and $\rho(B) = \rho(M)$. Therefore $\xi(M, A, B) = t$.

□

## 2. Matroid tangles

Let $t$ be a positive integer. A *tangle of order $t$* in $M$ is a set $\mathcal{T}$ of separations of $M$, each of order less than $t$ such that

(i) For every separation $(A, B)$ of $M$ such that $\xi(M, A, B) < t$, either $(A, B) \in \mathcal{T}$ or $(B, A) \in \mathcal{T}$;
(ii) If $(A_1, B_1), (A_2, B_2), (A_3, B_3) \in \mathcal{T}$, then $A_1 \cup A_2 \cup A_3 \neq S(M)$;
(iii) If $(A, B) \in \mathcal{T}$, then $\rho(A) < \rho(M)$.

We refer to these as the *first, second* and *third tangle axioms.*

The *tangle number* of $M$, denoted $\theta(M)$, is defined as follows: If there is a set $\mathcal{T}$ of separations of $M$ satisfying the second and third tangle axioms, and such that for every separation $(A, B)$ of $M$ either $(A, B) \in \mathcal{T}$ or $(B, A) \in \mathcal{T}$, then $\theta(M) = \infty$. Otherwise $\theta(M)$ is the maximum order of tangles in $M$, and $\theta(M) = 0$ if $M$ has no tangle.

If $\theta(M) = \infty$, then any set of separations of $M$ that satisfies the defining conditions for $\theta(M) = \infty$ is called a *maximal tangle* of $M$. Otherwise any tangle of $M$ of order $\theta(M)$ is called a *maximal tangle* of $M$. If $\rho(M) > 0$, then $\{(\emptyset, S(M))\}$ which is the unique tangle of order 1, is called the *trivial tangle* of $M$. As an example we find the tangle number of the Fano matroid $F_7$. Now $\theta(F_7) \geq 3$ because the set of separations $(A, B)$, where $|A| \leq 1$ is a tangle of order 3. To see that $\theta(F_7) = 3$ assume that $F_7$ has a tangle $\mathcal{T}$ of order $\geq 4$. Now if $(A, B)$ is a separation of $F_7$ where $A$ is circuit-hyperplane, then $(A, B) \in \mathcal{T}$. This violates the second tangle axiom.

Let us prove some tangle lemmas.

LEMMA 2.1.    1. $\theta(M) = \infty$ if and only if $M$ has a coloop;
2. $\theta(M) > 0$ if and only if $\rho(M) > 0$;
3. $\theta(M) \neq 1$;
4. If $\theta(M)$ is finite, then $M$ has a tangle of every positive order $n \leq \theta(M)$;

PROOF.    1. If $M$ has a coloop $x$ (say), then the set of separations $(A, B)$ of
$M$ such that $x \in B$, satisfies the second and third tangle axioms. Therefore
$\theta(M) = \infty$. Conversely, suppose $\theta(M) = \infty$. Let $T$ be a maximal tangle
of $M$. If $M$ has no coloop, then $(x, \{x\}^c) \in T$ for every $x \in S(M)$. Let $A_0$
be a maximal element of $\{A : (A, B) \in T\}$. Then by the third tangle axiom
$A_0 \not\subseteq S(M)$. Let $z \in A_0^c$. Then $((A_0 \cup z)^c, A_0 \cup z), (A_0, A_0^c), (z, \{z\}^c) \in T$.
This violates the second tangle axiom.

2. If $\rho(M) > 0$, then $\theta(M) > 0$ by the existence of the trivial tangle of $M$. The
converse follows from the third tangle axiom.

3. Assume $\theta(M) = 1$. Then $M$ has a separation of order 1 but no tangle of
order 2. Since $\theta(M) = 1$ by (2) it follows that $M$ has a component $X$ (say)
such that $\rho(X) > 0$. Let $T$ be the set of separations $(A, B)$ of order 1 such
that $X \subseteq B$. Then from (2) of (1.2) it follows that $T$ is a tangle of order 2.
This is a contradiction.

4. Suppose $T$ is a maximal tangle of $M$. Then the set of all separations in $T$
whose orders are less than $n$ is a tangle of order $n$.
□

LEMMA 2.2. Let $T$ be a tangle of order $\theta$ in $M$.  Then

1. If $(A, B) \in T$, then $(B, A) \notin T$;
2. If $(A, B), (A', B') \in T$ and $\xi(A \cup A', B \cap B') < \theta$, then $(A \cup A', B \cap B') \in T$.

PROOF.    1. This follows from the second tangle axiom.
2. By the second tangle axiom $(B \cap B', A \cup A') \notin T$. Hence $(A \cup A', B \cap B') \in T$
by the first tangle axiom.
□

LEMMA 2.3. Let $T$ be a set of separations of $M$, each of order less than $t$, that
satisfy the first and second tangle axioms. Then $T$ is a tangle if and only if there
is an $S_1 \subseteq S(M)$ such that the following conditions are satisfied:

(a) If $S_1 \neq \emptyset$, then $S_1$ consists of a single coloop;
(b) For every separation $(x, Y)$ of $M$ where $x \in S_1^c$, if $\xi(x, Y) < t$, then $(x, Y) \in T$.

PROOF. First suppose $T$ is a tangle. Let $S_1 = \{x \in S(M) : (\{x\}^c, x) \in T\}$.
Then by the first tangle axiom (b) holds. Also by the second and third tangle axioms
(a) holds. For the converse assume $T$ is not a tangle, and choose $(A, B) \in T$ such
that $\rho(A) = \rho(M)$ with $B$ is minimal. By the second tangle axiom $B \neq \emptyset$. Let
$x \in B$ and $Y = \{x\}^c$. Then by the first tangle axiom $(B \backslash x, A \cup x) \in T$, and
either $(x, Y) \in T$ or $(Y, x) \in T$. By the second tangle axiom $(x, Y) \notin T$. Hence by
(b) it follows that $x \in S_1$. Then (a) implies that $x$ must be a coloop. Therefore
$\rho(A) < \rho(M)$, which contradicts our original assumption.
□

Depending on the connectivity of $M$, it is possible to construct some of its
tangles solely by restricting the sizes of the small sides of separations. Let $M$ be

connected with $\rho(M) > 0$, and $n$ be an integer such that $2 \leq n \leq |S(M)|/2$. The *elementary pre-tangle* of $M$ of order $n$, denoted $\mathcal{P}_n(M)$, is defined by

$$\mathcal{P}_n(M) = \{(A, B) : (A, B) \text{ is a separation of } M \text{ and } |A| \leq n - 2\}.$$

When $M$ is understood, we simply write $\mathcal{P}_n$ instead of $\mathcal{P}_n(M)$. An elementary pre-tangle which is also a tangle is called an *elementary tangle*.

Obviously, $\mathcal{P}_2$ is the trivial tangle and $\mathcal{P}_i \not\subseteq \mathcal{P}_j$, for $i < j$.

LEMMA 2.4. *Let $M$ be $k$-connected where $k \geq 2$, and $|S(M)| \geq 2$. Also let $m = \min\{\lfloor |S(M)|/2 \rfloor, k - 1\}$ and $n$ be an integer such that $2 \leq n \leq m + 1$. Then*

(a) *$\mathcal{P}_2$ is the unique tangle of $M$ of order 1 as well as order 2;*

(b) *$\mathcal{P}_n$ satisfies the first and third tangle axioms for a tangle of order $n$;*

(c) *If $M$ has a tangle $\mathcal{T}$ of order $n$, then $\mathcal{T} = \mathcal{P}_n$;*

(d) *Let $n \geq 3$. Then $M$ has a tangle of order $n$ if and only if $|S(M)| \geq 3n - 5$;*

(e) *Let $|S(M)| \geq 3k' - 5$ where $2 \leq k' \leq k$. Then $\theta(M) = k'$ if and only if $M$ has precisely $k' - 1$ distinct tangles;*

PROOF.     (a) This follows from (4) of (1.7) and the third tangle axiom.

(b) By (a) let $n \geq 3$. That $\mathcal{P}_n$ satisfies the first and third tangle axioms follows from (5) and (3), respectively of (1.7).

(c) By (a) let $n \geq 3$. First suppose $(P, Q) \in \mathcal{T}$. Then by (3) of (1.7) and the third tangle axiom it follows that $|P| \leq |Q|$. Hence by (5) of (1.7) it follows that $(P, Q) \in \mathcal{P}_n$. Next suppose $(A, B) \in \mathcal{P}_n$. Then $|A| \leq n - 2 < m$ and $\xi(A, B) < n$. Now from (3) of (1.7) it follows that $(A, B) \in \mathcal{T}$.

(d) If $M$ has a tangle $\mathcal{T}$ of order $n$, then $\mathcal{T} = \mathcal{P}_n$, by (c). Now by the second tangle axiom $|S(M)| \geq 3n - 5$. Conversely, if $|S(M)| \geq 3n - 5$, then $\mathcal{P}_n$ satisfies the second tangle axiom and is therefore a tangle, by (b).

(e) From (2) of (1.7) it follows that $M$ has no coloop. Hence by (2.1) it follows that $M$ has a tangle of every positive order less than or equal to $\theta(M)$. From the hypothesis $k' \leq m + 1$.

If $\theta(M) = k'$, then by (a) and (c) it follows that $M$ has precisely $k' - 1$ distinct tangles. Conversely, suppose $M$ has precisely $k' - 1$ distinct tangles. Then $\theta(M) \geq k'$, and the tangles are $\mathcal{P}_2, \ldots, \mathcal{P}_{k'}$. From this it follows that $\theta(M) \leq k'$. Hence the result follows.

$\square$

## 3. A lemma about submodular functions

In this section we introduce the concepts of connectivity functions, efficient sets, biases and tree-labellings, and then state useful results about the interplay between these concepts. Because the mathematics in this section is independent of matroids we do not give any proofs, but rely on those given in [3]. This section will help us cross over from tangles to branch-decompositions and vice-versa, and prove the min-max theorem.

Let $F$ be a finite set. A *connectivity function* on $F$ is an integer-valued function $\kappa$ on the power set of $F$ such that

(i) $\kappa(X) = \kappa(F \backslash X)$ for every $X \subseteq F$;

(ii) $\kappa(X \cup Y) + \kappa(X \cap Y) \leq \kappa(X) + \kappa(Y)$ for every $X, Y \subseteq F$.

As an example let $F = S(M)$ and $\kappa(X) = \rho(X) + \rho(F \backslash X)$ for every $X \subseteq S(M)$.

A subset $X \subseteq F$ is *efficient* (with respect to $\kappa$) if $\kappa(X) \leq 0$. A *bias* is a set $\mathcal{B}$ of efficient sets such that

(i) if $X \subseteq F$ is efficient, then $\mathcal{B}$ contains one of $X$, $F \backslash X$;

(ii) if $X, Y, Z \in \mathcal{B}$, then $X \cup Y \cup Z \neq F$.

A bias $\mathcal{B}$ is said to *extend* a set $\mathcal{A}$ of efficient sets if $\mathcal{A} \subseteq \mathcal{B}$.

We are concerned with the problem of extending a given set of efficient sets to a bias. A *tree* is a connected non-null graph with no circuits. The *leaves* of a tree are its vertices of valence at most 1. A tree is *ternary* if every vertex has valence 1 or 3. Thus every ternary tree has at least 2 leaves. An *incidence* in a tree $T$ is a pair $(v, e)$ where $v \in V(T)$, $e \in E(T)$ and $e$ is incident with $v$.

Let $\mathcal{A}$ be a set of efficient sets that are subsets of $F$. A *tree-labeling* over $\mathcal{A}$ is a pair $(T, \alpha)$ where $T$ is a ternary tree and $\alpha$ is a function from the set of all incidences in $T$ to the set of all efficient sets of $F$ such that

(i) for every $e \in E(T)$ with incident vertices $u, v$ (say), $\alpha(u, e) = F \backslash \alpha(v, e)$;

(ii) for every incidence $(v, e)$ in $T$ such that $v$ is a leaf, either $\alpha(v, e) = F$ or there is an $X \in \mathcal{A}$ such that $\alpha(v, e) \cup X = F$;

(iii) if $v \in V(T)$ has valence 3, and is incident with the edges $e_1, e_2$ and $e_3$ (say), then $\alpha(v, e_1) \cup \alpha(v, e_2) \cup \alpha(v, e_3) = F$. (See Figure 1)

A *fork* in $T$ is an unordered pair $\{e_1, e_2\}$ of distinct edges of $T$ with a common end (the *nub* of the fork). A fork $\{e_1, e_2\}$ with nub $v$ is *exact* (for $\alpha$) if $\alpha(v, e_1) \cap \alpha(v, e_2) = \emptyset$. We say that the tree-labeling $(T, \alpha)$ is *exact* if every fork of $T$ is exact.

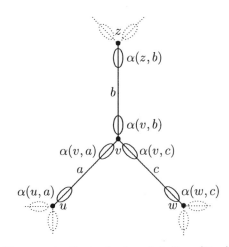

FIGURE 1. Part of a tree-labeling $(T, \alpha)$

LEMMA 3.1. *If there is a bias extending $\mathcal{A}$, then there is no tree-labelling over $\mathcal{A}$.*

LEMMA 3.2. *If there is a tree-labelling over $\mathcal{A}$, then there is an exact tree-labelling over $\mathcal{A}$, using the same tree.*

LEMMA 3.3. *Let $(T, \alpha)$ be an exact tree-labelling over $\mathcal{A}$ and $(u, f)$ be an incidence in $T$. Also let $T_0$ be the component of $T \backslash f$ which contains $u$. Then as $(v, e)$ ranges over all incidences of $T$ such that $v$ is a leaf of $T$ and $v \in V(T_0)$, the sets $F \backslash \alpha(v, e)$ are mutually disjoint and have union $F \backslash \alpha(u, f)$.*

LEMMA 3.4. *If there is no bias extending $\mathcal{A}$, then there is an exact tree-labelling over $\mathcal{A}$.*

LEMMA 3.5. *The following are equivalent:*

(i) *There is no bias extending $\mathcal{A}$;*
(ii) *There is a tree-labelling over $\mathcal{A}$;*
(iii) *There is an exact tree-labelling over $\mathcal{A}$.*

LEMMA 3.6. *If there is an exact tree-labelling over $\mathcal{A}$, then either $F = \emptyset$, or $F \in \mathcal{A}$, or there is an exact tree-labelling $(T, \alpha)$ over $\mathcal{A}$ such that for every incidence $(v, e)$ in $T$ where $v$ is a leaf, $\alpha(v, e) \neq F$.*

## 4. Branch-width of a Matroid

A *branch-decomposition* of a matroid $M$ is a pair $(T, \lambda)$ where $T$ is a ternary tree and $\lambda$ is a bijection from the set of leaves of $T$ to $S(M)$. The *order* of an edge $e$ of $T$ is equal to $\xi(M, \lambda(L_1), \lambda(L_2))$, where $L_1$ and $L_2$ are the sets of leaves of $T$ that are vertices of the 2 end-trees of $T \backslash e$. The *width* of $(T, \lambda)$ is the maximum order of the edges of $T$, and the *branch-width* $\beta(M)$ of $M$ is the minimum width of all branch-decompositions of $M$ (or 0 if $|S(M)| \leq 1$, when $M$ has no branch-decomposition). An *optimal branch-decomposition* of $M$ is a branch-decomposition whose width equals $\beta(M)$. Figure 2 illustrates a Euclidean representation and an optimal branch-decomposition of the Fano matroid $F_7$.

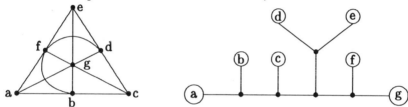

FIGURE 2. $F_7$ and an optimal branch decomposition of $F_7$

From the definition $\beta(M) = 0$ if and only if $|S(M)| \leq 1$. An upper bound for $\beta(M)$ may be established by constructing an appropriate branch-decomposition of $M$. Direct verification of a lower bound usually involves the following graph theoretic result known as the central-edge-lemma.

LEMMA 4.1. *If $T$ is a ternary tree, then there is an $e \in E(T)$ such that each of the two end-trees of $e$ has at least one third of the leaves of $T$, as vertices.*

We prove some results about branch-width.

LEMMA 4.2.  (a) $\beta(M^*) = \beta(M)$;
(b) *If $M_1$ is a minor of $M$, then $\beta(M_1) \leq \beta(M)$;*

PROOF. (1) This follows from (1.1).
(2) We may assume that $|S(M_1)| \geq 2$, for otherwise $\beta(M_1) = 0$. Also by induction and (1) it suffices to prove the result when $M_1$ is obtained from $M$ by deleting an element $x$ of the latter. Let $(T, \lambda)$ be an optimal branch-decomposition of $M$. Obtain the ternary tree $T_1$ from $T$ by deleting the leaf $\lambda^{-1}(x)$ of $T$ along with its incident pendant edge, and suppressing the resulting divalent vertex. Let $\lambda_1$ be the restriction of $\lambda$ to the set of leaves of $T_1$. Then $(T_1, \lambda_1)$ is a branch-decomposition of $M_1$. The result now follows from (1.4). $\qquad\square$

LEMMA 4.3. *Let $M$ be $n$-connected, where $n \geq 3$. Then $\beta(M) \geq n$ if and only if $|S(M)| \geq 3n - 5$.*

PROOF. First suppose $|S(M)| < 3n - 5$. Then there is a ternary tree $T$, with $|S(M)|$ leaves and a trivalent vertex $v$, so that each of the 3 pairwise disjoint end-trees of the edges that are incident with $v$ has at most $n - 2$ leaves of $T$, as vertices. Now by considering an an arbitrary bijection from the leaves of $T$ to $S(M)$ it follows that $\beta(M) < n$. The "only if" part follows from (4.1).                    □

LEMMA 4.4.      (a) $\beta(M) \leq 1$ if and only if $M$ has no non-loop circuit.
(b) $\beta(M) \leq 2$ if and only if $M$ is the polygon matroid of a series parallel graph.

PROOF. (1) The "if" part follows from (1.5), and the "only if" part follows from (4.2) because any non-loop circuit has branch-width 2.
(2) First suppose $M$ is the polygon matroid of a series parallel graph. By (2) of (1.2) we may assume that $M$ is connected. Also since $\beta(M) \leq 2$ if $|S(M)| \leq 2$, let $|S(M)| \geq 3$. We proceed by induction. By passing to the dual if necessary, we may assume that $M$ is a single-element parallel extension of a polygon matroid $M_1$ of a series parallel network. Let $S(M) \backslash S(M_1) = p$ and let $p_1 \in S(M_1)$ such that $p_1$ is parallel to $p$. Also let $(T_1, \lambda_1)$ be an optimal branch-decomposition of $M_1$. We form the branch-decomposition $(T, \lambda)$ of $M$ by letting $T$ be the ternary tree constructed by attaching two pendant edges to the leaf $\lambda_1^{-1}(p_1)$, and letting $\lambda$ agree with $\lambda_1$ on the leaves of $T$ that are also leaves of $T_1$ and letting $\lambda(p) = \lambda(p_1) = \lambda_1(p_1)$. Then $(T_1, \lambda_1)$ is of width at most 2.

Conversely, suppose $\beta(M) \leq 2$. It can be verified that each of $U_{2,4}$ (the uniform matroid of rank 2 on 4 elements), $M(K_4)$, $F_7$, $F_7^*$ and $M(K_{3,3})^*$ has branch-width 3, and that $M(K_5)^*$ has branch-width 4. Hence by (2) of (4.2) it follows that none of these 6 matroids is a minor of $M$. Therefore $M$ has to be the polygon matroid of a series parallel graph.                    □

## 5. The min-max theorem

THEOREM 5.1.      (5.1) $\beta(M) = \theta(M)$ if and only if $M$ has no coloop and $\beta(M) \neq 1$.

PROOF. If $\beta(M) = \theta(M)$, then from (2.1) and (4.4) it follows that $M$ has no coloop and $\beta(M) \neq 1$. Conversely, suppose $M$ has no coloop and $\beta(M) \neq 1$. Without loss of generality let $|S(M)| \geq 2$. Let $n$ be an integer $\geq 2$. Then define $\kappa(A) = \xi(A, B) - n$ for each $A \subseteq S(M)$. Also let $\mathcal{A} = \{\{x\} : x \in S(M)\}$. Then $\kappa$ is a connectivity function and $\mathcal{A}$ is a set of efficient sets (with respect to $\kappa$).

We prove that $\beta(M) = \theta(M)$ in 5 steps.

(1) Let $(T, \alpha)$ be an exact tree-labelling over $\mathcal{A}$ such that $\alpha(l, p) \neq S(M)$ for every incidence $(l, p)$ in $T$, where $l$ is a leaf. For any incidence $(v, e)$ in $T$, let $L(v, e)$ denote the set of leaves of $T$ that are vertices of the end-tree of $e$ that does not have $v$ as a vertex. (See Figure 3.)

Then there is a bijection $\tau$ from the set of all leaves of $T$ onto $S(M)$ such that $\alpha(l, p) = S(M) \backslash \tau(l)$ for each incidence $(l, p)$ in $T$ where $l$ is a leaf, and $\alpha(v, e) = \tau(L(v, e))$ for each incidence $(v, e)$ in $T$.

If $(l, p)$ is an incidence in $T$ where $l$ is a leaf, then by condition (ii) on tree-labellings there is an $x \in S(M)$ such that $\alpha(l, p) = S(M) \backslash x$. Define the function $\tau$ from the set of all leaves of $T$ into $S(M)$ by letting $\tau(l) = x$. Then $\alpha(l, p) = S(M) \backslash \tau(l)$.

Next suppose $(v, e)$ is an arbitrary incidence in $T$. Let $z \in L(v, e)$ and $d$ be the length of the path from $v$ to $z$. Then by induction on $d$ it can

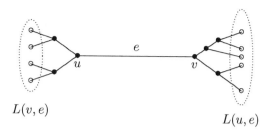

FIGURE 3. Sets $L(u, e)$ and $L(v, e)$, for incidences $(u, e)$ and $(v, e)$ of $T$

be proved that $\tau(z) \in \alpha(v, e)$. Therefore $\alpha(v, e) \supseteq \tau(L(v, e))$. The reverse containment can be shown by letting $d$ be the maximum length of a path from $v$ to any $z \in L(v, e)$ and proceeding by induction on $d$.

If $|S(M)| = 2$, then by condition (i) on tree-labellings $\tau$ is bijective. If $|S(M)| > 2$, then injectivity of $\tau$ may be proved by assuming otherwise and obtaining a contradiction. Surjectivity is proved by choosing a trivalent vertex $v$ of $T$ and applying condition (iii) on tree-labellings at $v$.

(2) There is a bias that extends $\mathcal{A}$ if and only if $M$ has a tangle of order $n + 1$.

First suppose $M$ has a tangle $\mathcal{T}$ of order $n+1$. Let $\mathcal{B} = \{A : (A, B) \in \mathcal{T}\}$. Then $\mathcal{B}$ is a bias. If $\mathcal{B}$ does not extend $\mathcal{A}$, then there is an $x \in S(M)$ such that $x \notin A$ for each $(A, B) \in \mathcal{T}$. Let $Y = S(M) \backslash x$. From (1) of (1.2) it follows that $(Y, x) \in \mathcal{T}$. Hence by the third tangle axiom $x$ must be a coloop of $M$ and this is a contradiction.

Conversely, suppose there is a bias $\mathcal{B}$ that extends $\mathcal{A}$. Let $\mathcal{T}$ consist of the separations $(A, B)$ of $M$ such that $\xi(A, B) \leq n$ and $A \in \mathcal{B}$. Then $\mathcal{T}$ satisfies the first and second tangle axioms. Also $\mathcal{T}$ satisfies the conditions of (2.3) with $S_1 = \emptyset$. Therefore $\mathcal{T}$ is a tangle.

(3) There is an exact tree-labelling over $\mathcal{A}$ if and only if $\beta(M) \leq n$.

First suppose $\beta(M) \leq n$. Let $(T, \tau)$ be an optimal branch-decomposition of $M$. Define the function $\alpha$ from the set of all incidences in $T$ to the set of all efficient sets of $S(M)$ by letting $\alpha(v, e) = \tau(L(v, e))$ for every incidence $(v, e)$ of $T$. Then $\alpha$ is an exact tree-labelling over $\mathcal{A}$.

Conversely, suppose there is an exact tree-labelling over $\mathcal{A}$. Then since $\emptyset \neq S(M) \notin \mathcal{A}$, by (3.6) there is an exact tree-labelling $(T, \alpha)$ over $\mathcal{A}$ such that for every incidence $(v, e)$ in $T$ where $v$ is a leaf, $\alpha(v, e) \neq S(M)$. Let $\tau$ be the bijection which was proved to exist in (1). Then $(T, \tau)$ is a branch-decomposition of width at most $n$.

(4) $M$ has a tangle of order $n + 1$ if and only if $n < \beta(M)$.

By (2) it follows that $M$ has a tangle of order $n + 1$ if and only if there is a bias extending $\mathcal{A}$, and by (3.5) the latter is equivalent to the non-existence of an exact tree-labelling over $\mathcal{A}$. Finally, by (3) this non-existence is equivalent to $n < \beta(M)$.

(5) $\beta(M) = \theta(M)$.

Letting $n = \theta(M)$ in (4) yields $\beta(M) \leq \theta(M)$, and letting $n = \theta(M) - 1$ in (4) yields $\theta(M) - 1 < \beta(M)$. Therefore $\beta(M) = \theta(M)$.

$\square$

Using (5.1) in conjunction with (2.4) it is possible to characterize highly connected matroids of a particular branch-width, in terms of the number of tangles.

COROLLARY 5.2. *Let $k$ and $k'$ be integers such that $2 \leq k' \leq k$ and $M$ is $k$-connected with $|S(M)| \geq 2$. Then $\beta(M) = k'$ if and only if $M$ has precisely $k' - 1$ distinct tangles.*

PROOF. $M$ has no coloop and $\beta(M) \neq 1$. Therefore by (5.1) it follows that $\beta(M) = k'$ if and only if $\theta(M) = k'$. For $k' = 2$ the result follows from (a) of (2.4). So suppose $k' > 2$. If $|S(M)| \geq 3k' - 5$, then the result follows by (e) of (2.4). Otherwise from (4.3) it follows that $\beta(M) < k'$. Then from (e) of (2.4) it follows that $M$ has less than $k' - 1$ distinct tangles. The result follows. $\quad\square$

From (5.2) it follows that if $|S(M)| \geq 2$, then $M$ is the polygon matroid of a series parallel network if and only if $M$ has no non-trivial tangle. Also if $M$ is 3-connected, then $\beta(M) = 3$ if and only if its only non-trivial tangle is that in which separations have singletons for their respective small sides.

We conclude with a result that follows from (4.2) and (5.1).

COROLLARY 5.3.    1. *If $M$ has both a loop and a coloop or neither, then $\theta(M^*) = \theta(M)$;*

2. *Let $M_1$ be a minor of $M$ that has a coloop only if $M$ does. Then $\theta(M_1) \leq \theta(M)$.*

**Acknowledgment:** I wish to thank my thesis supervisor, Professor G. Neil Robertson, for the suggestions, encouragement and support given throughout this research.

(While Jack Dharmatilake was preparing this paper, which is based on a portion of his 1994 Ph.D. dissertation, he was afflicted with a serious illness from which he did not recover. This, the final version of the paper was completed by his dissertation advisor, Neil Robertson, and presented by him at the conference.)

## References

[1] J. S. Dharmatilake, "Binary Matroids of Branch-width 3" Ph.D. thesis, Ohio State University, 1994.
[2] J. G. Oxley, "Matroid Theory" Oxford University Press, 1992.
[3] N. Robertson and P. D. Seymour *Graph Minors and Obstructions to Tree-Decomposition*, J. Combin. Theory Ser. B, 52, 1991, 153–167.

DEPARTMENT OF MATHEMATICS, OHIO STATE UNIVERSITY, COLUMBUS, OHIO 43210

Contemporary Mathematics
Volume **197**, 1996

# A greedoid characteristic polynomial

Gary Gordon and Elizabeth McMahon

ABSTRACT. We define a characteristic polynomial $p(G)$ for a greedoid $G$, generalizing the well studied matroid characteristic polynomial (which in turn generalizes the chromatic polynomial of a graph). We show several of the matroid expansions for $p(G)$ have direct greedoid analogs. We also develop a Möbius function formulation for $p(G)$ when $G$ is an antimatroid. We compute $p(G)$ when $G$ is a poset, a rooted tree and an unrooted tree and give an example to show the coefficient sequence of $p(G)$ (known as the *Whitney numbers of the first kind* when $G$ is a matroid) need not be unimodal.

## 1. Introduction

The characteristic polynomial of a matroid was introduced by Whitney [**18**] as a generalization of the chromatic polynomial of a graph. The characteristic polynomial has many interesting applications within matroid theory, especially to The Critical Problem of Crapo and Rota. A very readable account of this invariant and two important related invariants, the Möbius invariant and Crapo's beta invariant, appears in [**19**].

We are interested in extending this polynomial one step further, to the class of greedoids. Greedoids were introduced by Korte and Lovász and include several interesting combinatorial structures which are not matroidal. For example, partially ordered sets, rooted graphs, rooted digraphs, trees, chordal graphs, and finite convex sets all admit a greedoid structure in a natural way, while none of these objects is matroidal in a non-trivial way. Thus, a characteristic polynomial defined for greedoids gives an immediate application to these (and other) combinatorial objects.

The characteristic polynomial of matroid, $p(G)$, can also be obtained as an evaluation of a two-variable polynomial, the Tutte polynomial of the matroid. This is the viewpoint we will take to define our characteristic polynomial, but we will prove that many of the standard results which hold for $p(G)$ when $G$ is a matroid remain valid in the more general greedoid setting. Not only does this provide evidence that our definition of $p(G)$ is appropriate, it lends additional support to our view that the 2-variable Tutte polynomial defined in [**11**] and studied in

1991 *Mathematics Subject Classification*. Primary: 05B.
*Key words and phrases*. Greedoid, antimatroid, characteristic polynomial, Tutte polynomial.

[**5**, **12**, **7**, **8**, **13**, **10**] is the 'correct' generalization of the Tutte polynomial from matroids to greedoids.

In Section 2, we give several fundamental results, each of which extends a corresponding matroid result. This includes the Tutte polynomial formulation of $p(G)$ (our definition), a Boolean expansion, a feasible set expansion, a deletion-contraction recursion, a direct sum factorization and two algebraic results. We also define *Whitney numbers of the first kind* for greedoids.

In Section 3, we concentrate on antimatroids, where an analog of the Möbius function formulation of $p(G)$ is possible. We then use Möbius inversion to obtain an interesting equation involving the sum of the characteristic polynomials of sub-antimatroids of $A$.

Section 4 is devoted to examples. In particular, we compute $p(G)$ when $G$ is the edge pruning greedoid of a tree and also when $G$ is a poset. The tree example is then used to show that the coefficient sequence of $p(G)$ need not be unimodal. The corresponding question about unimodality for matroids is a famous open problem.

## 2. Definitions and fundamental properties

We assume the reader is familiar with matroid theory. Define a greedoid as follows:

DEFINITION 1. A *greedoid* $G$ on the ground set $E$ is a pair $(E, \mathcal{F})$ where $E$ is a finite set and $\mathcal{F}$ is a family of subsets of $E$ satisfying

1. For every non-empty $X \in \mathcal{F}$ there is an element $x \in X$ such that $X - \{x\} \in \mathcal{F}$;
2. For $X, Y \in \mathcal{F}$ with $|X| < |Y|$, there is an element $y \in Y - X$ such that $X \cup \{y\} \in \mathcal{F}$.

The independent sets in a matroid clearly satisfy these requirements. One significant difference between matroids and greedoids is that every subset of an independent set is independent in a matroid, but a feasible set in a greedoid will have non-feasible subsets in general. As with matroids, the rank of a set $A$, denoted $r(A)$, is the size of the largest feasible subset of $A$:

$$r(A) = \max_{S \in \mathcal{F}}\{|S| : S \subseteq A\}.$$

An extensive introduction to greedoids can be found in [**3**] or [**15**].

There are several equivalent ways to define the characteristic polynomial of a matroid. We use an evaluation of the 2-variable Tutte polynomial of a greedoid to define the characteristic polynomial of a greedoid.

DEFINITION 2. Let $G$ be a greedoid on the ground set $E$. The *Tutte polynomial* of $G$ is defined by

$$f(G; t, z) = \sum_{S \subseteq E} t^{r(G)-r(S)} z^{|S|-r(S)}.$$

This polynomial was introduced in [**11**], and has been studied for various greedoid classes. A deletion-contraction recursion (Theorem 3.2 of [**11**]) holds for this Tutte polynomial, as well as an activities interpretation (Theorem 3.1 of [**12**]).

DEFINITION 3. Let $G$ be a greedoid on the ground set $E$. The *characteristic polynomial* $p(G; \lambda)$ is defined by

$$p(G; \lambda) = (-1)^{r(G)} f(G; -\lambda, -1).$$

We will now use results developed in [11, 12] to generalize some matroid expansions of $p(G; \lambda)$.

PROPOSITION 1 (Boolean expansion).

$$p(G; \lambda) = \sum_{S \subseteq E} (-1)^{|S|} \lambda^{r(G) - r(S)}.$$

PROOF. This result follows immediately from Definition 3. □

In [12], a notion of external activity for feasible sets in a greedoid is developed. We now briefly recall the definitions and fundamental results we will need. A *computation tree* $T_G$ for a greedoid $G$ is a recursively defined, rooted, binary tree in which each vertex of $T_G$ is labeled by a minor of $G$. More precisely, if the vertex $v$ in $T_G$ receives label $H$ for some minor $H$ of $G$, we label the two children of $v$ by $H - e$ and $H/e$, where $\{e\}$ is some feasible set in $H$. The process terminates when $H$ consists solely of greedoid loops. (An element $e$ is a *greedoid loop* if $e$ is in no feasible set.) We label the root of $T_G$ with $G$ and note that $T_G$ obviously depends on the order in which elements are deleted and contracted. (In fact, unlike the matroid case, there may be no fixed order which can be adhered to throughout the procedure.) There is a natural bijection between the feasible sets of $G$ and the terminal vertices of $T_G$ which is given by listing the elements of $G$ which are contracted in arriving at the specified terminal vertex. Define the *external activity of a feasible set* $F$ with respect to the tree $T_G$ by $ext_T(F) = A$ where $A \subseteq E$ is the collection of greedoid loops which labels the terminal vertex corresponding to $F$. Thus, $ext_T(F)$ consists of the elements of $G$ which become loops after all the elements of $F$ have been contracted in $T_G$.

The next result extends Whitney's expansion of the chromatic polynomial [18].

PROPOSITION 2 (Feasible set expansion). *Let $T_G$ be a computation tree for $G$ and let $\mathcal{F}_T$ denote the set of all feasible sets of $G$ having no external activity. Then*

$$p(G; \lambda) = \sum_{F \in \mathcal{F}_T} (-1)^{|F|} \lambda^{r(G) - |F|}.$$

PROOF. This follows from Theorem 3.1 of [12]. □

The deletion-contraction recursion which the Tutte polynomial satisfies gives rise to one for $p(G; \lambda)$.

PROPOSITION 3 (Deletion-contraction). *Let $\{e\}$ be a feasible set in $G$. Then*

$$p(G; \lambda) = \lambda^{r(G) - r(G-e)} p(G - e; \lambda) - p(G/e; \lambda).$$

PROOF. Using the deletion-contraction formula for the Tutte polynomial (Proposition 3.2 of [11]) and Definition 3, we find

$$\begin{aligned}
p(G; \lambda) &= (-1)^{r(G)} f(G; -\lambda, -1) \\
&= (-1)^{r(G)} \{ f(G/e; -\lambda, -1) + (-\lambda)^{r(G) - r(G-e)} f(G - e; -\lambda, -1) \} \\
&= (-1)^{r(G)} \{ (-1)^{r(G/e)} p(G/e; \lambda) + \\
&\qquad (-\lambda)^{r(G) - r(G-e)} (-1)^{r(G-e)} p(G - e; \lambda) \} \\
&= \lambda^{r(G) - r(G-e)} p(G - e; \lambda) - p(G/e; \lambda),
\end{aligned}$$

since $r(G/e) = r(G) - 1$. □

We remark that since $r(G - e) = r(G)$ for all non-isthmuses $e$ in a matroid $G$, the formula above reduces to the familiar $p(G) = p(G - e) - p(G/e)$ for matroids.

PROPOSITION 4 (Direct sum property). $p(G_1 \oplus G_2) = p(G_1)p(G_2)$.

PROOF. This result follows immediately from Proposition 3.7 of [11] and the definition of $p(G)$.                                                                    □

The last two results in this section concern algebraic properties of $p(G)$. Both of these results generalize corresponding results for matroids.

PROPOSITION 5. $(\lambda - 1)|p(G)$.

PROOF. Note that if $G = \{e\}$ has only one element, then $p(G) = 0$ if $e$ is a greedoid loop and $p(G) = (\lambda - 1)$ otherwise. The result now follows by induction and the deletion-contraction formula of Proposition 3.                          □

A fundamental result concerning the chromatic polynomial of a graph is that the coefficients alternate in sign. This remains true for the characteristic polynomial of a matroid.

PROPOSITION 6 (Alternating signs). Let $p(G; \lambda) = \sum_{k=0}^{r(G)} w_k \lambda^{r(G)-k}$. Then the sign of $w_k$ is $(-1)^k$.

PROOF. This follows immediately from Proposition 2.                              □

When $G$ is a matroid, the coefficients of $p(G; \lambda)$ are called the *Whitney numbers of the first kind* for $G$. Proposition 6 then gives us a natural definition for Whitney numbers of the first kind for greedoids.

DEFINITION 4. The $k^{th}$ Whitney number $w_k$ of the first kind for a greedoid $G$ is the coefficient of $\lambda^{r(G)-k}$ in $p(G; \lambda)$.

The sequence $\{(-1)^k w_k\}$ (sometimes written $\{w_k^+\}$) is one of many sequences associated with matroids which is conjectured to be unimodal. (See [1] for an account of some results concerning this and other related conjectures.) This is false for greedoids: the sequence of Whitney numbers given below in Example 2 is not unimodal.

We also remark that Proposition 2 shows that $(-1)^k w_k$ equals the number of feasible sets of cardinality $k$ having no external activity with respect to a given computation tree $T_G$. Thus the number of such feasible sets of a fixed cardinality does not depend upon the computation tree $T_G$.

For matroids, the Whitney numbers of the first kind are the face enumerators for the *broken circuit complex*, i.e., the simplicial complex formed by all independent sets which contain no broken circuits. (See [2] for details.) For an arbitrary greedoid, there is no deep topological connection, but when $G$ is an *antimatroid*, we can say more. We explore this topic in the next section.

## 3. Antimatroids

Antimatroids form a particularly well-behaved class of greedoids. A greedoid $G$ is an antimatroid in which the feasible sets are closed under the process of forming unions. More precisely, we state the following definition.

DEFINITION 5. An *antimatroid* $A = (E, \mathcal{F})$ is a greedoid which satisfies $F_1, F_2 \in \mathcal{F}$ implies $F_1 \cup F_2 \in \mathcal{F}$.

For an antimatroid $A$, let $\mathcal{L}_\mathcal{F}$ denote the lattice of feasible sets of $A$. $\mathcal{L}_\mathcal{F}$ is a semimodular lattice—in fact, a greedoid $G$ is an antimatroid if and only if the poset $(\mathcal{F}, \subseteq)$ is a semimodular lattice (see [3] or [15]). This lattice has been studied by a number of people in connection with convexity, algorithm design and greedoids. In fact, antimatroids have been rediscovered several times, having been introduced by Dilworth in the 1940's. See [14] and [3, pages 343–4] for short and interesting accounts of the development of antimatroids.

Antimatroids are dual to *convex geometries*. See [3, 15] for a detailed account. For or an antimatroid $A = (E, \mathcal{F})$, let $\mathcal{C}$ be the collection of convex sets in $A$, i.e., $\mathcal{C} = \{C \subseteq E : E - C \in \mathcal{F}\}$. It will be more convenient for us to work with the lattice of convex sets, which we denote $\mathcal{L}_\mathcal{C}$, rather than the feasible set lattice $\mathcal{L}_\mathcal{F}$. (The Hasse diagram for $\mathcal{L}_\mathcal{C}$ is obtained by flipping the Hasse diagram for $\mathcal{L}_\mathcal{F}$—these are dual posets.) We call a convex set $K \subseteq E$ *free* if every subset of $K$ is also convex. The collection of all free sets forms an order ideal in $\mathcal{L}_\mathcal{C}$. Our first proposition translates the feasible set expansion of Proposition 2 into this setting.

PROPOSITION 7 (Convex set expansion). *Let $\mathcal{C}_F$ denote the set of all free convex sets of an antimatroid $A$. Then*

$$p(A; \lambda) = (-1)^{|E|} \sum_{K \in \mathcal{C}_F} (-1)^{|K|} \lambda^{|K|}.$$

PROOF. If $T$ is any computation tree for $A$, then it follows from Theorem 2.5 of [12] that $ext_T(F) = \emptyset$ precisely when $E - F$ is a free convex set. The result now follows from Proposition 2. □

The next theorem gives an expansion for $p(A; \lambda)$ for an antimatroid $A$ which is similar to the Möbius function formulation of the characteristic polynomial of a matroid. (See Section 7.2 of [19].) Let $\mu(C, D)$ denote the Möbius function on the lattice $\mathcal{L}_\mathcal{C}$.

THEOREM 1. *Let $A$ be an antimatroid and let $\mathcal{L}_\mathcal{C}$ be the lattice of convex sets. Then*

$$p(A; \lambda) = (-1)^{|E|} \sum_{C \in \mathcal{L}_\mathcal{C}} \mu(\emptyset, C) \lambda^{|C|}.$$

PROOF. From Theorem 4.3 of [6],

$$\mu(\emptyset, C) = \begin{cases} (-1)^{|C|}, & \text{if } C \text{ is free;} \\ 0 & \text{otherwise.} \end{cases}$$

Thus the formula follows from Proposition 7. □

Recall that if $G = (E, \mathcal{F})$ is a greedoid and $S \subseteq E$, then the *restriction of $G$ to $S$*, written $G|S$, is a greedoid on the ground set $S$ whose feasible sets are just the feasible sets of $G$ which are contained in $S$. Equivalently, $G|S = G - (E - S)$. Note that when $A$ is an antimatroid, $A|S$ is an antimatroid precisely when $S$ is a feasible set.

The characteristic polynomial of a matroid arises from using Möbius inversion on the lattice of closed sets of the matroid. This classical approach was originally used by to Whitney to compute the chromatic polynomial of a graph. If we apply Möbius inversion in $\mathcal{L}_\mathcal{C}$, then we obtain the following result.

PROPOSITION 8. *Let* $A = (E, \mathcal{F})$ *be an antimatroid with convex sets* $\mathcal{C}$. *Then*

$$\sum_{C \in \mathcal{C}} (-1)^{|A-C|} \lambda^{|C|} p(A - C; \lambda) = 1.$$

PROOF. For a convex set $C$, let

$$f(C) = \sum_{K: K \subseteq C} \mu(C, K) \lambda^{|K|}.$$

Note that $F$ is feasible in the antimatroid $A - C$ if and only if $F$ is feasible in $A$ and $F \cap C = \emptyset$, or, equivalently, if and only if $E - F$ is convex in $A$ and $E - F \supseteq C$.

Therefore, the convex sets in $A - C$ correspond to the convex sets in $A$ which contain $C$. Thus we may identify the lattice of convex sets of $A - C$ with the interval $[C, 1]$ in $\mathcal{L}_C$. Now applying Theorem 1 to the interval $[C, 1]$ of $\mathcal{L}_C$ gives

$$f(C) = (-1)^{|E|-|C|} \lambda^{|C|} p(A - C; \lambda).$$

Thus, by Möbius inversion (25.5 in [**17**]), we get

$$\lambda^{|C|} = \sum_{K: K \supseteq C} f(K) = \sum_{K: K \supseteq C} (-1)^{|E-K|} \lambda^{|K|} p(A - K; \lambda).$$

The result now follows by setting $C = \emptyset$.                    $\square$

## 4. Examples and counterexamples

We begin with an example of Proposition 8.

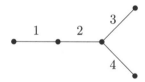

FIGURE 1

EXAMPLE 1. Let $A$ be the edge pruning antimatroid associated with the tree of Figure 1. (Thus, a set $F$ of edges is feasible if the edges of $E - F$ form a subtree.) In Table 1, for each feasible set $F$, we list the feasible sets of the antimatroid $A|F$ and the corresponding term from $\sum_{F \in \mathcal{F}} (-1)^{|F|} \lambda^{|A-F|} p(A|F; \lambda)$. For brevity in the table, we write $F = 123$ instead of $F = \{1, 2, 3\}$, and so on.

Then $\sum_{F \in \mathcal{F}} (-1)^{|F|} \lambda^{|A-F|} p(A|F; \lambda) = (1 - \lambda)(\lambda^3 + \lambda^2 + \lambda + 1) + \lambda^4 = 1$, as required in Proposition 8.

Partially ordered sets form a class of antimatroids. For a poset $P$, define a subset $F$ to be feasible if $F$ is an order ideal in $P$. Let $M(P)$ denote the collection of all maximal elements of $P$. We leave the proof of the next lemma to the interested reader.

LEMMA 1. *$C$ is a free convex set in a poset $P$ if and only if $C \subseteq M(P)$.*

We now compute $p(P; \lambda)$ for a poset $P$.

PROPOSITION 9. *Let $P$ be a poset and $M(P)$ its set of maximal elements. Then*

$$p(P; \lambda) = (-1)^{|P|} (1 - \lambda)^{|M(P)|}.$$

| Feasible Set $F$ | $\mathcal{F}(A\|F)$ | $p(A\|F;\lambda) \cdot \lambda^{4-\|F\|} \cdot (-1)^{\|F\|}$ |
|---|---|---|
| $\emptyset$ | $\emptyset$ | $\lambda^4$ |
| 1 | $\emptyset, 1$ | $(1-\lambda)\lambda^3$ |
| 3 | $\emptyset, 3$ | $(1-\lambda)\lambda^3$ |
| 4 | $\emptyset, 4$ | $(1-\lambda)\lambda^3$ |
| 12 | $\emptyset, 1, 12$ | $(1-\lambda)\lambda^2$ |
| 13 | $\emptyset, 1, 3, 13$ | $(1-\lambda)^2\lambda^2$ |
| 14 | $\emptyset, 1, 4, 14$ | $(1-\lambda)^2\lambda^2$ |
| 34 | $\emptyset, 3, 4, 34$ | $(1-\lambda)^2\lambda^2$ |
| 123 | $\emptyset\ 1, 3, 12, 13, 123$ | $(1-\lambda)^2\lambda$ |
| 124 | $\emptyset, 1, 4, 12, 14, 124$ | $(1-\lambda)^2\lambda$ |
| 134 | $\emptyset, 1, 3, 4, 13, 14, 34, 134$ | $(1-\lambda)^3\lambda$ |
| 234 | $\emptyset, 3, 4, 34, 234$ | $(1-\lambda)\lambda$ |
| 1234 | $\emptyset, 1, 3, 4, 12, 13, 14, 34,$ $123, 124, 134, 234, 1234$ | $(1-\lambda)(\lambda^2 - 3\lambda + 1)$ |

TABLE 1.

PROOF. By Lemma 1, $M(P)$ is the unique maximal free convex set. The result now follows from Proposition 7. $\qquad\square$

When $T$ is a tree rooted at a distinguished vertex $*$, we can define two antimatroids in a natural way. The feasible sets of the *branching greedoid* $B(T)$ are the subsets of edges which form a rooted subtree, while the feasible sets of the *pruning greedoid* $P(T)$ are the subsets of edges which form the *complement* of a rooted subtree. The Tutte polynomial of either of these greedoids uniquely determines the rooted tree (see [11] and [5]). These two greedoid structures are closely related; in fact, for a given tree $T$, the feasible sets induce a partial ordering on the edge set of $T$. Under this ordering, $B(T)$ and $P(T)$ are dual poset greedoids. (See [8] for more details.) Thus we can apply Proposition 9 to rooted trees.

PROPOSITION 10. *Let $T$ be a rooted tree with edge set $E$ and associated greedoids $B(T)$ and $P(T)$. Let $L(T)$ denote the set of leaves (edges incident to a vertex of degree 1) and let $deg(*)$ be the degree of the root vertex $*$. Then*

1. $p(B(T); \lambda) = (-1)^{\|E\|}(1 - \lambda)^{\|L(T)\|}$;
2. $p(P(T); \lambda) = (-1)^{\|E\|}(1 - \lambda)^{\|deg(*)\|}$.

PROOF. For $B(T)$, the maximal elements correspond to the leaves of $T$, while the maximal elements of the poset associated to $P(T)$ correspond to the edges incident to the root vertex. Both formulas now follow from Proposition 9. $\qquad\square$

We conclude this section by considering $p(T; \lambda)$ when $T$ is an unrooted tree with edge set $E$. As we remarked in Example 1, a subset $F$ of edges is feasible if the edges $E - F$ form a subtree. A *star* $S$ is a subtree in which there is a single vertex incident to all of the edges of $S$. The next Lemma follows from the definitions and is a standard result.

LEMMA 2. *$C$ is a free convex set in a tree $T$ if and only if $C$ is a star.*

PROPOSITION 11. *Let $T$ be a tree with vertex set $V$ and edge set $E$. Then*

$$p(T;\lambda) = (-1)^{|E|}\left(\sum_{v\in V}(1-\lambda)^{deg(v)} - |E|(1-\lambda)\right).$$

PROOF. By Proposition 2.3 of [10], we have $\sum_{v\in V}x^{deg(v)} = f(T;x-1,-1) + |E|x$, where $f(T;t,z)$ is the Tutte polynomial from Definition 2. Substituting $\lambda = 1-x$ in this equation and using Definition 3 gives us the result.    □

COROLLARY 1. *Let $T_1$ and $T_2$ be trees. Then $p(T_1) = p(T_2)$ if and only if $T_1$ and $T_2$ have the same degree sequence.*

We conclude this section with an example to show that the Whitney numbers of the first kind need not be unimodal for antimatroids. Recall that $w_k^+ = (-1)^k w_k$ is the $k^{th}$ (unsigned) Whitney number.

EXAMPLE 2. Let $T$ be a tree with one vertex of degree 10, 100 vertices of degree 3 and 110 vertices of degree 1. Then, by Proposition 11,

$$w_k^+ = \begin{cases} \binom{10}{k}, & \text{if } k \le 6; \\ 220, & \text{if } k = 7; \\ 345, & \text{if } k = 8; \\ 100, & \text{if } k = 9; \\ 1, & \text{if } k = 10. \end{cases}$$

Thus $w_0^+ < w_1^+ < \cdots < w_5^+ > w_6^+ < w_7^+ < w_8^+ > w_9^+ > w_{10}^+$ is not unimodal.

There are several possible directions for future research. We list three possibilities here:

1. Extend more of the algebraic properties of $p(G;\lambda)$ to greedoids. In particular, Stanley's modular factorization theorem (Theorem 2 of [16]) explains how $p(G)$ factors in a geometric lattice containing a modular element. Is there an analogous result which holds for greedoids?

2. Study $p(G)$ for other classes of greedoids. In particular, it would be interesting to determine what combinatorial information $p(G;\lambda)$ encodes when $G$ is a greedoid associated with a rooted graph, rooted digraph, chordal graph, or a convex set of points. These are all well studied, important combinatorial objects. Progress here could include a chromatic polynomial for these objects.

3. Generalize other matroid invariants to greedoids. It would be interesting to extend $\mu(M)$ and $\beta(M)$ to greedoids. This should be especially promising for antimatroids, where there is a semimodular lattice $\mathcal{L}_\mathcal{F}$ with which the invariants may be connected.

## References

[1] M. Aigner, *Whitney numbers*, in Combinatorial Geometries (N. White, ed.), Encyclopedia of Mathematics and Its Applications, Vol. 29, pp. 139-160, Cambridge Univ. Press, London, 1987.

[2] A. Björner, *Homology and shellability of matroids and geometric lattices*, in Matroid Applications (N. White, ed.), Encyclopedia of Mathematics and Its Applications, Vol. 40, pp. 226-283, Cambridge Univ. Press, London, 1992.

[3] A. Björner and G. Ziegler, *Introduction to Greedoids*, Matroid Applications (N. White, ed.), Encyclopedia of Mathematics and Its Applications, Vol. 40, pp. 284-357, Cambridge Univ. Press, London, 1992.

[4] T. Brylawski and J. Oxley, *The Tutte Polynomial and its Applications*, Matroid Applications (N. White, ed.), Encyclopedia of Mathematics and Its Applications, Vol. 40, pp. 123-225, Cambridge Univ. Press, London, 1992.

[5] S. Chaudhary and G. Gordon, *Tutte polynomials for trees*, J. Graph Theory, **15** (1991), 317-331.

[6] P. Edelman and R. Jamison, *The theory of convex geometries*, Geom. Ded. **19** (1985), 247-270.

[7] G. Gordon, *A Tutte polynomial for partially ordered sets*, J. Comb. Theory (B) **59** (1993), 132-155.

[8] G. Gordon, *Series-parallel posets and the Tutte polynomial*, to appear in Discrete Math.

[9] G. Gordon, *A beta invariant for greedoids and antimatroids*, submitted.

[10] G. Gordon, E. McDonnell, D. Orloff and N. Yung, *On the Tutte polynomial of a tree*, Cong. Numer. **108** (1995), 141-151.

[11] G. Gordon and E. McMahon, *A greedoid polynomial which distinguishes rooted arborescences*, Proc. Amer. Math. Soc., **107** (1989), 287-298.

[12] G. Gordon and E. McMahon, *Interval partitions and activities for the greedoid Tutte polynomial*, to appear in Adv. in Appl. Math.

[13] E. McMahon, *On the greedoid polynomial for rooted graphs and rooted digraphs*, J. Graph Theory, **17** (1993), 433-442.

[14] B. Monjardet, *A use for frequently rediscovering a concept*, Order **1** (1985), 415-417.

[15] B. Korte, L. Lovász and R. Schrader, *Greedoids*, Springer-Verlag, Berlin, 1991.

[16] R. Stanley, *Modular elements of geometric lattices*, Alg. Univ. **1** (1971), 214-217.

[17] J. H. van Lint and R. H. Wilson, *A Course in Combinatorics*, Cambridge Univ. Press, London, 1992.

[18] H. Whitney, *A logical expansion in mathematics*, Bull. Amer. Math. Soc. **38** (1932), 572-579.

[19] T. Zaslavsky, *The Möbius function and the characteristic polynomial*, in Combinatorial Geometries (N. White, ed.), Encyclopedia of Mathematics and Its Applications, Vol. 29, pp. 114-138, Cambridge Univ. Press, London, 1987.

DEPARTMENT OF MATHEMATICS, LAFAYETTE COLLEGE, EASTON, PA 18042
*E-mail address*, Gary Gordon: `gordong@lafayette.edu`

*E-mail address*, Elizabeth McMahon: `mcmahone@lafayette.edu`

Contemporary Mathematics
Volume **197**, 1996

# Monotactic Matroids

Robert E. Jamison

## 1. Introduction

The notion of monotaxis arose originally in very general studies of finite closure systems. Although a precise definition is rather technical, roughly speaking, a closure system is monotactic if and only if it possesses a unique "basis" of a certain type. In graphic matroids, this basis is closely related to the notion of a cycle basis. The basic ideas for general closures were worked out by Duquenne and Guiges [1] and Ganter[2], but the first really striking result was proved in the dissertation of Selma Strahringer [7]. She established that the disjunctive product [3] of order closures is always monotactic. This established a large class of interesting closures with the monotactic property. The disjunctive product of order closures arises naturally in concept analysis as developed by Wille [9] and his followers and plays a central role in ordinal data analysis.

The disjunctive product of order closures is in fact an anti-matroid – that is, a closure satisfying the anti-exchange axiom. Indeed, monotaxis has several useful characterizations in antimatroids which do not carry over to more general closures. Stimulated by Strahringer's dissertation, Jamison attempted but failed to give a straight-forward proof of her result. However, this effort resulted in a proof by Jamison and Strahringer [3] of monotaxis for the disjunctive product of several other antimatroid classes, such as trees and semilattices.

The goal here is to examine the meaning of monotaxis in the context of matroids. As it turns out, all binary matroids are monotactic, but so are several classes of non-binary matroids arising from "nonstandard" matroid structures on graphs such as those introduced by Pereira and some count matroids introduced by White and Whitely in connection with rigidity. These specific examples will be explored in a separate paper, while the goal here is to establish the general theory of monotaxis for matroids.

Let $h$ be a closure operator on a finite set $X$. A family $S$ of subsets of $X$ is a *premise system* for $h$ provided that for any subset $K$ of $X$, $K$ is closed if and only if $h(P)$ is contained in $K$ for all "premises" $P$ in $S$ which are contained in $K$.

1991 *Mathematics Subject Classification.* 52B40.

Work on this paper was begun while the author was a sabbatical visitor at Cornell University with support from a Packard fellowship.

A *premise basis* is a premise system which is minimal with respect to inclusion as a family of sets – that is, no proper subfamily is also a premise system. A closure $h$ is *monotactic* if it has a unique premise basis. Duquenne introduced an inductively defined canonical premise basis. A set $P$ is *pseudo-closed* if i) $P$ is not closed and ii) P contains the closure of any pseudo-closed proper subset. Thus to determine all pseudo-closed sets of $n$ points, we first must know all pseudo-closed sets of less than $n$ points. The induction starts with the empty set since it has no proper subsets. If the empty set is closed, then by i) it is not pseudo-closed. On the other hand, if the empty set is not closed, then ii) holds vacuously, so the empty set is pseudo-closed. Duquenne and Guiges [1] showed that for any closure, the pseudo-closed sets form a premise basis. The following result was established in [3]:

THEOREM 1.1. *Let $h$ be a closure on a finite set $X$. Then the following are equivalent:*

1. *$h$ is monotactic;*
2. *the family of pseudo-closed sets is an anti-chain;*
3. *every proper subset of a pseudo-closed set is closed.*

It is clear from this that to understand monotaxis, we must first understand the pseudo-closed sets. Our study of the pseudo-closed sets begins with chords of circuits. In a graph, a chord of a cycle is an edge joining two nodes of the cycle which are not joined in the cycle. Thus a chord breaks a circuit into two smaller cycles of which it is the modulo two sum.

In the following, unless stated otherwise, we will be working with a simple matroid – no loops and no parallel points. Let $C$ be a circuit. A chord of $C$ is a point $x$ not in $C$ such that $A \cup \{x\}$ is a circuit for some subset A of $C$. We call $x$ a *proper chord* and $A \cup \{x\}$ a *short-circuit* of $C$ through $x$ if $|A| < |C| - 1$. A point $x$ is a *monochord* of a matroid $M$ if it is a proper chord of some circuit $C$ of $M$ and there is a unique short-circuit of $C$ through $x$.

A matroid is *hereditarily monotactic* if it and all of its minors by deletion alone are monotactic. One of the main goals of this paper is to prove the following characterization:

THEOREM 1.2. *A matroid is hereditarily monotactic if and only if it contains no monochords.*

EXAMPLE 1.3 (A monotactic matroid). This is given by the matric matroid whose points are the column vectors below:

$$\begin{bmatrix} a & b & c & s & t \\ 1 & 0 & 0 & 1 & 1 \\ 0 & 1 & 0 & 1 & 1 \\ 0 & 0 & 1 & 0 & 1 \end{bmatrix}$$

This is realizable over any field (and is a regular matroid). Geometrically, $c, s, t$ are collinear and $a, b, t$ are collinear. There are three circuits: $\{a, b, c, s\}$, $\{a, b, t\}$ and $\{c, s, t\}$. Circuit $\{a, b, c, s\}$ has $t$ as a chord with $\{a, b, t\}$ and $\{c, s, t\}$ as short-circuits. The pseudo-closed sets of this matroid are

$$Y : \{a, b\}, \{b, t\}, \{a, t\}, \{c, s\}, \{c, t\}, \{s, t\}, \text{ and } \{a, b, c, s\},$$

and these constitute the unique premise basis.

EXAMPLE 1.4 (A polytactic matroid). Let $F$ be a field other than GF(2) and let $a$ be any element of $F$ other than 0 or 1. Form the matric matroid whose points are the column vectors below:

$$\begin{bmatrix} a & b & c & s & t \\ 1 & 0 & 0 & 1 & 1 \\ 0 & 1 & 0 & a & 1 \\ 0 & 0 & 1 & 0 & 1 \end{bmatrix}$$

Geometrically, $a, b, s$ are collinear and $c, t$ lie on a parallel line. There are four circuits of this matroid: $\{a, b, s\}$, $\{b, s, c, t\}$, $\{a, s, c, t\}$, and $\{a, b, c, t\}$. Thus $\{a, b, s\}$ is the unique short-circuit of each the 4-element circuits $\{b, s, c, t\}$, $\{a, s, c, t\}$, and $\{a, b, c, t\}$, with $a, b$, and $s$ as monochords, resp.

The pseudo-closed sets of this matroid are

$$Y : \{a, b\}, \{a, s\}, \{b, s\}, \{a, b, s, c\} \text{ and } \{a, b, s, t\}.$$

There are sixteen premise bases for this matroid, each derived from $Y$. Any premise basis must contain $\{a, b\}$, $\{a, s\}$, and $\{b, s\}$. In addition, it must contain either $\{a, b, s, c\}$ or a set obtained from $\{a, b, s, c\}$ by deleting $a$, $b$, or $s$. Hence there are four choices for this set. Likewise, a premise basis must contain either $\{a, b, s, t\}$ or a set obtained from $\{a, b, s, t\}$ by deleting $a$, $b$, or $s$. Thus there are also four choices for this set. These choices can be made independently, so there are $4 \times 4 = 16$ possible premise bases. Of these $Y$ is the "largest" in the sense that it contains the largest sets: three 2-sets and two 4-sets. There are six with three 2-sets, one 3-set, and one 4-set and nine "minimal" premise bases with three 2-sets and two 3-sets.

EXAMPLE 1.5 (Projective geometries). Any (finite) projective geometry with subspaces as closed sets forms a matroid. In the case of $\text{PG}(q, d)$ this is derived from $\text{GF}(q)d + 1$ by choosing one element from each equivalence class of "parallel" points. This matroid is trivially monotactic. Indeed, a subset is closed if and only if the line through any two of its points also lies in the set. This implies that the collection $Y$ of pseudo-closed sets consists of just the 2-point sets. Example 1.4 shows that if the order is not 2, then these geometries contain polytactic deletion minors. Thus monotaxis is definitely not inherited by minors.

EXAMPLE 1.6 (A smaller monotactic matroid with a monochord). Example 1.4 can in fact be embedded in a monotactic matroid by just adding two new points:

$$\begin{bmatrix} a & b & c & s & t & u & v \\ 1 & 0 & 0 & 1 & 1 & 1 & 0 \\ 0 & 1 & 0 & a & 1 & a & 1 \\ 0 & 0 & 1 & 0 & 1 & 1 & 1 \end{bmatrix}$$

This shares with the projective geometries the crucial property that a subset is closed if and only if the line through any two of its points also lies in the set. Thus again the pseudo-closed sets are just the 2-point sets. A closure in which the family of all $d$-sets forms a premise basis is said to have degree $d$.

QUESTION 1. In $\text{PG}(q, d)$, if a set $X$ of points is given, how many more points must be added to $X$ to produce a subset of degree 2?

PROBLEM 1. Characterize the monotactic subsets of $\text{PG}(q, d)$. Does one have to reduce the degree to 2 to force monotaxis?

## 2.  Proper parts, chords and short-circuits

In the following, unless stated otherwise, we will be working with a simple matroid – no loops and no parallel points. Let $C$ be a circuit. A chord of $C$ is a point $x$ not in $C$ such that $A \cup \{x\}$ is a circuit for some subset $A$ of $C$. We call $C \setminus A$ a *part of $C$ over $x$*.

LEMMA 2.1. *Let $x$ be a chord of a circuit $C$.  Then the parts of $C$ over $x$ partition $C$.*

PROOF. Let $A$ be a subset of $C$ such that $A \cup \{x\}$ is a circuit. Let $y$ be any element of $A$. We need to show that $y$ is in some part of $C$ over $x$. Since $y$ is common to the two circuits $A \cup \{x\}$ and $C$, there is a circuit contained in $(A \cup \{x\} \cup C) \setminus \{y\} = (C \cup \{x\}) \setminus \{y\}$. Such a circuit must contain $x$ as otherwise it would be a proper subset of $C$. Thus this circuit has the form $B \cup \{x\}$ for some subset $B$ of $C$. Moreover, $y$ belongs to the part $C \setminus B$. Thus the parts cover the elements of $C$. We now must show that they are disjoint.

Suppose there are two different parts $P$ and $Q$ of $C$ over $x$ which contain a common element $y$. Then $(C \setminus P) \cup \{x\}$ and $(C \setminus Q) \cup \{x\}$ are both circuits, so there is a circuit contained in $((C \setminus P) \cup \{x\} \cup (C \setminus Q) \cup \{x\}) \setminus \{x\} = (C \setminus P) \cup (C \setminus Q) = C \setminus (P \cap Q)$. Since $y$ belongs to $P \cap Q$, this circuit is a proper subset of $C$, contrary to the circuit axioms.  □

A part $P$ of a circuit $C$ over a chord $x$ is proper if $|P| > 1$. A chord is proper if it has a proper part. The *index* $\mathrm{ind}(C : x)$ [*proper index* $\mathrm{IND}(C : x)$] of $C$ over $x$ is the number of parts [proper parts] of $C$ over $x$. A *short-circuit* of $C$ through $x$ is a circuit $S$ with $|S| < |C|$ and $S$ contained in $C \cup \{x\}$. Equivalently, $S$ is a short-circuit of $C$ through $x$ if and only if $D = (C \setminus P) \cup \{x\}$ where $P$ is a proper part of $C$ over $x$. A *monochord* of $C$ is a chord $x$ of $C$ which is the chord of exactly one short-circuit of $C$. Equivalently, a monochord of $C$ is a chord $x$ of $C$ with exactly one proper part – i.e., $\mathrm{IND}(C : x) = 1$.

LEMMA 2.2. *Consider these three conditions on a chord $x$ of a circuit $C$:*
**C1)** *for all $y$ in $C$, there is a short-circuit through $x$ which avoids $y$;*
**C2)** *for all $y$ in $C$, there is a short-circuit through $x$ which contains $y$;*
**C3)** *$IND(C, x) > 1$.*
*Then* **C1)** $\Longrightarrow$ **C2)** $\Longleftrightarrow$ **C3)**.

PROOF. **C1)** $\Longrightarrow$ **C3)**. Condition **C1)** says that all parts of $C$ over $x$ are proper. Now $C$ cannot be a part by itself as this would force $x$ to be a loop. Thus $C$ has at least two parts.

**C2)** $\Longrightarrow$ **C3)**. A short-circuit contains $y$ if and only if its (proper) part avoids $y$. Since the parts are disjoint, two parts suffice to avoid all points.  □

A set $S$ is a Q-set if for some $x$ not in $S$, $C = S \cup \{x\}$ is a circuit all of whose short-circuits contain $x$. In particular, if $C$ is a chordless circuit, then $C \setminus \{x\}$ is a Q-set for every $x$ in $C$. In a general closure system, a non-closed set every proper subset of which is closed is called a quasi-closed set. Clearly, every quasi-closed set is pseudo-closed, but the converse fails as shown by the pseudo-closed sets $\{a, c, d, e\}$ and $\{b, c, d, e\}$ of Example 1.4. In fact, Theorem 1.1 of Jamison and Strahringer asserts that all pseudo-closed sets are quasi-closed if only if the closure space is monotactic. The next result characterizes the quasi-closed sets in a matroid.

PROPOSITION 2.1. *For a subset $S$ of a simple matroid, the following are equivalent:*

*1) $S$ is a Q-set;*

*2) $S$ is pseudo-closed and every proper subset of $S$ is closed;*

*3) $S$ is a minimal pseudo-closed set;*

*4) $S$ is an independent pseudo-closed set.*

PROOF. 1) $\implies$ 2) Let $C = S \cup \{x\}$ be a circuit all of whose short-circuits pass through $x \notin S$. Let $T$ be a proper subset of $S$, and suppose $y \notin T$ is in $\mathrm{cl}(T)$. Then $T \cup \{y\}$ contains a circuit which is a short-circuit of $C$ since $|T| < |S|$. But this is impossible since $x \notin T$. Hence $T$ is closed. Since every proper subset of $S$ is closed, $S$ properly contains no pseudo-closed set. Since $x$ is in $\mathrm{cl}(S)$, $S$ is not closed. Thus $S$ is pseudo-closed.

2) $\implies$ 3) If every proper subset of $S$ is closed, $S$ properly contains no pseudo-closed set.

3) $\implies$ 4) If $S$ is minimal pseudo-closed, then no proper subset of $S$ contains a pseudo-closed set and hence must be closed by the theorem of Duquenne and Guiges [1] that the pseudo-closed sets form a premise basis. Hence for any $x$ in $S$, $S \setminus \{x\}$ is closed, so $x \notin \mathrm{cl}(S \setminus \{x\})$. Therefore, $S$ is independent.

4) $\implies$ 2) Hence T is a proper subset of $S$ which is not closed. Since the pseudo-closed sets form a premise basis by Duquenne's theorem, there must be a pseudo-closed set $P$ in $T$ whose closure is not in $T$. Since $P$ is pseudo-closed and hence not closed, there is a $y \notin P$ with $y$ in $\mathrm{cl}(P)$. Now $P$ is a proper subset of $S$ since $T$ is, so since $S$ is pseudo-closed, $\mathrm{cl}(P)$ is in $S$. But then $y$ is in $S$ and in the closure of $P \subseteq S \setminus \{y\}$, contrary to the independence of $S$.

2) $\implies$ 1) Since $S$ is pseudo-closed, it is not closed, so there is an $x \notin S$ with $x$ in $\mathrm{cl}(S)$. Thus $S \cup \{x\}$ contains a circuit $C$ through $x$. Let $T = C \cap S$, so $C = T \cup \{x\}$. If $T$ is a proper subset of $S$, then it is closed by hypothesis. But $x \notin T$ is in $\mathrm{cl}(T)$. Thus $T$ is not a proper subset of $S$, so $T = S$ and $C = S \cup \{x\}$.

Let $D$ be a short-circuit of $C$ with chord $y$. To complete the proof, we must show that $x$ lies in $D$. Let $R = D \cap C$, so $D = R \cup \{y\}$. Suppose $R$ lies in $S$. Now $R$ is not closed since $y \notin R$ but $y$ is in $\mathrm{cl}(R)$. Thus since every proper subset of $S$ is closed, $R = S$ is forced. But then

$$|D| = |R \cup \{y\}| = |R| + 1 = |S| + 1 = |S \cup \{x\}| = |C|,$$

contrary to the assumption that $D$ is a short-circuit of $C$. Thus $R$ cannot lie in $S$. But the only point outside of $S$ in $C$ is $x$, so $R$ and hence $D$ must contain $x$ as desired. $\square$

THEOREM 2.3. *If a matroid $M$ has no monochords, then every pseudo-closed set is a Q-set.*

PROOF. Let $P$ be a pseudo-closed set. We first claim that $P$ contains the closure of every proper subset $S$. We induct on the cardinality $|S|$. The claim is obvious for $|S| = 0$ or $1$ since $M$ is simple. Now suppose $x$ is in $\mathrm{cl}(S)$. Then $x$ forms a circuit with some subset $S'$ of $S$. If $S'$ is a proper subset of $S$, then by induction, $x$ is in $P$. Thus without loss of generality, $C = S \cup \{x\}$ is a circuit.

Suppose first that every short-circuit of $C = S \cup \{x\}$ contains $x$. Then $S$ is a $Q$-set and hence pseudo-closed by Proposition 2.1. Thus since $P$ is pseudo-closed, $\mathrm{cl}(S)$ and hence $x$ lies to $P$ as desired.

On the other hand, suppose there is a short-circuit of $C = S \cup \{x\}$ through some $y$ which avoids $x$. Then this has the form $T \cup \{y\}$ where $T$ is a proper subset of $S$. Thus $|T| < |S|$, so $y$ is in $P$ by induction. Since $T \cup \{y\}$ is a short-circuit of $C$, $\text{IND}(C, y) > 0$. Since $M$ has no monochords by hypothesis, $\text{IND}(C, y) > 1$. Thus by Lemma 2.2, there is a short-circuit of $C = S \cup \{x\}$ through $y$ that contains $x$. This has the form $R \cup \{x, y\}$ where $R$ is a subset of $S$. Now $R \cup \{y\}$ is contained in $P$ and has $x$ in its closure. Also since $R \cup \{x, y\}$ is a short-circuit of $S \cup \{x\}$, we have $|R \cup \{y\}| < |S|$. Thus by induction, $x$ is in $P$ as desired.

Now P is pseudo-closed and hence not closed, so there is a $z \notin P$ in the closure $\text{cl}(P)$. Thus $z$ forms a circuit with a subset of $P$. If this subset is proper, then by the claim proved above, $z$ is in $P$, contrary to its choice. Thus $P \cup \{z\}$ is a circuit. We want to show that every short-circuit $D$ of $P \cup \{z\}$ contains $z$. Let $w$ be the chord of $D$. Now $|D \setminus \{w\}| < |P|$ since $D$ is a short-circuit. Hence if $D \setminus \{w\}$ is a subset of $P$, it would be a proper subset of $P$ with $w$ in its closure. This would force $w$ to be in $P$ by the claim. But as a chord, $w$ should not belong to $P \cup \{z\}$. Hence $D \setminus \{w\}$ is not a subset of $P$. Since $D \setminus \{w\}$ is a subset of $P \cup \{z\}$, this means $z$ is in $D$ as desired. Therefore, $P$ is a $Q$-set.                    □

## 3. Monochordal Matroids

PROPOSITION 3.1. *Let $M$ be a simple matroid on a finite set $X$. Assume that $M$ has a unique circuit $D$ with $|D| < |X| - 1$. Then either*

1) *$D$ is the only circuit or*

2) *$D$ and the sets $X/\{z\}$ for $z$ in $D$ form the complete system of circuits of $M$.*

PROOF. Without loss of generality we may assume $M$ has another circuit $C \neq D$. Then $|C| = |X| - 1$, so $X = C \cup \{x\}$. Now $x$ must be in $D$ since the circuits form an antichain. Since $M$ is simple, $|D| > 2$. For any $z \neq x$ in $D$, $z$ is also in $C$, so there is a circuit contained in $X \setminus \{z\} = (D \cup C) \setminus \{z\}$. Since $D$ is the unique short-circuit, $X \setminus \{z\}$ must be the circuit. Hence $X/\{z\}$ is a circuit for all $z$ in $D$. Now any subset of $X$ either contains $D$ or is contained in $X \setminus \{z\}$ for some $z$ in $D$. Thus since the circuits form an antichain, 2) describes all circuits of $M$.                    □

We call the matroid in the second case above a *monochordal matroid*. It is determined up to isomorphism by the parameters $n = |X|$ and $d = |D|$. Thus we may denote it by $\text{MC}(n, d)$. Of course, we must have $2 < d < n - 1$. Note that the matroid in Example 1.3 is $\text{MC}(5, 3)$, which is the smallest monochordal matroid. It is a minor by contraction of all $\text{MC}(n, d)$ – if loops are deleted. We now characterize the pseudo-closed subsets of $\text{MC}(n, d)$.

PROPOSITION 3.2. *Let $M$ be a monochordal matroid on a set $X$ with unique short-circuit $D$. Then the following constitutes a complete list of the pseudo-closed sets of $M$:*

i) *$D \setminus \{z\}$ for all $z$ in $D$;*

ii) *$X \setminus \{y, z\}$ for all $y \neq z$ in $D$;*

iii) *$X \setminus \{y\}$ for all $y$ not in $D$.*

*Moreover, types i) and ii) are quasi-closed, but type iii) is not quasi-closed.*

PROOF. If a set is not closed, then it must contain all but exactly one element of some circuit $C$. Consider $D \setminus \{z\}$ for $z$ in $D$. For any proper subset, there is no such $C$; hence every proper subset is closed. But $D \setminus \{z\}$ is not closed. Hence $D \setminus \{z\}$ is not only pseudo-closed but even quasi-closed.

Now let $P$ be a pseudo-closed set with associated circuit $C$. If $C = D$, then $D \setminus \{z\}$ lies in $P$ for some $z$ in $D$. If the containment is proper, then since $D \setminus \{z\}$ is pseudo-closed, this would force $z \in \text{cl}(D \setminus \{z\})$ to lie in $P$. But this is contrary to $P$ missing a point of $C$. Thus $C = D$, then $P = D \setminus \{z\}$.

Now suppose $C = X \setminus \{z\}$ for some $z$ in $D$. Let $y$ be the unique point of $C$ missing from $P$. First assume $y$ is in $D$. If $z$ is in $P$, then the pseudo-closed set $D \setminus \{y\}$ is a proper subset of $P$. Since $P$ is pseudo-closed, that forces $y \in \text{cl}(D \setminus \{y\})$ to lie in $P$, contrary to the supposition that $y \notin P$. Hence if $y \in D$, then $z$ is not in $P$. Thus $P = X \setminus \{y, z\}$. Since $y$ and $z$ are both in $D$, $P$ misses two points of every circuit except $X \setminus \{y\}$ and $X \setminus \{z\}$. It follows that every proper subset of $P$ is closed, whereas $\text{cl}(P) = X$. Thus $P$ is again quasi-closed.

Now assume $y$ is not in $D$. Since $P$ contains all points of $C$ except $y \notin D$ and $C$ contains all points of $D$ except $z$, it follows that $D \setminus \{z\}$ is a subset of $P$. Moreover, $|D \setminus \{z\}| = |D| - 1 < |C| - 1 = |P|$, so $D \setminus \{z\}$ is a proper subset of $P$. Since $D \setminus \{z\}$ and $P$ are pseudo-closed, this forces $z \in D = \text{cl}(D \setminus \{z\})$ to lie in $P$. Thus $P = X \setminus \{y\}$ as desired.

Now a set of the form iii) cannot contain a set of the form ii) as sets of the form ii) contain all of $X \setminus D$. Also a set of the form iii) cannot properly contain another set of the form iii) since all such sets have the same cardinality $|X| - 1$. However, a set of the form iii) does contain all sets of the form i), since it contains their common closure D. Thus all sets of the form iii) are pseudo-closed, but not quasi-closed.  □

PROPOSITION 3.3. *A simple matroid $M$ has a monochord if and only if and only if it has some monochordal matroid $MC(n, d)$ as a minor by deletion alone.*

PROOF. ($\Longrightarrow$) Let $x$ be a monochord of a circuit $C$. Then there is a unique short-circuit $D$ of $C$ through $x$. Take $X = C \cup \{x\}$. Then of course $D$ and $C$ are both circuits of $X$. Furthermore, any other circuit $E$ of $X$ cannot lie in $C$ and so must contain $x$. Since $D$ is the unique short-circuit of $C$ through $x$, $E$ must have the same cardinality as $C$. Thus $D$ is the only circuit of $X$ whose cardinality is less than $|X| - 1$. Since $D$ is not the only circuit altogether, 3.1 guarantees that $X$ is a monochordal matroid.

($\Longleftarrow$) In $MC(n, d)$, the short-circuit $D$ is the unique short-circuit of the circuit $X \setminus \{z\}$ with the chord $z$ for each $z$ in $D$. Since adding points does not change circuits, every $z$ in $D$ is a monochord in every matroid containing $MC(n, d)$.  □

We are now in a position to give a proof of Theorem 1.2, in the following slightly more general form.

THEOREM 3.1. *For a simple matroid $M$, the following are equivalent:*
*i) $M$ is hereditarily monotactic;*
*ii) $M$ has no monochords;*
*iii) $M$ does not have any monochordal matroid $MC(n, d)$ as a minor by deletion alone.*

PROOF. (i $\Longrightarrow$ iii) As we saw in (3.2), in $MC(n, d)$, the sets $X \setminus \{y\}$ for $y$ not in $D$ are pseudo-closed but not quasi-closed. Hence $MC(n, d)$ is not monotactic by [3].

(ii $\Longleftrightarrow$ iii) by (3.3).

(ii $\Longrightarrow$ i) If $M$ has no monochords, then by (1.16), all pseudo-closed sets are $Q$-sets. By (1.15.2) all $Q$-sets are quasi-closed. Thus by [3], M is monotactic. Since the property of having no monochords is hereditary to deletion minors, so is the monotactic property. □

PROPOSITION 3.4. *Every minor of a matroid M is monotactic if and only if* $MC(5,3)$ *is not a minor of* $M$.

PROOF. If $M$ has a polytactic minor, then that minor contains $MC(n,d)$ for some $n$ and $d$ by (3.1). As $MC(5,3)$ is a minor by contraction of $MC(n,d)$, it follows that $M$ has $MC(5,3)$ as a minor. Conversely, $MC(5,3)$ is not monotactic, so if $MC(5,3)$ is a minor of $M$, then $M$ has a polytactic minor. □

COROLLARY 3.2. *Every binary matroid is monotactic.*

PROOF. $MC(5,3)$ is not binary and the binary matroids are a minor-closed class. □

In fact, using Oxley's work on 3-connected matroids and minor-excluded classes of matroids, we can deduce the following dual characterization of minor monotactic matroids. Notice that the dual of $MC(5,3)$ is $U_{2,4}$, the four point line with a an additional element in parallel. I am grateful to James Oxley for pointing out this characterization.

COROLLARY 3.3. $M$ *is the dual of a matroid all of whose minors are monotactic if and only if* $M$ *can be obtained from binary matroids and uniform matroids by a sequence of direct sums and series extensions.*

## 4. Linear Matroids

THEOREM 4.1. *Let* $e$ *be a chord of a circuit* $C$ *in a linear matroid over a field* $F$. *Then* $\operatorname{ind}(C : e) \leq |F|$. *Moreover, if* $IND(C : e) = 1$, *then* $|S| \leq |F|$ *where* $S$ *is the unique short-circuit of* $C$ *through* $e$.

PROOF. Let $v_1, v_2, v_3, \ldots, v_n$ denote the points of $C$, and let $e, v_1, v_2, v_3, \ldots, v_k$ denote the points of a circuit $S$ through $e$. Then for some scalars $a_i$ and $b_i$ in $F$, we have
   (1) $a_1 v_1 + a_2 v_2 + a_3 v_3 + \ldots + a_k v_k + \ldots + a_n v_n = 0$ and
   (2) $e + b_1 v_1 + b_2 v_2 + b_3 v_3 + \ldots + b_k v_k = 0$.
Since $C$ and $S$ are circuits, these scalars are unique up to a constant multiple. We may normalize (2) to keep the coefficient of $e$ fixed at 1, as we wish to retain $e$ in our circuit in any event. Thus we are free only to multiple (1) by a constant $c$ and add to (2) to get a "new" circuit through $e$. In so doing, $v_i$ is eliminated from the "new" circuit provided $ca_i + b_i = 0$ or equivalently, $c = -b_i/a_i$. Each choice of $c$ results in a circuit through $e$ whose complement in $C$ consists of those $v_i$ with $c = -b_i/a_i$. (Note that $c = 0$ yields the circuit $S$ with which we started.) Thus the number of circuits through $e$ is at most $|F|$. Notice that a "new" circuit will be a short circuit if and only if there are two or more indices i with $c = -b_i/a_i$. Suppose we start with a short-circuit $S$ with $|S| > |F|$. Then $k > |F| - 1$, so at least two of the ratios $-b_i/a_i$ for $i$ from 1 to $k$ must coincide since none of these ratios can be zero. The resulting "new" circuit will be a second short-circuit through $e$. □

COROLLARY 4.2. *If* $e$ *is a chord of a circuit* $C$ *in a linear matroid over* $GF(2)$, *then* $IND(C : e) = 2$.

THEOREM 4.3. *The monochordal matroid $MC(n,d)$ is representable over a field $F$ if and only if $d \leq |F|$.*

PROOF. ($\Longrightarrow$) If $MC(n,d)$ is representable, then the circuit $D$ of length $d$ is a short-circuit. Hence by Theorem 4.1, $d = |D| \leq |F|$.

($\Longleftarrow$) Since the rank of $MC(n,d)$ is $n - 2$, take an $(n-2)$-dimensional $F$-vector space and let $e_1, e_2, \ldots, e_{n-2}$ be a basis. Let $t$ be the sum of these basis vectors so that $\{e_1, e_2, \ldots, e_{n-2}, t\}$ is a circuit. Now let $a_1, a_2, a_3, \ldots, a_{d-1}$ be $d - 1$ distinct non-zero scalars in $F$. Since $d \leq |F|$, these exist. Take $s := a_1 e_1 + a_2 e_2 + \cdots + a_{d-1} e_{d-1}$. Then $\{e_1, e_2, \ldots, e_{d-1}, s\}$ is a circuit. It is easy to see that there are no more circuits of length less than $n - 1$, so by Proposition 3.1, the set $\{e_1, e_2, \ldots, e_{n-2}, s, t\}$ must induce $MC(n,d)$ as desired. $\square$

# References

[1] V. Duquenne and J. L. Guiges, *Familles minimales d'implications informatives resultant d'un tableau de donnees binaires*, Math. Sci. Hun. 95(1986), 5-18.

[2] B. Ganter, *Algorithmen zur formalen Begriffsanalyse*, in: B. Ganter, R. Wille, K.E. Wolff, eds., Beitrage zur Begriffsanalyse (B.I.-Wissenschaftsverlag, Mannheim 1987), 241 - 254.

[3] R. Jamison and S. Strahringer, *Disjunctive products of antimatroids*, in preparation.

[4] James G. Oxley, *On singleton 1-rounded sets of matroids*, J Comb Theory Ser B 37(1984), 189 - 197.

[5] James G. Oxley, *On nonbinary 3-connected matroids*, Trans Am Math Soc 300(1987), 663 - 679.

[6] James G. Oxley, *A characterization of certain excluded-minor classes of matroids*, Europ. J. Combinatorics 10 (1989), 275 - 279.

[7] Selma Strahringer, *Direct products of convex-ordinal scales*, dissertation, Technische Hochschule Darmstadt, 1992.

[8] M. Wild, *Implicational bases for finite closure systems*, in W. Lex, ed., Arbeitstagung Begriffsanalyse und Künstliche Intelligenz (TU Clausthal 1991), 147- 170

[9] R. Wille, *Tensorial decomposition of concept lattices*, Order 2 (1985), 81-95.

DEPARTMENT OF MATHEMATICAL SCIENCES, CLEMSON UNIVERSITY, CLEMSON, SC 29634-1907
*E-mail address:*   rejam@clemson.edu

Contemporary Mathematics
Volume **197**, 1996

# On binary matroids with a $K_{3,3}$-minor

S.R. Kingan

ABSTRACT. We prove that every binary 3-connected matroid with an $M(K_{3,3})$-minor must also have an $M(K_5\backslash e)$- or $M^*(K_5\backslash e)$-minor, the only exceptions being $M(K_{3,3})$, the unique splitter $R_{10}$ for regular matroids, and a 10-element, rank-5, self-dual matroid called $M(E_5)$.

## 1. Introduction

In 1930, Kuratowski [5] characterized planar graphs by proving that a graph is planar if and only if it has no subgraph homeomorphic with $K_5$ or $K_{3,3}$. Wagner [10] proved that a graph is planar if and only if it has no minor isomorphic to $K_5$ or $K_{3,3}$. D.W. Hall [2] proved that every simple 3-connected graph with a $K_5$-minor must also have a $K_{3,3}$-minor, the only exception being $K_5$ itself. Seymour [9, 7.5] noted that the above result also holds for regular matroids. In [3] the author showed that Hall's result can be generalized to binary matroids as follows: Every 3-connected binary matroid with an $M(K_5)$-minor must also have an $M(K_{3,3})$- or $M^*(K_{3,3})$-minor, the only exceptions being $M(K_5)$, a highly symmetric, 12-element, rank-6, binary matroid called $T_{12}$, and any single-element contraction of $T_{12}$. This result implies that the excluded-minor classes $\mathcal{E}\mathcal{X}(M(K_{3,3}), M^*(K_{3,3}), M(K_5), M^*(K_5), U_{2,4})$ and $\mathcal{E}\mathcal{X}(M(K_{3,3}), M^*(K_{3,3}), U_{2,4})$ are almost the same, where $\mathcal{E}\mathcal{X}(M_1, M_2, \ldots, M_k)$ denotes the class of matroids having none of the matroids $M_1, M_2, \ldots, M_k$ as minors. Note that excluding $U_{2,4}$ guarantees that these matroids are binary.

In this paper we study the excluded-minor class $\mathcal{E}\mathcal{X}(M(K_{3,3}), M^*(K_{3,3}), M(K_5\backslash e), M^*(K_5\backslash e), U_{2,4})$. One reason for studying this class is as follows: It is well known that the three nonisomorphic binary 3-connected single-element extensions of the 4-wheel $M(W_4)$ are $M(K_5\backslash e)$, $M^*(K_{3,3})$, and a nonregular 9-element matroid $P_9$. In [6] Oxley determined the 3-connected members of the class $\mathcal{E}\mathcal{X}(P_9, P_9^*, U_{2,4})$. Therefore it would be interesting to know the 3-connected members of $\mathcal{E}\mathcal{X}(M(K_{3,3}), M^*(K_{3,3}), M(K_5\backslash e), M^*(K_5\backslash e), U_{2,4})$. We prove that the above class and $\mathcal{E}\mathcal{X}(M(K_5\backslash e), M^*(K_5\backslash e), U_{2,4})$ are almost the same. The main theorem of this paper states that every 3-connected binary matroid with

---

1991 *Mathematics Subject Classification.* Primary 05B35, 05C75.

an $M(K_{3,3})$-minor must also have an $M(K_5\backslash e)$- or $M^*(K_5\backslash e)$-minor, the only exceptions being $M(K_{3,3})$, $R_{10}$, and $M(E_5)$. Binary matrix representations for $R_{10}$ and $M(E_5)$ are shown below.

$$
\begin{array}{cccccccccc}
1 & 2 & 3 & 4 & 5 & 6 & 7 & 8 & 9 & 10
\end{array}
$$

$$
\left(
\begin{array}{ccccc|ccccc}
 & & & & & 1 & 1 & 0 & 0 & 1 \\
 & & & & & 1 & 1 & 1 & 0 & 0 \\
 & & I_5 & & & 0 & 1 & 1 & 1 & 0 \\
 & & & & & 0 & 0 & 1 & 1 & 1 \\
 & & & & & 1 & 0 & 0 & 1 & 1
\end{array}
\right)
\qquad
\left(
\begin{array}{ccccc|ccccc}
 & & & & & 1 & 0 & 0 & 1 & 1 \\
 & & & & & 1 & 1 & 0 & 1 & 0 \\
 & & I_5 & & & 1 & 1 & 1 & 1 & 1 \\
 & & & & & 0 & 1 & 1 & 1 & 0 \\
 & & & & & 0 & 0 & 1 & 1 & 0
\end{array}
\right)
$$

$$
\begin{array}{ccc}
R_{10} & \qquad\qquad\qquad & M(E_5)
\end{array}
$$

The matroid $R_{10}$ is self-dual and it is the unique splitter for regular matroids [9]. The linear transformation $(x_1,\ x_2,\ x_3,\ x_4,\ x_5)^T \longmapsto (x_3,\ x_2,\ x_4,\ x_1,\ x_5)^T$ maps the matrix representing $M^*(E_5)$ to the matrix representing $M(E_5)$; hence $M(E_5)$ is self-dual. It is non-regular since $M(E_5)\backslash 5/4, 8 \cong F_7$. Chula Jayavardane, a student of Neil Robertson at Ohio State University, independently showed that the matroid $M(E_5)$ is a splitter for the class of binary matroids with neither $M(K_5\backslash e)$- nor $M^*(K_5\backslash e)$-minors (see Lemma 2.3).

The matroid terminology in general follows Oxley [7]. A matroid $N$ is a *minor* of a matroid $M$ if $N \cong M\backslash X/Y$ for some disjoint subsets $X$ and $Y$ of $E(M)$. A circuit with $k$ elements is called a *k-circuit*. The *cycle matroid* of a graph $G$ is denoted by $M(G)$. The *vector matroid* of a matrix $A$ is denoted by $M(A)$. A matroid is *binary* if it can be represented by a matrix over $GF(2)$. A basic tool in this paper is the well-known fact that binary matroids are uniquely representable; that is, if $A$ and $A'$ are $r \times n$ matrices over $GF(2)$ such that the map which, for all $i \in \{1,2,\ldots,n\}$, takes the $i$ th column of $A$ to the $i$ th column of $A'$ is an isomorphism from $M(A)$ to $M(A')$, then $A'$ can be transformed into $A$ by a sequence of operations each of which consists of interchanging two rows or adding one row to another. We shall assume familiarity with the pivoting operation. In order to maintain a representation in the standard form $[I_r|D]$, every pivot will be followed by the appropriate column interchange. See, for example, [7, p. 209]. If $A$ is an $r \times n$ matrix with column labels $1, 2, \ldots, n$, and $\bar{x}$ is an $r \times 1$ column vector, then denote by $A \cup \bar{x}$ the $r \times (n+1)$ matrix $A$ with the column $\bar{x}$ affixed at the end. Label the columns of $A \cup \bar{x}$ as $1, 2, \ldots, n, x$. A matroid $M$ is *3-connected* if it is connected and $E(M)$ cannot be partitioned into subsets $X$ and $Y$, each having at least two elements, such that $r(X) + r(Y) - r(M) = 1$. Let $\mathcal{C}$ be a class of matroids that is closed under minors and under isomorphisms. A member $N$ of $\mathcal{C}$ is called a *splitter* for $\mathcal{C}$ if no 3-connected member of $\mathcal{C}$ has a proper minor isomorphic to $N$.

## 2. The main theorem

The following theorem is the main result of this paper. Computations involving single-element extensions may be found in the Appendix.

THEOREM 2.1. *Suppose $M$ is a 3-connected binary matroid with an $M(K_{3,3})$-minor. Then either $M$ has an $M(K_5\backslash e)$- or $M^*(K_5\backslash e)$-minor or $M$ is isomorphic to $M(K_{3,3})$, $R_{10}$, or $M(E_5)$.*

LEMMA 2.2. *The matroids $R_{10}$ and $M(E_5)$ have neither $M(K_5\backslash e)$- nor $M^*(K_5\backslash e)$-minors.*

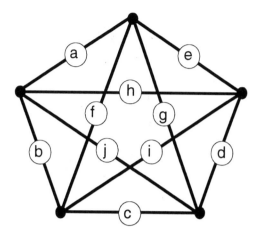

FIGURE 1. $K_5$.

PROOF. Since $R_{10}$ and $M(E_5)$ are self-dual, it is sufficient to show that neither of them has an $M^*(K_5\backslash e)$-minor. Every single-element deletion of $R_{10}$ is isomorphic to $M(K_{3,3})$. Therefore $R_{10}$ has no $M^*(K_5\backslash e)$-minor. The matroid $M(E_5)$ has nine 4-circuits, $\{1,2,3,6\}$, $\{2,3,4,7\}$, $\{1,4,6,7\}$, $\{3,4,5,8\}$, $\{2,5,7,8\}$, $\{4,5,6,9\}$, $\{1,5,7,9\}$, $\{1,2,8,9\}$, and $\{3,6,8,9\}$. Each element other than 10 appears in exactly four 4-circuits, and 10 appears in none of the 4-circuits. Suppose, if possible, $M(E_5)\backslash e \cong M^*(K_5\backslash e)$ for some element $e$ in $M(E_5)$. Since the circuits of $M(E_5)\backslash e$ are the circuits of $M(E_5)$ not containing $e$, $M(E_5)\backslash e$ will have either five or nine 4-circuits. This is a contradiction since $M^*(K_5\backslash e)$ has three 4-circuits. Therefore, $M(E_5)$ has no $M^*(K_5\backslash e)$-minor.                                    $\square$

PROOF OF THEOREM 2.1. Suppose $M$ is a 3-connected binary matroid with an $M(K_{3,3})$-minor. Seymour's Splitter Theorem [7, 11.2.1] implies that there is a chain $M_0$, $M_1$, ..., $M_n$ of 3-connected matroids such that $M_0 \cong M(K_{3,3})$, $M_n = M$, and for all $i \in \{0,1,\ldots,n-1\}$, $M_{i+1}$ is a single-element extension or coextension of $M_i$. If $M \cong M(K_{3,3})$, then there is nothing to prove. Therefore, assume this does not occur. Then, $M_0 \cong M(K_{3,3})$ and $M_1$ is an extension or coextension of $M(K_{3,3})$. Suppose $M_1$ is a coextension of $M(K_{3,3})$. Note that the coextensions of $M(K_{3,3})$ are the duals of the extensions of $M^*(K_{3,3})$. The matroid $M^*(K_{3,3})$ has precisely one binary 3-connected single-element extension denoted by $(K_{3,3}^*, ext1)$. The matrices representing $(K_{3,3}^*, ext1)$ and $(K_{3,3}^*, ext1)\backslash 1$ are shown below.

$$
\begin{array}{c}
\begin{array}{cccccccccc} 1 & 2 & 3 & 4 & 5 & 6 & 7 & 8 & 9 & 10 \end{array} \\
\left( \begin{array}{cccc|cccccc}
 & & & & 1 & 1 & 1 & 0 & 0 & 1 \\
 & \multicolumn{2}{c}{I_4} & & 0 & 1 & 1 & 1 & 0 & 1 \\
 & & & & 0 & 0 & 1 & 1 & 1 & 1 \\
 & & & & 1 & 1 & 1 & 1 & 1 & 0
\end{array} \right) \\
(K_{3,3}^*, ext1)
\end{array}
\qquad
\begin{array}{c}
\begin{array}{ccccccccc} 5 & 2 & 3 & 4 & 6 & 7 & 8 & 9 & 10 \end{array} \\
\left( \begin{array}{cccc|ccccc}
 & & & & 1 & 1 & 0 & 0 & 1 \\
 & \multicolumn{2}{c}{I_4} & & 1 & 1 & 1 & 0 & 1 \\
 & & & & 0 & 1 & 1 & 1 & 1 \\
 & & & & 0 & 0 & 1 & 1 & 1
\end{array} \right) \\
(K_{3,3}^*, ext1)\backslash 1
\end{array}
$$

Observe that columns $5,2,3,4,6,7,8,9,10$ of the matrix representing $(K_{3,3}^*, ext1)\backslash 1$ correspond to the edges $a,b,c,d,f,g,h,i,e$ of the graph $K_5$ in Figure 1. Therefore $(K_{3,3}^*, ext1)\backslash 1 \cong M(K_5\backslash e)$. So if $M_1 \cong (K_{3,3}^*, ext1)^*$, then $M_1$ has an $M^*(K_5 \backslash e)$-minor, and consequently so does $M$. Next, suppose $M_1$ is an extension of $M(K_{3,3})$. The matroid $M(K_{3,3})$ has precisely four non-isomorphic binary 3-connected single-element extensions denoted by $(K_{3,3}, exti)$ for $i \in \{1, 2, 3, 4\}$. Matrix representations for these matroids are shown below.

$$
\begin{array}{cccccccccc}
1 & 2 & 3 & 4 & 5 & 6 & 7 & 8 & 9 & 10
\end{array}
\left(
\begin{array}{c|ccccc}
 & & & & 1 & 0 & 0 & 1 & 1 \\
 & & & & 1 & 1 & 0 & 1 & 1 \\
 & I_5 & & & 1 & 1 & 1 & 1 & 0 \\
 & & & & 0 & 1 & 1 & 1 & 0 \\
 & & & & 0 & 0 & 1 & 1 & 0
\end{array}
\right)
\qquad
\begin{array}{cccccccccc}
1 & 2 & 3 & 4 & 5 & 6 & 7 & 8 & 9 & 10
\end{array}
\left(
\begin{array}{c|ccccc}
 & & & & 1 & 0 & 0 & 1 & 1 \\
 & & & & 1 & 1 & 0 & 1 & 0 \\
 & I_5 & & & 1 & 1 & 1 & 1 & 1 \\
 & & & & 0 & 1 & 1 & 1 & 0 \\
 & & & & 0 & 0 & 1 & 1 & 0
\end{array}
\right)
$$

$$(K_{3,3}, ext1) \qquad\qquad\qquad (K_{3,3}, ext2)$$

$$
\begin{array}{cccccccccc}
1 & 2 & 3 & 4 & 5 & 6 & 7 & 8 & 9 & 10
\end{array}
\left(
\begin{array}{c|ccccc}
 & & & & 1 & 0 & 0 & 1 & 1 \\
 & & & & 1 & 1 & 0 & 1 & 1 \\
 & I_5 & & & 1 & 1 & 1 & 1 & 0 \\
 & & & & 0 & 1 & 1 & 1 & 1 \\
 & & & & 0 & 0 & 1 & 1 & 0
\end{array}
\right)
\qquad
\begin{array}{cccccccccc}
1 & 2 & 3 & 4 & 5 & 6 & 7 & 8 & 9 & 10
\end{array}
\left(
\begin{array}{c|ccccc}
 & & & & 1 & 0 & 0 & 1 & 1 \\
 & & & & 1 & 1 & 0 & 1 & 0 \\
 & I_5 & & & 1 & 1 & 1 & 1 & 1 \\
 & & & & 0 & 1 & 1 & 1 & 0 \\
 & & & & 0 & 0 & 1 & 1 & 1
\end{array}
\right)
$$

$$(K_{3,3}, ext3) \qquad\qquad\qquad (K_{3,3}, ext4)$$

Observe that $(K_{3,3}, ext1) \cong M(K'_{3,3})$, the cycle matroid of the graph $K_{3,3}$ with an additional edge (see [1 p. 110]) and $(K_{3,3}, ext2) = M(E_5)$. The linear transformation $(x_1, x_2, x_3, x_4, x_5)^T \longmapsto (x_1, x_2 + x_1, x_3 + x_1, x_4, x_5)^T$ maps the matrix representing $(K_{3,3}, ext4)$ to the matrix representing $R_{10}$; hence $(K_{3,3}, ext4) \cong R_{10}$. Lemma 2.2 implies that $R_{10}$ and $M(E_5)$ have no $M(K_5 \backslash e)$- or $M^*(K_5 \backslash e)$-minor. Each of the matroids $(K_{3,3}, ext1)/4$ and $(K_{3,3}, ext3)/3$ is isomorphic to $M(K_5 \backslash e)$. If $M_1$ is isomorphic to either $(K_{3,3}, ext1)$ or $(K_{3,3}, ext3)$, then $M_1$ has an $M(K_5 \backslash e)$-minor, and therefore so does $M$. So assume $M_1 \cong R_{10}$ or $M(E_5)$. The next lemma completes the proof of the theorem.

LEMMA 2.3. *The matroids $R_{10}$ and $M(E_5)$ are splitters for the class of binary matroids with neither $M(K_5 \backslash e)$- nor $M^*(K_5 \backslash e)$-minors.*

PROOF. The matroid $R_{10}$ has two nonisomorphic binary 3-connected single-element extensions denoted by $(R_{10}, ext1)$ and $(R_{10}, ext2)$. It is shown in the Appendix that $(R_{10}, ext1)$ has a minor isomorphic to $M(K'_{3,3})$ and $(R_{10}, ext2)$ has a minor isomorphic to $(K_{3,3}, ext3)$, both of which have an $M(K_5 \backslash e)$-minor. The matroid $M(E_5)$ has seven nonisomorphic binary 3-connected single-element extensions denoted by $(E_5, exti)$ for $i \in \{1, 2, \ldots, 7\}$. Each of the matroids $(E_5, ext1)$ and $(E_5, ext4)$ has a minor isomorphic to $M(K'_{3,3})$. Each of the matroids $(E_5, ext3)$ and $(E_5, ext6)$ has a minor isomorphic to $(K_{3,3}, ext3)$. Let $(E_5, ext2)$, $(E_5, ext5)$, and $(E_5, ext7)$ be the matroids obtained by adjoining columns $(10010)$, $(10001)$, and $(10101)$, respectively, to $E_5$. The matrices representing the matroids $(E_5, ext2)/5\backslash 9$, $(E_5, ext5)/4\backslash 9$, and $(E_5, ext7)/4\backslash 9$ are shown below:

$$
\begin{array}{ccccccccc}
1 & 2 & 3 & 4 & 6 & 7 & 8 & 10 & 11
\end{array}
\left(
\begin{array}{c|ccccc}
 & & & & 1 & 0 & 0 & 1 & 1 \\
 & & & & 1 & 1 & 0 & 0 & 0 \\
 & I_4 & & & 1 & 1 & 1 & 1 & 0 \\
 & & & & 0 & 1 & 1 & 0 & 1
\end{array}
\right)
\qquad
\begin{array}{ccccccccc}
1 & 2 & 3 & 5 & 6 & 7 & 8 & 10 & 11
\end{array}
\left(
\begin{array}{c|ccccc}
 & & & & 1 & 0 & 0 & 1 & 1 \\
 & & & & 1 & 1 & 0 & 0 & 0 \\
 & I_4 & & & 1 & 1 & 1 & 1 & 0 \\
 & & & & 0 & 0 & 1 & 0 & 1
\end{array}
\right)
$$

$(E_5, ext2)/5\backslash 9$                                          $(E_5, ext5)/4\backslash 9$

$$
\begin{array}{ccccccccc}
1 & 2 & 3 & 5 & 6 & 7 & 8 & 10 & 11
\end{array}
$$

$$
\left(
\begin{array}{cccc|ccccc}
 & & & & 1 & 0 & 0 & 1 & 1 \\
 & & & & 1 & 1 & 0 & 0 & 0 \\
 & I_4 & & & 1 & 1 & 1 & 1 & 1 \\
 & & & & 0 & 0 & 1 & 0 & 1
\end{array}
\right)
$$

$(E_5, ext7)/4\backslash 9$

Observe that columns $1, 2, 3, 4, 6, 7, 8, 10, 11$ of the matrix representing $(E_5, ext2)/5\backslash 9$ corresponds to the edges $f, j, a, e, c, d, h, b, i$ of the graph $K_5$ in Figure 1. Therefore $(E_5, ext2)/5\backslash 9 \cong M(K_5\backslash e)$. Similarly, each of the matroids $(E_5, ext5)/4\backslash 9$ and $(E_5, ext7)/4\backslash 9$ is isomorphic to $M(K_5\backslash e)$. Therefore, each binary 3-connected extension of $R_{10}$ and $M(E_5)$ has a minor isomorphic to $M(K_5\backslash e)$. Finally, since $R_{10}$ and $M(E_5)$ are self-dual, each of their binary 3-connected coextensions has a minor isomorphic to $M^*(K_5\backslash e)$.               $\square$

For graphs the main theorem implies that every simple 3-connected graph with a $K_{3,3}$-minor must also have a $K_5\backslash e$- or $(K_5\backslash e)^*$- minor, the only exception being $K_{3,3}$ itself. The following corollary is a direct consequence of the main theorem.

COROLLARY 2.4. *The 3-connected binary matroids in* $\mathcal{EX}[M(K_5\backslash e),$ $M^*(K_5\backslash e)]$ *but not in* $\mathcal{EX}[M(K_5\backslash e),\ M^*(K_5\backslash e),\ M(K_{3,3}),\ M^*(K_{3,3})]$ *are precisely* $M(K_{3,3}),\ M^*(K_{3,3}),\ R_{10},$ *and* $M(E_5)$.              $\square$

## Appendix

The matroids $M(K_{3,3})$ and $M^*(K_{3,3})$ are represented by the matrices $X$ and $X^*$, respectively, shown below:

$$
\begin{array}{ccccccc}
1 & \ldots & 5 & 6 & 7 & 8 & 9
\end{array}
$$

$$
X = \left(
\begin{array}{ccc|cccc}
 & & & 1 & 0 & 0 & 1 \\
 & & & 1 & 1 & 0 & 1 \\
 & I_5 & & 1 & 1 & 1 & 1 \\
 & & & 0 & 1 & 1 & 1 \\
 & & & 0 & 0 & 1 & 1
\end{array}
\right),
\quad
X^* = \left(
\begin{array}{ccc|ccccc}
 & & & 1 & 1 & 1 & 0 & 0 \\
 & I_4 & & 0 & 1 & 1 & 1 & 0 \\
 & & & 0 & 0 & 1 & 1 & 1 \\
 & & & 1 & 1 & 1 & 1 & 1
\end{array}
\right).
$$

with column headers $\begin{array}{ccccccc}1 & \ldots & 4 & 5 & 6 & 7 & 8 & 9\end{array}$ for $X^*$.

Assume that the column $\bar{x} = (x_1, x_2, x_3, x_4, x_5)^T$ is adjoined to the matrix $X$ to obtain a 3-connected binary matroid. For convenience we will drop the transpose. There are 22 choices for $\bar{x}$. If $\bar{x} \in \{(11000), (01100), (00110), (11110), (00011),$ $(01111)\}$, then $M(X \cup \bar{x}) \cong (K_{3,3}, ext1)$. If $\bar{x} \in \{(10100), (10010), (01010), (10001),$ $(01001), (00101), (11101), (11011), (10111)\}$, then $M(X \cup \bar{x}) \cong (K_{3,3}, ext2)$. If $\bar{x} \in$ $\{(11010), (10110), (11001), (01101), (10011), (01011)\}$, then $M(X\cup\bar{x}) \cong (K_{3,3}, ext3)$. If $\bar{x} = (10101)$, then $M(X \cup \bar{x}) \cong (K_{3,3}, ext4)$. Observe that, $(K_{3,3}, ext1)$ has three 3-circuits and four 3-cocircuits, $(K_{3,3}, ext2)$ has two 3-circuits and two 3-cocircuits, $(K_{3,3}, ext3)$ has zero 3-circuits and two 3-cocircuits, and $(K_{3,3}, ext4)$ has zero 3-circuits and zero 3-cocircuits. Hence these extensions are nonisomorphic. To verify that columns in each class give rise to isomorphic extensions of $M(K_{3,3})$ observe that each of the following linear transformations on $X$ induces an automorphism on $M(K_{3,3})$:

$$
\alpha : (x_1,\ x_2,\ x_3,\ x_4,\ x_5)^T \longmapsto (x_1,\ x_5 + x_1,\ x_4 + x_1,\ x_3 + x_1,\ x_2 + x_1)^T,
$$
$$
\beta : (x_1,\ x_2,\ x_3,\ x_4,\ x_5)^T \longmapsto (x_1 + x_2,\ x_2,\ x_5 + x_2,\ x_4 + x_2,\ x_3 + x_2)^T,
$$

$\gamma : (x_1,\ x_2,\ x_3,\ x_4,\ x_5)^T \longmapsto (x_1,\ x_1 + x_3 + x_4,\ x_1 + x_3 + x_5,\ x_2 + x_3 + x_5,\ x_5)^T$.
Now observe that $\beta(01111)^T = (11000)^T$, $\alpha(11000)^T = (11110)^T$, $\beta(11110)^T = (01100)^T$, $\alpha(01100)^T = (00011)^T$, and $\beta(00011)^T = (00110)^T$. Therefore, adjoining any one of these columns to $X$ gives a matroid isomorphic to $(K_{3,3}, ext1)$. The other cases can be done similarly. It can be checked that $M^*(K_{3,3})$ has precisely one binary 3-connected single-element extension.

Next, the matroids $R_{10}$ and $M(E_5)$ are represented by the matrices $Y$ and $Z$, respectively, shown below:

$$Y = \left( \begin{array}{ccccc} & & & & \\ & I_5 & & & \\ & & & & \\ & & & & \\ & & & & \end{array} \left| \begin{array}{ccccc} 1 & 0 & 0 & 1 & 1 \\ 1 & 1 & 0 & 1 & 0 \\ 1 & 1 & 1 & 1 & 1 \\ 0 & 1 & 1 & 1 & 0 \\ 0 & 0 & 1 & 1 & 1 \end{array} \right. \right), \quad Z = \left( \begin{array}{ccccc} & & & & \\ & I_5 & & & \\ & & & & \\ & & & & \\ & & & & \end{array} \left| \begin{array}{ccccc} 1 & 0 & 0 & 1 & 1 \\ 1 & 1 & 0 & 1 & 0 \\ 1 & 1 & 1 & 1 & 1 \\ 0 & 1 & 1 & 1 & 0 \\ 0 & 0 & 1 & 1 & 0 \end{array} \right. \right).$$

For convenience, $R_{10}$ is represented as a single-element extension of $M(K_{3,3})$. Assume that the column $\bar{x} = (x_1, x_2, x_3, x_4, x_5)^T$ is adjoined to the matrix $Y$ to obtain a 3-connected binary matroid. There are 21 choices for $\bar{x}$. If $\bar{x} \in \{(11000), (10100), (01100), (10010), (01010), (00110), (11110), (10001), (01001), (00101), (11101), (00011), (11011), (10111), (01111)\}$, then $M(Y \cup \bar{x}) \cong (R_{10}, ext1)$. If $\bar{x} \in \{(11010), (10110), (11001), (01101), (10011), (01011)\}$, then $M(Y \cup \bar{x}) \cong (R_{10}, ext2)$. These extensions are nonisomorphic since $(R_{10}, ext1)$ has three 3-circuits and zero 3-cocircuits and $(R_{10}, ext2)$ has zero 3-circuits and zero 3-cocircuits. Observe that each of the following linear transformations on $Y$ induces an automorphism on $R_{10}$:

$\alpha : (x_1,\ x_2,\ x_3,\ x_4,\ x_5)^T \longmapsto (x_5,\ x_1 + x_5,\ x_1 + x_2 + x_5,\ x_1 + x_3,\ x_4)^T$,
$\beta : (x_1,\ x_2,\ x_3,\ x_4,\ x_5)^T \longmapsto (x_1,\ x_1 + x_2,\ x_1 + x_4,\ x_1 + x_3,\ x_1 + x_5)^T$.

These automorphisms can be used to verify that columns in each class give rise to isomorphic extensions. Notice that $(R_{10}, ext1)$ is obtained by adjoining column $(11000)$ to $Y$. Therefore, $(R_{10}, ext1)$ has a minor isomorphic to $(K_{3,3}, ext1)$. Similarly, $(R_{10}, ext2)$ is obtained by adjoining column $(11010)$ to $Y$. Therefore, $(R_{10}, ext2)$ has a minor isomorphic to $(K_{3,3}, ext3)$.

Assume that the column $\bar{x} = (x_1, x_2, x_3, x_4, x_5)^T$ is adjoined to the matrix $Z$ to obtain a 3-connected binary matroid. There are 21 choices for $\bar{x}$. If $\bar{x} \in \{(11000), (01100)\}$, then $M(Z \cup \bar{x}) \cong (E_5, ext1)$. If $\bar{x} \in \{(10010), (01010), (11011), (10111)\}$, then $M(Z \cup \bar{x}) \cong (E_5, ext2)$. If $\bar{x} \in \{(11010), (10110), (10011), (01011)\}$, then $M(Z \cup \bar{x}) \cong (E_5, ext3)$. If $\bar{x} \in \{(00110), (11110), (00011), (01111)\}$, then $M(Z \cup \bar{x}) \cong (E_5, ext4)$. If $\bar{x} \in \{(10001), (01001), (00101), (11101)\}$, then $M(Z \cup \bar{x}) \cong (E_5, ext5)$. If $\bar{x} \in \{(11001), (01101)\}$, then $M(Z \cup \bar{x}) \cong (E_5, ext6)$. If $\bar{x} = (10101)$, then $M(Z \cup \bar{x}) \cong (E_5, ext7)$. Observe that, $(E_5, ext1)$ has five 3-circuits and two 3-cocircuits, $(E_5, ext2)$ has four 3-circuits and one 3-cocircuits, $(E_5, ext3)$ has three 3-circuits and one 3-cocircuit, $(E_5, ext4)$ has five 3-circuits and one 3-cocircuit, $(E_5, ext5)$ has four 3-circuits and zero 3-cocircuits, $(E_5, ext6)$ has two 3-circuits and zero 3-cocircuits, and $(E_5, ext7)$ has three 3-circuits and zero 3-cocircuits. Hence these extensions are nonisomorphic. Observe that each of the following linear transformations on $Z$ induces an automorphism on $M(E_5)$:

$\alpha : (x_1,\ x_2,\ x_3,\ x_4,\ x_5)^T \longmapsto (x_2 + x_3,\ x_1 + x_3,\ x_3,\ x_4,\ x_5)^T$
$\beta : (x_1,\ x_2,\ x_3,\ x_4,\ x_5)^T \longmapsto (x_3 + x_4,\ x_2 + x_4,\ x_1 + x_4,\ x_4,\ x_5 + x_4)^T$

These automorphisms can be used to verify that columns in each class give rise to isomorphic extensions.

*Acknowledgment:* The author thanks Joe Bonin, James Oxley, and the referee for many helpful comments and suggestions.

## References

[1] B. Bollobás, *"Extremal Graph Theory"*, Academic Press, London (1978).

[2] D.W. Hall, *A note on primitive skew curves*, Bull. Amer. Math. Soc. **49** (1943), 935-937.

[3] S.R. Kingan, *A generalization of a graph result of D.W. Hall*, Discrete Math., to appear..

[4] J.P.S. Kung, *Excluding the cycle geometries of the Kuratowski graphs from binary geometries*, Proc. London Math. Soc. (3) **55** (1987), 209-242.

[5] K. Kuratowski, *Sur le problème des courbes gauches en topologie*, Fund. Math. **15** (1930), 271-283.

[6] J.G. Oxley, *The binary matroids with no 4-wheel minor*, Trans. Amer. Math. Soc. **154** (1987), 63-75.

[7] J.G. Oxley, *"Matroid Theory"*, Oxford University Press, New York (1992).

[8] N. Robertson, P.D. Seymour, *Generalizing Kuratowksi's Theorem*, Congressus Numerantium **45** (1984), 129-138.

[9] P.D. Seymour, *Decomposition of regular matroids*, J. Combin. Theory Ser. B **28** (1980), 305-359.

[10] K. Wagner, *Über eine Eigenschaft der ebeben Komplexe*, Math. Ann. **114** (1937), 570-590.

DEPARTMENT OF MATHEMATICAL SCIENCES, OAKLAND UNIVERSITY, ROCHESTER, MI 48309

*Current address*: Department of Mathematics, Westminster College of Salt Lake City, Salt Lake City, UT 84105

*E-mail address*: s-kingan@wcslc.edu

Contemporary Mathematics
Volume **197**, 1996

# Randomised Approximation of the Number of Bases

Laura Chávez Lomelí and Dominic Welsh

ABSTRACT. It is known that the exact enumeration of the number of bases of
a matroid is #$P$-hard. Azar, Broder and Frieze (1994) have shown that using
only deterministic methods, it is not even possible to get good approximations
to this number. Here we show that there exists a fully polynomial randomised
approximation scheme for this quantity for a large class of all matroids.

## Introduction

It is well known that exact enumeration of the number of bases of a matroid
is a difficult computational problem. Indeed in several instances where the input
has a succinct representation such as by a matrix over a finite field this has been
rigorously proved by showing that the problem is #$P$-complete. However, since
there are several applications of practical significance, there has been considerable
effort expended on achieving good approximations. In a recent paper Azar, Broder
and Frieze [2] have shown that it is impossible to get a good approximation in
deterministic polynomial time if the matroid is presented by a basis or independence
oracle.

This contrasts with the hopes expressed in recent work on approximation for
#$P$–hard problems using randomised algorithms, in particular the Markov chain
approach initiated by Broder [3]. Dyer and Frieze [4] and Feder and Mihail [5] give
examples of this approach applied to counting matroid bases.

Here we show that in contrast to the negative result of [2] and the compara-
tively difficult approaches in [4] and [5] which work only for very restricted classes
of matroids, the very simple randomised algorithm described below gives a good
approximation for a very large subset of all matroids.

## 1. A fully polynomial randomised approximation scheme

Our matroid notation is that of Oxley [7] and we assume that the matroid
presentation is as in [2], namely through an independence oracle which, when presented with a set $A$, determines if it is independent, and in such a case, provides a
base of the matroid containing $A$. Such a call to the oracle is called a *probe*. As far
as polynomial time computations are concerned, this is computationally equivalent
to the standard independence oracle. For more on the complexity status of these

oracles see Robinson and Welsh [8]. If $M$ is a matroid on a set $E$, we let $b(M)$ denote the number of bases of $M$.

The main result of Azar, Broder and Frieze [2] is the following.

Consider algorithms whose only knowledge of $M$ is obtained through probes. It is well known that such algorithms can be used to optimise very efficiently and it is always the hope in a matroid problem that there is such an algorithm which can be used to solve it.

THEOREM 1.1. *Let $|E| = n$ and let $A$ be a deterministic oracle algorithm which outputs a number $\beta$ approximating the number of bases of a given matroid $M$ on the set $E$. Suppose $A$ makes $k = 2^{o(n)}$ probes. Then $A$ can only guarantee that*

$$2^{-\Omega(n/(\log k)^2)}|b(M)| \leq \beta \leq 2^{\Omega(n/(\log k)^2)}|b(M)|.$$

*In particular*

(a) *If $A$ makes only a polynomial number of probes then its estimate can only be guaranteed accurate to within $2^{\Omega(n/(\log n)^2)}$.*

(b) *Suppose that $A$ always computes an $\alpha$-approximation $\beta$ to $b(M)$ where $0 < \alpha$ is a constant. Then in the worst case $A$ requires $2^{\Omega(\sqrt{n})}$ probes.*

*A randomised approximation scheme* for estimating $b(M)$ is a probabilistic algorithm that takes a matroid $M$ and a rational number $\epsilon, 0 < \epsilon < 1$, as input and produces as output a random variable $Z$ such that

$$Pr\left\{ \left| \frac{Z}{b(M)} - 1 \right| > \epsilon \right\} \leq 1/4.$$

As with the deterministic version of these algorithms we allow information about $M$ to be obtained only through probes and as with all oracle machines charge one unit of time for each probe. If the probabilistic algorithm runs in time polynomial in the size of $M$ and $\epsilon^{-1}$ then we say that it is a *fully polynomial randomised approximation scheme (fpras)* for estimating $b(M)$.

Although the main result of [2] rules out the possibility of a deterministic polynomial time approximation scheme for $b(M)$, as far as we are aware there is no obvious obstacle to the existence of a randomised scheme. Indeed the recent results of [1] have extended the classes of problems for which such schemes exist for estimating numerical invariants of matroids. Here we describe a very simple algorithm which we believe works for a very large class, perhaps even the majority of all matroids.

We say that a class $\mathcal{C}$ of matroids is *frequent* if there exists a polynomial $p$ such that if $M \in \mathcal{C}$ on $n$ elements has rank $r$, then

$$b(M)p(n) \geq \binom{n}{r}.$$

EXAMPLE 1.2. **Paving Matroids.** *A matroid of rank $r$ is paving if every circuit has cardinality $r$ or $r + 1$. Paving matroids contain all Steiner systems and it is widely believed that paving matroids predominate in the class of all matroids. For example the best lower bound known for the number of matroids was obtained by Knuth [6] who constructed a family of paving matroids achieving this bound. For more on this see Oxley [7].*

PROPOSITION 1.3. *The class of paving matroids is frequent.*

The proof of this will follow as an application of Proposition 1.8 proved below. Our main result is the following.

THEOREM 1.4. *There exists an fpras for estimating the number of bases of any matroid in a frequent class.*

PROOF. We claim that if $C$ is frequent then the algorithm DART-THROW, described below, is an fpras for estimating $b(M)$.

**Algorithm** DART-THROW.
**begin**
    Use oracle to determine rank $r$ of input $M = (S, \mathcal{B})$
    $n := |S|$
    $t := 4p(n)\epsilon^{-2}$
    **for** $i := 1$ to $t$ **do**
    **begin**
        Select uniformly at random an $r$-subset $A$ of $S$.
        **if** $A$ is base of $M$ **then** $Z_i := 1$
        **else** $Z_i := 0$
    **end**
    $\hat{Z} := \frac{Z_1 + Z_2 + \cdots + Z_t}{t}$
    output $Z := \hat{Z} \begin{pmatrix} n \\ r \end{pmatrix}$
**end**

To substantiate our claim, we use Chebychev's inequality to note that

$$Pr\left\{ \left| \frac{Z}{b(M)} - 1 \right| \geq \epsilon \right\} \leq \epsilon^{-2} \frac{1}{b(M)^2} \text{var}(Z).$$

But

$$\text{var}(Z) = \frac{1}{t} b(M) \left( \begin{pmatrix} n \\ r \end{pmatrix} - b(M) \right),$$

therefore,

$$\begin{aligned} Pr\left\{ \left| \left( \frac{Z}{b(M)} \right) - 1 \right| \geq \epsilon \right\} &\leq \epsilon^{-2} \frac{1}{b(M)} \frac{1}{t} \left( \begin{pmatrix} n \\ r \end{pmatrix} - b(M) \right) \\ &\leq \epsilon^{-2} t^{-1} (p(n) - 1) \\ &\leq 1/4, \end{aligned}$$

provided $t \geq 4(p(n) - 1)\epsilon^{-2}$. $\qquad\square$

Note that in fact we have shown more, namely: if $C$ is a frequent class with bounding polynomial $p(n) = O(n^\alpha)$, then the running time of our fpras is $O(n^\alpha \epsilon^{-2})$.

We next consider how frequency is preserved under standard operations. The following statement is an immediate consequence of the definition.

PROPOSITION 1.5. *If $C$ is a frequent class, then the* dual class $C^* = \{M : M^* \in C\}$ *is frequent.*

Let $C$ be a class of matroids. We define the *k–truncation* $C_k$ of $C$ as follows: $M \in C_k$ if and only if there exists $N \in C$ such that $M \simeq T^k(N)$. (Note that if $N$ has rank $r \geq k$, then $T^k(N)$ has rank $r - k$.)

PROPOSITION 1.6. *If $C$ is a frequent class, then for any $k$, the $k$–truncation $C_k$ is frequent.*

PROOF. Let $C$ be frequent with bounding polynomial $p$. Clearly it is sufficient to show that $C_1$, the 1–truncation of $C$, is also frequent. So let $M \in C_1$ have rank $r$ on a set of size $n$, so that we know there exists $N \in C$ with $M = T(N)$. Since $N \in C$,

$$b(N) \geq \binom{n}{r+1} \frac{1}{p(n)}.$$

Consider the bipartite graph $\Delta \langle \mathcal{B}(N), \mathcal{B}(M) \rangle$ where a vertex $B \in \mathcal{B}(N)$ is connected to a vertex in $B' \in \mathcal{B}(M)$ if $B' \subset B$. Each vertex $B$ has degree $r+1$ and each $B'$ has degree at most $n - r$. Hence

$$b(N)(r+1) = |E(\Delta)| \leq (n-r)b(M).$$

Thus

$$b(M) \ \geq \ \frac{r+1}{n-r} \binom{n}{r+1} \frac{1}{p(n)}$$

$$= \ \binom{n}{r} \frac{1}{p(n)}.$$

$\square$

Let $\mathcal{E}_t(C)$ be the class of matroids obtained from the class $C$ by *elongating* members of $C$ by $t$. In other words, $M \in \mathcal{E}_t(C)$ if and only if there exists $N \in C$ such that the bases of $M$ are the spanning sets of $N$ which have cardinality $t + r(N)$, where $r(N)$ is the rank of $N$.

Thus $\mathcal{E}_0(C) = C$. It is easy to see that elongation is the dual of truncation, so that using Proposition 1.5 we get:

PROPOSITION 1.7. *If $C$ is a frequent class then $\mathcal{E}_t(C)$ is frequent, for any positive integer $t$.*

We turn to another useful operation. The operator $\partial$ produces a new class $\partial(C)$ of matroids from a given class $C$ as follows: $M$ is in $\partial(C)$ if and only if $T(M)$, the 1-truncation of $M$, is in $C$.

We prove:

PROPOSITION 1.8. *If $C$ is a frequent class, then so is $\partial(C)$.*

PROOF. Let $p(x)$ be a polynomial guaranteeing the frequency of $C$, and suppose that $M \in \partial(C)$ is a matroid of rank $r$ on $n$ points. Let $\Delta$ be the bipartite graph with vertex set $V_1 \cup V_2$, where $V_1$ denotes the set of bases of $T(M)$ and $V_2$ the set of bases of $M$, and an edge joins $B \in V_1$ to $B' \in V_2$ if and only if $B \subset B'$.

Each vertex in $V_1$ has degree at least 1, and each vertex in $V_2$ has degree $r$. Hence

$$b(T(M)) \leq |E(\Delta)| = rb(M).$$

But using the frequency of $C$, we know

$$b(T(M)) \geq \frac{1}{p(n)} \binom{n}{r-1}$$

and hence

$$b(M) \geq \frac{1}{r} \frac{1}{p(n)} \binom{n}{r-1}.$$

Taking $q$ to be the polynomial $q(x) = xp(x)$, we see that $q$ guarantees the frequency of $\partial(\mathcal{C})$.                                                                                      □

As an application of Proposition 1.8, we prove Proposition 1.3. Take $\mathcal{C}$ in Proposition 1.8 to be the class $\mathcal{U}$ of uniform matroids. This is clearly frequent, and the class of paving matroids is just $\partial(\mathcal{U})$.

A further consequence of Proposition 1.8 is the following.

For any non-negative integer $k$, let $\mathcal{W}_k$ be the class of matroids defined as follows:

$M \in \mathcal{W}_k$ if and only if the cardinality of a circuit of $M$ lies in the set $\{r - k, r - k + 1, \ldots, r + 1\}$, where $r$ is the rank of $M$.

Thus $\mathcal{W}_0$ is exactly the class of paving matroids.

PROPOSITION 1.9. *For all fixed $k \geq 0$, $\mathcal{W}_k$ is frequent.*

PROOF. It is easy to see that $\mathcal{W}_k$ is exactly the class $\partial^{k+1}(\mathcal{U})$ and since $\partial$ is an operator which preserves frequency, the result follows.                        □

Note also that, since the application of $\partial$ increases the degree of the frequency guaranteeing polynomial $p$ by $n$, we have proved:

COROLLARY 1.10. *The running time of our fpras on an input matroid of size $n$ from the class $\mathcal{W}_k$ is $O(n^{k+1}e^{-2})$.*

This highlights the sort of matroids on which our methods fail to give a polynomial time approximation, typically a matroid on $n$ elements of rank $n/2$ and with circuits of size $n/4$.

Thus, in contrast to the sophisticated methods of Dyer and Frieze [4] and Feder and Mihail [5] who give ingenious methods for estimating the number of bases for very restricted classes of matroids (regular and balanced respectively) this very crude approach deals with what seems to be a very substantial proportion of all matroids.

In particular, any class which can be obtained from the class of uniform matroids by some finite sequence of the various operations shown above to preserve frequency is also frequent. Paving matroids, believed to predominate in the class of all matroids, is a relatively small subclass of this class.

However, we should emphasise, that it is not possible to have a strong negative result comparable to that of [2] for any frequent class. The trivial approximation gives a polynomial ratio. We cannot settle the question of whether there exists a deterministic $(1 + \epsilon)$–approximation for any frequent class. We suspect there does not. For example, a specific question which we have not been able to settle is the following:

**Question** Find a deterministic polynomial time algorithm which will estimate the number of bases of a paving matroid to within a ratio 2, or show that this is impossible.

### Acknowledgements

We are very grateful to Joseph Bonin for spotting and correcting a mistake in an argument in an earlier draft of this paper. We also wish to acknowledge that this research has been supported by CONACYT and UNAM Mexico and also partially supported by RAND-REC EC US030.

# References

[1] N. Alon, A. M. Frieze, and D. J. A. Welsh, *Polynomial time randomised approximation schemes for Tutte-Grothendieck invariants: the dense case*, Random Structures Algorithms **6** (1995), 459–478.

[2] Y. Azar, A. Z. Broder, and A. M. Frieze, *On the problem of approximating the number of bases of a matroid*, Inform. Process. Lett. **50** (1994), 9–11.

[3] A. Z. Broder, *How hard is it to marry at random? (On the approximation of the permanent)*, Proceedings of the 18th Annual ACM Symposium on Theory of Computing, 1986, pp. 50–58.

[4] M. E. Dyer and A. M. Frieze, *Random walks, totally unimodular matrices and a randomised dual simplex algorithm*, Proceedings of the Second IPCO Conference, Carnegie Mellon University, 1992, pp. 72–84.

[5] T. Feder and M. Mihail, *Balanced matroids*, 24th annual ACM Symposium on Theory of Computing, 1992, pp. 26–38.

[6] D. E. Knuth, *The asymptotic number of geometries*, J. Combin. Theory Ser. A **17** (1974), 398–401.

[7] J. G. Oxley, *Matroid Theory*, Oxford University Press, New York, 1992.

[8] G. C. Robinson and D. J. A. Welsh, *The computational complexity of matroid properties*, Math. Proc. Camb. Phil. Soc. **87** (1980), 29–45.

MATHEMATICAL INSTITUTE, 24-29 ST GILES', OXFORD, OX1 3LB

MATHEMATICAL INSTITUTE, 24-29 ST GILES', OXFORD, OX1 3LB

Contemporary Mathematics
Volume **197**, 1996

# On Representable Matroids Having Neither $U_{2,5}-$ Nor $U_{3,5}-$minors

Charles Semple and Geoff Whittle

ABSTRACT. Consider 3–connected matroids that are neither binary nor ternary and have neither $U_{2,5}-$ nor $U_{3,5}-$minors: for example, $AG(3,2)'$, the matroid obtained by relaxing a circuit-hyperplane of $AG(3,2)$. The main result of the paper shows that no matroid of this sort is representable over any field. This result makes it possible to extend known characterisations of the binary and ternary matroids representable over a field $\mathbf{F}$ to ones of the matroids representable over $\mathbf{F}$ that have neither $U_{2,5}-$ nor $U_{3,5}-$minors.

## 1. Introduction

For a field $\mathbf{F}$, Tutte [**8, 9**] characterised the matroids that are representable over $GF(2)$ and $\mathbf{F}$. If $\mathbf{F}$ has characteristic 2, the class is just the class of binary matroids; otherwise it is the class of regular matroids. Characterisations of the matroids that are representable over $GF(3)$ and $\mathbf{F}$ are given in [**10, 11**]. These results are analogues of Tutte's results. Since a matroid is binary if and only if it has no $U_{2,4}-$minor, one can regard Tutte's results as characterising the matroids representable over $\mathbf{F}$ that have no $U_{2,4}-$minor. It is natural to ask if this perspective can be generalised. Given that the next uniform matroids of interest are $U_{2,5}$ and its dual $U_{3,5}$, it is natural to ask for a characterisation of the matroids representable over $\mathbf{F}$ that have neither $U_{2,5}-$ nor $U_{3,5}-$minors. Such a characterisation is given in Theorem 5.2.

A key result toward proving this characterisation is Theorem 4.2, which is the main result of this paper: a 3–connected matroid that is representable over some field and has neither $U_{2,5}-$ nor $U_{3,5}-$minors is either binary or ternary. Note that the hypothesis of 3–connectedness is crucial. For example, the 2–sum of $U_{2,4}$ and the Fano plane, which has neither $U_{2,5}-$ nor $U_{3,5}-$minors, is representable over $GF(4)$, but over neither $GF(2)$ nor $GF(3)$.

The paper is structured as follows. In Section 2 it is shown that, apart from $U_{2,5}$ and $U_{3,5}$, no 3–connected excluded minor for the class of matroids that are either binary or ternary is representable over any field. This fact follows easily from results in [**3**]. Because [**3**] is not yet widely available, we provide an independent proof. Unfortunately, not all excluded minors for the matroids that are either binary or

---

1991 *Mathematics Subject Classification.* 05B35.

ternary are 3–connected. This creates a problem that is dealt with by Theorem 4.1, where it is shown that a 3–connected matroid that is neither binary nor ternary always contains a minor that is a 3–connected excluded minor for this class. The 3–connectivity result of Section 3 is needed as a lemma for Theorem 4.1. The main result of the paper, Theorem 4.2, is an immediate corollary of earlier results. Finally, Section 5 gives characterisations of the matroids representable over a given field that have neither $U_{2,5}$– nor $U_{3,5}$–minors. Classes that were not considered in [10, 11] arise only for fields of characteristic 2. These classes consist of matroids obtained by taking 2–sums and direct sums of binary matroids and certain classes of ternary matroids.

Familiarity is assumed with the elements of matroid theory as set forth in [4]. In particular it is assumed that the reader is familiar with the theory of matroid connectivity. For an excellent presentation of this theory [4, Chapters 8 and 11] is recommended to the reader. Notation and terminology follows [4] with the following exceptions. We denote the simple matroid canonically associated with a matroid $M$ by $si(M)$, and the class of matroids representable over $GF(q)$ by $\mathcal{L}(q)$. By a *coline* of $M$ we mean a flat of $M$ whose rank is two less than the rank of $M$.

## 2. Excluded Minors

In this section we prove that the only 3–connected excluded minors for $\mathcal{L}(2) \cup \mathcal{L}(3)$ that are representable over some field are $U_{2,5}$ and $U_{3,5}$. The matroids $U_{2,4} \oplus F_7$, $U_{2,4} \oplus_2 F_7$, and their duals show that the hypothesis of 3–connectivity is needed.

LEMMA 2.1. *Let $M$ be a 3–connected excluded minor for $\mathcal{L}(2) \cup \mathcal{L}(3)$ that is not $U_{2,5}$ or $U_{3,5}$. Then there exist distinct elements $x$ and $y$ of $E(M)$ such that either $M\backslash x$, $M\backslash y$, and $M\backslash x,y$ are all binary and connected, or $M/x$, $M/y$, and $M/x,y$ are all binary and connected.*

PROOF. Since $M$ has no minor isomorphic to $U_{2,5}$ or $U_{3,5}$, it follows by the excluded-minor characterisation of ternary matroids [2] that $M$ has a minor isomorphic to the Fano matroid $F_7$ or its dual $F_7^*$. By duality, we can assume without loss of generality that $M$ has an $F_7$-minor. Moreover, as $F_7$ is binary, $F_7$ is a proper minor of $M$. Then, by Seymour's Splitter Theorem [5] (see also [4, Theorem 11.1.2, Corollary 11.2.1]), there is a sequence $M_0, M_1, \ldots, M_n$ of 3–connected matroids such that $M_0 \cong F_7$, $M_n = M$, and, for all $i$ in $\{0, 1, \ldots, n-1\}$, $M_i$ is a single-element deletion or a single-element contraction of $M_{i+1}$. The rest of the proof is a case analysis based on the number of matroids in this sequence.

Suppose that $n = 1$. Then there is an element $x$ of $E(M)$ such that either $M\backslash x$ or $M/x$ is isomorphic to $F_7$. If $M\backslash x \cong F_7$, then $M$ is a 3–connected non-binary single-element extension of $F_7$. But it is easily seen that every 3–connected single-element extension of $F_7$ has a $U_{2,5}$–minor, contradicting the fact that $M$ has no $U_{2,5}$–minor. Therefore $M/x \cong F_7$ and so $M$ is a 3–connected non-binary single-element coextension of $F_7$. A straightforward check (see also [3]) shows that the only non-binary 3–connected coextension of $F_7$ that has no $U_{2,5}$– and no $U_{3,5}$–minor is the matroid $AG(3,2)'$ obtained by relaxing a circuit-hyperplane of $AG(3,2)$. Certainly $AG(3,2)'$ is an excluded minor for $\mathcal{L}(2) \cup \mathcal{L}(3)$, and it is easily checked (see [4, p. 508]) that there exist elements $x$ and $y$ of the ground set of $AG(3,2)'$ such that $M/x$, $M/y$, and $M/x,y$ are all binary and connected. Thus the lemma holds if $n = 1$.

Suppose that $n \geq 2$. Say $i \in \{0, 1, \ldots, n-1\}$. Then for some $z \in E(M)$, $M_i = M_{i+1} \backslash z$ or $M_i = M_{i+1}/z$. Assume the former. Then $M \backslash z$ has an $F_7$–minor so that this matroid is not ternary. But $M \backslash z$ is either binary or ternary. Hence $M \backslash z$ is binary. Similarly, if $M_i = M_{i+1}/z$, then $M/z$ is binary. In the case analysis that follows we repeatedly use this fact and the well-known fact that a matroid obtained by deleting or contracting an element from a 3–connected matroid is connected [4, Proposition 8.1.13].

Assume first that $n = 2$. Then there exists $\{x, y\} \subset E(M)$ such that $M$ extends or coextends $M_1$ by $x$ and $M_1$ extends or coextends $F_7$ by $y$. If $M_1 \backslash y \cong F_7$, then $M_1$ is a single-element extension of $F_7$ which is 3–connected and binary. But there are no 3–connected binary single-element extensions of $F_7$. Therefore $M_1$ must be a coextension of $F_7$. If $M/x = M_1$ and $M_1/y \cong F_7$, then it is easily seen that $M/x$, $M/y$, and $M/x, y$ are all binary and connected. Say $M \backslash x = M_1$ and $M_1/y \cong F_7$. Then $M_1$ is a 3–connected binary single-element coextension of $F_7$. It is known [7] that the only 3–connected binary single-element coextensions of $F_7$ are $AG(3, 2)$ and a certain matroid called $S_8$ (see [4, p. 357]). Another straightforward check (again see [3]) shows that any 3–connected non-binary single-element extension of either $AG(3, 2)$ or $S_8$ has a $U_{2,5}$–minor. Therefore this case does not arise and we have established the lemma in the case that $n = 2$.

Now assume that $n > 2$. Consider $M_{n-1}$, $M_{n-2}$, and $M_{n-3}$. If $M/a = M_{n-1}$ and either $M_{n-1}/b = M_{n-2}$ or $M_{n-2}/c = M_{n-3}$, then the argument used in the case that $n = 2$ applies. That same argument, applied to deletions in place of contractions, works if $M \backslash a = M_{n-1}$ and either $M_{n-1} \backslash b = M_{n-2}$ or $M_{n-2} \backslash c = M_{n-3}$.

There are two other cases. Suppose that $M/a = M_{n-1}$, $M_{n-1} \backslash b = M_{n-2}$, and $M_{n-2} \backslash c = M_{n-3}$. Since $M$ is 3–connected, $M \backslash b$ and $M \backslash c$ are both connected. If $M \backslash b, c$ is connected, then the lemma follows by choosing $x = b$ and $y = c$. Assume that $M \backslash b, c$ is not connected. Then, as $M/a \backslash b, c$ is 3–connected, $a$ is a coloop of $M \backslash b, c$. Furthermore, as $M \backslash b$ and $M \backslash c$ are both connected, $\{a, c\}$ and $\{a, b\}$ are 2–element cocircuits of $M \backslash b$ and $M \backslash c$, respectively. Therefore, as $M$ is 3–connected, $\{a, b, c\}$ is a triad of $M$ and so $E(M) - \{a, b, c\}$ is a hyperplane $H$ of $M$. Since $M|H = M/a \backslash b, c$, $M|H$ is a binary matroid with an $F_7$–minor. Consider $M/b$. Since $M$ is 3–connected, $M/b$ is certainly connected. Moreover, $M|H$ is a minor of $M/b$, so $M/b$ has an $F_7$–minor. Therefore, as $M$ is an excluded minor for $\mathcal{L}(2) \cup \mathcal{L}(3)$, $M/b$ is also binary. Hence $M/a$, $M/b$, and $M/a, b$ are all binary and connected. Hence, in this case, the lemma follows upon choosing $x = a$ and $y = b$. The case of $M \backslash a = M_{n-1}$, $M_{n-1}/b = M_{n-2}$, and $M_{n-2}/c = M_{n-3}$ is treated similarly, completing the proof. $\square$

LEMMA 2.2. *Let $M$ be a matroid that is representable over a field $\mathbf{F}$ of characteristic two. If $M$ has a pair of elements $x$ and $y$ such that $M \backslash x$, $M \backslash y$ and $M \backslash x, y$ are all binary and connected, then $M$ is binary and connected.*

PROOF. Evidently $M$ is connected. It is known [1] that a binary matroid is uniquely representable over any field over which it is representable. It is easily seen that a representation of a matroid over $GF(2)$ can be interpreted as a representation over $\mathbf{F}$. Thus any matrix representation of a binary matroid over $\mathbf{F}$ is equivalent to one in which all the entries are either 0 or 1. Moreover, any matroid that can be represented over $\mathbf{F}$ by such a matrix is binary.

We now recall some facts on representations. Let $N$ be a matroid represented over $\mathbf{F}$ by a matrix $[I|D]$. Associated with $D$ is a simple bipartite graph $G(D)$ whose parts are the index sets of the rows and columns of $D$. Two vertices $v_i$ and $v_j$ are adjacent if and only if the entry of $D$ in row $v_i$ and column $v_j$ is non-zero. It is known ([1] see also [4, Theorem 6.4.7]) that the rows and columns of $D$ can be scaled so that the entries corresponding to the edges of any fixed spanning forest of $G(D)$ are all one. Moreover, if $N$ is uniquely representable over $\mathbf{F}$, then, up to such a scaling, all entries of $D$ are unique. It is also the case that $G(D)$ is connected if and only if $N$ is connected.

Consider $M\backslash x, y$. This matroid is binary so it can be represented over $\mathbf{F}$ by a matrix $[I|D']$ all of whose entries are in $\{0,1\}$. Also $M\backslash x, y$ is connected, so $G(D')$ is connected. Since $M\backslash x, y$ is binary, this representation is unique, so it extends to a representation $[I|D'|\mathbf{x}]$ of $M\backslash y$. Since $M\backslash y$ is connected, $G([D'|\mathbf{x}])$ is connected. The graph $G([D'|\mathbf{x}])$ has one more vertex than $G(D')$ so a spanning tree of $G([D'|\mathbf{x}])$ has one more edge than a spanning tree of $G(D)$. It follows that if $\mathbf{x}$ is scaled to have leading non-zero entry one, the choice of $\mathbf{x}$ is unique. Moreover, since $M\backslash y$ is binary, all entries of $[I|D'|\mathbf{x}]$ are in $\{0,1\}$. Similarly we deduce that $[I|D']$ extends uniquely to a matrix $[I|D'|\mathbf{y}]$ where $\mathbf{y}$ has leading non-zero entry one. The entries of $\mathbf{x}$ and $\mathbf{y}$ are all in $\{0,1\}$, so that $[I|D'|\mathbf{x},\mathbf{y}]$ represents a binary matroid. But $[I|D']$ extends to an $\mathbf{F}$–representation $[I|D'|\mathbf{x}',\mathbf{y}']$ of $M$, where we scale so that the leading non-zero entries in $\mathbf{x}'$ and $\mathbf{y}'$ are 1. Since $[I|D'|\mathbf{y}']$ and $[I|D'|\mathbf{x}']$ are $\mathbf{F}$–representations of $M\backslash x$ and $M\backslash y$ respectively, we have that $\mathbf{x} = \mathbf{x}'$ and $\mathbf{y} = \mathbf{y}'$. It follows that $[I|D'|\mathbf{x},\mathbf{y}]$ represents $M$ and we conclude that $M$ is binary.                                                                                         $\square$

THEOREM 2.3. *Let $M$ be a 3–connected excluded minor for $\mathcal{L}(2) \cup \mathcal{L}(3)$. If $M$ is representable over some field, then $M$ is either $U_{2,5}$ or $U_{3,5}$.*

PROOF. Say that $M$ is not $U_{2,5}$ or $U_{3,5}$. It was noted in the proof of Lemma 2.1 that $M$ has either an $F_7-$ or an $F_7^*$–minor. Thus $M$ is not representable over a field whose characteristic is not 2. Assume that $M$ is representable over a field $\mathbf{F}$ of characteristic 2. By Lemma 2.1, dualising if necessary, we may assume that $M$ has a pair of elements $\{x, y\}$ with the property that $M\backslash x$, $M\backslash y$, and $M\backslash x, y$ are all connected and binary. But then, by Lemma 2.2, $M$ is binary, contradicting the fact that $M$ is an excluded minor for $\mathcal{L}(2) \cup \mathcal{L}(3)$.                                   $\square$

Consider a 3–connected matroid $N$ that has neither $U_{2,5}-$ nor $U_{3,5}-$minors. If $N$ is neither binary nor ternary, then it has an excluded minor for $\mathcal{L}(2) \cup \mathcal{L}(3)$ as a minor. If this excluded minor is 3–connected, it follows from Theorem 2.3 that $N$ is not representable over any field. But it is plausible that $N$ has no minor that is a 3–connected excluded minor for $\mathcal{L}(2) \cup \mathcal{L}(3)$. We turn attention to this question now. We begin by establishing a result on 3–connectivity.

## 3. A 3–connectivity Theorem

Recall that a matroid $M$ *uses* a set $S$ if $S \subseteq E(M)$. The following result is needed as a lemma for Theorem 4.1, but it may be of independent interest so we call it a theorem. The proof makes frequent use of standard facts on matroid connectivity, as presented in [4, Chapter 8].

THEOREM 3.1. *Let $\{A, B\}$ be a 3–separation of the 3–connected non-binary matroid $M$, and let $p$ be in $\mathrm{cl}(A) \cap \mathrm{cl}(B)$. Then $M$ has a 3–connected non-binary minor $N$ using $A$ with the properties that $N|A = M|A$ and that $A$ spans $N$.*

We first note some preliminary results. The next result is proved in [6] (see also [4, Proposition 11.3.8]). It is used frequently in arguments on non-binary 3–connected matroids.

3.2. *Let $x$ and $y$ be elements of the ground set of the 3–connected non-binary matroid $M$. Then $M$ has a $U_{2,4}$–minor that uses $\{x, y\}$.*

The next result is proved in Kahn and Seymour [2] (see also [4, Lemma 10.2.4]).

3.3. *Let $M$ be a connected simple matroid whose rank $r$ is at least two, and let $X = \{x \in E(M) : M/x \text{ is disconnected}\}$. Then*

(a) *$|X| \leq r - 2$; and*

(b) *if $|X| = r - 2$, then there are lines $L_0, L_1, \ldots, L_{r-2}$ of $M$, and an ordering $x_1, x_2, \ldots, x_{r-2}$ of $X$ such that*

    (i) *$|L_i| \geq 3$ for all $i$ in $\{0, 1, \ldots, r - 2\}$;*

    (ii) *$E(M) = \cup_{i=0}^{r-2} L_i$; and*

    (iii) *$L_i \cap \mathrm{cl}(L_0 \cup L_1 \cup \cdots \cup L_{i-1}) = \{x_i\}$ for all $i$ in $\{1, 2, \ldots, r - 2\}$.*

Our need for 3.3 is to prove

LEMMA 3.4. *Let $M$ be a simple connected matroid whose rank $r$ is at least four, and let $F$ be a coline of $M$. Then there is an element $x \in F$ with the property that $M/x$ is connected.*

PROOF. Let $X$ denote the set of elements whose contraction from $M$ results in a disconnected matroid. By 3.3, $|X| \leq r - 2$. But $F$ has rank $(r - 2)$, so the lemma holds unless $|X| = r - 2$, and $F = X$. In this case $M$ has the structure given by 3.3(b). But it follows easily from 3.3(b) that if $r(M) \geq 4$, then $X$ is not a flat of $M$, so that $F \neq X$. $\qquad\square$

We now prove Theorem 3.1.

PROOF. If $\mathrm{cl}(A) = E(M)$, the result is immediate. If $A$ has rank 2, the result follows from 3.2. Hence we may assume that $r(A) \geq 3$ and that $A$ does not span $M$. Clearly $r(B) \geq 3$.

Choose a pair of distinct elements $p_1, p_2$ in $A$. Again by 3.2, $M$ has a $U_{2,4}$–minor using $\{p_1, p_2\}$. Thus there exists a basis $I \cup \{p_1, p_2\}$ of $M$ such that $M/I$ is non-binary. Since $\mathrm{cl}(A) \neq M$ there is an element $i$ in $I$ that is not in $\mathrm{cl}(A)$. Consider $M/i$. Again, either $\mathrm{cl}_{M/i}(A) = M/i$ or there exists $i' \in I - \{i\}$ that is not in $\mathrm{cl}_{M/i}(A)$. Repeating the process clearly results in a matroid $N'$ that uses $A$ and has the property that $\mathrm{cl}_{N'}(A) = N'$. Evidently $N'$ is non-binary and $N'|A = M|A$. The problem is that $N'$ may not be 3–connected. The substance of the proof is devoted to dealing with this. We first note

3.5. *Either $M|\mathrm{cl}(B)$ is connected or $M|\mathrm{cl}(B)$ has a single coloop $y$, where $y \notin \mathrm{cl}(A)$.*

PROOF. Assume that $M|\mathrm{cl}(B)$ is not connected. Then this matroid has a separation $\{X, Y\}$ where $p \in X$. From the submodular inequality and the facts that $\{X, Y\}$ is a separation of $M|\mathrm{cl}(B)$, that $\{A, B\}$ is a 3–separation of $M$, and that $r(\mathrm{cl}(A) \cap X) \geq r(p) \geq 1$ we get

$$
\begin{aligned}
r(Y) + r(\mathrm{cl}(A) \cup X) &\leq r(Y) + r(X) + r(A) - r(\mathrm{cl}(A) \cap X) \\
&= r(A) + r(B) - r(\mathrm{cl}(A) \cap X) \\
&\leq r(M) + 1.
\end{aligned}
$$

It follows from this that if $|Y| \geq 2$, then $\{Y, E - Y\}$ is a 2–separation of the 3–connected matroid $M$. Hence $|Y| = 1$. Say $Y = \{y\}$. If $y \in \mathrm{cl}(A)$, then it is easily checked that $\{X, E - X\}$ is a 2–separation of $M$, again contradicting the fact that $M$ is 3–connected. Thus $y \notin \mathrm{cl}(A)$ and 3.5 follows. $\qquad\square$

The minor $N'$ of $M$ has been constructed in a certain way. We wish to establish properties of minors of $M$ that have been constructed in similar ways. Let $Q$ be a minor of $M$ using $A$ of the form $M/Z$ with the properties that $Q|A = M|A$ and that $A$ spans $Q$. It is clear that $Z$ spans a coline of $M|\mathrm{cl}(B)$. Hence $\mathrm{cl}(B) - Z$ is a line of $Q$. Let $l$ be the corresponding line of $\mathrm{si}(Q)$, the simple matroid associated with $Q$.

3.6. *If $|l| \geq 3$, then $\mathrm{si}(Q)$ is 3–connected.*

PROOF. In what follows, cl denotes closure in $\mathrm{si}(Q)$. Assume that $\mathrm{si}(Q)$ is not 3–connected. Then this matroid has a 2–separation $\{S, T\}$. Since $|l| \geq 3$, either $S$ or $T$ contains at least two points of $l$, so either $\mathrm{cl}(S)$ or $\mathrm{cl}(T)$ contains $l$. Say $l \subseteq \mathrm{cl}(S)$. If $\{\mathrm{cl}(S), T - \mathrm{cl}(S)\}$ is not a 2–separation of $\mathrm{si}(Q)$, then $|T - \mathrm{cl}(S)| = 1$ and, since $\mathrm{si}(Q)$ is simple, $r_{\mathrm{si}(Q)}(T - \mathrm{cl}(S)) < r_{\mathrm{si}(Q)}(T)$, thus $\{\mathrm{cl}(S), T - \mathrm{cl}(S)\}$ is a separation of $\mathrm{si}(Q)$. Hence, $\{\mathrm{cl}(S), T - \mathrm{cl}(S)\}$ is either a 2–separation of $\mathrm{si}(Q)$ or a separation of $\mathrm{si}(Q)$. Since $\mathrm{cl}(S)$ contains $l$, $T - \mathrm{cl}(S)$ is a subset of $A$, so that $r_M(T - \mathrm{cl}(S)) = r_{\mathrm{si}(Q)}(T - \mathrm{cl}(S))$. It follows routinely that $\{T - \mathrm{cl}(S), E - (T - \mathrm{cl}(S))\}$ is a 2–separation of $M$ if $\{\mathrm{cl}(S), T - \mathrm{cl}(S)\}$ is a 2–separation of $\mathrm{si}(Q)$, and $\{T - \mathrm{cl}(S), E - (T - \mathrm{cl}(S))\}$ is a separation of $M$ if $\{\mathrm{cl}(S), T - \mathrm{cl}(S)\}$ is a separation of $\mathrm{si}(Q)$. In either case we contradict the assumption that $M$ is 3–connected. Hence $\mathrm{si}(Q)$ is 3–connected. $\qquad\square$

Return attention to the minor $N'$ defined above. Consider $\mathrm{si}(N')$. We may assume without loss of generality that $A \cup \{p\} \subseteq \mathrm{si}(N')$. Now $\mathrm{cl}(B) \cap E(N')$ spans a line of $N'$. If this line has more than two points, then, by 3.6, $\mathrm{si}(N')$ is 3–connected and we are done. Thus we may assume that the line contains two points. One of them is $p$. By 3.5, there are two cases that need to be considered.

For the first case assume that $M|\mathrm{cl}(B)$ is connected. Let $x$ be the other point on the line spanned by $\mathrm{cl}(B) \cap E(N')$. It is clear that we may assume that $N'$ is obtained by contracting a coline $F$ of $M|\mathrm{cl}(B)$. We now show that there exists a flat $F' \subset F$ having rank one less than that of $F$ and having the property that $(M|\mathrm{cl}(B))/F'$ is connected. If $r(F) = 1$ this is immediate. Assume $r(F) \geq 2$. Then $r(M|\mathrm{cl}(B)) \geq 4$, so, by 3.4, there is an element $f \in F$ such that $(M|\mathrm{cl}(B))/f$ is connected. By simplifying this matroid and repeating the process if necessary we deduce that there is indeed a flat $F'$ with the claimed properties. Let $N'' = \mathrm{si}(M/F')$. (Since $M/F$ is a minor of $M/F'$, we may assume that $p$ and $x$ are in the ground set of $N''$.) Now $N''|(E(N'') \cap \mathrm{cl}(B))$ is a rank–3 connected matroid. This matroid has an element $f$ corresponding to the parallel class $F - F'$ of $M/F'$. Thus $N''/f$ has $N'$ as a restriction. The line joining $f$ and $p$, and the line joining $f$ and $x$ cover the ground set of $N''|(E(N'') \cap \mathrm{cl}(B))$. For $N''|(E(N'') \cap \mathrm{cl}(B))$ to be connected there must exist other points $p'$ and $x'$ on these lines respectively. One of $x$ or $x'$ is not in $\mathrm{cl}_{N''}(A)$. Assume without loss of generality that $x'$ is not in $\mathrm{cl}_{N''}(A)$. It is clear that $N''/x'$ has $N'$ as a restriction, so this matroid is non-binary. But $\{p, x, p'\}$ is a circuit of this matroid. Hence, by 3.6, $\mathrm{si}(N''/x')$ is 3–connected. The result follows in this case by letting $N = \mathrm{si}(N''/x')$.

Consider the second case that arises from 3.5. In this case $M|\mathrm{cl}(B)$ has a single coloop $y$. Moreover, $y \notin \mathrm{cl}(A)$, so $y \in B$. Now $r(\mathrm{cl}(B) - \{y\}) = r(B) - 1$, and $r(A \cup \{y\}) = r(A) + 1$. Hence $\{\mathrm{cl}(B) - \{y\}, E - (\mathrm{cl}(B) - \{y\})\}$ is either a 3–separation of $M$ or at least one of $\mathrm{cl}(B) - \{y\}$ and $E - (\mathrm{cl}(B) - \{y\})$ has cardinality less than 3. But it is routinely seen that $|E - (\mathrm{cl}(B) - \{y\})| \geq 3$. Also $r(\mathrm{cl}(B) - \{y\}) \geq 2$, and, by 3.5, $M|(\mathrm{cl}(B) - \{y\})$ is connected. Hence $|\mathrm{cl}(B) - \{y\}| \geq 3$. It follows that $\{\mathrm{cl}(B) - \{y\}, E - (\mathrm{cl}(B) - \{y\})\}$ is indeed a 3–separation of $M$.

We now show that the result holds if $r(\mathrm{cl}(B) - \{y\}) = 2$. In this case $\mathrm{cl}(B)$ consists of the coloop $y$ together with a non-trivial line $l'$ containing $p$. There is a point $f$ in $B$ such that $M/f = N'$. Clearly this point is not $p$. Moreover $f$ cannot be $y$, for then the line of $\mathrm{si}(N')$ corresponding to $\mathrm{cl}(B) - \{f\}$ would have at least three points contradicting the assumption that it has two. Thus $f$ is a point on $l' - \{p\}$. By 3.6, $\mathrm{si}(M/y)$ is 3–connected. We now show that $\mathrm{si}(M/y)$ is non-binary. Evidently $\{f, y\}$ is a series pair of $M \backslash (l' - \{f, p\})$. Hence $M \backslash (l' - \{f, p\})/f \cong M \backslash (l' - \{f, p\})/y$. But $M \backslash (l' - \{f, p\})/f \cong \mathrm{si}(M/f)$. Also $M/f = N'$ so this matroid is non-binary. We deduce that $M/y$ has a non-binary minor. Hence $\mathrm{si}(M/y)$ is 3–connected and non-binary as required.

Assume that $r(\mathrm{cl}(B) - \{y\}) > 2$. Then, since $M|(\mathrm{cl}(B) - \{y\})$ is connected, we may apply the method of the first part of this case analysis and obtain a non-binary 3–connected minor $N''$ of $M$ using $A \cup \{y\}$ with the properties that $r(N'') = r(A) + 1$, that $N''|(A \cup \{y\}) = M|(A \cup \{y\})$, and that $E(N'') \cap (\mathrm{cl}(B) - \{y\})$ consists, for some $r \geq 2$, of a line $\{p, q_1, q_2, \dots, q_r\}$. Moreover $p$ is the only element of $\{p, q_1, q_2, \dots, q_r\}$ in $\mathrm{cl}_{N''}(A)$. Arguing as above we see that there is an element $q_i$ of $\{q_1, q_2, \dots, q_r\}$ that can be contracted from $N''$ to give a non-binary matroid and that $N''/y$ contains $\mathrm{si}(N''/q_i)$ as a restriction. It follows that $N''/y$ is non-binary. Moreover, by 3.6, $\mathrm{si}(N''/y)$ is 3–connected. $\qquad\square$

## 4. Main Results

The following result is essentially a lemma for Theorem 4.2. However, as with Theorem 3.1 it may be of independent interest, so we call it a theorem. The class of matroids that are either binary or ternary does have excluded minors that are not 3–connected. Theorem 4.1 shows that if our interest is in 3–connected matroids, it often suffices to focus on the 3–connected excluded minors. It would be interesting to know of other classes of matroids that have similar properties.

THEOREM 4.1. *Let $M$ be a 3–connected matroid that is neither binary nor ternary. Then $M$ contains a minor that is a 3–connected excluded minor for the class of matroids that are either binary or ternary.*

PROOF. Recall that $\mathcal{L}(q)$ denotes the class of matroids representable over $GF(q)$. The proof is by induction on the cardinality of $|E(M)|$. Using the proof of Lemma 2.1 it is easily checked that the result holds if $|E(M)| \leq 8$. Assume that $|E(M)| > 8$, and that the result holds for all 3–connected matroids that are not in $\mathcal{L}(2) \cup \mathcal{L}(3)$ and whose ground sets have cardinality less than $|E(M)|$.

If $M$ has a $U_{2,5}-$ or a $U_{3,5}-$minor, then the result certainly holds. Assume that $M$ has no $U_{2,5}-$ and no $U_{3,5}-$minor. If $M$ is an excluded minor for $\mathcal{L}(2) \cup \mathcal{L}(3)$, then again the result is immediate, so assume that $M$ is not an excluded minor for $\mathcal{L}(2) \cup \mathcal{L}(3)$. It follows that there exists an element $p$ of $E(M)$ having the property that at least one of $M \backslash p$ or $M/p$ is not in $\mathcal{L}(2) \cup \mathcal{L}(3)$. By taking the dual if necessary we may assume without loss of generality that $M/p$ is not in $\mathcal{L}(2) \cup \mathcal{L}(3)$. If $M/p$ is 3–connected, then the result follows from the induction assumption. Assume that $M/p$ is not 3–connected. In this case $M/p$ has a 2–separation $\{A, B\}$ corresponding to a 2–sum decomposition $M_A \oplus_2 M_B$ of $M/p$. Now $M/p$ is not ternary, and has no $U_{2,5}-$ and no $U_{3,5}-$minor. Therefore, by the excluded-minor characterisation of ternary matroids [2], $M/p$ has a minor isomorphic to either $F_7$ or $F_7^*$. Since these are both 3–connected matroids, we deduce that either $M_A$ or $M_B$ has an $F_7-$ or $F_7^*$–minor. Assume that $M_A$ has such a minor. Consider $M$ again. Evidently, $\{A \cup \{p\}, B\}$ is a 3–separation of $M$ having the property that $p \in \mathrm{cl}(B)$. By Theorem 3.1, $M$ has a 3–connected non-binary minor $N$ using $A \cup \{p\}$ with the properties that $N|(A \cup \{p\}) = M|(A \cup \{p\})$ and that $A \cup \{p\}$ spans $N$. Moreover, it is straightforward to check that $\mathrm{si}(N/p) \cong \mathrm{si}(M_A)$. Hence $N$ contains either an $F_7-$ or an $F_7^*$–minor. Thus $N$ is not ternary. Therefore $N$ is a 3–connected matroid that is not in $\mathcal{L}(2) \cup \mathcal{L}(3)$. Certainly $N$ is a proper minor of $M$. By the induction assumption, $N$, and hence $M$, has a 3–connected excluded minor for $\mathcal{L}(2) \cup \mathcal{L}(3)$ as a minor.                                                                                    $\square$

The next theorem, the main result of this paper, follows immediately upon combining Theorem 2.3 with Theorem 4.1.

THEOREM 4.2. *Let $M$ be a 3–connected matroid that is representable over some field and has no minor isomorphic to $U_{2,5}$ or $U_{3,5}$. Then $M$ is either binary or ternary.*

## 5. A Characterisation

Let $\mathbf{F}$ be a field. Characterisations of the matroids representable over $GF(3)$ and $\mathbf{F}$ are given in [10, 11]. By combining Theorem 4.2 with the results of [10, 11] and the classical characterisation of the binary matroids representable over $\mathbf{F}$ it is possible to give a characterisation of the class of matroids that have no $U_{2,5}-$ and no $U_{3,5}-$minor and are representable over $\mathbf{F}$. We first recall some definitions from [10, 11].

A *dyadic matrix* is a matrix over the rationals all of whose non-zero subdeterminants are signed integral powers of 2. A *dyadic matroid* is a matroid that can be represented over the rationals by the columns of a dyadic matrix. A $\sqrt[6]{1}-$*matrix* is a matrix over the complex numbers, all of whose non-zero subdeterminants are complex sixth roots of unity. A $\sqrt[6]{1}-$*matroid* is a matroid that can be represented over the complex numbers by the columns of a $\sqrt[6]{1}-$matrix. Let $\mathbf{Q}(\alpha)$ denote the field obtained by extending the rationals by the transcendental $\alpha$. A matrix over $\mathbf{Q}(\alpha)$ is *near-unimodular* if all of its non-zero subdeterminants are in $\{\pm \alpha^i(\alpha-1)^j : i, j \in \mathbf{Z}\}$. A matroid is *near-regular* if it can be represented over $\mathbf{Q}(\alpha)$ by the columns of a near-unimodular matrix. The following theorem is a straightforward consequence of a number of results in [11].

THEOREM 5.1. *Let $\mathbf{F}$ be a field, and let $\mathcal{T}$ denote the class of ternary matroids that are representable over $\mathbf{F}$.*

1. *If* **F** *has odd characteristic and does not have a root of* $\alpha^2 - \alpha + 1$, *then* $\mathcal{T}$ *is the class of dyadic matroids.*
2. *If* **F** *has odd characteristic and has a root of* $\alpha^2 - \alpha + 1$, *then* $\mathcal{T}$ *is the class obtained by taking direct sums and 2–sums of dyadic and* $\sqrt[6]{1}$-*matroids.*
3. *If* **F** *is not* $GF(2)$, *has characteristic 2, and has no root of the polynomial* $\alpha^2 - \alpha + 1$ *(in particular, if* **F** $= GF(2^k)$ *for some odd integer* $k > 1$), *then* $\mathcal{T}$ *is the class of near-regular matroids.*
4. *If* **F** *has characteristic 2 and has a root of the polynomial* $\alpha^2 - \alpha + 1$ *(in particular, if* **F** $= GF(2^k)$ *for some even positive integer* $k$), *then* $\mathcal{T}$ *is the class of* $\sqrt[6]{1}$-*matroids.*

On combining Theorem 5.1 with Theorem 4.2 we obtain the following characterisation of the **F**–representable matroids that have no $U_{2,5}$- and no $U_{3,5}$–minor.

THEOREM 5.2. *Let* **F** *be a field and let* $\mathcal{U}$ *denote the class of matroids representable over* **F** *that have no* $U_{2,5}$- *and no* $U_{3,5}$-*minor.*

1. *If* **F** *does not have even characteristic, then* $\mathcal{U}$ *is the class of matroids representable over* $GF(3)$ *and* **F**.
2. *If* **F** *is not* $GF(2)$, *has characteristic 2, and has no root of the polynomial* $\alpha^2 - \alpha + 1$ *(in particular, if* **F** $= GF(2^k)$ *for some odd integer* $k > 1$), *then* $\mathcal{U}$ *is the class of matroids that can be obtained by taking direct sums and 2–sums of binary and near-regular matroids.*
3. *If* **F** *has characteristic 2 and has a root of the polynomial* $\alpha^2 - \alpha + 1$ *(in particular, if* **F** $= GF(2^k)$ *for some even positive integer* $k$), *then* $\mathcal{U}$ *is the class of matroids that can be obtained by taking direct sums and 2–sums of binary matroids and* $\sqrt[6]{1}$-*matroids.*

## Acknowledgements

We thank the referee whose detailed and constructive comments led to a significant improvement in the exposition.

## References

[1] Brylawski, T. H. and Lucas, D. (1976). Uniquely representable combinatorial geometries. In *Teorie Combinatorie* (Proc. 1973 Internat. Colloq.), pp. 83–104. Accademia Nazionale del Lincei, Rome.

[2] Kahn, J., and Seymour, P. (1988). On forbidden minors for $GF(3)$. *Proc. Amer. Math. Soc.* **102**, 437–440.

[3] Oporowski, B., Oxley, J. G., and Whittle, G. On excluded minors for the class of matroids that are either binary or ternary, in preparation.

[4] Oxley, J. G. (1992). *Matroid Theory.* Oxford University Press, New York.

[5] Seymour, P. D. (1980). Decomposition of regular matroids. *J. Combin. Theory Ser. B* **28**, 305–359.

[6] Seymour, P. D. (1981). On minors of non-binary matroids. *Combinatorica* **1**, 387–394.

[7] Seymour, P. D. (1985). Minors of 3–connected matroids. *European J. Combin.* **6**, 375–382.

[8] Tutte, W. T. (1958). A homotopy theorem for matroids, I, II. *Trans. Amer. Math. Soc.* **88**, 144–174.

[9] Tutte, W. T. (1965). Lectures on matroids. *J. Res. Nat. Bur. Standards Sect. B* **69B**, 1–47.

[10] Whittle, G. (1995). A characterisation of the matroids representable over $GF(3)$ and the rationals. *J. Combin. Theory Ser. B* **65**, 222–261.

[11] Whittle, G. On matroids representable over $GF(3)$ and other fields. To appear in *Trans. Amer. Math. Soc.*

Department of Mathematics, Victoria University, PO Box 600 Wellington, New Zealand

*E-mail address*: semple@kauri.vuw.ac.nz, whittle@kauri.vuw.ac.nz

Contemporary Mathematics
Volume **197**, 1996

# Skeletal rigidity of p.l.-spheres

Tiong-Seng Tay

ABSTRACT. The notion of skeletal rigidity, which generalizes infinitesimal rigidity of bar frameworks, was introduced by Tay et al. In this paper we prove that $d$-dimensional p.l.-spheres realized in $d$-space are $r$-rigid for $1 \leq r \leq d+1$. Immediate consequences are (i) p.l.-spheres are Cohen-Macaulay; (ii) the $h$-vector of a p.l.-sphere is symmetric and has non-negative entries. An open conjecture is that $d$-dimensional p.l.-spheres can be realized in $(d+1)$-space such that they are $r$-rigid for $1 \leq r \leq \lceil (d+2)/2 \rceil$. This conjecture implies that the entries of the $g$-vector of a p.l.-sphere are non-negative. This would give an elementary and geometric proof of the necessity part of the well known $g$-theorem for p.l.-spheres.

## 1. Introduction

In [**6**, **7**] the notion of skeletal rigidity of simplicial complexes was introduced. This generalizes infinitesimal (equivalently static) rigidity of bar frameworks. (See [**2**] and references therein). In this paper we use the notion of skeletal rigidity to study the $h$- and $g$-vector of p.l.-spheres. The significance of these two vectors are well-known. Our work is similar in spirit to the work of Carl Lee [**4**] and Paul Filliman [**3**] and is also connected to that of Peter McMullen [**5**].

This paper is organized as follows. In Section 2 we fix the notation and briefly discuss the algebra of extensors as well as the geometric realization of our simplicial complexes in projective space. For a fuller treatment of extensors, see [**6**, **7**]. In Section 3 we give a sketch of the notion of skeletal rigidity and quote some essential results from [**6**, **7**]. The connection of the $h$- and $g$-vector with stresses is also pointed out.

Typically, we prove our main theorem by inductive arguments. This is done by decomposing each complex into its *star* and *antistar*. Section 4 includes all the technical results needed to do this.

In Section 5 we prove that a $(d-1)$-shellable complex realized in $(d-1)$-space is $r$-rigid for all $r \in [1, d]$. As a corollary, we prove that shellable complexes are Cohen-Macaulay. Even though the results here are implied by the more general result to be proved in the next section, they are included because the proofs are different and brief and may be of independent interest.

In Section 6 we prove that a $d$-dimension p.l.-sphere realized in $d$-space is $r$-rigid for all $r \in [1, d+1]$. As corollaries, we prove that a p.l.-sphere is Cohen-Macaulay and that its $h$-vector is symmetric.

In Section 7 the connection between the $g$-vector of a p.l.-sphere and skeletal rigidity is discussed. Essentially, to prove the $g$-theorem for p.l.-spheres, we need to prove that $d$-dimensional p.l.-spheres can be realized in $(d+1)$-space so that they are $r$-rigid for $1 \le r \le \lceil d + 1/2 \rceil$. This is still an open conjecture.

## 2. Preliminaries

Let $\Delta$ denote a simplicial complex on the set $X$. We use lower case Greek letters to denote its faces. However, vertices will be denoted by lower case Roman letters. We will write $\Delta = \langle \sigma_1, \sigma_2, \dots, \sigma_k \rangle$, for $\sigma_i \subseteq X$, to mean the simplicial complex $\{\tau : \tau \subseteq \sigma_i \text{ for some } i\}$. The complete complex on $n$ vertices, i.e., the $(n-1)$-simplex, will be denoted by $K_n$. The *dimension* of a face $\sigma$ is $\dim \sigma := |\sigma| - 1$. The *dimension* of $\Delta$ is $\dim \Delta := \max\{\dim \sigma : \sigma \in \Delta\}$. The $r$-*skeleton* of $\Delta$ is $\Delta^{(r)} := \{\sigma \in \Delta : |\sigma| = r+1\}$ and $f_r := |\Delta^{(r)}|$. For all non-negative integers $r$, $s$, define the function

$$\theta_r^s(\Delta) := \sum_{j=0}^{r} (-1)^{j+r} \binom{s-j}{s-r} f_{j-1}, \qquad (2.1)$$

where $f_{-1} := 1$. If $\Delta$ is a $(d-1)$-dimensional simplicial complex, then the $r^{\text{th}}$ entry of the $h$-vector and the $g$-vector are given by

$$h_r(\Delta) = \theta_r^d(\Delta), \quad g_r(\Delta) = \theta_r^{d+1}(\Delta).$$

Unless otherwise stated, $\mathbb{V}$ denotes the $(d+1)$-dimensional real vector space $\mathbb{R}^{d+1}$ and $\bigwedge \mathbb{V}$ denotes the exterior algebra on $\mathbb{V}$. Members of $\bigwedge \mathbb{V}$ will usually be denoted by lowercase boldface letters. We will denote the exterior product of $\mathbf{a}$ and $\mathbf{b}$ by $\mathbf{a} \vee \mathbf{b}$ or simply $\mathbf{ab}$. If $\mathbf{a}$ is an exterior product of $k$ elements of $\mathbb{V}$, we say that $\mathbf{a}$ is a *decomposable* $k$-tensor, or a $k$-*extensor*. If $\mathbf{a}$ is a linear combination of $k$-extensors, we say that $\mathbf{a}$ is a $k$-tensor. If $\bigwedge^k \mathbb{V}$ denotes the subspace of $\bigwedge \mathbb{V}$ consisting of all $k$-tensors, then $\bigwedge \mathbb{V} = \bigoplus_{k=0}^{d+1} \bigwedge^k \mathbb{V}$ as a vector space. Furthermore, $K = \bigwedge^0 \mathbb{V}$, $\mathbb{V} = \bigwedge^1 \mathbb{V}$. If $E = \{\mathbf{e}_1, \mathbf{e}_2, \dots, \mathbf{e}_{d+1}\}$ is a basis of $\mathbb{V}$, then

$$E^{(k)} := \{\mathbf{e}_{i_1} \mathbf{e}_{i_2} \cdots \mathbf{e}_{i_k} : 1 \le i_1 < i_2 < \dots < i_k \le d+1\}$$

is a basis of $\bigwedge^k \mathbb{V}$, hence $\dim \bigwedge^k \mathbb{V} = \binom{d+1}{k}$.

We want to realize $\Delta$ in $d$-space. When this is the case we use the notation $(\Delta, d)$ or simply $\Delta$ when the context is clear. So for each $x \in X$, let $\tilde{x}$ denote a fixed choice of homogeneous coordinates of $x$ in $d$-space, i.e., $\tilde{x}$ is a $(d+1)$-tuple, or a 1-extensor in $\mathbb{V}$. The standard way to construct such homogeneous coordinates is to take the usual Euclidean coordinates and append an additional coordinate of value 1. (In fact, any realization in the real projective $d$-space is good enough, provided we fix the homogeneous coordinates for each point.)

We often regard simplices in $\Delta$ as square-free monomials, and we often employ notation appropriate to this context, for example, $\sigma \mid \rho$ for $\sigma \subseteq \rho$ and $\rho/\sigma$ for $\rho - \sigma$ if $\sigma \mid \rho$. We also impose an arbitrary linear order on the set $X$ of vertices. Placing each face in this order imposes an orientation on the faces. If $\pi$ and $\mu$ are disjoint subsets of $X$, we denote by $\text{Sg}[\pi, \mu]$ the sign of the permutation required to bring the elements of the sequence $\pi, \mu$ into the given linear order, assuming that the elements of $\pi$ and $\mu$ are already in the linear order. Similarly, if $\sigma \subseteq \rho$,

Sg$[\sigma, \rho] := $ Sg$[\sigma, \rho/\sigma]$. If $\rho$ is the monomial $x_1 x_2 \cdots x_r$, and $x_1 \leq x_2 \leq \cdots \leq x_r$ in the linear order on the set of vertices, then $\tilde{\rho}$ denotes the $r$-extensor $\tilde{x}_1 \tilde{x}_2 \cdots \tilde{x}_r$. Thus $\tilde{\rho} = \mathbf{0}$ if $\rho$ is not square free or if the $\tilde{x}_i$'s are linearly dependent. Also, if $\sigma, \rho$ are faces such that $\rho = \sigma x$ for some vertex $x$, we write $\rho \succ \sigma$ or $\sigma \prec \rho$. An explanation of the summation notation is also in order, viz, $\sum_{\rho \succ \sigma}$ means $\sum_{\rho : \rho \succ \sigma}$ and $\sum_{\sigma \prec \rho}$ means $\sum_{\sigma : \sigma \prec \rho}$.

When working with $r$-rigidity of $(\Delta, d)$ and related concepts to be defined in the next section, where $r \in [1, d+1]$ is an integer, we assume that the vertices of $\Delta$ are realized in such a way that $\tilde{\rho} \neq 0$ for every simplex $\rho \in \Delta^{(r-1)}$, in other words, the vertices of $\rho$ are affinely independent.

## 3. The Projective Matrix

Let $(\Delta, d)$ be a simplicial complex realized in $d$-space and $\mathbb{V} = \mathbb{R}^{d+1}$. Let $\mathbf{R}_r(\Delta)$ be a matrix whose entries are extensors of step $r$ in $\bigwedge^r \mathbb{V}$, whose rows are indexed by $\Delta^{(r-1)}$ and whose columns are indexed by $\Delta^{(r-2)}$. The entry in row $\rho$ and column $\sigma$ is

$$\mathbf{R}_r(\rho, \sigma) := \begin{cases} \text{Sg}[\sigma, \rho]\tilde{\rho} & \text{if } \rho \succ \sigma \\ \mathbf{0} & \text{if } \sigma \not\prec \rho. \end{cases}$$

Note that Sg$[\sigma, \rho]\tilde{\rho} = \tilde{\sigma}\tilde{x}$ if $\rho = \sigma x$. Since each entry is an extensor which lies in a space of dimension $\binom{d+1}{r}$ we can also think of $\mathbf{R}_r(\Delta)$ as having $f_{r-2}(\Delta)\binom{d+1}{r}$ columns, organized in $f_{r-2}(\Delta)$ blocks. This matrix is the *(projective) rigidity matrix* of $(\Delta, d)$. We denote its row space by $Row_r(\Delta)$. This matrix is denoted with a superscript $P$ in [6, 7] but we drop it because we will use exclusively this matrix in our presentation here.

An $r$-*stress* of $\Delta$ is a function $\lambda : \Delta^{(r-1)} \to \mathbb{R}$ satisfying for each $\sigma \in \Delta^{(r-2)}$, the equilibrium equation

$$\sum_{\rho \succ \sigma} \lambda_\rho \text{Sg}[\sigma, \rho]\tilde{\rho} = \mathbf{0}. \tag{3.1}$$

This means the space of all $r$-stresses is the cokernel of $\mathbf{R}_r(\Delta)$. We denote the space of (projective) $r$-stresses by $Stress_r(\Delta)$. The simplicial complex $\Delta$ is said to be $r$-*independent* if dim $Stress_r(\Delta) = 0$, i.e., if the rows of the rigidity matrix are linearly independent over $\mathbb{R}$.

An $r$-*load* of $\Delta$ is a function $L : \Delta^{(r-2)} \to \bigwedge^r \mathbb{V}$ satisfying for all $\sigma \in \Delta^{(r-2)}$,

$$L(\sigma) = \mathbf{s}_\sigma \tilde{\sigma} \quad \text{for some } \mathbf{s}_\sigma \in \bigwedge^1 \mathbb{V} \tag{3.2}$$

and satisfying, for all $\tau \in \Delta^{(r-3)}$, the equilibrium equations,

$$\sum_{\sigma \succ \tau} \text{Sg}[\tau, \sigma]L(\sigma) = \mathbf{0}. \tag{3.3}$$

The space of all $r$-loads is denoted by $Load_r(\Delta)$. It is clear that $Row_r(\Delta) \subseteq Load_r(\Delta)$.

An $r$-load $L$ is said to be *resolved* if there is function $\lambda : \Delta^{(r-1)} \to \mathbb{R}$ such that

$$\sum_{\rho \in \Delta^{(r-1)}} \lambda_\rho \text{Row}(\rho) + L = 0.$$

We say that $\Delta$ is $r$-*rigid* if all $r$-loads are resolved.

Let $\mathbb{A}_j^i$ denote the space of all functions from $\Delta^{(i)}$ to $\bigwedge^j \mathbb{V}$. Thus $Row_r(\Delta) \subseteq Load_r(\Delta) \subseteq \mathbb{A}_r^{r-2}$. We shall also write $N \vee Q := \sum_{\sigma \in \Delta^{(r-2)}} N(\sigma) \vee Q(\sigma)$, for $N \in \mathbb{A}_r^{r-2}$, $Q \in \mathbb{A}_{d+1-r}^{r-2}$.

An $r$-center of $\Delta$ is a function $C : \Delta^{(r-2)} \to \bigwedge^{d+1-r} \mathbb{V}$, i.e, $C \in \mathbb{A}_{d+1-r}^{r-2}$ satisfying for all $\rho \in \Delta^{(r-1)}$,

$$C \vee \mathrm{Row}(\rho) = \sum_{\sigma \prec \rho} \mathrm{Sg}[\sigma, \rho] C(\sigma)\tilde{\rho} = 0 \tag{3.4}$$

where $\mathrm{Row}(\rho)$ is the row of the rigidity matrix indexed by $\rho$, regarded as a function in $\mathbb{A}_r^{r-2}$. We denote the space of (projective) centers by $Motion_r(\Delta)$.

There are two types of trivial centers, which will occur for a given $(r-2)$-skeleton no matter which $r-1$ faces are present. The space of $trivial$ $r$-$centers$ $of$ $the$ $first$ $kind$, denoted by $Triv_{r,1}(\Delta)$, is generated by the $r$-centers $T_{\sigma,x,\mathbf{s}}$ for every pair $x, \sigma$, where $x \in \sigma \in \Delta^{(r-2)}$ and every tensor $\mathbf{s} \in \bigwedge^{d-r} \mathbb{V}$:

$$T_{\sigma,x,\mathbf{s}}(\mu) := \begin{cases} \mathbf{s}\tilde{x} & \text{if } \mu = \sigma \\ \mathbf{0} & \text{otherwise.} \end{cases} \tag{3.5}$$

Such a generator is localized to the columns of $\sigma \in \Delta^{(r-2)}$.

The space of $trivial$ $r$-$centers$ $of$ $the$ $second$ $kind$, denoted by $Triv_{r,2}(\Delta)$, is generated by $T_{\pi,\mathbf{s}}$, for every $\pi \in \Delta^{(r-3)}$ and every tensor $\mathbf{s} \in \bigwedge^{d+1-r} \mathbb{V}$:

$$T_{\pi,\mathbf{s}}(\sigma) := \begin{cases} \mathrm{Sg}[\pi, \sigma]\mathbf{s} & \text{if } \sigma \succ \pi \\ \mathbf{0} & \text{otherwise.} \end{cases} \tag{3.6}$$

The space of $trivial$ $r$-$centers$, denoted by $Triv_r(\Delta)$, is generated by the trivial centers of the first and second kind. We define the space of $non$-$trivial$ $r$-$centers$, $NonTriv_r(\Delta)$, to be the quotient space $Motion_r(\Delta)/(Triv_r(\Delta))$.

We also need the following theorems from [6, 7].

THEOREM 3.1. ([6], Theorem 3.6) $An$ $r$-$center$ $is$ $trivial$ $if$ $and$ $only$ $if$ $for$ $all$ $r$-$loads$ $L$, $C \vee L = 0$.

THEOREM 3.2. ([6], Corollary 3.7) $A$ $simplicial$ $complex$ $\Delta$ $is$ $r$-$rigid$ $if$ $and$ $only$ $if$ $NonTriv_r(\Delta) = 0$.

THEOREM 3.3. ([7], Corollary 1.2) $Let$ $\Delta' := \Delta * a$ $denote$ $the$ $one$-$point$ $cone$ $over$ $\Delta$, $where$ $a$ $is$ $not$ $a$ $vertex$ $of$ $\Delta$. $Realize$ $\Delta'$ $in$ $(d+1)$-$space$ $and$ $project$ $it$ $from$ $a$ $to$ $a$ $d$-$dimensional$ $subspace$ $\mathbb{H}$. $Then$ $\Delta'$ $is$ $r$-$rigid$ $if$ $and$ $only$ $if$ $its$ $image$ $\Delta$ $is$ $r$-$rigid$ $in$ $\mathbb{H}$.

THEOREM 3.4. ([7], Theorem 1.6) $Let$ $\Delta = K_n$ $be$ $realized$ $in$ $general$ $position$ $in$ $d$-$space$, $i.e.$, $the$ $vertices$ $of$ $every$ $d$-$dimensional$ $faces$ $are$ $affinely$ $independent$. $If$ $d \geq r-1$, $then$ $\Delta$ $is$ $r$-$rigid$. $If$ $d+1 \geq n$, $then$ $\Delta$ $has$ $only$ $the$ $zero$ $r$-$stress$.

The idea of skeletal rigidity is connected to the face ring of the simplicial complex in the following way.

Let $\Delta$ be a $d$-dimensional simplicial complex realized in $n$-space. Let the vertices of $\Delta$ be $a_1, \ldots, a_k$ and their respective homogeneous coordinates be $\mathbf{a}_1, \ldots, \mathbf{a}_k$. Define the real polynomial ring $R := \mathbb{R}[x_1, \ldots, x_k]$ and let $I$ be the ideal generated by monomials whose supports do not correspond to faces of $\Delta$. The Stanley-Reisner ring $A := R/I = A_0 \oplus A_1 \oplus \cdots$ is graded by degree. Let $\mathbf{a}_i = (a_{i,1}, \ldots, a_{i,n+1})$,

$i = 1, \ldots, k$. For $1 \leq j \leq n + 1$, let $\theta_j := a_{1,j}x_1 + a_{2,j}x_2 + \cdots + a_{k,j}x_k$ and $B := A/\langle \theta_1, \cdots, \theta_{n+1} \rangle = B_0 \oplus B_1 \oplus \cdots$. As noted in [4] and [8], we have the following result.

THEOREM 3.5. $\dim B_i = \dim Stress_i(\Delta)$, for all $i$.

As quoted in [4], $\Delta$ is Cohen-Macaulay if $\dim B_i = h_i$. Thus we have the following corollary:

COROLLARY 3.6. Let $D$ be a $d$-dimensional simplicial complex. Then $\Delta$ is Cohen-Macaulay if it can be realized in $d$-space so that $\dim Stress_i(\Delta) = h_i(\Delta)$ for all $i$.

Suppose $\Delta$ is a convex $d$-polytope. We can think of $\Delta$ as realized in projective $(d-1)$-space by regarding the Euclidean coordinates of the vertices as their homogeneous coordinates. Then $h_i = \dim B_i$. Stanley proved the necessity of the $g$-theorem by showing that one can realize $\Delta$ is projective $d$-space by appending an extra coordinate to the Euclidean coordinates so that $g_i = \dim B_i$.

## 4. The link

For any $\sigma \in \Delta^{(i-1)}$, the *star* and *antistar* are, respectively, $\mathrm{St}_\Delta(\sigma) := \{\tau \in \Delta : \sigma \mid \tau\}$, $\mathrm{Ast}_\Delta(\sigma) := \Delta - \langle \mathrm{St}_\Delta(\sigma) \rangle$. The *link* of $\sigma$ in $\Delta$ is $\mathrm{Lk}_\Delta(\sigma) := \{\tau/\sigma : \tau \in \mathrm{St}(\sigma)\}$. Subscripts will be dropped if the context is clear. Even though $\mathrm{St}(\sigma)$ is not a simplicial complex, the notions of $r$-centers, trivial $r$-centers of the first kind and $r$-stresses still apply. However, trivial $r$-centers of the second kind have to be defined slightly differently. The space of trivial $r$-centers of the second kind, $Triv_{r,2}(\mathrm{St}(\sigma), d)$, is generated by $T_{\sigma\tau,\mathbf{s}}$ for every $(r-i-3)$-face $\tau \in \mathrm{Lk}(\sigma)$, and for every $\mathbf{s} \in \bigwedge^{d+1-r} \mathbb{V}$ where

$$T_{\sigma\tau,\mathbf{s}}(\sigma\rho) := \begin{cases} \mathrm{Sg}[\tau, \rho]\mathbf{s} & \text{if } \rho \succ \tau \\ \mathbf{0} & \text{otherwise.} \end{cases}$$

The space of trivial centers of the first kind, generated by $T_{\sigma\pi,x,\mathbf{s}}$ where $x \in \sigma$, is denoted by $Triv_{r,1}(\mathrm{St}(\sigma), d)$.

Our purpose is to derive some relationship between motions of $\Delta$ and motions of $\mathrm{St}(\sigma)$ and to show that motions of $\Delta$ can be decomposed into motions of $\mathrm{St}(\sigma)$ and $\mathrm{Ast}(\sigma)$. As usual we assume that $\Delta$ is in $d$-space. Choose an extensor $\mathbf{s} = \mathbf{a}_1\mathbf{a}_2\cdots\mathbf{a}_{d+1-i} \in \bigwedge^{d+1-i}\mathbb{V}$ such that $\tilde{\sigma}\mathbf{s} \neq 0$. Let $\mathbb{S}$ be the subspace spanned by $\{\mathbf{a}_1, \mathbf{a}_2, \ldots, \mathbf{a}_{d+1-i}\}$. If we project $\sigma$ from $\sigma$ into $\mathbb{S}$, then the image is $\mathrm{Lk}(\sigma)$. We assume that $\mathrm{Lk}(\sigma)$ is the image of such a projection $\Phi$. The map $\Phi$ extends linearly to a projection from $\bigwedge\mathbb{V}$ to $\bigwedge\mathbb{S}$ which we also denote by $\Phi$. We also assume that for all tensors $\mathbf{x}$, $\tilde{\sigma}\mathbf{x} = \tilde{\sigma}\Phi(\mathbf{x})$. (For those who are familiar with Cayley algebra, $\Phi(\mathbf{x}) = \frac{\tilde{\sigma}\wedge\mathbf{s}}{[\tilde{\sigma}\mathbf{s}]}$.) Note that we think of $\mathrm{Lk}(\sigma)$ as a complex realized in $\mathbb{S}$ but for convenience we continue to write the coordinates of its vertices as points in $\mathbb{V}$.

Before we present the theorems in this section, it is useful to note that the $r$-rigidity matrix of $\Delta$ can be partitioned as

$$\begin{bmatrix} S & X \\ Y & A \end{bmatrix},$$

where $S$ is $r$-rigidity matrix of $(\mathrm{St}_\Delta(\sigma), d)$, $A$ is that of $(\mathrm{Ast}_\Delta(\sigma), d)$, and $Y$ is the matrix with all entries 0.

THEOREM 4.1. *For any $(n-1)$-dimensional simplicial complex $(\Delta, d)$ realized in $d$ space and for every $\sigma \in \Delta^{(i-1)}$, $1 \le i \le n$, we have, for $i < r \le \dim(\mathrm{St}(\sigma))+1$,*

    **(i):** $Motion_r(\mathrm{St}(\sigma), d)/\,Triv_{r,1}(\mathrm{St}(\sigma), d) \simeq Motion_{r-i}(\mathrm{Lk}(\sigma), d-i)$
    **(ii):** $Stress_r(\mathrm{St}(\sigma), d) \simeq Stress_{r-i}(\mathrm{Lk}(\sigma), d-i)$.

PROOF. (i) $\Phi$ induces a surjection from $Motion_r(\mathrm{St}(\sigma))$ to $Motion_{r-i}(\mathrm{Lk}(\sigma))$ as follows. If $C$ is an $r$-center of $\mathrm{St}(\sigma)$, then $\Phi(C') : \mathrm{Lk}(\sigma)^{(r-i-2)} \to \bigwedge^{d+1-r} \mathbb{S}$ where $\Phi(C')(\tau) := \Phi(C(\sigma\tau))$ is an $(r-i)$-center of $\mathrm{Lk}(\sigma)$. Also, if $C'$ is an $(r-i)$-center of $\mathrm{Lk}(\sigma)$, then $C : \mathrm{St}(\sigma) \to \bigwedge^{d+1} \mathbb{V}$ where $C(\sigma\tau) := C'(\tau)$ for all $(r-i-2)$-faces $\tau \in \mathrm{Lk}(\sigma)$ is an $r$-center of $\mathrm{St}(\sigma)$ and $\Phi(C) = C'$. The kernel of this map is clearly $Triv_{r,1}(\mathrm{St}(\sigma))$.

(ii) Let $\lambda$ be an $r$-stress of $\mathrm{St}(\sigma)$. Then for all $(r-i-2)$-face $\tau \in \mathrm{Lk}(\sigma)$,

$$\sum_{\rho \succ \tau} \lambda_{\sigma\rho} \mathrm{Sg}[\tau, \rho] \tilde{\sigma}\tilde{\rho} = \mathbf{0}.$$

Thus $\tilde{\sigma} \sum_{\rho \succ \tau} \lambda_{\sigma\rho} \mathrm{Sg}[\tau, \rho] \Phi(\tilde{\rho}) = \mathbf{0}$. Therefore $\sum_{\rho \succ \tau} \lambda'_\rho \mathrm{Sg}[\tau, \rho] \Phi(\tilde{\rho}) = \mathbf{0}$, where $\lambda'_\rho := \lambda_{\sigma\rho}$. Thus $\lambda'$ is an $(r-i)$-stress of $(\mathrm{Lk}(\sigma), d-i)$.

In exactly the same way, every $(r-i)$-stress of $(\mathrm{Lk}(\sigma), d-i)$ corresponds to an $r$-stress of $\mathrm{St}(\sigma)$. $\square$

THEOREM 4.2. *Suppose $(\Delta, d)$ is an $(n-1)$-dimensional simplicial complex realized in $d$-space. If $\sigma \in \Delta^{(i-1)}$ and $(\mathrm{Lk}(\sigma), d-i)$ is $(r-i)$-independent, where $1 \le i \le n$ and $i < r \le \dim(\mathrm{St}(\sigma))+1$, then*

    **(i):** $Motion_r(\Delta, d) \simeq Motion_r(\mathrm{Ast}(\sigma, d))$
$$\oplus Motion_{r-i}(\mathrm{Lk}(\sigma), d-i) \oplus Triv_{r,1}(\mathrm{St}(\sigma), d);$$
    **(ii):** $Triv_r(\mathrm{Ast}(\sigma, d)) \oplus Triv_{r-i}(\mathrm{Lk}(\sigma), d-i) \oplus Triv_{r,1}(\mathrm{St}(\sigma), d)$ *is isomorphic to a subspace of $Triv_r(\Delta, d)$;*
    **(iii):** $Non\,Triv_r(\Delta, d)$ *is isomorphic to a subspace of*

$$Non\,Triv_r(\mathrm{Ast}(\sigma, d)) \oplus Non\,Triv_{r-i}(\mathrm{Lk}(\sigma), d-i).$$

PROOF. (i) It suffices to prove that

$$Motion_r(\Delta) \simeq Motion_r(\mathrm{Ast}(\sigma)) \oplus Motion_r(\mathrm{St}(\sigma)).$$

From the partitioning of the $r$-rigidity matrix, we see that any $r$-center of $\Delta$ restricted to $\mathrm{Ast}(\sigma)$ is an $r$-center of $\mathrm{Ast}(\sigma)$. Thus the restriction map $f : Motion_r(\Delta) \to Motion_r(\mathrm{Ast}(\sigma))$ is well defined. The kernel of this map is precisely those $r$-centers of $\Delta$ which are zero on $\mathrm{Ast}(\sigma)$, i.e., $r$-centers of $\mathrm{St}(\sigma)$. Since $\mathrm{Lk}(\sigma)$ has no $(r-i)$-stress, every $r$-center of $\mathrm{Ast}(\sigma)$ extends to an $r$-center of $\Delta$. (This extension is not unique in general.) Thus the map is onto. This completes the proof of the first part.

(ii) We note that trivial $r$-centers in $Triv_r(\mathrm{Ast}(\sigma))$ can be extended to trivial centers in $Triv_r(\Delta)$, and that trivial centers in $Triv_r(\mathrm{St}(\sigma), d)$ extend to trivial $r$-centers of $Triv_r(\Delta, d)$. Moreover $Triv_r(\mathrm{St}(\sigma), d) \simeq Triv_{r-i}(\mathrm{Lk}(\sigma), d-i) \oplus Triv_{r,1}(\mathrm{St}(\sigma), d)$. Thus the result follows.

Part (iii) then follows from the first two parts. $\square$

COROLLARY 4.3. *Let $\sigma \in \Delta^{(i-1)}$ and $r > i$. If $(\mathrm{Lk}(\sigma), d-i)$ is $(r-i)$-rigid and $(\mathrm{Ast}(\sigma, d))$ is $r$-rigid, then $(\Delta, d)$ is also $r$-rigid.*

PROOF. We remove some appropriate $(r-i+1)$-faces from $\Delta$ so that $(\mathrm{Lk}(\sigma), d-i)$ is $(r-i)$-independent but remains $(r-i)$-rigid. This does not change $\mathrm{Ast}(\sigma)$. Thus the result follows from Theorem 4.2 part (iii).  □

COROLLARY 4.4. *Let $\sigma \in \Delta^{(i-1)}$ and $r > i$.*

(i): *If $(\mathrm{Lk}(\sigma), d-i)$ is $(r-i)$-rigid, then*

$$NonTriv_r(\Delta, d) \simeq NonTriv_r(\mathrm{Ast}(\sigma, d)).$$

(ii): *If $(\mathrm{Lk}(\sigma), d-i)$ is $(r-i)$-independent and $(\Delta, d)$ is $r$-rigid, then $(\mathrm{Ast}(\sigma, d))$ is also $r$-rigid.*

PROOF. Let $L$ be an $r$-load of $(\mathrm{Ast}(\sigma, d))$. Then it extends to an $r$-load $L'$ of $(\Delta, d)$ by assigning $\mathbf{0}$ to $(r-2)$-faces of $\mathrm{St}(\sigma)$.

First we prove part (ii). Since $\Delta$ is $r$-rigid, $L'$ is resolved, i.e., there exist scalars $\lambda_\rho$ such that $\sum_{\rho \in \Delta^{(r-1)}} \lambda_\rho \mathrm{Row}(\rho) + L' = 0$. Since $(\mathrm{Lk}(\sigma), d-i)$ is $(r-i)$-independent, i.e., $(\mathrm{St}(\sigma), d)$ is $r$-independent, $\lambda_\rho = 0$ if $\rho \in \mathrm{St}(\sigma)$. This means $L$ itself is resolved. So $(\mathrm{Ast}(\sigma., d))$ is $r$-rigid.

To prove part (i), we consider the space $\mathbb{L}$ of $r$-loads of $\Delta$ which are zero on $\mathrm{St}(\sigma)$. Since $(\mathrm{Lk}(\sigma), d-i)$ is $(r-i)$-rigid, the orthogonal complement of the space generated by $\mathbb{L} \cup \{\mathrm{Row}(\rho) : \rho \in \mathrm{St}(\sigma)\}$ is $Triv_{r,1}(\Delta)$. Thus $Load_r(\Delta) \simeq \mathbb{L} \oplus Row(\mathbf{R}_r(\mathrm{St}(\sigma)))$. From this the conclusion follows.  □

REMARK 4.5. Note that a non-trivial $r$-center of $(\Delta, d)$ which is zero on $\mathrm{Ast}(\sigma)$ can correspond to a trivial $(r-i)$-center of $(\mathrm{Lk}(\sigma), d-i)$ in general. Thus $\Delta$ can be $r$-rigid without $\mathrm{Lk}(\sigma)$ being $(r-i)$-rigid (see Example 4.6). The $(r-i)$-rigidity of $(\mathrm{Lk}(\sigma), d-i)$ for all $\sigma \in \Delta^{(i-1)}$ is not even sufficient to guarantee the $r$-rigidity of $(\Delta, d)$ (see Example 4.7). However, the non-trivial $(r-i)$-centers of the links often give rise to non-trivial $r$-centers of $(\Delta, d)$ (see Example 4.8).

EXAMPLE 4.6. Consider the 2-dimension simplicial complex $\Delta := \langle abc, ade \rangle$. Realize $\Delta$ in 2-space. By the results in [**6**, Section 4] and [**7**], $\Delta$ is 3-rigid since $\beta_1 = 0$ for $\Delta$. However, $\mathrm{Lk}(a)$ is disconnected and hence is not 2-rigid in 1-space. Note that $\mathrm{Ast}(a)$ is 3-rigid in 2-space.

EXAMPLE 4.7. Let $\Delta$ be the boundary complex of a 4-polytope with 7 vertices and 12 facets:

$$\Delta := \langle abde, abef, abfg, abdg, acde, acef, acfg, acdg, bcde, bcef, bcfg, bcdg \rangle.$$

Realize $\Delta$ in 4-space as a convex polytope. The link of every vertex is a triangulated 3-polytope which is 2-rigid in 3-space. However, not all 3-centers of $\Delta$ are trivial. The following 3-motion is such an example. Let $C$ be the 3-center which is $\mathbf{0}$ on every edge except the following: $C(ab) := \tilde{d}\tilde{e}$, $C(af) := \alpha\tilde{c}\tilde{e}$, $C(ag) := \beta\tilde{c}\tilde{d}$, $C(fg) := \gamma\tilde{b}\tilde{c}$. where $\alpha, \beta, \gamma$ are the scalars

$$\alpha := [\tilde{d}\tilde{e}\tilde{a}\tilde{b}\tilde{f}]/[\tilde{c}\tilde{e}\tilde{a}\tilde{f}\tilde{b}], \ \beta := [\tilde{d}\tilde{e}\tilde{a}\tilde{b}\tilde{g}]/[\tilde{c}\tilde{d}\tilde{a}\tilde{g}\tilde{b}], \ \gamma := (\alpha[\tilde{c}\tilde{e}\tilde{a}\tilde{f}\tilde{g}] + \beta[\tilde{c}\tilde{d}\tilde{a}\tilde{g}\tilde{f}])/[\tilde{b}\tilde{c}\tilde{f}\tilde{g}\tilde{a}]$$

$C$ is not a trivial 3-center because $C \vee L \neq 0$ where $L$ is the 3-load represented by the missing face $abc$. The figure below shows the relevant part of the $\mathbf{R}_3(\Delta)$.

|       | $ab$          | $af$         | $ag$         | $fg$         |
|-------|---------------|--------------|--------------|--------------|
| $abd$ | $\tilde{a}\tilde{b}\tilde{d}$ | $0$ | $0$ | $0$ |
| $abe$ | $\tilde{a}\tilde{b}\tilde{e}$ | $0$ | $0$ | $0$ |
| $abf$ | $\tilde{a}\tilde{b}\tilde{f}$ | $\tilde{a}\tilde{f}b$ | $0$ | $0$ |
| $abg$ | $\tilde{a}\tilde{b}\tilde{g}$ | $0$ | $\tilde{a}\tilde{g}\tilde{b}$ | $0$ |
| $acf$ | $0$ | $\tilde{a}\tilde{f}\tilde{c}$ | $0$ | $0$ |
| $acg$ | $0$ | $0$ | $\tilde{a}\tilde{g}\tilde{c}$ | $0$ |
| $adf$ | $\tilde{a}\tilde{f}\tilde{d}$ | $0$ | $0$ | $0$ |
| $adg$ | $0$ | $0$ | $\tilde{a}\tilde{g}\tilde{d}$ | $0$ |
| $afg$ | $0$ | $\tilde{a}\tilde{f}\tilde{g}$ | $\tilde{a}\tilde{g}\tilde{f}$ | $\tilde{f}\tilde{g}\tilde{a}$ |
| $bfg$ | $0$ | $0$ | $0$ | $\tilde{f}\tilde{g}\tilde{b}$ |
| $cfg$ | $0$ | $0$ | $0$ | $\tilde{f}\tilde{g}\tilde{c}$ |

| $L$ | $\tilde{a}\tilde{b}\tilde{c}$ | $0$ | $0$ | $0$ |
|-----|---------------|-----|-----|-----|

| $C$ | $\tilde{d}\tilde{e}$ | $\alpha\tilde{c}\tilde{e}$ | $\beta\tilde{c}\tilde{d}$ | $\gamma\tilde{b}\tilde{c}$ |
|-----|----------------------|----------------------------|----------------------------|----------------------------|

EXAMPLE 4.8. Let $\Delta$ be the boundary complex of the triangular bipyramid

$$\Delta := \langle abd, abe, ace, acd, bcd, bce\rangle.$$

Then $\mathrm{Lk}(a)$ is the quadrilateral $bdce$. This is not 2-rigid in 2-space. It has a 2-center which is not trivial. This gives rise to the following 3-center $C$ of $\Delta$ which is not trivial: $C$ is $\mathbf{0}$ on every edge except $ac$ and $ae$, and $C(ac) := \tilde{d}$, $C(ae) := \alpha\tilde{b}$, where $\alpha[\tilde{a}\tilde{e}\tilde{c}\tilde{b}] := [\tilde{a}\tilde{c}\tilde{e}\tilde{d}]$. The 3-center $C$ is not a trivial 3-center because $C \vee L \neq 0$ where $L$ is the 3-load given by the non-facial triangle $abc$. The figure below shows $\mathbf{R}_3(\Delta)$.

|       | $ab$          | $ac$          | $ad$          | $ae$          | $bc$          | $bd$          | $be$          | $cd$          | $ce$          |
|-------|---------------|---------------|---------------|---------------|---------------|---------------|---------------|---------------|---------------|
| $abd$ | $\tilde{a}\tilde{b}\tilde{d}$ | $0$ | $\tilde{a}\tilde{d}\tilde{b}$ | $0$ | $0$ | $\tilde{b}\tilde{d}\tilde{a}$ | $0$ | $0$ | $0$ |
| $abe$ | $\tilde{a}\tilde{b}\tilde{e}$ | $0$ | $0$ | $\tilde{a}\tilde{e}\tilde{b}$ | $0$ | $0$ | $\tilde{b}\tilde{e}\tilde{a}$ | $0$ | $0$ |
| $ace$ | $0$ | $\tilde{a}\tilde{c}\tilde{e}$ | $0$ | $\tilde{a}\tilde{e}\tilde{c}$ | $0$ | $0$ | $0$ | $0$ | $\tilde{c}\tilde{e}\tilde{a}$ |
| $acd$ | $0$ | $\tilde{a}\tilde{c}\tilde{d}$ | $\tilde{a}\tilde{d}\tilde{c}$ | $0$ | $0$ | $0$ | $0$ | $\tilde{c}\tilde{d}\tilde{a}$ | $0$ |
| $bcd$ | $0$ | $0$ | $0$ | $0$ | $\tilde{b}\tilde{c}\tilde{d}$ | $\tilde{b}\tilde{d}\tilde{c}$ | $0$ | $\tilde{c}\tilde{d}\tilde{b}$ | $0$ |
| $bce$ | $0$ | $0$ | $0$ | $0$ | $\tilde{b}\tilde{c}\tilde{e}$ | $0$ | $\tilde{b}\tilde{e}\tilde{c}$ | $0$ | $\tilde{c}\tilde{e}\tilde{b}$ |

| $C$ | $0$ | $\tilde{d}$ | $0$ | $\alpha\tilde{b}$ | $0$ | $0$ | $0$ | $0$ | $0$ |
|-----|-----|-------------|-----|-------------------|-----|-----|-----|-----|-----|

| $L$ | $\tilde{a}\tilde{b}\tilde{c}$ | $\tilde{a}\tilde{c}\tilde{b}$ | $0$ | $0$ | $\tilde{b}\tilde{c}\tilde{a}$ | $0$ | $0$ | $0$ | $0$ |
|-----|-------------------------------|-------------------------------|-----|-----|-------------------------------|-----|-----|-----|-----|

We also have a corresponding theorem for stresses.

THEOREM 4.9. Let $\sigma \in \Delta^{(i-1)}$. Suppose $r > i$ and $(\mathrm{Ast}(\sigma, d))$ is $r$-rigid or $(\mathrm{Lk}(\sigma), d - i)$ is $(r - i)$-independent. Then

$$Stress_r(\Delta, d) \simeq Stress_r(\mathrm{Ast}(\sigma, d)) \oplus Stress_{r-i}(\mathrm{Lk}(\sigma), d - i).$$

PROOF. The restriction of an $r$-stress $\lambda$ of $(\Delta, d)$ to $\mathrm{St}(\sigma)$ is an $r$-stress of $(\mathrm{St}(\sigma), d)$. If $(\mathrm{Lk}(\sigma), d - i)$ is $(r - i)$-independent, then $\mathrm{St}(\sigma)$ is $r$-independent. Thus $\lambda$ is 0 on $\mathrm{St}(\sigma)$. Hence its restriction to $\mathrm{Ast}(\sigma)$ is an $r$-stress of $(\mathrm{Ast}(\sigma, d))$. Since every $r$-stress of $(\mathrm{Ast}(\sigma, d))$ is an $r$-stress of $(\Delta, d)$, the result holds.

Next we consider the case where $(\mathrm{Ast}(\sigma, d))$ is $r$-rigid. The kernel of the restriction map is clearly the space of $r$-stresses of $\mathrm{Ast}(\sigma)$. Thus it suffices to prove that every $r$-stress $\lambda$ of $(\mathrm{St}(\sigma), d)$ extends to an $r$-stress of $\Delta$.

For all $(r - 2)$-faces $\tau$ in $\mathrm{Ast}(\sigma)$, define $L(\tau) := \sum_{\rho \succ \tau} \lambda_\rho \mathrm{Sg}[\tau, \rho] \tilde{\rho}$. We claim that $L \in Load_r(\mathrm{Ast}(\sigma))$. Clearly (3.2) is satisfied. To prove (3.3), we note that for all $(r - 3)$-faces $\pi$ in $\mathrm{Ast}(\sigma)$,

$$\sum_{\tau \succ \pi} \mathrm{Sg}[\pi, \tau] L(\tau) = \sum_{\tau \succ \pi} \sum_{\rho \succ \tau} \mathrm{Sg}[\pi, \tau] \mathrm{Sg}[\tau, \rho] \lambda_\rho \tilde{\rho}$$

$$= \sum_{\rho : \pi | \rho} \Big( \sum_{\tau : \rho \succ \tau \succ \pi} \mathrm{Sg}[\pi, \tau] \mathrm{Sg}[\tau, \rho] \Big) \lambda_\rho \tilde{\rho}$$

There are two cases. First, there are exactly two faces, say $\tau_1, \tau_2$, in $\mathrm{Ast}(\sigma)$ such that $\rho \succ \tau_1, \tau_2 \succ \pi$. Then

$$\mathrm{Sg}[\pi, \tau_1] \mathrm{Sg}[\tau_1, \rho] + \mathrm{Sg}[\pi, \tau_2] \mathrm{Sg}[\tau_2, \rho] = 0$$

Second, there is one face $\tau \in \mathrm{Ast}(\sigma)$ and one face $\tau' \in \mathrm{St}(\sigma)$ such that $\rho \succ \tau, \tau' \succ \pi$. Instead of indexing the summation by $\tau$, we can index it by $\tau'$. Thus the sum becomes

$$-\sum_{\tau'} \mathrm{Sg}[\pi, \tau'] \Big( \sum_{\rho \succ \tau'} \mathrm{Sg}[\tau', \rho] \lambda_\rho \tilde{\rho} \Big).$$

Since $\lambda$ is an $r$-stress of $\mathrm{St}(\sigma)$, the sum is $\mathbf{0}$.

Thus

$$\sum_{\tau \succ \pi} \mathrm{Sg}[\pi, \tau] L(\tau) = \mathbf{0}$$

and (3.3) is satisfied and $L$ is a an $r$-load of $(\mathrm{Ast}(\sigma, d))$. Since $\mathrm{Ast}(\sigma)$ is $r$-rigid, $L$ is resolved, i.e., for all $(r - 1)$-faces $\rho \in \mathrm{Ast}(\sigma)$, there exist scalars $\lambda_\rho$ such that

$$\sum_\rho \lambda_\rho \mathrm{Row}(\rho) + L = \mathbf{0}.$$

Thus $\lambda$ extends to an $r$-stress of $\Delta$. $\square$

## 5. Shellable complexes

A pure simplicial complex $\Delta$ is shellable if the facets of $\Delta$ can be arranged in a *shelling order* $\sigma_1, \sigma_2, \ldots, \sigma_m$, such that for $j = 2, \ldots, m - 1$, there is a unique minimal face $\pi_j$ of $\sigma_j$ such that $\pi_j$ is not a face of $\sigma_i$, for all $i < j$.

THEOREM 5.1. *A $(d - 1)$-dimensional shellable complex $\Delta$ realized in $(d - 1)$-space is $r$-rigid for all $r \in [1, d]$*

PROOF. Let $\sigma_1, \sigma_2, \ldots, \sigma_m$ be a shelling order. We shall prove the theorem by induction. Since $\langle \sigma_1 \rangle$ is a complete complex, it is $r$-rigid for all $r \in [1, d]$ by Theorem 3.4. We shall prove that if $\Delta_1 = \langle \sigma_1, \sigma_2, \ldots, \sigma_{j-1} \rangle$ is $r$-rigid for all $r \in [1, d]$, then so is $\Delta_2 = \langle \sigma_1, \sigma_2, \ldots, \sigma_j \rangle$. Suppose $\pi_j \in \Delta^{(k-1)}$, where $\pi_j$ is the unique minimal face of $\sigma_j$ in the shelling order. Then $\Delta_1^{(i)} = \Delta_2^{(i)}$ if $i \in [0, k - 2]$. Thus $\Delta_2$ is $r$-rigid if $r \in [1, k - 1]$.

For $r \geq k$, $\mathrm{Lk}_{\Delta_2}(\pi_j) = K_{d-k}$ is both $(r-k)$-rigid and independent in $(d-1-k)$-space. Also $\mathrm{Ast}_{\Delta_2}(\pi_j) = \Delta_1$ which is $r$-rigid in $d$-space. So by Corollary 4.3, $\Delta_2$ is $r$-rigid.                                                                        $\square$

THEOREM 5.2. *With the same notation as in the proof Theorem 5.1, if $\pi_j \in \Delta^{(k-1)}$, then*

$$\dim Stress_r(\Delta_2) = \begin{cases} \dim Stress_r(\Delta_1) + 1 & \text{if } r = k \\ \dim Stress_r(\Delta_1) & \text{otherwise.} \end{cases}$$

PROOF. From the proof of the previous result, it follows that $\dim Stress_r(\Delta_2) = \dim Stress_r(\Delta_1)$ for $r \in [1, k-1]$.

For $r = k$, since $\Delta_1$ is $r$-rigid, addition of $\pi_j$ without any change in $\Delta_1^{(k-1)}$ increases the dimension of the space of stresses by 1.

For $r > k$, we have $\mathrm{Lk}_{\Delta_2}(\pi_j) = K_{d-k}$ which is $(r-k)$-independent in $(d-1-k)$-space. So the result follows from Theorem 4.9.                              $\square$

THEOREM 5.3. *Let $\Delta$ be a $(d-1)$-dimensional shellable complex in $(d-1)$-space. Then $h_r = \dim Stress_r(\Delta)$.*

PROOF. The proof follows from the following well known result:

$$h_r(\Delta_2) = \begin{cases} h_r(\Delta_1) + 1 & \text{if } r = k \\ h_r(\Delta_1) & \text{otherwise.} \end{cases}$$

$\square$

The following is an immediate corollary.

COROLLARY 5.4. *Shellable complexes are Cohen-Macaulay.*

## 6. The $h$-vector of p.l.-spheres

Let $\Delta$ be a $d$-dimensional simplicial complex. The *boundary* of any face $\sigma$ of $\Delta$ is the complex $\partial\sigma := \langle\sigma\rangle - \sigma$. For any two simplicial complexes $\Delta_1$, $\Delta_2$ on disjoint vertex sets, $\Delta_1 * \Delta_2 := \{\sigma_1 \cup \sigma_2 : \sigma_i \in \Delta_i\}$. Suppose $\sigma \in \Delta^{(k-1)}$, $k \geq 1$ and $\tau$ is a square free monomial of degree $\ell$ which is not a face of $\Delta$ such that $\mathrm{Lk}_\Delta(\sigma) = \partial\tau$ and $k + \ell = d + 2$. Then the *bistellar subdivision* of $\Delta$ with respect to $\sigma$ and $\tau$ is

$$\mathrm{Bist}_\Delta(\tau, \sigma) := \mathrm{Ast}_\Delta(\sigma) \cup (\partial\sigma * \langle\tau\rangle).$$

Roughly speaking is such a subdivision, we remove the face $\sigma$, replace it by $\tau$, which is of complementary dimension, and join $\tau$ to the boundary of $\sigma$.

Our purpose is to show that for $\Delta$ in $d$-space, a bistellar operation preserves $r$-rigidity, for $0 \leq r \leq d$. We also show how it changes the dimension of stress spaces.

LEMMA 6.1. *Let $\Delta$ be a $d$-dimensional simplicial complex in $d$-space. Suppose $\sigma \in \Delta^{(k-1)}$ such that $\mathrm{Lk}(\sigma) = K_{d+2-k}$. Then*

$$\dim Stress_r(\mathrm{Ast}(\sigma)) = \begin{cases} \dim Stress_r(\Delta) - 1 & \text{if } d+1 \geq r \geq k \\ \dim Stress_r(\Delta) & \text{if } 1 \leq r < k \end{cases}$$

*and for $1 \leq r \leq d+1$*

$$\dim NonTriv_r(\mathrm{Ast}(\sigma)) = \dim NonTriv_r(\Delta).$$

PROOF. Since the $j$ faces of $\mathrm{Ast}_\Delta(\sigma)$ and $\Delta$ are the same for $j \in [0, k-2]$, the results are as claimed, for $r < k$.

For $d+1 \geq r \geq k$ let $\Delta_1 := \langle\sigma\rangle * \mathrm{Lk}(\sigma)$. Then $\Delta_1 = K_{d+2}$ is an $r$-circuit which is also $r$-rigid in $d$-space by Theorem 3.4. Let $\pi$ be an $(r-1)$-face of $\Delta_1$ such that $\sigma \mid \pi$, and let $\Delta' := \Delta - \mathrm{St}(\pi)$. Since $\pi$ is contained in an $r$-circuit,

$$\dim Stress_r(\Delta, d) = \dim Stress_r(\Delta', d) + 1$$

and

$$NonTriv_r(\Delta, d) = NonTriv_r(\Delta', d).$$

Since $\mathrm{Lk}_{\Delta'}(\sigma)$ is $(r-k)$-independent in $(d-k)$-space, by Theorem 4.9

$$\dim Stress_r(\Delta', d) = \dim Stress_r(\mathrm{Ast}_{\Delta'}(\sigma), d).$$

But $\mathrm{Ast}_{\Delta'}(\sigma) = \mathrm{Ast}_\Delta(\sigma)$, hence

$$\dim Stress_r(\Delta, d) - 1 = \dim Stress_r(\mathrm{Ast}_\Delta(\sigma, d)).$$

Since $\mathrm{Lk}_{\Delta'}(\sigma)$ is $(r-k)$-rigid, by Corollary 4.4

$$NonTriv_r(\mathrm{Ast}_{\Delta'}(\sigma)) \simeq NonTriv_r(\Delta'),$$

i.e.,

$$NonTriv_r(\mathrm{Ast}_\Delta(\sigma)) \simeq NonTriv_r(\Delta).$$

$\square$

Since every $d$-dimensional p.1.-sphere can be obtained from $\partial K_{d+2}$ by a sequence of bistellar operations (this is a result of Pachner, see [4]), and $\partial K_{d+2}$ is $r$-rigid in $d$-space, for $1 \leq r \leq d+1$, we have the following two corollaries.

COROLLARY 6.2. *Every $d$-dimensional p.1.-sphere in $d$-space is $r$-rigid, for $1 \leq r \leq d+1$.*

COROLLARY 6.3. *Let $\Delta$ be a $d$-dimensional p.1.-sphere in $d$-space. Then for $1 \leq r \leq d+1$, $\dim Stress_r(\Delta) = h_r$. Also the $h$-vector of a p.1.-sphere is symmetric, i.e., $h_i = h_{d+1-i}$, $i = 0, 1, \ldots, d+1$.*

PROOF. The results are clearly true for $\partial K_{d+2}$. Suppose $\dim Stress_r(\Delta) = h_r(\Delta)$. Consider $\mathrm{Bist}_\Delta(\tau, \sigma)$, with $|\tau| = \ell$, $|\sigma| = k$ and $k + \ell = d + 2$. Then

$$\dim Stress_r(\mathrm{Bist}_\Delta(\tau, \sigma)) - \dim Stress_r(\Delta) = \begin{cases} 1 & \text{if } \ell < k \text{ and } \ell \leq r < k \\ -1 & \text{if } k < \ell \text{ and } k \leq r < \ell \\ 0 & \text{otherwise.} \end{cases}$$

However

$$h_r(\mathrm{Bist}_\Delta(\tau, \sigma)) - h_r(\Delta) = \begin{cases} 1 & \text{if } \ell < k \text{ and } \ell \leq r < k \\ -1 & \text{if } k < \ell \text{ and } k \leq r < \ell \\ 0 & \text{otherwise.} \end{cases}$$

Thus $\dim Stress_r(\mathrm{Bist}_\Delta(\tau, \sigma)) = h_r(\mathrm{Bist}_\Delta(\tau, \sigma))$.

Finally, the above considerations show that if the $h$-vector of $\Delta$ is symmetric, then so is the $h$-vector of $\mathrm{Bist}_\Delta(\tau, \sigma)$. Since the $h$-vector of $\partial K_{d+2}$ is symmetric, so is the $h$-vector of every p.1.-sphere, $\square$

Note that the $r$-stresses referred to in the proof are what Carl Lee called linear stresses [4]. The next corollary follows from Corollary 3.6.

COROLLARY 6.4. *All p.l.-spheres are Cohen-Macaulay.*

## 7. The $g$-vector of p.l.-spheres

We shall indicate in this section the relationship between the $g$-vector of a p.l.-sphere and skeletal rigidity.

LEMMA 7.1. *Let $\Delta$ be a $d$-dimensional simplicial complex in $(d+1)$-space. Suppose $\sigma \in \Delta^{(k-1)}$ such that $\mathrm{Lk}(\sigma) = K_{d+2-k}$. If $\mathrm{Ast}\Delta(\sigma)$ is $k$-rigid, then*

$$\dim Stress_k(\mathrm{Ast}(\sigma)) = \dim Stress_k(\Delta) - 1.$$

*If $\mathrm{Ast}\Delta(\sigma)$ is $k$-independent, then*

$$\dim NonTriv_k(\mathrm{Ast}(\sigma)) = \dim NonTriv_k(\Delta) + 1.$$

*For $r \neq k$, we have*

$$\dim Stress_r(\mathrm{Ast}(\sigma)) = \dim Stress_r(\Delta)$$

*and*

$$\dim NonTriv_r(\mathrm{Ast}(\sigma)) = \dim NonTriv_r(\Delta).$$

PROOF. If $r < k$, then the $(r-1)$-faces of $\Delta$ and $\mathrm{Ast}(\sigma)$ are the same, as are the $(r-2)$-faces. So the results hold.

If $r = k$, then the $(r-2)$-faces of $\Delta$ and $\mathrm{Ast}(\sigma)$ are the same, while $\Delta$ has one more $(r-1)$-face than $\mathrm{Ast}(\sigma)$, namely $\sigma$. So the results are as claimed.

For $r > k$, since $\mathrm{Lk}(\sigma)$ is the $(d+1-k)$-simplex, $K_{d+2-k}$, it is $(r-k)$-independent and $(r-k)$-rigid in $(d+1-k)$-space. So the results follow from Theorem 4.9 and Corollary 4.4.                                       □

THEOREM 7.2. *Suppose $\Delta$ is a $d$-dimensional simplicial complex which is obtained from $\Delta_0 := \partial K_{d+2}$ by a sequence of bistellar subdivisions*

$$\Delta_i := \mathrm{Bist}_{\Delta_{i-1}}(\tau_i, \sigma_i), \qquad i = 1, 2, \dots, n$$

*where $\Delta_n := \Delta$ and $|\tau_i| < |\sigma_i|$ for all $i$. If $\Delta$ is realized in $(d+1)$-space, then $\Delta$ is $r$-rigid for $1 \leq r \leq \frac{d+1}{2}$ and is $r$-independent for $\frac{d+1}{2} \leq r \leq d+1$. Moreover,*

$$\dim Stress_r(\Delta) = g_r, \quad \text{if } 1 \leq r \leq (d+1)/2,$$

*and*

$$\dim NonTriv_r(\Delta) = -g_r, \quad \text{if } (d+1)/2 \leq r \leq d+1.$$

PROOF. We shall prove the theorem by induction. The results hold for $\Delta_0$. Assume that they hold for $\Delta_{i-1}$. Then by Lemma 7.1, they hold for $\Delta_i$ as well.   □

Note that the complexes in Theorem 7.2 are p.l.-spheres. The stresses involved what Carl Lee called linear stresses [4]. In order to extend the theorem to all p.l.-spheres, we need a proof that works for $|\tau_i| \geq |\sigma_i|$. This will be the case if the following conjecture is true.

CONJECTURE 7.3. *Let $\Delta$ be a $d$-dimensional p.l.-sphere, where $d$ is even. Then $\Delta$ can be realized in $(d+1)$-space so that it is $r$-rigid and $r$-independent for $r = (d+2)/2$.*

Cauchy's rigidity theorem for convex 3-polytopes [1] implies the truth of this theorem for $d = 2$.

# References

[1] A. Cauchy, *Deuxiéme memoire sur les polygons et les polyédres*, J. École Polytechnique XVIe Cahier (1831), 87–98.

[2] H. Crapo and W. Whiteley, *Stresses on frameworks and motions of panel structures: a projective geometric introduction*, Structural Topology **6** (1982), 42–82.

[3] P. Filliman, *Face numbers of pl-spheres*, manuscript, 1991.

[4] C. Lee, *Some recent results on convex polytopes*, Contemporary Math. **114** (1990), 3–19.

[5] P. McMullen, *On simple polytopes*, Invent. Math., **113** (1993), 419–444.

[6] T-S. Tay, N. White, and W. Whiteley, *Skeletal rigidity of simplicial complexes I*, European J. Combin. **16** (1995), 381–403.

[7] T-S. Tay, N. White, and W. Whiteley, *Skeletal rigidity of simplicial complexes II*, European J. Combin. in press.

[8] T-S. Tay, N. White, and W. Whiteley, *A homological interpretation of skeletal rigidity*, in preparation.

DEPARTMENT OF MATHEMATICS, NATIONAL UNIVERSITY OF SINGAPORE, 10 KENT RIDGE CRESCENT, SINGAPORE 119260

*E-mail address*: mattayts@math.nus.sg

Contemporary Mathematics
Volume **197**, 1996

# The Coxeter Matroids of Gelfand et al.

Neil L. White

ABSTRACT. First we show how ordinary matroids may be viewed in relation to the Coxeter group $S_n$, the symmetric group. Then we generalize, defining Coxeter matroids for an arbitrary Coxeter group $W$ and standard parabolic subgroup $P$. We note, in particular, the example $W = \mathcal{B}C_n$, the symmetry group of the $n$-cube; Coxeter matroids in this case are called symplectic matroids. The Coxeter matroid point of view leads us to a new basis axiomatization for ordinary matroids. We conclude with a number of open problems.

## 1. Introduction

Coxeter matroids, formerly known as $WP$-matroids, are a generalization of ordinary matroids, and are based on a Coxeter group $W$ and a standard parabolic subgroup $P$ of $W$. They have been studied by Gelfand, Serganova, Borovik, and others ([**BG1, BG2, BR, GGMS, GS1, GS2**]), but are relatively unknown to most of the community of matroid theorists. This paper is an attempt to remedy this situation.

## 2. Ordinary matroids as Coxeter matroids

Let $\mathcal{B}$ be the collection of bases of a matroid of rank $k$ on the set $E = [n] = \{1, 2, \dots, n\}$. It is well-known ([**Bry**]) that one of the many equivalent forms of the matroid basis axioms is

1. $\mathcal{B} \neq \emptyset$,
2. $B \in \mathcal{B}$ implies $|B| = k$,
3. (Gale maximality) For every total ordering $<$ on $E$, there exists $B \in \mathcal{B}$ such that for all $B' \in \mathcal{B}$, if we write $B = \{b_1, b_2, \dots, b_k\}, B' = \{b'_1, b'_2, \dots, b'_k\}$ with $b_i \leq b_{i+1}$ and $b'_i \leq b'_{i+1}$ for all $i \leq k-1$, then $b_i \geq b'_i$ for all $i \leq k$.

In other words, (3.) says that for every total ordering on $E$, there is a unique maximal basis in the *Gale ordering* (see [**Gale**]), which is just componentwise ordering on the bases, assuming the elements of each base are themselves listed in order.

Now let $S_n$ be the symmetric group on the set $[n]$. We know that $S_n$ is generated by the set of adjacent transpositions, $\{s_1, s_2, \dots, s_{n-1}\}$, where $s_i = (i, i+1)$. Let $P_k$ be the subgroup of $S_n$ generated by $\{s_1, s_2, \dots, s_{k-1}, s_{k+1}, \dots, s_{n-1}\}$. Then

1991 *Mathematics Subject Classification.* 05B35,05E15,20F55.
Supported in part by NSA grant MDA904-95-1-1056.

$P_k$ is called a *maximal standard parabolic subgroup* of $S_n$, and is the stabilizer of $\{1, 2, \ldots, k\}$ (as well as of $\{k+1, k+2, \ldots, n\}$).

Now let $B \in \binom{[n]}{k}$, that is, $B$ is a subset of $[n]$ of cardinality $k$. Let $\sigma$ be any permutation in $S_n$ which, when written out as a word in the symbols $[n]$, has some permutation of $B$ as its first $k$ symbols. Then the left coset $\sigma P_k$ consists of all $k!(n-k)!$ permutations which have some permutation of $B$ as their first $k$ symbols (we are multiplying permutations from right to left). Thus every such subset $B$ corresponds to a particular left coset of $P_k$ in $S_n$, and $\mathcal{B}$ corresponds to a subset $M$ of the factor set $S_n/P_k$. (Note: $P_k$ need not be a normal subgroup of $S_n$, hence the factor set need not have a group structure.) This subset is called a *Coxeter matroid*, for $S_n$ and $P_k$. We still need to see how the Gale maximality axiom translates into this setting, but first let us pause for an easy example.

EXAMPLE 2.1. Consider the matroid of rank 2 on $[4]$ whose bases $\mathcal{B}$ consist of all 2-element subsets except $\{3, 4\}$. Then $P_2 = \{s_1, s_3\}$ and here is the correspondence between the bases of the matroid and cosets of $P_2$ in $S_4$.

| Subset | | | | Coset |
|--------|---|-----------|---|-------|
| $\{1,2\}$ | $\leftrightarrow$ | $P_k$ | $=$ | $\{1234, 2134, 1243, 2143\}$ |
| $\{1,3\}$ | $\leftrightarrow$ | $(2,3)P_k$ | $=$ | $\{1324, 3124, 1342, 3142\}$ |
| $\{1,4\}$ | $\leftrightarrow$ | $(2,4)P_k$ | $=$ | $\{1423, 4123, 1432, 4132\}$ |
| $\{2,3\}$ | $\leftrightarrow$ | $(1,3)P_k$ | $=$ | $\{2314, 3214, 2341, 3241\}$ |
| $\{2,4\}$ | $\leftrightarrow$ | $(1,4)P_k$ | $=$ | $\{2413, 4213, 2431, 4231\}$ |

It turns out that the Gale ordering on $k$-element subsets of $[n]$ corresponds to the Bruhat ordering on $S_n/P_k$, where Bruhat ordering on cosets is induced from Bruhat ordering on $S_n$ by saying $\tau P_k \geq \rho P_k$ if and only if $\sigma \geq \pi$ for some $\sigma \in \tau P_k, \pi \in \rho P_k$. For a definition of Bruhat ordering, see the next section. Furthermore, given a total ordering on $[n]$, we can write $\sigma$ for the permutation of $[n]$ which lists the elements of $[n]$ in increasing order. Then $B \geq B'$ in the Gale ordering induced by the given total ordering if and only if $\sigma^{-1}B \geq \sigma^{-1}B'$ in the Gale ordering induced by natural order if and only if $\sigma^{-1}\tau P_k \geq \sigma^{-1}\rho P_k$ in the natural Bruhat order, where $\tau P_k$ and $\rho P_k$ are the cosets corresponding to $B$ and $B'$, respectively.

Thus we define $M \subseteq S_n/P_k$ to be a *Coxeter matroid* (for $S_n$ and $P_k$) if and only if

(MP) : For every $\sigma \in S_n$ there exists a $\sigma$-*maximal* member $\tau P_k \in M$, such that $\sigma^{-1}\tau P_k \geq \sigma^{-1}\rho P_k$ for all $\rho P_k \in M$.

Condition (MP) is called the Maximality Property, and although it is a rather nice, clean condition from a theoretical point of view, it is rather difficult to check directly even on rather small examples. Fortunately, we will soon come to an equivalent geometric condition which is easier to check. First, however, let us see how the above definition generalizes to arbitrary Coxeter groups.

## 3. Coxeter matroids for arbitrary finite Coxeter groups

A *Coxeter group* (see [**Hum**]) is a group $W$ which is defined by a finite generating set $S = \{s_1, s_2, \ldots, s_m\}$ together with the relations $(s_i s_j)^{m_{ij}} = 1$ for all $i$ and $j$, where $m_{ii} = 1$ for all $i$, and $m_{ij} \geq 2$ or $m_{ij} = \infty$ for all $i \neq j$. We call $S$ the set of *special generators*.

We can define *Bruhat ordering* on $W$ as follows. Let $u, v \in W$. Then $u \leq v$ if and only if there exists a reduced (or shortest length) expression $v = s_{i_1} s_{i_2} \cdots s_{i_p}$ for $v$ in terms of the special generators, such that $u = s_{i_{j_1}} s_{i_{j_2}} \cdots s_{i_{j_q}}$ for some $j_1, j_2, \ldots, j_q$ with $1 \leq j_1 < j_2 < \ldots < j_q \leq p$.

Let $W$ be a finite Coxeter group with special generators $S$, and $P$ a *standard parabolic subgroup* of $W$, that is, a subgroup generated by a subset of $S$. As in the case of $W = S_n$ above, it is possible to show ([**Deo**]) that Bruhat order on $W$ induces a well-defined partial order (also called Bruhat order) on the factor set $W/P$, where $tP \leq rP$ if there exist $s \in tP, q \in rP$ such that $s \leq q$ in ordinary Bruhat order. Then we define $M \subseteq W/P$ to be a *Coxeter matroid* for $W$ and $P$ if $M$ satisfies the *Maximality Property*:

(MP) for every $w \in W$, there exists a *$w$-maximal* member $uP \in M$, that is, $w^{-1}uP \geq w^{-1}vP$ for all $vP \in M$.

## 4. A more geometric viewpoint

Associated with each finite Coxeter group $W$ is the *Coxeter complex* $\Gamma$ of $W$, a cell complex whose maximal dimensional cells (or *chambers*) are in bijection with the elements of $W$. Furthermore, $W$ may be realized as a group generated by reflections in $\mathbf{R}^n$ for appropriate $n$. The fixed hyperplanes of all the reflections in the resulting subgroup of the orthogonal group $O(n)$ give a hyperplane arrangement which, if intersected with the unit sphere, produce a cell complex combinatorially isomorphic to $\Gamma$. The root system of $W$ is a set of vectors, each orthogonal to one of the hyperplanes in the arrangement, with each hyperplane having a pair of roots. The lengths of the roots need not concern us here. For details, see [**Hum**].

There are two examples of Coxeter groups that will concern us the most. One is $W = S_n$, also known as $\mathcal{A}_{n-1}$. As we have seen, its special generators are the adjacent transpositions, $s_1, s_2, \ldots, s_{n-1}$. The Coxeter complex $\Gamma$ is the barycentric subdivision of the regular $n - 1$-dimensional simplex, and the roots are parallel to the edges of the simplex. This complex is shown in Figure 1.

The second example is $W = \mathcal{BC}_n$, the hyperoctahedral group. This is the group of symmetries of the $n$-cube (or, equivalently, of the $n$-cross polytope, which is dual to the $n$-cube). We can represent $W$ as a group of permutations on the set $J = \{1, 2, \ldots, n, 1^*, 2^*, \ldots, n^*\}$, corresponding to the facets of the $n$-cube (with $i$ the facet opposite $i^*$), and having as special generators the involutions (in cycle notation) $s_1 := (1, 2)(1^*, 2^*), s_2 := (2, 3)(2^*, 3^*), \ldots, s_{n-1} := (n-1, n)((n-1)^*, n^*)$, $s_n := (n, n^*)$. Its Coxeter complex $\Gamma$ is the barycentric subdivision of the $n$-cube, and its roots are parallel to the edges of the $n$-cube and to the diagonals of the 2-dimensional faces of the $n$-cube. A Coxeter matroid for $W = \mathcal{BC}_n$ is called a *symplectic* matroid. The Coxeter complex of this example shown in Figure 2.

In the theory of Coxeter groups (see [**Hum**]) each parabolic subgroup of $W$ has a well-defined *type*. In each of our two main examples, the type of $P$ is just the set of indices of the omitted special generators. These types carry over to faces of $\Gamma$, where each vertex of type $\{k\}$ is the barycenter of a face of cardinality $k$ of the simplex, in the case of $\mathcal{A}_{n-1}$, or the barycenter of a face of the cube of dimension $n - k$ in the case of $\mathcal{BC}_n$. The type of a larger dimensional face of $\Gamma$ is just the union of the types of its vertices. For example, in Figure 2, any edge connecting a vertex of the cube with the barycenter of an edge of the cube would be a face of $\Gamma$ of type $\{2, 3\}$, whereas an edge connecting an edge-barycenter to a face-barycenter

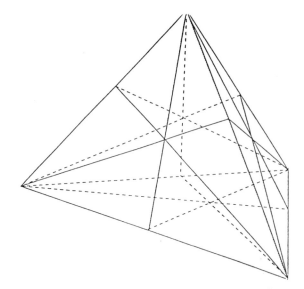

FIGURE 1. The Coxeter complex of $\mathcal{A}_3$.

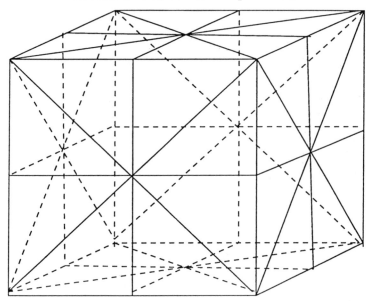

FIGURE 2. The Coxeter complex of $\mathcal{BC}_3$.

would be a face of $\Gamma$ of type $\{1, 2\}$. The cosets of the parabolic subgroup $P$ of type $T$ are in bijection with the faces of the complex of type $T$. Thus, if $M$ is any subset of the cosets of $P$ in $W$, then $M$ corresponds to a collection of faces of type $T$. Let $N$ denote the set of barycenters of the faces of $\Gamma$ which correspond to $M$. Note that if $P$ is a non-maximal parabolic subgroup, then $T$ has cardinality larger than 1, and we are actually taking barycenters of faces of $\Gamma$, which is itself the barycentric subdivision of the simplex or cube; in the maximal parabolic case, however, $N$ is just a subset of the vertices of $\Gamma$. Now we define the *hypersimplex* of $M$, or $H(M)$, to be the convex hull of $N$.

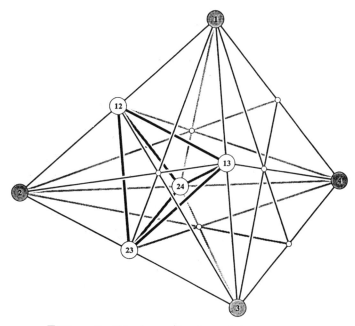

FIGURE 3. The hypersimplex of Example 4.2.

If $M$ is an ordinary matroid of rank $k$ on a set of cardinality $n$, then realizing $M$ as a Coxeter matroid for $W = \mathcal{A}_{n-1}$ and $P = P_k$, we see that $H(M)$ is combinatorially isomorphic to a face of the familiar matroid polytope, which by definition is the convex hull of the incidence vectors of the independent sets of $M$.

THEOREM 4.1 (Gelfand-Serganova,[**GS2**]). *Let $M$ be a subset of $W/P$, where $P$ is a standard parabolic subgroup of the finite Coxeter group $W$. Then $M$ is a Coxeter matroid for $W$ and $P$ if and only if every edge of $H(M)$ is parallel to a root of $W$.*

EXAMPLE 4.2. The collection $M = \{12, 13, 23, 24\}$ is not the collection of bases of an ordinary matroid of rank two on a four-element set. This is easily checked directly from the matroid axioms, but is also easily seen from the Gelfand-Serganova Theorem. We see that $H(M)$ is the convex hull of the barycenters of the four edges $\{12, 13, 23, 24\}$ of the 3-simplex with vertices labeled $\{1, 2, 3, 4\}$, as shown in Figure 3. Clearly, $\{13, 24\}$ is an edge of $H(M)$ which is not parallel to any edge of the 3-simplex.

EXAMPLE 4.3. Let $P_2$ be the maximal standard parabolic subgroup of type $\{2\}$ in $\mathcal{B}C_3$. Thus

$$P_2 = < s_1, s_3 > = < (1, 2)(1^*, 2^*), (3, 3^*) >$$

$$= \{1233^*2^*1^*, 2133^*1^*2^*, 123^*32^*1^*, 213^*31^*2^*\},$$

where the last representation comes from thinking of the permutations in $\mathcal{B}C_3$ as permuting the word $1233^*2^*1^*$, hence this word itself represents the identity element of the group. In fact, the group $\mathcal{B}C_3$ in this representation is the set of all words in the symbols $J = \{1, 2, 3, 3^*, 2^*, 1^*\}$ which have the property that the last half of the word is the first half, except that order is reversed and each symbol has been starred, where a doubly-starred symbol is an unstarred symbol. Similarly, the

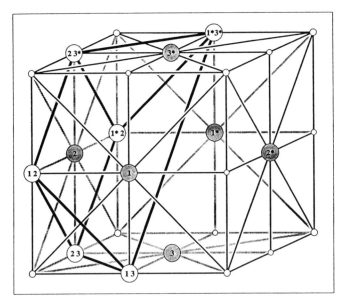

FIGURE 4. The hypersimplex of Example 4.3.

elements of a left coset may be represented by words, such as

$$(13^*)(1^*3)P_2 = \{3^*21^*12^*3, 23^*1^*132^*, 3^*211^*2^*3, 23^*11^*32^*\}.$$

Similarly to Example 2.1 above, every left coset of $P_2$ corresponds to a 2-element subset of $J$, namely, the two elements which appear, in some order, as the first two symbols in each word of the coset. Thus a symplectic matroid of type 2 in $\mathcal{B}C_3$ may be represented by a collection of 2-element subsets of $J$, which must, of course, correspond to cosets satisfying the Maximality Property. For example, let $M = \{12, 13, 1^*2, 1^*3^*, 23, 23^*\}$. Each pair listed gives an edge of the 3-cube as an intersection of the two listed facets, and $H(M)$ is the convex hull of their barycenters, as shown in Figure 4. In this case, we can visually check that the edges of $H(M)$ are all parallel to roots of $\mathcal{B}C_n$, so $M$ is a symplectic matroid. Even for symplectic matroids on a somewhat larger set, for which $H(M)$ is embedded in a larger-dimensional cube, checking the Gelfand-Serganova criterion remains a feasible task.

In similar fashion, we may check that the left cosets of

$$P_k = <s_1, s_2, \dots, s_{k-1}, s_{k+1}, \dots, s_n>$$

correspond to $k$-element subsets of $J$, and hence to barycenters of $n-k$-dimensional faces of the $n$-cube.

## 5. Represented symplectic matroids

Let $V$ be a standard symplectic space over the field $F$. That is, $V$ has a basis $E = \{1, 2, \dots, n, 1^*, 2^*, \dots, n^*\}$ and an antisymmetric bilinear form $(,)$ such that $(i, j) = (i, j^*) = (i^*, j^*) = 0$ for all $i \neq j$, and $(i, i^*) = -(i^*, i) = 1$ for all $i$. Let $U$ be a totally isotropic subspace of $V$ with basis $\{u_1, u_2, \dots, u_k\}$, that is, $(u_i, u_j) = 0$ for all $i, j$. We now expand each $u_i$ as a linear combination of elements of $E$, and put the coefficients as a row of the matrix $A$. We then define the collection $\mathcal{B}$ of subsets $B \subseteq E$ by saying that $B \in \mathcal{B}$ if (1.) $|B| = k$, (2.) for all $i \leq n, i \in B$ implies $i^* \notin B$, and (3.) the columns of $A$ corresponding to $B$ form a non-singular $k \times k$ submatrix of $A$.

THEOREM 5.1 (Borovik-White). *As defined above, $\mathcal{B}$ is a symplectic matroid.*

EXAMPLE 5.2. Consider over characteristic 0 the matrix

$$A = \begin{array}{c} \\ u_1 \\ u_2 \\ u_3 \end{array} \begin{array}{cccccc} 1 & 1^* & 2 & 2^* & 3 & 3^* \\ \left( \begin{array}{cccccc} 1 & 0 & 0 & 1 & 0 & 1 \\ 0 & 1 & 1 & 0 & 0 & 1 \\ 0 & 1 & 0 & 1 & 1 & 0 \end{array} \right) \end{array}.$$

To check that the corresponding subspace $U$ of $V$ is totally isotropic amounts just to observing that for each pair of distinct rows, the $2 \times 2$ minor in columns $j$ and $j^*$, summed over $j$, gives 0. The resulting collection $\mathcal{B}$ is

$$\{123, 12^*3^*, 1^*23^*, 1^*2^*3, 1^*2^*3^*\},$$

which, as we may check via the Gelfand-Serganova criterion, is indeed a symplectic matroid.

## 6. Exchange axioms for ordinary matroids

Investigation of Coxeter matroids led to what appeared to be a new form of the basis exchange axiom for ordinary matroids, (4) in the following theorem. We recently learned that A. Kelmans proved the equivalence of this axiom and another, seemingly weaker one, (5), to the usual matroid axioms in 1973 [**Kel**]. Since these results are not widely known, at least in the West, we present Kelmans' proof here. The condition for arbitrary Coxeter matroids corresponding to (4) turns out to be strictly stronger than the definition of Coxeter matroid, unlike the situation for ordinary matroids, although we will not attempt to present this condition for arbitrary Coxeter matroids here.

THEOREM 6.1. *Let $\mathcal{B}$ be a non-empty collection of subsets of $E$. Then the following are equivalent. Consequently, each is an axiomatization of the collection of bases of a matroid.*

**(1):** *For every $A, B \in \mathcal{B}$ and $a \in A \setminus B$ there exists $b \in B \setminus A$ such that $A \setminus \{a\} \cup \{b\} \in \mathcal{B}$.*

**(2):** *For every $A, B \in \mathcal{B}$ and $a \in A \setminus B$ there exists $b \in B \setminus A$ such that $B \setminus \{b\} \cup \{a\} \in \mathcal{B}$.*

**(3):** *For every $A, B \in \mathcal{B}$ and $a \in A \setminus B$, there exists $b \in B \setminus A$ such that $A \setminus \{a\} \cup \{b\} \in \mathcal{B}$ and $B \setminus \{b\} \cup \{a\} \in \mathcal{B}$.*

**(4):** *For every $A, B \in \mathcal{B}$, $A \neq B$, there exist $a \in A \setminus B$ and $b \in B \setminus A$ such that $A \setminus \{a\} \cup \{b\} \in \mathcal{B}$ and $B \setminus \{b\} \cup \{a\} \in \mathcal{B}$.*

**(5):** *For every $A, B \in \mathcal{B}$, $A \neq B$, there exist $a \in A \setminus B$, $b \in B \setminus A$ and $b' \in B \setminus A$ such that $A \setminus \{a\} \cup \{b\} \in \mathcal{B}$ and $B \setminus \{b'\} \cup \{a\} \in \mathcal{B}$.*

PROOF. Conditions (1), (2) and (3) are well known to be equivalent forms of matroid basis exchange. Since (3) implies (4) and (4) implies (5) are obvious, we need only show (5) implies (2).

First, we note that (5) (or, indeed, any of the above five conditions) implies that the members of $\mathcal{B}$ are equal in cardinality, as is verified by an easy induction. We prove (2) by induction on $|A \setminus B|$. If $|A \setminus B| = 1 = |B \setminus A|$, the statement is clearly true. Let $|A \setminus B| = n \geq 2$. By (5), there are $a \in A \setminus B$, $b \in B \setminus A$ and $b' \in B \setminus A$ such that $A' := A \setminus \{a\} \cup \{b\} \in \mathcal{B}$ and $B \setminus \{b'\} \cup \{a\} \in \mathcal{B}$. Now, $A' \setminus B = (A \setminus B) \setminus \{a\} \subset A \setminus B$ and $B \setminus A' = (B \setminus A) \setminus \{b\} \subset B \setminus A$. Since $|A' \setminus B| = n - 1$, by the induction hypothesis, condition (2) holds for $A'$ and $B$, so for every $c \in (A \setminus B) \setminus \{a\}$, there exists $d \in (B \setminus A) \setminus \{b\}$ such that $B \setminus \{d\} \cup \{c\} \in \mathcal{B}$. Since $B \setminus \{b'\} \cup \{a\} \in \mathcal{B}$ also, we have condition (2) for $A$ and $B$.

$\square$

## 7. Flags of matroids

We have described ordinary matroids in terms of *maximal* standard parabolic subgroups of $W = S_n$, but our definition of Coxeter matroid allowed an arbitrary standard parabolic subgroup of $W$. If we take an arbitrary standard parabolic subgroup of $S_n$, we get a *flag of matroids*.

Let $P_I = < \{s_i : i \notin I\} >$ be an arbitrary standard parabolic subgroup of $S_n$, where $I = \{k_1, k_2, \ldots, k_t\}, 1 \leq k_1 < k_2 < \ldots < k_t \leq n - 1$. Indeed, $P_I$ is the parabolic subgroup of type $I$, as mentioned in Section 4. Let $\sigma P_I$ be a left coset of $P_I$. Similarly to Example 2.1, $\sigma P_I$ corresponds to a chain of subsets $B_1 \subset B_2 \subset \ldots \subset B_t$ such that, for each $i$, $|B_i| = k_i$.

Now let $M$ be a Coxeter matroid for $S_n$ and $P_I$, that is, a collection of left cosets of $P_I$ which satisfy the Maximality Property. Then we define the flag of ordinary matroids $M_1, M_2, \ldots, M_t$ as follows: $M_i$ is a matroid of rank $k_i$ on $E = \{1, 2, \ldots, n\}$ with collection of bases $\mathcal{B}_i = \{B : \text{for some } \sigma P_I \in M, B \text{ is the } i\text{-th member of the chain of subsets corresponding to } \sigma P_I\}$. It can then be shown that not only is each $M_i$ a matroid, but that, furthermore, the identity function is a strong map $M_i \to M_{i-1}$ for each $i, 2 \leq i \leq t$. That is, every closed set in $M_{i-1}$ is also closed in $M_i$. The Maximality Property says that for every total ordering on $E$, there is a single chain of bases $B_1 \subset B_2 \subset \ldots \subset B_t$ such that $B_i$ is the unique Gale maximal basis of $M_i$ for each $i$. A flag of matroids is also equivalent to the notion of a *Gaussian greedoid*, see [**BZ**].

## 8. Open questions

1. Pick a finite Coxeter group $W$, work out the details of Coxeter matroids for $W$, and find elementary axioms which characterize them. Is there a notion of representability in some kind of vector space for this choice of $W$? Some Coxeter matroids over $\mathcal{D}_n$, for example, should be representable in terms of an orthogonal vector space, in a manner analogous to represented symplectic matroids. A more general type of geometric representation, in terms of chambers in a building, may be found in [**BG1, BG2**].

2. Even for symplectic matroids, we don't have a good set of elementary axioms. We also don't know how to characterize those symplectic matroids which are representable.

3. Generalize oriented matroids (see [**BLSWZ**]) to the Coxeter matroid setting.

4. For $W = S_n$, polytope duality of the Coxeter complex corresponds to matroid duality. What does polytope duality correspond to in general?

5. Are there other new characterizations of ordinary matroids and ordinary oriented matroids derivable from the Coxeter matroid point of view?

# References

[**BLSWZ**] A. Bjorner, M. Las Vergnas, B. Strumfels, N. White, G. M. Ziegler, **Oriented Matroids**, Cambridge University Press, 1993.

[**BZ**] A. Bjorner, G. M. Ziegler, *Introduction to greedoids* in **Matroid Applications**, N. White, ed., Cambridge University Press, Cambridge, 1992.

[**BG1**] A. V. Borovik and I. M. Gelfand, *WP-matroids and thin Schubert cells on Tits systems*, Adv. Math. **103** (1994) 162–179.

[**BG2**] A. V. Borovik and I. M. Gelfand, *Matroids on chamber systems*, Publ. LaCIM, **14** 1993, 25–62.

[**BR**] A. V. Borovik and K. S. Roberts, *Coxeter groups and matroids*, in **Groups of Lie Type and Geometries**, W. M. Kantor and L. Di Martino, eds., Cambridge University Press, 1995, pp. 13–34.

[**Bry**] T. Brylawski, *Appendix of Matroid Cryptomorphisms*, in N. White, ed., **Theory of Matroids**, Cambridge University Press, Cambridge, 1986.

[**Deo**] V. Deodar, *A splitting criterion for the Bruhat ordering on Coxeter groups*, Communications in Algebra **15** (1987) 1889-1894.

[**Gale**] D. Gale, *Optimal assignments in an ordered set: an application of matroid theory*, J. Combinatorial Theory **4** (1968) 1073–1082.

[**GGMS**] I. M. Gelfand, M. Goresky, R. D. MacPherson and V. V. Serganova, *Combinatorial Geometries, convex polyhedra, and Schubert cells*, Adv. Math. **63** (1987) 301–316.

[**GS1**] I. M. Gelfand and V. V. Serganova, *On a general definition of a matroid and a greedoid*, Soviet Math. Dokl. **35** (1987) 6–10.

[**GS2**] I. M. Gelfand and V. V. Serganova, *Combinatorial geometries and torus strata on homogeneous compact manifolds*, Russian Math. Surveys **42** (1987) 133–168; see also I. M. Gelfand, **Collected Papers**, vol. III, Springer-Verlag, New York a.o., 1989, 926–958.

[**Hum**] J. Humphreys, **Reflection Groups and Coxeter Groups**, Cambridge University Press, Cambridge, 1990.

[**Kel**] A. Kelmans, *Introduction to the matroid theory*, Lectures at the All-Union Conference on Graph Thoery and Algorithms, Odessa, September, 1973.

[**Ronan**] M. Ronan, **Lectures on Buildings**, Academic Press, Boston, 1989.

DEPARTMENT OF MATHEMATICS, UNIVERSITY OF FLORIDA, GAINESVILLE, FL 32611
*E-mail address*: white@math.ufl.edu

Contemporary Mathematics
Volume **197**, 1996

# Open Problems

Below are a number of open problems contributed by conference participants. In addition, the reader will find many open problems in the survey articles by Joseph P. S. Kung, James G. Oxley, and Walter Whiteley in this volume. For more open problems, the reader is referred to Chapter 14 of James Oxley's book "Matroid Theory" and to the several collections of open problems referenced there.

## 1. Conjectures on Matroids Representable over $GF(3)$ and other Fields

Let $\mathcal{F}$ be a set of fields containing $GF(3)$ and consider the class $\mathcal{M}$ of matroids representable over all fields in $\mathcal{F}$. It is shown in [**2, 3**] that if $\mathcal{M}$ is not the class of ternary matroids or regular matroids, then $\mathcal{M}$ is either the class of "near-regular matroids", "dyadic matroids", "$\sqrt[6]{1}$-matroids", or the class of matroids obtained by taking direct sums and 2-sums of dyadic and $\sqrt[6]{1}$-matroids. The problems we pose here concern finding excluded minors for these classes. Since these matroids are all ternary and the excluded minors for ternary matroids are known, we focus on the ternary excluded minors.

Let $\mathbf{Q}(\alpha)$ denote the field obtained by extending the rationals by the transcendental $\alpha$. A matrix over $\mathbf{Q}(\alpha)$ is *near-unimodular* if all of its non-zero subdeterminants are in $\{\pm\alpha^i(\alpha-1)^j : i,j \in \mathbf{Z}\}$. A matroid is *near-regular* if it can be represented over $\mathbf{Q}(\alpha)$ by the columns of a near-unimodular matrix. If $\mathcal{F}$ consists of all fields other than $GF(2)$, or $\mathcal{F} = \{GF(3), GF(8)\}$, then $\mathcal{M}$ is the class of near-regular matroids. The following matroids are straightforwardly checked to be excluded minors for near-regular matroids: the non-Fano matroid $F_7^-$ and its dual; the self-dual matroid $P_8$ defined in [**1**, p. 512]; the matroid $AG(2,3)\backslash p$ obtained by deleting a point from the ternary affine plane, and its dual; and the self-dual matroid $(AG(2,3)\backslash p)_{\triangle Y}$ obtained by performing a delta-wye exchange on $AG(2,3)\backslash p$.

CONJECTURE 1.1. *The ternary excluded minors for the class of near-regular matroids are* $F_7^-$, $(F_7^-)^*$, $P_8$, $AG(2,3)\backslash p$, $(AG(2,3)\backslash p)^*$, *and* $(AG(2,3)\backslash p)_{\triangle Y}$.

A *dyadic matrix* is a matrix over the rationals with the property that all of its subdeterminants belong to the set $\{0, \pm 2^i : i \in \mathbf{Z}\}$. A *dyadic matroid* is a matroid that can be represented over the rationals by the columns of a dyadic matrix. If $\mathcal{F}$ consists of $GF(3)$ and the reals, $GF(3)$ and the rationals, or $GF(3)$ and $GF(5)$, then $\mathcal{M}$ is the class of dyadic matroids.

CONJECTURE 1.2. *The ternary excluded minors for the class of dyadic matroids are* $AG(2,3)\backslash p$, $(AG(2,3)\backslash p)^*$, *and* $(AG(2,3)\backslash p)_{\triangle Y}$.

A $\sqrt[6]{1}$-*matrix* is a matrix over the complex numbers with the property that all of its non-zero subdeterminants are complex sixth roots of unity. A $\sqrt[6]{1}$-*matroid* is a matroid that can be represented over the complex numbers by the columns of a $\sqrt[6]{1}$-matrix. If $\mathcal{F} = \{GF(3), GF(4)\}$, then $\mathcal{M}$ is the class of $\sqrt[6]{1}$-matroids. Note also that if $\mathcal{F}$ consists of $GF(3)$ and the complex numbers, then $\mathcal{M}$ is the class obtained by taking direct sums and 2-sums of dyadic matroids and $\sqrt[6]{1}$-matroids.

CONJECTURE 1.3. *The ternary excluded minors for the class of $\sqrt[6]{1}$-matroids are $F_7^-$, $(F_7^-)^*$, and $P_8$.*

### References

[1] J. G. Oxley, *Matroid Theory*, Oxford University Press, New York, 1992.
[2] G. Whittle, *A characterisation of the matroids representable over $GF(3)$ and the rationals*, J. Combin. Theory Ser. B, **65** (1995), 222–261.
[3] G. Whittle, *On matroids representable over $GF(3)$ and other fields*, Trans. Amer. Math. Soc., to appear

*Contributed by James Oxley, Dirk Vertigan, and Geoff Whittle.*

## 2. A Conjecture on Rank-Preserving Weak Map Images

### In Memory of Dean Lucas

A rank-preserving weak map image of $M(S)$ is (for us) a matroid $M'(S)$ whose collection of bases is a proper subset of the collection of bases of $M$.

In the early 1970's, Lucas [2] proved that every rank-preserving weak map image of a binary matroid is both binary and separable. In fact, these are the compositions of rank-preserving weak map images $M(S) \mapsto M|A \oplus M/A$.

Lucas also (with Brylawski) [1] defined a projectively unique representation $A(M)$ over $F$ as a matrix representation $A$ of $M$ such that any other matrix representation $A'$ of $M$ is of the form $A' = N\overline{A}D$ where $N$ is a nonsingular matrix, $D$ is a nonsingular diagonal matrix, and $\overline{A} = A$, with, perhaps, a field automorphism applied to its entries.

Call a matroid *completely projectively unique* over $F$ if it is projectively unique over every extension field of $F$.

CONJECTURE 2.1. *A rank-preserving weak map image of a matroid that is completely projectively unique over $F$ is also representable over $F$ and is separable. Can it always be factored as above?*

Geoff Whittle has pointed out that the condition that the rank-preserving weak map image is representable is necessary as the Fano plane is a rank-preserving weak map image of the completely projectively unique non-Fano matroid (the matroid obtained by relaxing a circuit-hyperplane of the Fano matroid).

### References

[1] T. H. Brylawski and D. Lucas, *Uniquely representable combinatorial geometries*, Teorie Combinatoire (Proc. 1973 Internat. Colloq.), Accademia Nazionale dei Lincei, Rome, 1976, pp. 83–104.
[2] D. Lucas, *Weak maps of combinatorial geometries*, Trans. Amer. Math. Soc. **206** (1975), 247–279.

*Contributed by Thomas H. Brylawski.*

## 3. A Conjectured Matroid on the Set

Let $P$ be a finite set, $2^P$ its Boolean algebra of subsets, and $\binom{P}{2}$ the set of 2-element subsets of $P$. Let $f : 2^P \to \mathbf{Z}$ be defined by

$$f(A) = \begin{cases} 3|A| - 6, & \text{if } |A| \geq 3; \\ 1, & \text{if } |A| = 2; \\ 0, & \text{otherwise.} \end{cases}$$

An *antichain* $\mathcal{E} = (A_1, A_2, \dots, A_t)$ is a family of subsets $A_i \subseteq P$, no one of which contains another. Call the subsets $A_i$ the *nodes* of the antichain. An antichain $\mathcal{E} = (A_1, A_2, \dots, A_t)$ is *thin* if $|A_i \cap A_j| \leq 2$ whenever $i \neq j$. An antichain $\mathcal{E}$ *covers* an antichain $\mathcal{F}$ if every node of $\mathcal{F}$ is a subset of some node of $\mathcal{E}$.

An antichain $\mathcal{B}$ is a *bar* antichain if each of its nodes is a 2-element subset of $P$. Thus, bar antichains are subsets of the set $\binom{P}{2}$; we intend to construct a matroid on $\binom{P}{2}$.

The *characteristic* $\chi(\mathcal{E})$ of an antichain is defined as the alternating sum

$$\chi(\mathcal{E}) = \sum_i f(A_i) - \sum_{i<j} f(A_i \cap A_j) + \sum_{i<j<k} f(A_i \cap A_j \cap A_k) - \cdots .$$

Define $r(\mathcal{B}) = \min \chi(\mathcal{Z})$, where the minimum is over the thin antichains $\mathcal{Z}$ which cover $\mathcal{B}$.

**CONJECTURE 3.1.** *The function $r$ is a matroid rank function on $\binom{P}{2}$.*

*Contributed by Henry H. Crapo and T. S. Tay.*

## 4. Problems on Bar Frameworks

A *bar framework* $(\Gamma, \alpha)$ is a graph $\Gamma(V, E)$ together with a mapping $\alpha : V \to \mathbf{R}^d$, giving a *placement* $\alpha_b$ for each vertex $b$ of $\Gamma$. For any bar framework $(\Gamma, \alpha)$, let $M_\alpha$ be the space of infinitesimal motions $\phi : V \to \mathbf{R}^d$ of the vertices of $\Gamma$ which preserve, to first order, the lengths of all edges of $\Gamma$, that is:

$$M_\alpha = \{\phi : V \to \mathbf{R}^d \mid \text{ for all } (a,b) \in E, \ (\phi_b - \phi_a) \cdot (\alpha_b - \alpha_a) = 0\}.$$

This is the local property holding whenever $\phi$ is the time derivative $\alpha'(0)$ of a motion $\alpha(t)$ of the vertex set that preserves all bar-lengths. Let $\beta^0(\Gamma, \alpha)$ be the dimension of the vector space $M_\alpha$, and let $\chi(\Gamma) = d|V| - |E|$.

A graph $\Gamma(V, E)$ is said to be *generically $d$-independent* if there is a placement $\alpha$ of $\Gamma$ such that

$$\beta^0(\Gamma, \alpha) = \chi(\Gamma),$$

and is said to be *generically $d$-isostatic* if there is a placement $\alpha$ of $\Gamma$ such that

$$\beta^0(\Gamma, \alpha) = \chi(\Gamma) = \binom{d+1}{2}.$$

For bar frameworks in the plane, there are several equivalent characterizations of generically 2-isostatic frameworks. We mention two:

**THEOREM 4.1.** *For any graph $\Gamma$ with at least two vertices, the following are equivalent:*

**(0):** $\Gamma$ *is generically 2-isostatic.*

**(1):** $\chi(\Gamma) = 3$, and for every subset $A \subseteq V$ with at least 2 vertices, the induced subgraph $\Gamma_A$ has $\chi(\Gamma_A) \geq 3$.

**(2):** The edge set $E$ is the disjoint union of three trees, exactly two of which are incident with each vertex, and such that no two of the trees cospan any subset of two or more vertices.

The equivalence of properties (0) and (1) was proved by Laman. We refer to property (2) as the "3T2 condition". Analogous characterizations of generic 3-isostatic frameworks are not known. Those of the preceding theorem break down due to the presence of 'hinges', permitting relative movements about *pairs* of vertices.

PROBLEM 4.1 (J. Baracs, H. Crapo, W. Whiteley, et al). *For frameworks in 3-space, find an analog of the above characterizations.*

The estimation of rigidity of bar frameworks is best carried out with reference to the possibility of rigid components which contain more than two vertices. To this end, use hypergraphs. A hypergraph $H(V, \mathcal{E})$ consists of a vertex set $V$ and a family $\mathcal{E}$ of subsets of $V$, called its *nodes* or *hyperedges*. For our purposes, we may assume that the nodes are incomparable. A hypergraph $H(V, \mathcal{E})$ is said to be a *covering* of a graph $\Gamma$ if every edge of $\Gamma$ is a subset of a node of $H$. It is said to be *d-thin* if no two nodes have more than $d - 1$ vertices in common.

We need both a value of $\beta^0$ and a characteristic $\chi$ for hypergraphs. First define a rank function on subsets $A \subseteq V$ which measures the number of degrees of freedom for rigid motion of the set $A$ of vertices:

$$r(A) = \begin{cases} \binom{d+1}{2}, & \text{if } d < n; \\ nd - \binom{n}{2}, & \text{if } n \leq d. \end{cases}$$

We extend this to a characteristic $\chi(H)$ by

$$\chi(H) = \sum_{A \in \mathcal{E}} r(A) - \sum_{A,B \in \mathcal{E}} r(A \cap B) + \sum_{A,B,C \in \mathcal{E}} r(A \cap B \cap C) - \cdots.$$

The space of infinitesimal motions of a hypergraph framework $(H, \alpha)$ is defined as above, replacing the quantification *"for all $(a, b) \in E$"* by *"for all $a, b$ common to a node of $H$"*. In the plane, there is an exact calculation for the number of degrees of freedom of a generic plane framework:

THEOREM 4.2. *For any graph $\Gamma$, the following are equal:*

**(1):** $\beta^0_{2\text{-}gen}(\Gamma)$,

**(2):** $\max \chi(\mathcal{E})$, where the maximum is over all 2-thin hypergraph coverings $\mathcal{E}$ of $\Gamma$, and

**(3):** $\chi(\mathcal{R})$, where $\mathcal{R}$ is the hypergraph of maximal rigid components of $\Gamma$.

PROBLEM 4.2 (H. Crapo, A. Dress, T.-S. Tay). *Determine whether the analogous equalities hold in 3-space, that is, is the following true?*
*For any graph $\Gamma$, the following are equal:*

**(1):** $\beta^0_{3\text{-}gen}(\Gamma)$,

**(2):** $\max \chi(\mathcal{E})$, where the maximum is over all 3-thin hypergraph coverings $\mathcal{E}$ of $\Gamma$, and

**(3):** $\chi(\mathcal{R})$, where $\mathcal{R}$ is the hypergraph of maximal rigid components of $\Gamma$.

These are adaptations of a conjecture of Dress, stated in terms of counts of incidences of vertices, hinges, and rigid components, and a conjecture of Crapo and Tay, stated in terms of cohomology (proved by Tay to be equivalent to that of Dress).

The analogous calculations are known to be false in 4-space. A convenient counterexample is the complete bipartite graph $K_{6,6}$ for which the above counts would predict 12 degrees of freedom, but which has 13 degrees of freedom in generic placement. The maximal rigid components are the single edges. For an alternative formula perhaps more likely to find satisfactory extensions to arbitrary dimension, see the discussion of "cofactor matroids" in W. Whiteley's article in this volume. *Contributed by Henry H. Crapo.*

## 5. A Problem About Common Covectors and Bases in Oriented Matroid Pairs

A *sign matrix* is a matrix with entries $+$, $-$, and $0$. A square sign matrix $A$ is called *sign non-singular* (SNS) when every real matrix $F$ with sign pattern $\sigma(F) = A$ is non-singular. This is one of many notions detailed in [1] used to analyze what can be deduced about systems of linear equations from sign information. The facts below appear in this book and the papers referenced therein.

Let $Z$ be the determinant of the matrix of 0s and signed distinct variables corresponding to the entries of $A$. Consider the three mutually exclusive cases:

**(1):** The polynomial $Z$ is identically zero. Thus, all real matrices $F$ with sign pattern $\sigma(F) = A$ are singular.

**(2):** The polynomial $Z$ has both positive and negative terms. Thus, some real $F$ with $\sigma(F) = A$ are singular and some are non-singular. We call such sign matrices $A$ *sometimes not sign non-singular* (SNSNS).

**(3):** The polynomial $Z$ is not identically zero and all of its terms have the same sign. Thus, $A$ is SNS.

In this note, we state two properties of certain pairs of oriented matroids with common ground set $E$ that each generalize how case (2) is distinguished from case (3) when case (1) is excluded. (Matroid and oriented matroid analyses relevant to case (1) are treated elsewhere, see [**4, 3**].) Our two properties are equivalent when both oriented matroids are realizable. The open problem is whether the two properties are equivalent when at least one of the oriented matroids is non-realizable.

All real $F$ with $\sigma(F) = A$ can be factored as $F = M_1 D M_2^t$ where

**(1):** $D$ is a diagonal matrix with positive entries on the diagonal, and

**(2):** $M_1$ and $M_2$ are $\{0, \pm 1\}$ matrices in which each column has a unique non-zero entry; $M_1$ and $M_2$ depend only on the sign pattern $A$, not on the matrix $F$.

In fact, if we instead let $D$ be a diagonal matrix of distinct variables, then the polynomial $Z$ is the Cauchy-Binet expansion of $\det F$. Thus our first generalization of the SNSNS case is:

PROPERTY 5.1. *For oriented matroids $\mathcal{M}_1$, $\mathcal{M}_2$ with a common basis, there exist $B_1, B_2 \subseteq E$ for which*

$$\chi_1(B_1)\chi_2(B_1)\chi_1(B_2)\chi_2(B_2) = -$$

*where $\chi_i$ is the chirotope function of $\mathcal{M}_i$.*

Here, case (1) is excluded by the requirement that $\mathcal{M}_1$, $\mathcal{M}_2$ have a common basis, so we will assume this henceforth.

The polynomial $\det F$ is a non-zero multiple of the determinant of another matrix, namely (see [2])

$$\begin{pmatrix} M_1 D \\ M_2^{\perp} \end{pmatrix}$$

where $D$, $M_1$, and $M_2$ are as above, and where $M_2^{\perp}$ is any matrix whose rows are a basis for the orthogonal complement of the row space of $M_2$. The condition that this matrix is square and non-singular when $D$ is a diagonal matrix of variables is equivalent to our assumption that excludes case (1). This can be shown easily using duality, rank analysis, and Laplace's expansion for this determinant. Property 5.2 below has a requirement on $\mathcal{M}_1$ and the dual $\mathcal{M}_2^*$ that is equivalent to our common basis assumption. The case of SNSNS then means there exists a real $D > 0$ for which the row space of $M_1 D$ intersects the row space of $M_2^{\perp}$ at a non-zero member of $\mathbf{R}^E$. Thus our second generalization of the SNSNS case is:

PROPERTY 5.2.  *For oriented matroids $\mathcal{M}_1$, $\mathcal{M}_2^*$ whose matroid union is free and $\mathrm{rank}\mathcal{M}_1 + \mathrm{rank}\mathcal{M}_2^* = |E|$, $\mathcal{M}_1$ and $\mathcal{M}_2^*$ have a common (non-zero) covector.*

In [3] it is proved that Property 5.1 implies Property 5.2. The converse for oriented matroid pairs in which at least one is non-realizable is the open problem. It is easy to reduce the general case to the case with one realizable oriented matroid by doubling the ground set.

PROBLEM 5.1.  *Does Property 5.2 imply Property 5.1?*

Property 5.1 is preserved by dualizing, so a positive answer to the next question is weaker than a positive answer to Problem 5.1 above.

PROBLEM 5.2.  *Given $\mathcal{M}_1$ and $\mathcal{M}_2^*$ that satisfy the (unoriented) matroid assumptions in Property 5.2, is it true that $\mathcal{M}_1$ and $\mathcal{M}_2^*$ have a common covector if and only if they have a common vector?*

Motivations from electrical network problems, details, and other results for the general common covector problem are given in [3]. For example, if the rank of the matroid union $\mathcal{M}_1 \cup \mathcal{M}_2^*$ is less than $\mathrm{rank}(\mathcal{M}_1) + \mathrm{rank}(\mathcal{M}_2^*)$, then $\mathcal{M}_1$ and $\mathcal{M}_2^*$ have a common covector. This union rank condition is naturally abstracted from linear algebra. It is shown that the common covector problem for cases when this condition does not hold is NP-complete. The NP-completeness proof fails when the problem is restricted to the cases under discussion in this note. Specifically, the reduction of our NP-completeness proof only constructs instances with $|E| > \mathrm{rank}(\mathcal{M}_1) + \mathrm{rank}(\mathcal{M}_2^*)$.

We note that the SNSNS property raises recognized hard combinatorial questions and its computational complexity is unknown; it is polynomial time equivalent to the even cycle problem for digraphs [1, 5]. Our properties, even for the realizable case, are generalizations of such problems.

## References

[1] R. A. Brualdi and B. L. Shader, *Matrices of Sign-Solvable Linear Systems*, Cambridge University Press, New York, NY, 1995.

[2] T. Brylawski, *A determinantal identity for resistive networks*, SIAM J. Appl. Math. **32** (1977), 1–22.

[3] S. Chaiken, *Oriented matroid pairs, theory and an electric application*, this volume.

[4] K. Murota, *Some recent results in combinatorial approaches to dynamical systems*, Linear Algebra Appl. **122/123/124** (1989), 725–759.

[5] V. V. Vazirani and M. Yannakakis, *Pfaffian orientations, 0-1 permanents, and even cycles in directed graphs*, Disc. Appl. Math. **25** (1989), 179–190.

*Contributed by Seth Chaiken.*

## 6. A Problem on Dowling Lattices

A number of recent papers have illustrated that Dowling lattices are group-theoretic analogs of projective spaces; they do not have all the structure of projective spaces, but the similarities are striking. See, for example, [1] and [5].

We recall the definition of the rank-$d$ Dowling lattice $Q_d(A)$ over a (finite or infinite) group $A$. The ground set of the matroid $Q_d(A)$ consists of two types of points: the *joints* $p_1, p_2, \ldots, p_d$, which form a basis; and the *internal points* $\alpha_{ij}$, as $\alpha$ ranges over all elements of $G$ and $1 \leq i < j \leq d$. There are two types of non-trivial lines (lines having more than two points): the *coordinate lines* $\{p_i, p_j\} \cup \{\alpha_{ij} \mid \alpha \in G\}$; and the *transversal lines* $\{\alpha_{ij}, \beta_{jk}, (\alpha\beta)_{ik}\}$ where the product $\alpha\beta$ is the product in the group $G$. Thus, there are $\binom{n}{2}$ coordinate lines and $\binom{n}{3}|G|^2$ transversal lines. The flats of the Dowling lattice $Q_d(A)$ are the sets $F$ of points satisfying the following property: for all pairs of elements $x, y \in F$, the line spanned by $x$ and $y$ is in $F$. (For the original definition of Dowling lattices, see [3] or [1]. For another view, see Section 4.5 of Joseph Kung's article "Critical Problems" in this volume.)

To motivate the problem below on Dowling lattices, recall the following result of Richard Rado for geometries that embed in projective spaces (i.e., representable geometries). (See [4]. See also [2, Theorem 7.3.4].)

THEOREM 6.1. *Every finite geometry representable over a field is representable over a finite field.*

We ask if the corresponding result is true for geometries embeddable in Dowling lattices.

PROBLEM 6.1. *If a finite geometry $M$ embeds in the Dowling lattice $Q_r(A)$ for some infinite group $A$, does $M$ necessarily embed in the Dowling lattice $Q_r(A')$ for some finite group $A'$?*

R. T. Tugger has observed that the answer is affirmative if $A$ is abelian. First note that $M$ embeds in the Dowling lattice $Q_r(A'')$ where $A''$ is the subgroup of $A$ generated by the finite set

$$\{\alpha \mid \text{for some } i \text{ and } j, \text{ the internal point } \alpha_{ij} \text{ is in } M\}.$$

Since $A''$ is a finitely generated abelian group, it is isomorphic to a direct sum of a finite number of cyclic groups, say

$$A'' \simeq \mathbf{Z} \oplus \cdots \oplus \mathbf{Z} \oplus (\mathbf{Z}/m_1\mathbf{Z}) \oplus \cdots \oplus (\mathbf{Z}/m_t\mathbf{Z}),$$

where there are $s$ infinite cyclic groups $\mathbf{Z}$ in the direct sum. It follows that $M$ can be embedded in the Dowling lattice $Q_r(A')$ where $A'$ is the finite group

$$A' = (\mathbf{Z}/n_1\mathbf{Z}) \oplus \cdots \oplus (\mathbf{Z}/n_s\mathbf{Z}) \oplus (\mathbf{Z}/m_1\mathbf{Z}) \oplus \cdots \oplus (\mathbf{Z}/m_t\mathbf{Z})$$

for suitably large $n_1, \ldots, n_s$.

Tugger has also observed that because there are no finite skew fields which are not (commutative) fields, the failed Pappian configuration is a finite matroid representable over some infinite skew field but no finite skew field. Therefore, if the answer to Problem 6.1 is affirmative, then it would be a result which is qualitatively different from Rado's theorem.

## References

[1] M. K. Bennett, K. P. Bogart, and J. Bonin, *The geometry of Dowling lattices*, Advances in Math. **103** (1994), 131–161.

[2] T. H. Brylawski, *Constructions*, Theory of Matroids (ed. N. White), Cambridge University Press, 1986, pp. 127–223.

[3] T. A. Dowling, *A class of geometric lattices based on finite groups*, J. Combin. Theory Ser. B **14** (1973), 61–86. Erratum, same journal, **15** (1973), 211.

[4] R. Rado, *Note on independence functions*, Proc. London Math. Soc. **7** (1957), 300–320.

[5] G. Whittle, *Dowling group geometries and the critical problem*, J. Combin. Theory Ser. B **47** (1989), 80–92.

*Contributed by Joseph E. Bonin.*

# Selected Titles in This Series

(*Continued from the front of this publication*)

(See the AMS catalog for earlier titles)